ENGINEERING THERMODYNAMICS

JAMES B. JONES, P.E.

Professor and Head, Department of Mechanical Engineering
Virginia Polytechnic Institute

GEORGE A. HAWKINS, P.E.

Professor of Thermodynamics and Vice-President for Academic Affairs
Purdue University

NEW YORK • LONDON, JOHN WILEY & SONS, INC.

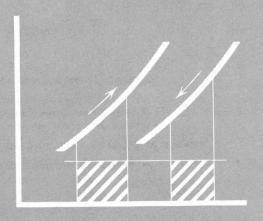

ENGINEERING
THERMODYNAMICS

An Introductory Textbook

Preface

This textbook is intended for use in undergraduate engineering courses in thermodynamics. Its purpose is to help develop in the student (1) an understanding of the first law, the second law, and some physical property relationships and (2) some competence in the application of these principles to engineering systems. This book is written directly to students, and this is the implication of the use of the second person. In this manner we hope to free the teacher from the necessity of interpreting the text to his students. His talents are more effectively used if classroom time is devoted to those teaching activities that require a face-to-face exchange of thoughts and therefore cannot be accomplished by a textbook.

It is well to state here what this book does not do. It does not describe design practices or equipment, except insofar as such descriptions are needed to illustrate the applications of the basic principles. It does not present performance data of actual systems or extensive physical property data. It gives no details on the physical arrangement of equipment. These things are important in engineering practice, but they are better left for the more specialized literature to which the students should be introduced at some time, but not necessarily in an introductory course in thermodynamics.

We make no pretense of touching on all the engineering applications of thermodynamics. If an engineering student completes a course in thermodynamics and has no familiarity with the first law, the second law, and some of their corollaries, this is a matter of concern; but we see no reason for alarm if he has never heard of a feedwater heater or an intercooler or a thermodynamic analysis of a thermocouple. It may be that he has acquired his grasp of the fundamentals by means of other examples. Furthermore, we believe that not everything pertinent to modern engineering thermodynamics needs to be mentioned in a first course. Statements such as "Steam turbines (or the Onsager relations or the Maxwell equations) are not even mentioned" should be regarded more as observations than as criticism of an introductory course or textbook.

The general plan of the book is influenced by our conviction that during the early part of a thermodynamics course sequence students need copious explanation and illustration. The person who has studied thermodynamics at length is capable of stating the basic principles very concisely and from them deducing many far-reaching conclusions. A thorough familiarity with the subject provides the perspective that reveals the simplicity as well as the importance of the fundamentals; but people who have achieved this familiarity often do not recognize the need of the neophyte for repeated explanations and illustrations of the fundamentals. Experienced teachers realize this when in subsequent courses they find that it is precisely the fundamentals on which too many students are weak. Consequently, the explanations in the early chapters of this book are often exhaustive, and we have placed particular emphasis on various points that we have found to be stumbling blocks for students. There are many fully solved example problems in the early chapters. As the students gain maturity in the subject, less explanation is needed, and more reliance can be placed on their reasoning powers; so both the amount of explanation and the number of solved example problems are decreased in later chapters.

The order of material has been selected more from pedagogical considerations than for reasons of logical economy. (This point is called to the students' attention in Art. 10·8.) Thus, after the introductory chapter and Chapter 2 on the first law, there are three chapters on physical properties. The problems following these chapters involve extensive applications of the first law and material from the introductory chapter, as well as physical property relationships. The student can thereby get ample practice in applying the first law to various systems before he takes up the new material on the second law.

Separate chapters are devoted to the second-law statement, reversibility, the Carnot principle and cycle, and entropy. This is done to emphasize the sequence. Reversibility has meaning only in light of the second law; the Carnot principle and cycle can be established only if reversibility is understood; and the definition of entropy involves a reversible process and also thermodynamic temperature, which is most easily explained after the Carnot principle is introduced. Chapter 10 then treats physical property relationships, which follow from the first and second laws combined, and Chapter 11 introduces availability and irreversibility. A problem posed by the inclusion of availability and irreversibility calculations in an introductory course is that although the conclusions are simple as well as highly useful the general derivation of these conclusions is somewhat involved. Some instructors may wish to use the conclusions without devoting appreciable time to their derivation.

The purpose of Chapters 15 to 19 is to illustrate the application of the basic principles covered in earlier chapters to various systems. In order to keep the emphasis on fundamentals, special techniques have been omitted. For example, in Chapter 15 some of the problems can be solved very quickly by use of the one-dimensional flow parameters which are tabulated in various places, including the Keenan and Kaye *Gas Tables;* but these special techniques are not introduced. It seems to us that their place is not in an introductory thermodynamics course. Certainly nothing prevents an instructor from introducing them in the classroom. It is much easier, in fact, to introduce such special material as a supplement to the basic approach in the textbook than to convince students to rely on the basic approach if their textbook always uses more specialized methods.

As already mentioned, the amount of explanation is decreased in the later chapters. Our intention is to describe some engineering systems only in sufficient detail that they can be the subject of problems to give the student practice in applying the basic principles. No attempt is made to describe actual systems in detail or to give typical performance figures. This is the function of handbooks the student should own or have ready access to. Engineering students should be encouraged to use a library regularly. If this is done, there is no need in a thermodynamics text for descriptions of equipment. If this is not done, a supplementary text or handbook should perhaps be assigned to accompany this book. A few of the problems require property data that are not included in this book but can be found in several handbooks.

At the end of the book is a short chapter on the elements of heat transfer. Although heat transfer is not part of the subject of thermodynamics, all engineering students should have some knowledge of heat-transfer fundamentals. In a number of schools an undergraduate course in heat transfer is offered. In such cases the final chapter of this volume would not be covered in the classroom. However, if a formal course is not given, the chapter on heat transfer may prove of value even though it is very brief.

Over seven hundred problems of varying difficulty are included, and answers to approximately one third are in the appendix. Many problems are highly "cumulative"; that is, their solutions involve material from several previous chapters. There are few problems presented that can be solved by finding an equation, plugging numbers into it, and cranking out the answer; however, a number of simple problems are included so that for illustrating some specific point the teacher can use one of these rather than make up a problem on the spur of the moment and have his students end up with the solution in their notes but not the statement of the problem. Some problems involve physical property data that must be obtained from other sources, and many problems involve data from *Thermodynamic Properties of Steam* by Keenan and Keyes and *Gas Tables* by Keenan and Kaye.

The references listed with most chapters are those in which students can find more information or different approaches to various topics. The listings are selective rather than exhaustive. We have listed only books and papers that are likely to be available in any engineering college library.

We are indebted to Professor H. L. Solberg, Associate Dean of Engineering and former head of the School of Mechanical Engineering, Purdue University, who suggested the writing of this book, for his active encouragement and assistance, which in certain ways made possible the completion of the work. We should also like to express our thanks to Professors C. L. Brown, R. A. Olsen, J. K. Stene, and O. W. Witzell and Mr. R. A. Comparin, who reviewed parts of the manuscript and made valuable suggestions. Professor Brown also assembled most of the tabular data used in Chapter 13. We are indebted to Jane Hardcastle Jones, wife of one of the authors, who gave unsparingly of her time to prepare the figures and perform some of the calculations.

J. B. J.
G. A. H.

Purdue University
February 1960

Contents

Symbols   xv

1. Fundamental Concepts and Definitions   1

1. Thermodynamics. 2. Engineering thermodynamics. 3. On definitions in general. 4. The language of mathematics. 5. The undefined
terms. 6. Thermodynamic systems. 7. Ideal and actual systems.
8. Properties, states, and processes. 9. Density, specific volume,
and specific weight. 10. Pressure. 11. Temperature. 12. Temperature scales. 13. Work. 14. Work of a frictionless process, closed
system. 15. Steady flow. 16. Work of a frictionless steady-flow
process. 17. Heat. 18. Point and path functions. 19. Summary.
References. Problems.

2. The First Law of Thermodynamics   54

1. The first law of thermodynamics. 2. The proportionality factor J.
3. The first law for noncyclic processes. Energy. 4. The nature of E.
5. Enthalpy. 6. The first law applied to (stationary) closed systems.
7. The first law applied to open systems. 8. The first law applied to
open systems—steady flow. 9. The first law applied to open systems—general formulations. 10. Heat engines, thermal efficiency;
refrigerators, coefficient of performance. 11. Limitation of the first
law. 12. Historical note on the first law. 13. Summary. References.
Problems.

3. Physical Properties I   106

1. Phases of substances; solids, liquids, and gases. 2. Equilibrium of
phases of a pure substance. 3. Phase diagrams. 4. Other property
diagrams. 5. Specific heat and latent heat. 6. Phase changes.
7. The critical point. 8. Tables of properties. 9. Summary. References. Problems.

4. Ideal Gases 151

1. The ideal gas. 2. Real gases and the ideal-gas equation of state. 3. The ideal-gas thermometer scale. 4. Internal energy and enthalpy of ideal gases. 5. Specific heats of ideal gases. 6. Special relations for ideal gases with constant specific heats. 7. The ideal-gas equation of state and kinetic theory. 8. Specific heats of ideal gases and kinetic theory. 9. Summary. References. Problems.

5. Real Gases 188

1. Compressibility factors. 2. Reduced coordinates. 3. The van der Waals equation of state. 4. The Beattie-Bridgeman equation of state. 5. Virial equations of state. 6. Specific heats of real gases. 7. Summary. References. Problems.

6. The Second Law 210

1. Limitations of the first law. 2. The second law of thermodynamics. 3. Perpetual-motion machines. 4. The value of the second law. 5. Conclusion.

7. Reversible and Irreversible Processes and Cycles 218

1. Reversible and irreversible processes. Definitions. 2. Reversible and irreversible processes. Characteristics; illustrations. 3. Internal and external reversibility. 4. $\int p\,dv$ and $\int v\,dp$ in irreversible processes. 5. Reversible and externally reversible cycles. 6. The Carnot cycle. 7. The reversed Carnot cycle. 8. Other externally reversible cycles. 9. Irreversible processes and molecular disorder. 10. Summary. References. Problems.

8. Some Consequences of the Second Law 250

1. The Carnot principle. 2. The efficiency of reversible engines. 3. The thermodynamic temperature scale. 4. Summary. References. Problems.

9. Entropy 266

1. The property entropy. 2. Calculation of entropy changes. 3. Entropy as a coordinate. 4. A useful relationship among properties. 5. The increase of entropy principle. 6. Available and unavailable energy. 7. Helmholtz (A) and Gibbs (G) functions. 8. Uses of entropy. 9. Entropy and probability. 10. Summary. References. Problems.

10. Physical Properties II   320

1. The Maxwell equations. 2. The Clapeyron equation. 3. The Joule-Thomson coefficient. 4. General equations for changes in entropy, internal energy, and enthalpy in terms of p, v, T, and specific heats. 5. Specific heat relations. 6. Ideal-gas property tables. 7. Property diagrams. 8. The rigorous approaches. 9. Summary. References. Problems.

11. Availability and Irreversibility   363

1. Maximum work. 2. Availability. 3. Irreversibility. 4. Availability accounting. 5. Summary. References. Problems.

12. Gas and Gas-Vapor Mixtures   391

1. Mass fraction; mole fraction. 2. Partial pressure; partial volume. 3. Dalton's law or the law of additive pressures. 4. Amagat's law, Leduc's law, or the law of additive volumes. 5. Properties of ideal-gas mixtures. 6. Mixing of ideal gases initially at different pressures and temperatures. 7. Mixtures of real gases. 8. Mixtures of ideal gases and vapors. 9. Atmospheric air. 10. Relative humidity and humidity ratio. 11. Temperatures used in the determination of the properties of atmospheric air. 12. Psychrometric charts. 13. Processes of air-vapor mixtures under constant total pressure. 14. Summary. References. Problems.

13. Chemical Reactions: Combustion   436

1. The basic combustion reactions. 2. The composition of dry air. 3. Ideal combustion. 4. Actual combustion mass balance. 5. Energy balance for a chemical reaction. 6. Enthalpy of reaction. 7. Internal energy of reaction. 8. Maximum adiabatic combustion temperature. 9. Chemical equilibrium. 10. Second-law analysis of chemical reactions. 11. Summary. References. Problems.

14. Chemical Equilibrium in Ideal-Gas Reactions   482

1. Criteria of equilibrium. 2. The equilibrium constant. 3. The relationship between K_p and ΔH_R. 4. The relationship between K_p and ΔG_R. 5. Summary. References. Problems.

15. Thermodynamic Aspects of Fluid Flow   503

1. One-, two-, and three-dimensional steady flow. 2. Total enthalpy, total temperature, and total pressure. 3. The dynamic equation for

steady one-dimensional flow.   4. Sonic velocity; Mach number.
5. The basic relations. 6. Area variation for the isentropic flow of any
fluid.   7. Adiabatic flow of ideal gases.   8. Adiabatic flow of vapors.
9. Flow through orifices.   10. The Fanno line; flow in pipes.   11. The
Rayleigh line; conditions across a normal shock.   12. Summary.
References. Problems.

16. Compression and Expansion Processes: Fluid Machines   **540**

1. Steady-flow compression processes. 2. Steady-flow expansion processes. 3. Incompressible flow through machines. 4. Energy transfer
between a fluid and a rotor. 5. Dynamic compressors. 6. Turbines.
7. Reciprocating machines. 8. Summary. References. Problems.

17. Gas Power Cycles   **565**

1. Air-standard analyses. 2. The simple gas-turbine cycle. 3. The
regenerative gas-turbine cycle. 4. Intercooling and reheating in gas-
turbine cycles. 5. Gas-turbine jet propulsion. 6. The air-standard
Otto cycle. 7. The air-standard Diesel cycle. 8. The dual cycle and
others. 9. Compound power plants. 10. Summary. References.
Problems.

18. Vapor Power Cycles   **596**

1. The Carnot cycle using steam. 2. The Rankine cycle. 3. The regenerative steam power cycle. 4. The reheat cycle. 5. Cycles for
heating and power. 6. Binary vapor cycles. 7. Summary. References. Problems.

19. Refrigeration   **622**

1. The reversed Carnot cycle. 2. Definition of the ton of refrigeration. 3. The reversed Brayton cycle. 4. Vapor-compression refrigeration. 5. Absorption refrigeration. 6. Liquefaction of gases.
7. Summary. References. Problems.

20. Binary Mixtures   **644**

1. The phase rule. 2. Miscibility. 3. Liquid-vapor equilibrium; miscible liquids. 4. Liquid-vapor equilibrium; immiscible and partially
miscible liquids. 5. Solid-liquid equilibrium; immiscible solids and
miscible liquids. 6. Summary. References. Problems.

21. Heat Transfer   **661**

1. Steady-state one-dimensional conduction.   2. Convection.   3. Radiation.   References.   Problems.

Appendix A: Dimensions and Units   **681**

Appendix B: Note on Partial Derivatives   **687**

Tables and Charts   **692**

Tables A·1, 2, 3   Properties of steam
Tables A·4, 5, 6   Properties of ammonia
Table A·7   Properties of Freon 12
Table A·8   Properties of air
Chart A·1   Temperature-entropy diagram for air
Chart A·2   Temperature-entropy diagram for steam
Chart A·3   Enthalpy-entropy diagram for steam
Chart A·4   Pressure-enthalpy diagram for ammonia
Chart A·5   Properties of aqua ammonia
Chart A·6   Psychrometric chart

Problem Answers   **713**

Index   **717**

Symbols

A area; Helmholtz function, $U - TS$

a linear acceleration; specific Helmholtz function, $u - Ts$; velocity of a pressure wave

b Darrieus function, $h - T_0 s$

C a constant; number of components (in the phase rule)

C_p molar specific heat at constant pressure

C_v molar specific heat at constant volume

c constant-temperature coefficient, $(\partial h/\partial p)_T$; velocity of sound

c_p specific heat at constant pressure, $(\partial h/\partial T)_p$

c_v specific heat at constant volume, $(\partial u/\partial T)_v$

E stored energy

e specific stored energy, E/m

F force; maximum number of independent intensive properties (in the phase rule)

F_A configuration factor for radiant heat transfer

F_ϵ emissivity factor for radiant heat transfer

f number of degrees of freedom of a molecule

G Gibbs function, $H - TS$

g gravitational acceleration or the acceleration of a freely falling body; specific Gibbs function, $h - Ts$

g_c dimensional constant

H enthalpy, $U + pV$

ΔH_f enthalpy (change) of formation

ΔH_R enthalpy (change) of reaction

h specific enthalpy, $u + pv$; height of a fluid column; convective heat-transfer coefficient

I irreversibility

i specific irreversibility, I/m

J conversion factor, 778 ft-lb/B

k	ratio of specific heats, c_p/c_v; thermal conductivity
K_p	equilibrium constant
KE	kinetic energy
L	length
M	mass rate of flow; molecular weight
m	mass
m'	mass of a molecule (Chapter 4); mass of extracted steam per pound of steam entering turbine
N	number of moles
N_M	Mach number, V/c
n	polytropic exponent
P	power; number of phases (in the phase rule)
p	pressure
p_r	relative pressure
PE	potential energy
Q	heat
$\dot{Q}$	time rate of heat transfer
q	heat transfer per unit mass
R	gas constant
R_u	universal gas constant
r	radius; compression ratio
r_c	cut-off ratio
S	entropy
s	specific entropy
T	absolute temperature
t	temperature
U	internal energy; over-all heat-transfer coefficient
ΔU_R	internal energy (change) of reaction
u	specific internal energy; velocity; velocity of a point on a rotor
V	volume, velocity
v	specific volume
v_r	relative specific volume
W	work
w	work per unit mass; weight
X	mass fraction (Chapters 19 and 20)
x	quality; mole fraction; a property in general; distance in the direction of heat conduction
Y	stream availability
y	specific stream availability; a property in general

Z compressibility factor, $Z \equiv pV/mRT$

z elevation

Greek letters

α absorptivity

β coefficient of performance; coefficient of volume expansion, $(\partial v/\partial T)_p/v$

γ specific weight

ϵ emissivity

η efficiency; number of molecules

Θ Debye's constant or characteristic temperature

θ temperature on any nonthermodynamic scale

κ_s isentropic compressibility, $-(\partial v/\partial p)_s/v$

κ_T isothermal compressibility, $-(\partial v/\partial p)_T/v$

μ Joule–Thomson coefficient, $(\partial T/\partial p)_h$

ν stoichiometric coefficient (number of moles in chemical equation)

ρ density; reflectivity

σ Stefan–Boltzmann constant

τ time; transmissivity

Φ availability of a closed system

ϕ specific availability of a closed system, $\dfrac{\Phi}{m}$; $\displaystyle\int \dfrac{c_p dT}{T}$; relative humidity

ω humidity ratio

Subscripts

a air

c critical state; (see also g_c in list of symbols)

dg dry gas

f final state; saturated liquid; fuel

fg difference between property of saturated liquid and property of saturated vapor at the same pressure and temperature

g saturated vapor

H high temperature (as in T_H and Q_H)

i initial state; ice point; ideal or isentropic; intermediate (as intermediate pressure in multistage compression)

if difference between property of saturated solid and saturated liquid at the same pressure and temperature

ig difference between property of saturated solid and saturated vapor at the same pressure and temperature

L low temperature (as in T_L and Q_L)

m mixture

N molar (as in v_N for molar specific volume)

0 base state; standard state; state of the atmosphere

R reduced coordinate; energy reservoir

r relative

s steam point

t total or stagnation

u universal

v vapor (in gas-vapor mixtures)

σ referring to an open-system boundary

1, 2, 3   referring to different states of a system or different locations in space

CHAPTER 1

Fundamental Concepts and Definitions

The study of any science must begin with an understanding of certain definitions and conventions. A sound knowledge of these definitions and conventions at the outset, just like an understanding of the ground rules at the start of a baseball game, will prevent many later misunderstandings.

The beginning student of thermodynamics is sometimes dismayed by the amount of time or number of words used in establishing and explaining the definitions; however, precise definitions, well understood, pave the way toward a sound understanding of the science.

This chapter is concerned primarily with definitions and conventions which are used repeatedly in later chapters. Careful study of this chapter is therefore essential for ready understanding of topics which follow.

1·1 Thermodynamics

Thermodynamics is the science dealing with energy transformations, including heat and work, and the physical properties of substances that are involved in energy transformations.

The origin of thermodynamics may be traced to early studies of the performance of steam engines. Its range of application was then broadened to cover other types of heat engines, or devices which convert heat or fuel energy into work, and the early refrigerating machines. Since the middle of the nineteenth century the scope of thermodynamics has grown so greatly that today an understanding of thermodynamics is essential for much of the work of the engineer, physicist, and chemist.

1·2 Engineering thermodynamics

Engineering thermodynamics is that part of the science which deals with all types of heat engines, refrigeration, air conditioning, combustion, the compression and expansion of fluids, and the physical properties of the substances used in these applications.

The automobile engine is an example of a device which converts part of the chemical energy of a fuel into work. The remainder of the energy obtained from the fuel is discharged to the surroundings by way of the exhaust gases and the cooling water. By thermodynamic analysis it is possible to predict the amount of fuel and the amount of air required by the engine to provide a certain work output. The amount of energy carried away by the cooling water and by the exhaust gases can be predicted. The effects of increasing the engine compression ratio can be made clear by application of the basic laws of thermodynamics.

A household electric refrigerator is another example of a device which is designed in accordance with the principles of thermodynamics. Suppose the temperature to be maintained in the refrigerator compartment and the amount of heat to be removed from the compartment are known. The problem is to design a refrigerating unit which will perform this service. Typical questions which can be answered by the use of thermodynamics are: What will the normal power consumption be? Of the many different refrigerating fluids available, is there one which will result in a lower power requirement than the others? What pressure must the units be built to withstand? Can the pressure range be changed by using a different refrigerant? How much air must be blown across the warm condenser coils during normal operation?

Steam engines were commercially successful long before the basic laws of thermodynamics were formulated, and the early builders of refrigerating machines and internal-combustion engines had little or no knowledge of thermodynamics as we now know it. However, while it was the practical problems concerned with these early machines that called for the development of thermodynamics, the resulting science has led the way toward improvements and new processes undreamed of by the pioneer builders and inventors. Thus engineering practice and thermodynamics have advanced together with now one and now the other in the lead. Today, the continuing work of engineers toward improvements and innovations in equipment and processes and the need for accurate predictions of performance make thermodynamics an indispensable engineering tool.

1·3   On definitions in general

In order for people to communicate effectively with one another, they must agree as to the meaning of the terms they use. That is, each term or word used must relate to the same (or at least to a similar) experience, object, or operation for each of the people involved.

Even aside from words which are entirely new to someone, it is sometimes difficult to achieve such agreement on terms. We know that many words have multiple meanings. For example, consider the many different meanings of the nouns "run," "break," and "point" and of the verbs "run" and "draw." These obvious examples cause little misunderstanding, however, because people are readily aware that the words have multiple meanings and the intended meaning is usually made clear by the context.

Serious difficulties in communication and understanding result, however, when it is not realized that some of the words used have different meanings for the various people involved. This causes much trouble in the study of engineering and science. To many people a statement about "the power in a gallon of gasoline" may have some meaning, but as power is defined in physics and engineering, such a statement is nonsense. Also, people who use the words speed and velocity synonymously think a physicist is talking nonsense when he refers to the difference in velocity of an automobile moving north at 50 mph and another one moving west at 50 mph, because they do not realize that the physicist, for sound reasons, considers direction as well as magnitude in his definition of velocity. Thus the need for precise definitions is obvious.

A definition of a word must relate the word to some experience, with experience understood to be an inclusive term covering both events and objects. Now we shall investigate how definitions should be made in order to establish clearly the intended relation between a word and an experience.

The best way to explain the meaning of a word to someone who has no idea of its meaning is to point out as many objects or operations as possible to which the word relates. This would amount to a nonverbal definition.

For many reasons, definitions usually must be verbal; that is, a word is usually defined by means of other words. To be of value, a verbal definition must use only words which are understood or independently defined. Violations of this rule can be found in any poor dictionary. For example, suppose we were entirely ignorant of the meaning of the word *shrill*. We could refer to a dictionary and find:

> *shrill:* having a high-pitched tone or sound.

Now if we do not know the meaning of *high* as used with *pitch*, we look and find:

> *high:* (Music) acute in pitch.

We are still no better off than at first unless we learn the meaning of *acute*, so we turn again to the dictionary:

> *acute:* high or shrill.

We are obviously going in a circle, and as long as we use only verbal definitions we shall continue to go in circles. This is the same difficulty we shall have if we try to learn a foreign language by using a dictionary in that language alone. Each word we look up will be defined in terms of other words we do not know, and these other words in turn are defined by still others we do not know. We must start by knowing the meaning of a few words in the foreign language in terms of words in a language we understand.

By the same reasoning, we can see that the meaning of words in our own language can be made clear by verbal definitions only if we start with some words which we directly relate to physical events or objects. These words are *undefined* verbally. Other words can then be defined in terms of these *undefined* words.

The idea that definitions of some words cannot be stated is surprising to some people, but the logical structure of any science must be based on the acceptance of certain undefined terms as starting points. Precisely which terms are accepted as undefined is usually a matter of convenience. The undefined terms which will be used in this book are listed in Art. 1·5.

Specifying a word as undefined does not mean that we are unable to explain its meaning to someone, but rather that we are unable to express its meaning only in terms of simpler words. If X is an undefined term (say mass, time, temperature, or length), we cannot complete a simple defining statement which begins, "X is $\cdots$". However, we can describe operations and experiments which demonstrate the effects of X and which allow us to assign numbers to the magnitude of X. In brief, we can tell *about* X but we cannot answer the question "What *is* X?"

An *operational* definition is one which specifies a method of measuring the defined quantity or specifies a test to be applied to an event or object to see whether it fits the definition. It gives directions for performing the operations which relate the defined word to nonverbal events or objects. It is therefore more valuable than a nonoperational definition.

As an example of a nonoperational definition, there is:

> *translational kinetic energy:* energy of a body which is due to its translational motion.

An operational definition of the same term is:

> *translational kinetic energy:* the energy of a body which is evaluated by $mV^2/2g_c$, where m is the mass of the body, V its translational velocity, and g_c a dimensional constant.

The terms energy, mass, and velocity which are used in these definitions must be independently defined or must be accepted as undefined terms.

In the operational definition given above, the operations are partly paper-and-pencil operations; but they are nevertheless operations which result in a definite number for translational kinetic energy.

In order for the definition to be of value, the specified measurement or test operations must be possible. We might define length in terms of operations with a yardstick or a foot rule. These operations would be possible for the measurement of the length of a tennis court, but they would not serve for measuring the dimensions of an atom. As far as operations are concerned, these two "lengths" are entirely different kinds of quantities, since they cannot be measured by the same operations.

Summarizing this discussion of definitions:

1. Precise definitions are essential for effective communication and understanding.

2. Some words must be accepted as undefined on the verbal level.

3. All other words should be defined in terms of these undefined words in order to avoid "circularity" in definitions.

4. Definitions are most effective in relating words to events or objects if the definitions are operational. An operational definition includes directions for measuring the defined quantity or for testing an event or object to see if it fits the definition.

1·4   The language of mathematics

The language we use in everyday communication and in much of our thinking is not a precise language; that is, the meaning of a written statement may not be the same for all readers. Let us list some reasons why the meaning of a statement differs among various readers.

1. As mentioned in the preceding article, many words have multiple meanings. (What connections are there among a heavy weight, a heavy line, a heavy opera, a heavy motor oil, and a heavy accent?)

2. Many words have "biased" meanings. For example, we think of steam as being "hot" and are therefore surprised when we first learn of a home being cooled by steam. Similarly, if we are told that someone put his finger into molten metal we think of the event as tragic until we consider that he might have put his finger into a cup of mercury at room temperature. Our conceptions of steam and of molten metal are "biased" toward steam and molten metal which are at high temperatures.

3. We deal largely with two-valued properties. Our habit of classifying as good or bad, extrovert or introvert, hard or soft, and so forth tends to obscure the fact that these are all multivalued properties, that there are many degrees of hardness and of introversion and so forth.

We do not encounter these same difficulties when we use a mathematical language. One reason for the clarity of mathematical language is that it is an operational language. One way of interpreting the equation

$$x^2 - x + 4 = 0$$

is: "The number for which x stands is such that, if it is multiplied by itself and then this product is diminished by the number itself and increased by four, the result is zero." Thus the equation gives us directions for specific operations which will test whether any given number can be substituted for x.

A further advantage of a mathematical statement is that it is more concise than an equivalent word statement. Mathematical notation is sometimes referred to as a "shorthand." Consider how many words would be required to express the same information given by

$$\left(\frac{\partial p}{\partial v}\right)_T = 0 \qquad \text{or} \qquad T_1 = T_2 e^{\mu\alpha}$$

A third advantage of mathematics as a language is that it is exact. The result of a specified operation on x is the same regardless of who performs the operation or when or where or why it is performed. This point probably needs no supporting discussion except the observation that the variation in numerical answers obtained by different people performing the same operations on calculating machines, slide rules, or paper does not result from any ambiguity of the mathematical statement. It results from variations in the degree of precision involved in carrying out the specified operations.

A final comment on mathematics is that the operations are performed on abstract numbers only. A useful equation expresses a relationship among physical quantities, and the solution of the equation yields a numerical value for some physical quantity. However, the mathematical operations involved in solving the equation are in no way influenced by these physical relationships.

1·5 The undefined terms

In this textbook, terms which will be accepted as undefined verbally are time, length, temperature, mass, and force. A relationship among some of these is given by Newton's relation

$$F = \frac{1}{g_c} \frac{d}{d\tau} (mV) \tag{1·1}$$

in which F is the net force acting on a body of mass m which has a velocity V, τ is time, and g_c is a dimensional constant whose value depends only on the units selected for the other quantities (see Appendix A). It is also possible to choose *either* mass or force as an undefined term and then to define the other term by means of Newton's relation. In such case, whether mass or force is selected as undefined is a matter of convenience or personal preference. The selection may be entirely arbitrary.

In the same manner, the selection of the other undefined terms is entirely arbitrary. As an illustration of this point, it would be possible to select as undefined quantities time, velocity, temperature, and mass or force. Length could then be defined in terms of time and velocity. Such a procedure may not appeal to us, but it could be used.

A few terms, such as matter and acceleration, which are used frequently can be defined in terms of the undefined words listed, but the definitions are not repeated here because they are usually covered at length in elementary college physics courses with which you should be familiar.

Temperature is sometimes defined in terms of molecular activity. Such a definition may have some value, but it does not lend itself to any test by physical operations nor does it describe a relationship between temperature and other observable physical events. Occasionally temperature is defined in terms of heat, and such definitions are acceptable if heat is defined independently or is accepted as an undefined term. In this book, however, we will select the alternative approach and define heat by using temperature as an undefined term.

1·6   Thermodynamic systems

A thermodynamic system is defined as any quantity of matter or any region of space to which attention is directed for purposes of analysis. The quantity of matter or region of space must be within a prescribed boundary, although this boundary may be deformable and may be imaginary.

If a system is defined as a particular quantity of matter, then the system always contains the same matter and there can be no transfer of mass across the boundary. However, if a system is defined as a region of space within a prescribed boundary, then mass may cross the system boundary. In order to distinguish between these two types of systems, the type which has no mass transfer across its boundary we call a *closed system* or *fixed-mass system*. An *open system* is a region of space within a boundary which mass may cross. An open system is also called a *control volume* and its boundary is called a *control surface*.

Everything outside the system boundary is referred to as the *surroundings*. Usually the term surroundings is restricted to those things outside the system which in some way interact with the system or affect the behavior of the system.

A special case of a closed system is an *isolated system*. An *isolated system* is a system which in no way interacts with its surroundings. Notice that an isolated system must be a closed system, since the requirement that there be no interaction of the system with its surroundings prohibits any transfer of mass across the system boundary.

Examples of systems used in thermodynamic analysis range from tiny particles to complete, complex power plants and even to large regions in the earth's atmosphere. The most important step in the solution of a problem in thermodynamics is often the selection and careful specification of the system which is to be considered. The importance of this step will be emphasized frequently later in this book. A few examples of thermodynamic systems will now be considered.

In studying the flow of a gas through a pipe, the system might be defined as the gas within a certain length of pipe. For the study of gas compression, a gas trapped within a cylinder and being compressed by a piston can be considered as a system, in which case part of the system boundary is movable. Notice that, although the boundary moves, as long as it always encloses the same material, the system under consideration is a closed system.

In studying the operation of an automobile engine, the entire engine can be considered as an open system. Such a system interacts with the surroundings in several ways. Air and gasoline are drawn in and hot exhaust gases are discharged. The turning of the output shaft against a resisting torque is an interaction between the system and its surroundings. The engine also causes a rise in temperature of the air blown across its radiator. In making a thermodynamic analysis of the entire engine, all these interactions with the surroundings must be considered.

In order to study particular aspects of the engine operation, other systems may be selected. For example, a convenient system to use in a study of the combustion process might be the contents of one cylinder during the time interval between the closure of the intake valve and the opening of the exhaust valve. During this time interval no mass enters or leaves the cylinder; hence the contents of the cylinder constitute a closed system. The interactions between this system and its surroundings include the electric impulse to the spark, the action of the gas against the moving piston, and the transfer of heat between the system and its surroundings.

For a study of the exhaust process, the system selected might be one cylinder while its exhaust valve is open. This system is bounded by the piston face, the cylinder walls, the cylinder head, the intake valve, and the exhaust-valve port opening. While the exhaust valve is open, mass flows across this boundary, so the system must be classified as an open system. The interactions between this system and its surroundings include the action of the gas against the moving piston, heat transfer, and the flow of mass from the system to the surroundings.

1·7 Ideal and actual systems

In solving physical problems, we often focus our attention not on the actual system at hand but instead on some idealized system which is similar to, but simpler than, the actual system. For example, in calculating the mechanical advantage of a system of ropes and pulleys (actual system), it is customary to start with the consideration of frictionless pulleys and weightless, nonstretching ropes (ideal system). An ideal system differs from the corresponding actual system in that it can be completely described in terms of a few characteristics. An actual system has many characteristics, some of which are highly pertinent to the behavior under study, many of which are immaterial, and some of which may have slight or unknown influence. The ideal system may be described in terms of only those characteristics which have a major influence on the actual system's behavior. Then this ideal system is analyzed under the assumption that no other system characteristics influence its behavior.

In order to obtain an accurate prediction of the behavior of an actual system, the result of the calculation on a corresponding ideal system must be adjusted to account for the fact that the ideal and actual systems do not behave in exactly the same way. Nevertheless, an ideal system is helpful in solving the problem. Another example of the use of an ideal system is in the calculation of the stress in a simple beam. Part of this calculation is generally made by using an ideal beam which is assumed, among other things, to be homogeneous and undistorted by the application of a load. No actual beam meets these conditions, even though for many applications the behavior of the ideal beam simulates that of the actual beam so closely that no correction need be made when applying the result for one to the other.

Many other examples of the substitution of an ideal system for an actual one for the purposes of analysis can be given. It is important to recognize such a substitution when it is made in order to avoid the error of predicting the behavior of an actual system by an analysis of an ideal system which may behave quite differently. This is the error which frequently leads to statements such as "Theoretically yes, but actually no." No contradiction troubles us if we realize that we are probably talking about different systems when we speak of a "theoretical" result and an "actual" result.

1·8 Properties, states, and processes

A *property* is any observable characteristic of a system. Examples of properties are pressure, temperature, modulus of elasticity, volume, and dynamic viscosity. We also consider as properties any combination of observable characteristics such as, for example, the product of pressure and temperature. Such properties can be thought of as *indirectly* observable characteristics of a system. Any number of such properties can be defined, but only a few are useful. Another type of property is the kind which cannot be directly observed and cannot be obtained by mathematical operations on other properties but can be defined only by means of the laws of thermodynamics. Two such properties, internal energy and entropy, will be introduced later. The *state* or condition of a system is specified by the values of its properties. Since there are numerous relationships among the properties of particular systems, the values of a few properties will often identify a state completely because all other properties can be determined in terms of these few. Precisely how many properties are required to specify the state of a system depends on the complexity of the system.

If a system has the same values of its properties at two different times, the system is in identical states at these two times.

A system is said to be in an equilibrium state (or in equilibrium) if no changes can occur in the state of the system without the aid of an external stimulus. A test to see if a system is in equilibrium is to isolate the system and observe whether any changes in its state occur. Obviously the temperature must be the same throughout a system which is in equilibrium, for otherwise when the system is isolated there would be a transfer of heat from one part of it to another to change the temperature distribution. Also, there can be no eddying motions of a fluid in a system in equilibrium, because, when the system is isolated, these motions will eventually cease and thus the state of the system will have changed without any external effects. In order to be in equilibrium, a system must be homogeneous or must consist of a finite number of homogeneous parts in contact. Such homogeneity is not sufficient to insure equilibrium, however. For example, a system comprised of iron, water vapor, and air at room temperature consists of a finite number of homogeneous parts in contact, but it is not in equilibrium because it will certainly change state through the oxidation of the iron without any interaction with the surroundings. Notice that the properties of a system such as pressure, temperature, and velocity can each be represented by a single number only if the system is in a state of equilibrium. For this reason, equilibrium states are much easier to specify than nonequilibrium states and elementary thermodynamics is concerned chiefly with equilibrium states and the changes of systems from one equilibrium state to another.

A transformation of a system from one state to another is called a *process*. The *path* of the process is the series of states through which the system passes during the process. A *cycle* or *cyclic process* is a process (or a series of processes) which returns the system to the state it was in before the process began. The properties of the system vary during the execution of a cycle, but at the completion of a cycle all properties have been restored to their initial values. In other words, the net change in a property is zero for any cycle. This is concisely stated by

$$\oint dx = 0$$

where x is any property and the symbol $\oint$ indicates integration around a cycle.

By definition, the properties of a system are characteristics which can be directly or indirectly observed while the system is in any given state. The system may have reached that state by means of any one of an infinite number of different processes, but the properties of the system in that state are independent of the history of the system. Thus, when a system changes from one state to another, the properties of the system undergo a change which depends only on the end states and not on the path followed between the two end states. Since the values of properties do depend only on the states of systems and not on the paths followed by systems in changing states, properties are called *state functions* or *point functions*.

A quantity whose value depends on the particular path followed in passing from one state to another is called a *path function*. The distinction between point functions and path functions is considered in detail in Art. 1·18. The terms are introduced here so that one important characteristic of point functions can be introduced: Point functions (properties) can be used as coordinates on diagrams representing states of a system. Property diagrams are used widely in thermodynamics.

Consider a system for which two properties are sufficient to determine all other properties, and thus the state, of the system. Let these two properties be X and Y. (X and Y might stand for pressure and volume, for example.) Each state of the system can then be represented by a point on XY coordinates. In Fig. 1·1, point A represents the state for which $X = X_A$ and $Y = Y_A$. Any other property Z is a function of the state and hence of X and Y.

$$Z = f(X, Y) \qquad Z_A = f(X_A, Y_A)$$

Another state of the system is state B. At state B, the properties have values X_B, Y_B, and Z_B. The differences in values of the properties between the two states are

$$\Delta X = X_B - X_A \qquad \Delta Y = Y_B - Y_A \qquad \Delta Z = Z_B - Z_A$$

and no information is needed regarding any path between A and B in order to evaluate these differences. Conversely, measurements made on the system only at states A and B can give no information as to which of the many possible paths between A and B was actually followed.

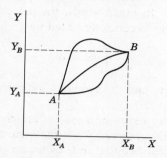

Fig. 1·1   Property diagram showing three paths between states A and B.

If a system which is homogeneous is divided into two parts, the mass of the whole system is equal to the sum of the masses of the two parts. The volume of the whole is also equal to the sum of the volumes of the parts. On the other hand, the temperature of the whole is not equal to the sum of the temperatures of the parts. In fact, the temperature, pressure, and density of the whole are the same as of the parts. This brings us to the distinction between *extensive* and *intensive* properties.

If the value of a property for a system is equal to the sum of the values for the parts of the system, that property is an *extensive* property. Mass, volume, weight, and several other properties (energy, enthalpy, entropy) which will be introduced later are *extensive* properties. An *intensive* property is one which has the same value for any part of a homogeneous system as it does for the whole system. The measurement of an intensive property can be made without knowledge of the total mass or extent of the system. Pressure, temperature, and density are examples of intensive properties.

If the value of any extensive property is divided by the mass of the system, the resulting property is intensive and is called a specific property. For example, specific volume is obtained by dividing the volume (an extensive property) of a system by its mass. This ratio of volume to mass is the same for any part of a homogeneous system and for the system as a whole; therefore it is an intensive property. The symbol convention usually followed is to use a capital letter for an extensive property and the same lower-case letter for the corresponding specific property. Thus V is used for volume and v is used for specific volume.

$$v = \frac{V}{m}$$

where m is used for mass (an exception to the convention of using capital letters for extensive properties).

If all possible physical measurements on a system indicate that it is in the same state it was in at some previous time, we refer to the two states as identical states. This does not mean that we believe each molecule to have the same location and velocity that it previously had. It means only that on a *macroscopic* level the states are identical; on the *microscopic* level we can make no direct measurements and consequently have no evidence for conclusions regarding individual molecules. The macroscopic viewpoint is used almost exclusively in thermodynamics; hence no assumptions regarding the ultimate structure of matter need be made. We will occasionally use a molecular picture to augment our understanding of some phenomenon, but it must be clearly understood that the laws of thermodynamics are based solely on macroscopic observations and in no way depend on molecular theory. (The explanation of physical phenomena on the basis of molecular behavior is the goal of *kinetic theory* which is based on the application of the laws of mechanics to individual molecules. Another approach is that of *statistical thermodynamics* in which the behavior of individual molecules is not treated but probability considerations are applied to the very large numbers of molecules which comprise any macroscopic quantity of matter. The approach to thermodynamics followed in this book is often called *classical thermodynamics* to distinguish it from statistical thermodynamics.)

1·9 Density, specific volume, and specific weight

Density (ρ) is defined as the mass of a substance divided by its volume, or the mass per unit volume.

$$\rho \equiv \frac{\text{mass}}{\text{volume}} = \frac{m}{V}$$

Specific volume (v) is defined as the reciprocal of density or the volume per unit mass.

$$v \equiv \frac{V}{m} = \frac{1}{\rho}$$

Specific weight (γ) is defined as the weight of a substance divided by its volume, or the weight per unit volume.

$$\gamma \equiv \frac{\text{weight}}{\text{volume}} = \frac{w}{V}$$

The relation between specific weight and density can be developed by applying Newton's second law of motion to a body of fixed mass to get

$$F = \frac{1}{g_c} ma \qquad (1\cdot2)$$

If the only external force acting on a body is the gravitational force which we call weight, the resulting acceleration is the gravitational acceleration g.

$$w = \frac{1}{g_c} mg \qquad (1\cdot3)$$

This equation is the basic relation between weight and mass. If each side of this equation is divided by the volume of the body under consideration, the basic relation between specific weight and density is obtained.

$$\gamma = \rho \frac{g}{g_c} \qquad (1\cdot4)$$

g_c is a dimensional constant, not a conversion factor, and so it is included in equations where needed. A different approach, also valid, which is not used in this book is that g_c is a conversion factor or unitary constant. Within this approach, g_c need not be written in equations and equation 1·4 appears as $\gamma = \rho g$. This point is discussed in Appendix A.

Specific gravity is defined as the ratio of the density of a substance to some standard density. The standard density used with solids and liquids is often that of water at some specified temperature such as 32 F, 39 F (the temperature of maximum density for water at a pressure of one atmosphere), or 60 F. Specific gravity can also be considered as the ratio of the specific weight of a substance to some standard specific weight if both are measured in the same gravitational field. Since specific gravity is a dimensionless ratio, its numerical value is independent of any system of units.

1·10 Pressure

Pressure is defined as the force exerted by a system on a unit area of its boundary. It is possible for the pressure to vary from place to place on the system boundary, even when the system is in equilibrium. For example, consider a system comprised of a fluid (either gas or liquid) in a closed tank. A simple force balance on the fluid shows that the pressure increases toward the bottom of the tank as a result of the weight of the fluid which acts downward. In many applications it is assumed that the variation in pressure caused by gravity is negligible.

Most pressure-measuring instruments measure the difference between the pressure of a fluid and the pressure of the atmosphere. This pressure *difference* is called *gage pressure*. The absolute pressure of the fluid is then obtained by the relation

$$p_{abs} = p_{atm} + p_{gage}$$

If a fluid exists at a pressure lower than atmospheric pressure, its gage pressure is negative and the term *vacuum* is applied to the magnitude of the

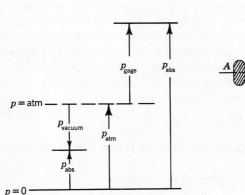

Fig. 1·2 Relationships among absolute, gage, and vacuum pressures.

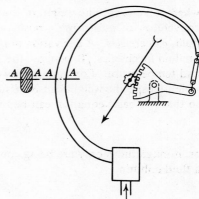

Fig. 1·3 Schematic diagram of a Bourdon gage.

gage pressure. For example, a gage pressure of −5 psi is spoken of as a *vacuum* of 5 psi. The relationships among absolute pressure, gage pressure, atmospheric (or barometric) pressure, and vacuum are shown graphically in Fig. 1·2.

In engineering practice, pressures are generally measured by means of Bourdon tube gages or manometers. A Bourdon tube gage is shown schematically in Fig. 1·3. One end of a bent tube having an elliptical cross section is rigidly fixed. The other end is closed and is connected to a pointer by means of a linkage. When a fluid under pressure is admitted to the tube, the elliptical section tends to become circular. This causes the tube to become straighter and thus move the pointer along a graduated scale. If a pressure less than atmospheric is applied to the tube, the curvature of the tube increases and the pointer is moved in the opposite direction. The gage is calibrated so that the scale reading gives in some convenient units the difference between the pressure of the fluid inside the tube and that of the fluid surrounding the tube. If the fluid surrounding the tube is at atmospheric pressure, then the gage reading is the gage pressure of the fluid inside the tube.

A manometer indicates a pressure difference by balancing a measurable length of fluid column against the pressure difference. For a fluid in static equilibrium, the relationship between pressure and elevation within the fluid is given by the basic equation of fluid statics,

$$dp = -\gamma \, dz \tag{1.5}$$

where γ is the specific weight of the fluid. The minus sign results from the convention of measuring z positively upward. Thus, as z increases in a fluid, p decreases. A derivation of this equation can be found in textbooks on fluid mechanics. In general, the specific weight is a function of pressure and temperature. For liquids, however, which are only slightly compressible, the specific weight can be assumed constant with respect to pressure so that the basic equation can be integrated to give

$$\Delta p = -\gamma \, \Delta z$$

or, if magnitudes only are being considered and h stands for the height of a fluid column,

$$\Delta p = \gamma h$$

As a result of the use of manometers and the direct proportionality between pressures and manometric fluid heights, pressures are often expressed in units such as inches of mercury, inches of water, millimeters of mercury. Vacuum readings, no matter how they are obtained, are generally expressed in inches of mercury. A pressure which is less than atmospheric pressure by 10 in. of mercury is spoken of as a "vacuum of 10 inches of mercury" and is written "10 in. Hg vac."

EXAMPLE 1·1. Determine the barometric pressure in pounds per square inch if the barometer reading is 76.0 cm of mercury. The specific gravity of mercury is 13.59.

Solution. Converting the barometric reading to English units,

$$h = \frac{76[cm]}{2.54[cm/in.]} = 29.9 \text{ in. Hg}$$

The specific weight of mercury is obtained by multiplying its specific gravity by the specific weight of water.

$$\gamma = 13.59(62.4) = 848 \text{ lb/cu ft}$$

Then, applying the basic equation of fluid statics for an incompressible fluid,

$$p = p - 0 = \Delta p = \gamma h$$

$$= \frac{848[\text{lb/cu ft}]\ 29.9[\text{in.}]}{1728[\text{cu in./cu ft}]} = 14.7\ \text{psia}$$

EXAMPLE 1·2. Determine the pressure difference represented by (a) 1 in. of mercury, (b) 1 ft of water.

Solution. (a) For 1 in. of mercury,

$$\Delta p = \gamma h = 13.6(62.4)\tfrac{1}{12}(\tfrac{1}{144}) = 0.491\ \text{psi}$$

(b) For 1 ft of water,

$$\Delta p = \gamma h = 62.4(1)\tfrac{1}{144} = 0.433\ \text{psi}$$

EXAMPLE 1·3. A Bourdon gage reads 20.0 psi when the barometer stands at 28.2 in. of mercury. Compute the absolute pressure of the fluid in the gage.

Solution. In the solution of Example 1·2 above it was shown that a pressure of 1 in. of mercury is equivalent to 0.491 psi.

$$p_{\text{barometric}} = 28.2[\text{in. Hg}]0.491[\text{psi/in. Hg}] = 13.85\ \text{psia}$$

$$p = p_{\text{barometric}} + p_{\text{gage}} = 13.85 + 20.0 = 33.9\ \text{psia}$$

EXAMPLE 1·4. A vacuum gage reads 10 in. of mercury when the atmospheric pressure is 29.4 in. of mercury. Compute the absolute pressure.

Solution.

$$p = 29.4 - 10 = 19.4\ \text{in. Hg abs or } 9.54\ \text{psia}$$

1·11 Temperature

The familiar sense perceptions of "hot" and "cold" are qualitative indications of the *temperature* of a body. No definition of temperature is given here because temperature is one of the terms (such as mass, length, and time) which we will consider as undefined verbally. We cannot make a simple, direct statement which defines temperature in terms of words which are either independently defined or accepted as undefined. We will, however, specify some operations by which numerical values can be assigned to various temperatures.

It is customary to speak of a hot body as having a higher temperature than a cold body. Our sense of touch readily indicates which of two bodies of the same material is "hotter" or at the higher temperature, but numerical values cannot be assigned to various temperatures on the basis of physiological sensations alone. Fortunately, when the temperature of a body changes, several other properties also change. Any one of these temperature-dependent properties might be used as an indirect measurement of temperature. For example, the volume of a bar of steel increases as the steel gets "hotter." The electrical resistance of the bar also increases as the temperature rises. Many other temperature-dependent properties of materials can be brought to mind, and several different ones are actually used in the measurement of temperature. Before the measurement of temperature can be discussed further, the concept of equality of temperature must be introduced.

If a hot body and a cold body are brought into contact with each other while isolated from all other bodies, the hot body becomes colder or the cold body becomes hotter, or both of these changes occur.* Finally, all changes in the properties of the bodies cease. The bodies are then at the same temperature and are said to be in *thermal equilibrium* with each other. It should be noted that such *equality of temperature* is possible even though the bodies have equal values of no other properties. Two bodies may be at the same temperature although the mass of one is many times the mass of the other.

It is a matter of experience that *two bodies each in temperature (or thermal) equilibrium with a third body are in temperature equilibrium with each other*. (This statement is sometimes called the zeroth law of thermodynamics.) In view of this fact, it is possible to determine if two bodies are at the same temperature without bringing them into contact with each other; it is necessary only to see if they are each in thermal equilibrium with a third body. The third body is usually what we call a thermometer. A thermometer is a body which has a readily measurable property which is a function of temperature. In a mercury-in-glass thermometer, the volume of the mercury depends on its temperature. In a resistance thermometer, the electrical resistance of the thermometer element is a temperature-dependent property. In order for a thermometer to indicate the temperature of another body, the thermometer and the other body must be in contact with each other long enough and must be sufficiently isolated from other bodies so that they will attain temperature equilibrium with each other. The temperature of the thermometer is then the temperature of the other body.

1·12   Temperature scales

We now consider the establishment of a numerical scale of temperature which will permit the temperature of a body to be specified quantitatively. One way to establish a temperature scale is first to assign numerical values to certain accurately reproducible temperatures. The reproducible temperatures so selected as reference points are usually (1) the equilibrium

---

* If the hot body is one pound of steel at 100 F and the cold body is ten pounds of ice at one atmosphere, 32 F, then the temperature of only the hot body will change. You can readily think of other cases in which the temperature of only one of the bodies changes.

temperature of ice and air-saturated water under a pressure of 14.696 psia, and (2) the equilibrium temperature of pure liquid water in contact with its vapor at 14.696 psia. These two temperatures are referred to as the *ice point* and the *steam point*, respectively. They are used as reference temperatures because they are accurately reproducible in any laboratory. On the Fahrenheit* scale, the ice point is assigned the value 32 and the steam point is assigned the value 212.

We establish a mercury-in-glass thermometer scale by first bringing such a thermometer to the ice point and marking the position of the mercury surface in the stem 32, and then bringing the thermometer to the temperature of the steam point and marking the position of the mercury surface 212. The stem is then divided into 180 equal parts or degrees. We can establish a resistance thermometer scale by first noting the electrical resistance of a wire at the ice point and at the steam point and then making a straight-line plot of temperature versus resistance. A similar procedure can be followed with a thermocouple, resulting in a straight-line plot (based on two points) of temperature versus emf for a fixed cold-junction temperature. If these three thermometers are placed together in a fluid which is at the ice point, all will read 32. If they are placed together in a fluid at the steam point, all will read 212. Agreement at the ice and steam points results, of course, from the calibration of these thermometers at these two temperatures which are used to define the Fahrenheit scale. If the three thermometers are placed in a fluid at a temperature A which causes the mercury-in-glass thermometer to read 122 F, the other two thermometers will generally indicate temperatures slightly different from 122 F. This means that, while the expansion of mercury between the ice point and temperature A is one half of its expansion between the ice and steam points, the changes in the thermometric properties of the other thermometers do not have the same one-to-two ratio for these two temperature differences. This sort of discrepancy is found even among thermometers based on the same thermometric property, say, the expansion of a liquid. (Strictly speaking, the volume is the thermometric property, but

---

* Gabriel Daniel Fahrenheit (1686–1736), German physicist and instrument maker, was the first to use mercury-in-glass thermometers. Alcohol and linseed oil had earlier been used as thermometric fluids. Fahrenheit's scale was a modification of one proposed by Sir Isaac Newton with 0 for the ice point and 12 for normal human body temperature. Fahrenheit lowered the zero of the scale to the temperature of a salt–ice mixture and made the degree smaller so that body temperature was 96. His measurements showed the ice and steam points to be at 32 and 212, respectively, based on the reference points at 0 and 96. Subsequently, the 32 and 212 were adopted as reference points, and refinements in thermometers have revealed that the salt–ice-mixture minimum temperature and normal body temperature are not exactly 0 and 96 on the present Fahrenheit scale.

only the change of volume is measured.) If three thermometers, all calibrated at 32 and 212 F read 122, 120, and 126 F when at the same temperature, which one is "correct"? This question cannot be answered from the data given. One may be tempted to say that two of the thermometers are "nonlinear" with temperature, but notice that there is no reason to establish any one as a standard in preference to the others. Thus a shortcoming of any temperature scale defined in terms of the physical properties of a substance is apparent. In Chapter 8 we shall see how it is possible to establish a *thermodynamic scale of temperature* which is independent of the properties of any substance.

Still, for convenience and for the purpose of having some scale as a reference until we develop the thermodynamic scale, we must define a temperature scale in terms of a readily measurable property of some substance. For reasons which will be brought out in Arts. 4·3 and 8·3, one of the best temperature scales related to physical properties is based on the variation with temperature of the pressure or volume of certain gases at low pressures.

A constant-volume gas thermometer consists of a gas, usually hydrogen or helium, contained in a constant-volume vessel provided with a means for measuring the gas pressure. The gas pressure varies with the temperature of the gas. Constant-volume gas thermometers calibrated at the ice point and the steam point agree closely with each other at other temperatures, even though different gases may be used. This agreement becomes better as the pressure of the gases (hence the mass in a given volume) is reduced. Extrapolation shows that the agreement becomes exact as the pressure approaches zero. Temperatures are measured on the constant-volume gas thermometer scale by the use of a linear relationship between temperature and pressure as shown in Fig. 1·4. The equation of the line shown is

$$t = t_0 + \left(\frac{t_s - t_i}{p_s - p_i}\right)p = t_0 + \frac{t_s - t_i}{p_s/p_i - 1}\left(\frac{p}{p_i}\right)$$

where the subscripts i, s, and 0 denote respectively conditions at the ice point, at the steam point, and at the temperature at which the gas pressure is zero. The value of t_0 can be obtained by the following procedure: The ratio of the pressure at the steam point to the pressure at the ice point is measured for several different pressures at the ice point, the pressure at the ice point being varied by changing the amount of gas in the constant-volume thermometer. It is found that the measured pressure ratio p_s/p_i is a function of the ice-point pressure as shown in Fig. 1·5. In that figure, four measurements of the ratio are shown for some gas A. Measurements on some other gas B give slightly different values. It is an important fact that when the measurements are extrapolated to $p_i = 0$, the value of the ratio p_s/p_i is the same for all gases and is 1.3661. Using this value in the equation of the line in Fig. 1·4, and substituting t_i and p_i as one possible pair of corresponding values of t and p,

$$t_0 = t - \frac{t_s - t_i}{p_s/p_i - 1}\left(\frac{p}{p_i}\right) = 32 - \frac{212 - 32}{1.3661 - 1}(1) = -459.69 \text{ F}$$

The *absolute* Fahrenheit gas thermometer scale is defined as the scale on which (1) t_0 in the equation above is assigned the numerical value of zero,

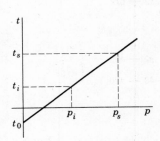

Fig. 1·4   Constant-volume gas thermometer relationship.

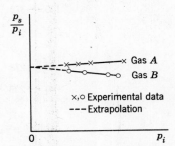

Fig. 1·5   Determination of t_0 on a constant-volume gas thermometer.

and (2) the interval between the ice and steam points is 180 degrees, i.e., the degree is the same "size" as the Fahrenheit degree. The absolute Fahrenheit scale is called the Rankine* scale.

Notice that the definition of a gas thermometer absolute-temperature scale does not imply that a temperature equal to or lower than zero on that scale is unattainable, nor does it involve any assumption regarding the behavior of any substance at or near that temperature.

Four temperature scales are encountered frequently in engineering practice: Fahrenheit, Rankine, centigrade, and Kelvin. The relationships among them are shown in Fig. 1·6 and are given by the following equations in which temperatures on the various scales are distinguished by subscripts and absolute temperatures are denoted by T instead of t.

$$T_R = t_F + 459.69 = \tfrac{9}{5}T_K$$
$$T_K = t_C + 273.16 = \tfrac{5}{9}T_R$$

The values 459.69 and 273.16 are replaced by the approximate values 460

---

* William John MacQuorn Rankine (1820–1872), Scotch engineer and professor of civil engineering at the University of Glasgow, made several outstanding contributions to the development of thermodynamics and its engineering applications. He was the author of several books and more than 150 papers on thermodynamics, mechanics, canals, shipbuilding, steam engines, and water supply systems.

and 273 in this textbook. For conversions between the Fahrenheit and centigrade scales a convenient, easy-to-remember relation which is based on the fact that -40 C $= -40$ F is as follows:

$$t_F = (t_C + 40)\tfrac{9}{5} - 40$$
$$t_C = (t_F + 40)\tfrac{5}{9} - 40$$

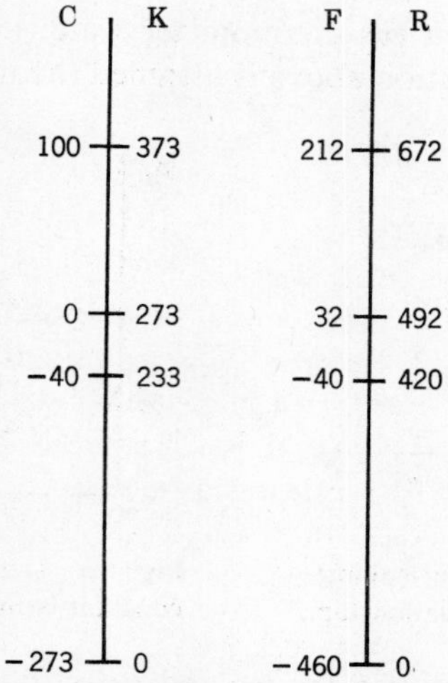

C	K		F	R
100	373		212	672
0	273		32	492
−40	233		−40	420
−273	0		−460	0

Fig. 1·6 Comparison of temperature scales.

1·13 Work

Work is an interaction between a system and its surroundings. Work is done by a system on its surroundings if the sole external effect of the interaction could be the lifting of a body. The magnitude of work is the product of the weight of the body lifted and the distance it could be lifted if the lifting of the body were the sole external effect of the interaction. This definition points out that work involves both a system and something outside the system, whether it is called the surroundings or another system. In two systems *A* and *B* interacting only with each other, the work done *by* system *A* is work done *on* system *B* and vice versa. The definition tells how to identify and measure the work done *by* a system. Work done *on* a system must be identified as work done *by* some other system. This roundabout method is necessary because the definition of work when reworded as "work is done on a system if the sole external effect could be the fall of a body" is *not true*, as is shown in Example 1·10.

Consider a system comprised of a compressed coil spring. As the spring expands against some part of its surroundings, the action of the spring on its surroundings could be reduced to the lifting of a weight. It does not matter whether the spring is actually being used to move an object against frictional resistance, to accelerate a body, or to push a plunger which in turn forces a fluid to flow through a small opening. The important fact is that the sole external effect *could be* the lifting of a weight while the spring undergoes the same process.

Consider a system comprised of a gas trapped in a cylinder behind a movable piston. If the gas expands, pushing the piston outward, the sole effect external to the gas *could be* the lifting of a body. If frictional effects are present in the surroundings, there may actually be effects other than the lifting of a body. For example, the temperature of some part of the surroundings may increase. However, if the frictional effects are reduced, the limiting case in which the sole external effect is the lifting of a weight is approached. The limiting condition of no friction in the surroundings is a useful concept in the identification and measurement of work. The use of this concept does not restrict us to the consideration of processes that involve no friction. It must be remembered that in deciding whether a certain interaction of a system with its surroundings is work, we ask, not if the sole external effect *is* the lifting of a weight, but rather: "*Could* the sole external effect be the lifting of a weight?" In seeking an answer to this question we consider as one possibility the limiting case of no friction in the surroundings.

A system comprised of a storage battery interacts with its surroundings by means of the electric current passing through its terminals. The electric current can be used to run a motor which in turn lifts a weight. For the limiting case of no frictional effects in the surroundings, the lifting of the weight would be the only effect outside the system, so the storage battery has done work on its surroundings. (The turning of the motor is not in itself an effect on the surroundings because, after the process is completed and the motor is brought to rest, it is in a state identical with its initial state. There has been no net change in the state of the motor. The weight, on the other hand, does show an effect of the process: The elevation of the weight after the process is different from its initial elevation.)

There is a widespread convention that work done *by* a system is expressed by *positive* numbers and work done *on* a system is expressed by *negative* numbers. Of course, since work is an interaction between systems, work done by one system must be done on some other system, so the same work is positive with respect to one system and negative with respect to another. Suppose that system A does 1000 ft-lb of work on system B. Following the convention described, we express this as

$$W_A = 1000 \text{ ft-lb} \quad \text{or} \quad W_B = -1000 \text{ ft-lb}$$

In this textbook, the work of a system is often specified as work$_{in}$ (meaning work done on the system) or work_{out} (meaning work done by the system) in order to avoid dependence on the sign convention. Where the subscript indicating direction is not used, however, the usual convention is followed: The term work, without a subscript indicating direction, means work done by the system to which the term is applied. As an illustration of both the sign convention and the use of directional subscripts, suppose again that system A does 1000 ft-lb of work on system B. We can then write

$$W_{in,A} = -1000 \text{ ft-lb} \qquad W_{in,B} = 1000 \text{ ft-lb}$$

$$W_{out,A} = 1000 \text{ ft-lb} \qquad W_{out,B} = -1000 \text{ ft-lb}$$

$$W_A = 1000 \text{ ft-lb} \qquad W_B = -1000 \text{ ft-lb}$$

Even though we speak of the work of a system, it is important to remember that work is an interaction between two systems.

The state of a system changes as work is done on or by the system. Work is not a characteristic which can be observed while a system is in a particular state. Thus work is not a property of a system. The change in value of a property is the same for all processes between two given end states; the amount of work done depends on the path of the process between the two end states. For this reason, work is called a *path function*. It was pointed out in Art. 1·8 that properties are *point functions*. The distinction between point and path functions is the subject of Art. 1·18.

Work which is done by means of an electric current is called electrical work. Work done by means of a magnetic field is called magnetic work. Work which is done by the action of a force at a moving boundary of a system is called mechanical work. The actions of the spring and the expanding gas discussed above are examples of mechanical work. *Mechanical work is work which is due to the action of a force on a moving boundary of a system. Its magnitude is equal to the product of the force and the displacement of its point of application in the direction of the force.* In many engineering applications of thermodynamics, mechanical work is the only form of work involved. However, thermodynamics deals with all forms of work; consequently, this article was opened with a general definition which includes all forms of work which come within the broad scope of thermodynamics.

In this textbook of engineering thermodynamics, the term *work* without modifiers will generally mean mechanical work. Exceptions to this rule will be made clear by the context.

The definition of mechanical work does not require that the system boundary move in a direction normal to itself. Also, shear forces at the system boundary as well as normal forces are to be considered. An illustration of these two points is provided by a system comprised of the gas inside a rigid tank. A shaft extends through the wall of the tank, and on the end of the shaft inside the tank is a thin circular disk. When the shaft and disk are turned at high speed, they do work on the gas even though (1) the volume of the gas remains constant, and (2) there is no movement of the system boundary in a direction normal to the boundary. The part of the gas near the shaft and disk is moving, however, and there is a force exerted by the shaft and disk on this moving part of the system. This illustration can also be made by taking as the system everything inside the tank, including the disk and that part of the shaft which is within the tank. An interaction between this system and its surroundings occurs where the shaft crosses the system boundary. Work is done on the system by means of the torque on the rotating shaft. If that part of the system boundary which is a plane cutting the shaft is considered to be moving (rotating) because the part of the system adjacent to it is moving, this interaction between the system and its surroundings comes within the given definition of mechanical work.

The definition of mechanical work specifies that its magnitude is equal to the product of a force and the displacement of the point of application of the force in the same direction. This method of calculating work is familiar to anyone who has studied mechanics. If the force F acts on a body which is displaced a distance s in the direction of the force, then the work done is given by

$$\text{Work} = Fs$$

(If the line of action of the force and the total displacement are not in the same direction, then either F is taken as the force component in the direction of the displacement, or s is taken as the displacement component in the direction of the force.) The work done during a differential displacement ds is a differential amount of work, δ work, and is given by

$$\delta \text{ work} = F\,ds \qquad (1\cdot6a)$$

The differential of a path function is written with the symbol δ instead of the symbol d. This point is discussed further in Art. 1·18. For a finite displacement, the total amount of work done is given by

$$\text{Work} = \int F\,ds \qquad (1\cdot6b)$$

Integration of this expression requires a knowledge of the functional relationship between F and s.

1·14   Work of a frictionless process, closed system

Derivation of a useful expression from mechanics. There are a number of cases in which the work done in a process can be calculated by expressing $\int F\,ds$ in terms of a relationship between two properties of a system.* This article and Art. 1·16 discuss two of these cases.

An expression will now be developed for the work done by a system during a process which satisfies the following conditions:

1. The system is closed.
2. There are no frictional effects within the system. This precludes fluid shear forces on any part of the system.
3. The pressure is the same on all boundaries of the system; thus a single number represents the pressure of the system. (Conditions 2 and 3 can be established by requiring that the system be at any instant in a state of equilibrium or infinitesimally close to an equilibrium state. A process carried out under such conditions is sometimes called a *quasistatic* process.)
4. There are no effects of electricity, magnetism, motion, gravity, or capillarity. (Effects of motion, gravity, and capillarity are also ruled out by strict adherence to condition 3 above.)

An explanation of the condition of no gravity is required. How can any expression developed for this condition be of value? The answer to this question is that, although the relation to be developed is exactly correct only for this condition, it is sufficiently accurate for many situations encountered in practice where gravitational effects are negligible in comparison with other effects. If we are told that air at 50 psia, 80 F, is stored in a 6-ft-diameter spherical tank, we generally do not ask where in the tank the air pressure is 50 psia. The reason we do not ask is that the difference in pressure between air at the highest point and the lowest point in the tank is only about 0.01 psi, and for most purposes this slight variation in pressure caused by gravity can be neglected. Similarly, the effects of motion such as the acceleration of part of the system by means of a moving piston are often negligible.

As an example of a system which satisfies the conditions listed above, consider a gas trapped in a cylinder and expanding against a piston as shown in Fig. 1·7. The gas expands from an initial state 1 to a final state 2. The piston moves slowly so that effects of motion on the system are negligible. The pressure is uniform throughout the system at any stage of the expansion, but the value of this uniform pressure changes as the expansion proceeds. At any stage of the expansion, the force on the piston is the product of the pressure of the gas and the area of the piston. Since this force acts in the direction of motion of the piston, the work done by the gas on the piston while the piston moves a distance ds is

$$\delta \text{ work} = F\,ds = pA\,ds$$

* See M. W. Zemansky, *Heat and Thermodynamics*, McGraw-Hill Book Co., 4th. ed., 1957, chapter 3.

A ds is the volume increase *dV* of the system as the piston travels the distance *ds*, and so

$$\delta \text{ work} = p \, dV \tag{1·7a}$$

and the total amount of work done by the gas on the piston as the gas expands from state 1 to state 2 is

$$\text{Work}_{1\text{-}2} = \int_1^2 p \, dV \tag{1·7b}$$

The *pV* diagram. The area beneath a curve on pressure–volume coordinates is $\int p \, dV$, and so the work of the process described above is

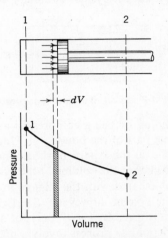

Fig. 1·7   Pressure–volume diagram for a gas expanding in a cylinder.

represented by an area on a plot of the system pressure versus its volume as shown in the lower part of Fig. 1·7. The crosshatched area represents the work done by the gas as its volume increases by an amount *dV*. The total area beneath curve 1-2 is $\int_1^2 p \, dV$ and represents the work done by the system as it passes from state 1 to state 2.

Many different paths can be followed by a closed system as it changes from one particular state to another by means of frictionless processes. If these paths are plotted on a *pV* diagram, it is seen that in general the area beneath each path is different from that beneath other paths. This result was expected, because it has been pointed out that work is a path function and its value therefore depends on the path of the process between any two states and not on the states themselves.

The sign convention. Work done as the system expands is work done by the system, because the sole external effect could be the lifting of a body.

When work is done by a system, $\int p\, dV$ is positive. The process executed by the system may be a compression instead of an expansion. When a system is compressed frictionlessly, work is done *on* the system and $p\, dV$ is negative. Thus the equation

$$\text{Work} = \int p\, dV \qquad (1\cdot 7c)$$

agrees with the sign convention of work out of (or by) the system as positive and work into (or on) the system as negative.

A special application. There are cases in which $\int p\, dV$ has significance even though shear forces at the system boundary are present. Consider a

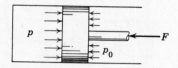

Fig. 1·8   Effect of atmospheric pressure.

system which is expanding or being compressed at the same time that a shear force acts at some part of the boundary. Under these conditions, if the pressure is uniform over those parts of the boundary which are moving in such a manner as to change the volume of the system, then $\int p\, dV$ is the work done which is associated with the change in volume. It is not the total work done by the system, however. (See Example 1·7.) The total work done by a system is given by $\int p\, dV$ only for a frictionless process of a closed system. A frictionless process involves no fluid shear forces. (A gas stirred by a paddle wheel inside a rigid tank serves to show that work cannot be calculated by $\int p\, dV$ for all processes of closed systems. For this system, $\int p\, dV$ is zero because the volume is constant; but the work is not zero as long as the paddle wheel is stirring the gas. Therefore, work $\neq \int p\, dV$.)

Absolute or gage pressure in $\int p\, dV$? Absolute pressure must be used when the work of a system is evaluated by $\int p\, dV$. However, sometimes the result obtained by using gage pressure is significant. Referring to Fig. 1·8, the work done on the piston by the gas expanding frictionlessly in this system is given by

$$\text{Work} = \int p\, dV \qquad (1\cdot 7c)$$

where p is the absolute pressure of the gas. Part of this work is used to push back the atmosphere, and the rest is used to move the piston against a resistance made up of the force F on the piston rod and the frictional force of the cylinder wall on the piston. (Notice that this frictional effect is outside the system; the system is expanding frictionlessly.) The atmosphere is assumed to be so large that its pressure p_0 is unaffected by changes in volume of the order of that caused by the expansion of the system. Therefore, the work done by the system on the atmosphere is given by

$$\text{Work} = \int p_0 \, dV = p_0 \int dV = p_0 \, \Delta V$$

The work done on the piston rod and to overcome the cylinder wall friction is the work of the expanding gas minus the work done in pushing back the atmosphere.

$$(\text{Total work of system}) - (\text{work done on atmosphere}) = \int p \, dV - \int p_0 \, dV$$

$$= \int (p - p_0) \, dV$$

$$= \int p_{\text{gage}} \, dV$$

Generalizing, the use of gage pressure in $\int p \, dV$ for a closed-system frictionless process gives the work of the system excluding the work done on the surrounding atmosphere. We make little use of this fact because (1) we frequently deal with cyclic processes in which the net work on the atmosphere is zero, and (2) in our later work we find that it is the total work done by a system that we can most conveniently relate to various system properties and to other interactions of the system with its surroundings.

The work of a cyclic frictionless process of a closed system. A closed system may pass by means of frictionless processes from a state 1 to a state 2 along a path such as 1-a-2 in Fig. 1·9. It may then complete a cycle by returning to state 1. During the return process, the system may pass through different states from those it passed through during the initial processes 1-a-2. Let one of the states passed through during the return process be state b, as shown in Fig. 1·9.

During some of the processes of the cycle the system does work on its surroundings; during other processes work is done on the system. The net work of the system for the cycle is the sum of the work of all the processes making up the cycle. Considering the cycle to be made up of four processes,

$$\binom{\text{Work of closed system}}{\text{during frictionless cycle}} = \int_1^a p \, dV + \int_a^2 p \, dV + \int_2^b p \, dV + \int_b^1 p \, dV$$

$$= \oint p \, dV$$

where the symbol $\oint$ denotes integration along a closed or cyclic path.

The work done by the system during each process is represented by the area beneath the pV plot of the process, and Fig. 1·9 shows that the net work of the cycle is represented by the area enclosed within the diagram. Notice that the net work of a cycle is generally not zero, even though (by definition of a cycle) the system is returned to its initial state. This is another reminder that work is a path function and cannot be evaluated from only the end states of a process.

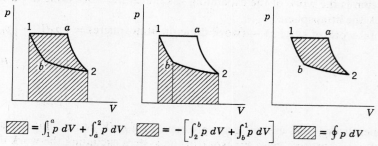

$$\boxed{\hspace{0.8cm}} = \int_1^a p\, dV + \int_a^2 p\, dV \quad \boxed{\hspace{0.8cm}} = -\left[\int_2^b p\, dV + \int_b^1 p\, dV\right] \quad \boxed{\hspace{0.8cm}} = \oint p\, dV$$

Fig. 1·9 Cyclic, frictionless process of a closed system.

Indicator diagrams. The pressure inside the cylinder of a reciprocating engine or compressor can be measured and plotted against the piston position or cylinder volume automatically by means of a device called an indicator. From the resulting pressure–volume record or indicator diagram, the work done on the piston can be determined. The indicator diagram is not the same as the pressure–volume diagrams shown with this article because the pV diagrams shown here are for closed systems, whereas the cylinder of an engine or compressor is not a closed system during a complete cycle of operations.

EXAMPLE 1·5. A fluid expands frictionlessly in a closed system from a volume of 3 to 7 cu ft in such a manner that the pressure is given by $p = CV^{-2}$, where C is a constant. The initial pressure is 45 psia. Calculate the amount of work done.

Solution. Since a frictionless process of a closed system is involved and the relation between pressure and volume implies that the pressure is uniform throughout the system, the work done by the system is given by

$$\text{Work} = \int_1^2 p\, dV$$

In order to integrate this expression, the relation between p and V must be used. Thus,

$$\text{Work} = \int_1^2 p\, dV = \int_1^2 \frac{C\, dV}{V^2} = -C\left[\frac{1}{V_2} - \frac{1}{V_1}\right]$$

The numerical value of C could be computed and then substituted with the values of

V_2 and V_1 into the equation above. Less numerical computation is required if the value of C from the given pV relation is substituted: $C = pV^2 = p_1V_1^2 = p_2V_2^2$.

$$\text{Work} = -C\left[\frac{1}{V_2} - \frac{1}{V_1}\right] = -p_1V_1^2\left[\frac{1}{V_2} - \frac{1}{V_1}\right] = -p_1V_1\left[\frac{V_1}{V_2} - 1\right]$$

$$= -45(144)3[\tfrac{3}{7} - 1] = 11{,}110 \text{ ft-lb}$$

The numerical value obtained is the work *out* or the work done *by* the system. If the numerical value obtained were negative, the conclusion would be that work had been done *on* the system.

EXAMPLE 1·6. The cylinder shown in the figure is closed at its upper end and has a cross-sectional area of A sq ft. Initially it contains V_1 cu ft of a gas at atmospheric

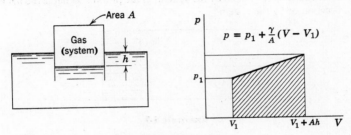

Example 1·6

pressure. The outer vessel, which contains a liquid with a free surface exposed to the atmosphere, is filled to the point of overflowing. How much work must be done on or by the gas if it expands until the liquid level in the cylinder is h ft lower than that in the surrounding vessel?

Solution. The gas trapped in the cylinder constitutes a closed system. Assuming that the expansion of the gas occurs slowly so that frictional effects within the gas are negligible and the pressure throughout the gas is uniform, the work done by the gas is given by

$$\text{Work} = \int_{V_1}^{V} p\, dV$$

where the subscript 1 refers to the initial condition, and properties without subscripts are those at any stage of the expansion. In order to integrate this expression, we must find a relationship between p and V. Initially, since the gas in the cylinder is at atmospheric pressure, the liquid level is the same inside and outside the cylinder or $h = 0$. The volume of the gas at any stage of the expansion is given by

$$V = V_1 + Ah$$

and then, since V_1 and A are constants,

$$dV = A\, dh$$

The pressure can also be expressed in terms of h. Making use of the pressure–height relation for incompressible fluids,

$$\Delta p = \gamma h$$

where γ is the specific weight of the liquid, we have

$$p = p_1 + \gamma h$$

Since we now have both p and dV in terms of h, we can use h as the variable of integration.

$$\text{Work} = \int_{V_1}^{V} p\,dV = \int_{h=0}^{h} (p_1 + \gamma h)A\,dh$$

Integration and substitution of the limits gives

$$\text{Work} = A\left[p_1 h + \frac{\gamma h^2}{2} \right] = Ah\left[p_1 + \frac{\gamma h}{2} \right]$$

This work is represented by the crosshatched area on the pV diagram shown.

EXAMPLE 1·7. Consider as a system the fluid contained in the cylinder as shown in the figure. The fluid expands from a volume of 1.40 to 1.60 cu ft while the pressure remains constant at 100 psia and while the paddle wheel does 3600 ft-lb of work on the system. How much work is done by the system on the piston? What is the net amount of work done on or by the system?

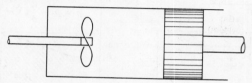

Example 1·7

Solution. This process is obviously not frictionless because fluid shear forces are involved in the interaction between the paddle wheel and the gas (system). However, *if the action of the paddle wheel is such that the pressure at the piston face is uniform and of known value at each stage of the process*, the work done on the piston (or in other words the work associated with a change in volume of the system) can be calculated by

$$\text{Work} = \int p\,dV$$

For the special case of a constant pressure, this relation becomes

$$\text{Work} = p\int_{1}^{2} dV = p(V_2 - V_1)$$
$$= 100(144)(1.60 - 1.40) = 2880 \text{ ft-lb}$$

Since the paddle-wheel work is work done on the system, we write in accordance with the usual sign convention, work = -3600 ft-lb. The net work of the system (meaning work done *by* the system in accordance with the convention) is

$$\text{Net work} = \text{work}_{\text{piston}} + \text{work}_{\text{paddle}}$$
$$= 2880 + (-3600) = -720 \text{ ft-lb}$$
$$\text{Net work}_{\text{in}} = 720 \text{ ft-lb}$$

Recall that these results are based on the assumption that the pressure on the piston face is 100 psia all through the process.

1·15 Steady flow

The last article concerned a formulation for the mechanical work of a frictionless process of a closed system. There is no analogous method for determining the work of a frictionless process of an open system except for the special case of *steady flow* through the open system. This article will discuss steady flow, and the next one will present a means of calculating the work of a frictionless steady-flow process.

The flow through an open system is *steady flow* (and the system is often called a *steady-flow system*) if all properties at each point within the system remain constant with respect to time. This definition requires that the following particular conditions be met:

1. The properties of the fluids crossing the boundary remain constant at each point on the boundary.

2. The flow rate at each section where mass crosses the boundary is constant. (The flow rate cannot change as long as all properties, including velocity, at each point remain constant.)

3. The rate of mass flow into the system equals the rate of mass flow out of it, or the amount of mass enclosed by the boundary is constant. (If this were not true, the density in some parts of the system or the volume of the system would change in violation of the defining condition of steady flow.)

4. All interactions with the surroundings occur at a steady rate.

Notice that the four conditions enumerated above are in terms of observations that can be made at the boundary of the system, so that no knowledge of the inner workings of a system is needed in order to determine whether steady-flow conditions prevail.

Some examples of steady-flow systems are a section of pipe line, a gas turbine, a welding torch, a carburetor, a boiler, and an air-conditioning unit. (If all the listed conditions are met except that the properties at various points within the system or at the system boundary vary cyclically with time, periodically returning to the same values, the flow may be treated as steady flow. For example, the flow through a reciprocating engine can sometimes be treated as steady flow.)

The mass rate of flow of a fluid passing through a cross-sectional area A is

$$M = \frac{AV}{v} \tag{1·8a}$$

where V is the average velocity of the fluid in a direction normal to the plane of the area A, and v is the specific volume of the fluid.* For steady

---

* A more general expression is

$$M = \int \frac{u \, dA}{v} \tag{1·8b}$$

where u and v are values of velocity and specific volume which may vary across the flow cross section.

flow with fluid entering a system at a section 1 and leaving at a section 2,

$$M_1 = M_2 = \frac{A_1 V_1}{v_1} = \frac{A_2 V_2}{v_2} \tag{1.9}$$

This is the *continuity equation of steady flow*. It is an important relation which is frequently used. It can readily be extended to any number of system inlets and outlets.

1·16 Work of a frictionless steady-flow process

An expression for the work of a frictionless process of a *closed system* was derived in Art. 1·14. A useful expression for the work of a frictionless

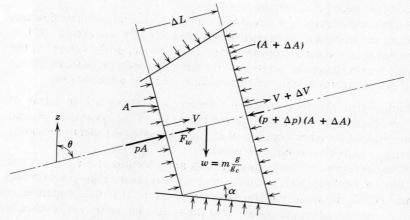

Fig. 1·10 Element of fluid in frictionless steady flow.

steady-flow process will now be derived. The derivation procedure is (*a*) make a free-body diagram of an element of fluid, (*b*) evaluate the external forces on the free body, (*c*) relate the sum of the external forces to the mass and acceleration of the free body, (*d*) solve the resulting relation for the force by which work is done on the fluid, and (*e*) apply the definition of work as $\int F\,ds$.

The absence of friction means that no shearing forces act on the fluid. An element of a fluid flowing under these conditions is shown in Fig. 1·10 where ΔL is to be considered small enough so that the variations of p, A, and V along ΔL are very nearly linear. This does not mean that the p, A, and V vary linearly with L, but only that ΔL is so small that a linear relation is a good approximation for the short distance ΔL. This approximation becomes better as ΔL becomes smaller, and later in the derivation an exact expression will be obtained by letting ΔL approach the differential length dL. The forces acting on this element in a direction parallel to the direction of flow are as follows:

1. The force of the adjacent fluid on the upstream face of the element, pA.

2. The force of the adjacent fluid on the downstream face of the element, $(p + \Delta p)(A + \Delta A)$.

3. The component of the weight of the element, weight $\cos \theta$ or $m(g/g_c) \cos \theta$.

4. The component of the normal wall forces in the direction of flow, $p_{avg} A_{surface} \sin \alpha$. Since it is assumed that the element is small enough so that p varies almost linearly along ΔL, the average pressure is the arithmetic mean of p and $(p + \Delta p)$, and the normal wall force component in the direction of flow is $(p + \Delta p/2)A_{surface} \sin \alpha$ or $(p + \Delta p/2) \Delta A$.

5. The force on the element F_w, by which work is being done on the fluid. This force is applied to the fluid by means of some impeller which is not shown in the figure.

The sum or resultant of these forces is

$$\sum F = pA - (p + \Delta p)(A + \Delta A) - m\frac{g}{g_c}\cos \theta + \left(p + \frac{\Delta p}{2}\right) \Delta A + F_w$$

$$= -A\,\Delta p - \frac{\Delta p\,\Delta A}{2} - m\frac{g}{g_c}\cos \theta + F_w \tag{a}$$

Applying Newton's second law of motion, the sum of the external forces on the fluid element must equal ma/g_c. The mass of the element is $\rho(A + \Delta A/2)\,\Delta L$, and the acceleration is approximately $\Delta V/\Delta \tau$. Thus

$$\sum F = \frac{ma}{g_c} = \frac{\rho}{g_c}\left(A + \frac{\Delta A}{2}\right)\Delta L\,\frac{\Delta V}{\Delta \tau}$$

Noting that $\Delta L/\Delta \tau = V_{avg} = V + \Delta V/2$,

$$\sum F = \frac{\rho}{g_c}\left(A + \frac{\Delta A}{2}\right)\left(V + \frac{\Delta V}{2}\right)\Delta V \tag{b}$$

Combining equations (a) and (b) and neglecting differences of the order of $\Delta p\,\Delta A$ and $\Delta A\,\Delta V$,

$$-A\,\Delta p - \frac{mg}{g_c}\cos \theta + F_w = \frac{\rho A V\,\Delta V}{g_c}$$

or

$$F_w = A\,\Delta p + \frac{\rho A V\,\Delta V}{g_c} + \frac{mg}{g_c}\cos \theta$$

The work done on the element (or the work put into the element) is

$$\text{Work}_{in} = F_w\,\Delta L = A\,\Delta L\,\Delta p + \frac{\rho A\,\Delta L V\,\Delta V}{g_c} + \frac{mg}{g_c}\,\Delta L\cos \theta$$

If differences of the order of $\Delta A \, \Delta L$ are neglected, then $A \, \Delta L$ is the volume of the element and $\rho A \, \Delta L$ is its mass. $\Delta L \cos \theta$ is Δz. Then

$$\text{Work}_{\text{in}} = F_w \, \Delta L = (\text{volume}) \, \Delta p + \frac{mV \, \Delta V}{g_c} + \frac{mg}{g_c} \, \Delta z$$

and per unit mass

$$\text{Work}_{\text{in}} = v \, \Delta p + \frac{V \, \Delta V}{g_c} + \frac{g}{g_c} \, \Delta z$$

Now, if ΔL is made to approach dL, then the other differences also approach differentials, and the work (per unit mass) done on the fluid in the distance dL is

$$\delta \, \text{work}_{\text{in}} = v \, dp + \frac{V \, dV}{g_c} + \frac{g}{g_c} \, dz \qquad (1 \cdot 10a)$$

or for flow between sections a finite distance apart

$$\text{Work}_{\text{in}} = \int v \, dp + \Delta \left(\frac{V^2}{2g_c} \right) + \frac{g}{g_c} \, \Delta z \qquad (1 \cdot 10b)$$

This is an important relation for the *mechanical work done on a unit mass of fluid in a frictionless steady-flow process.* Notice that it was derived from the principles of mechanics just as the analogous expression for the work of a frictionless closed-system process was derived.

EXAMPLE 1·8. A fluid flowing at a steady rate of 3.0 lb/sec through an open system expands frictionlessly according to the relation $pv^2 =$ constant from an initial pressure of 45 psia to a final pressure of 15 psia. The density of the fluid entering the system is 0.25 lb/cu ft. Changes in velocity and elevation are negligible. Calculate the power delivered by the fluid.

Solution. The power, or the rate at which work is done, can be calculated by multiplying the work done per pound by the mass rate of flow. Since the expansion is a frictionless steady-flow process, the work done by the fluid is given by

$$\text{Work}_{\text{out}} = w = -\int_1^2 v \, dp - \frac{V_2^2 - V_1^2}{2g_c} - \frac{g}{g_c} \, (z_2 - z_1)$$

Noting that the changes in velocity and elevation are negligible and that $pv^2 = C = p_1 v_1^2$,

$$w = -\int_1^2 v \, dp = -C^{1/2} \int_1^2 p^{-1/2} \, dp = -C^{1/2}(2)[p_2^{1/2} - p_1^{1/2}]$$

$$= -p_1^{1/2} v_1 (2)[p_2^{1/2} - p_1^{1/2}] = -2 p_1 v_1 \left[\left(\frac{p_2}{p_1} \right)^{1/2} - 1 \right] = 2 \frac{p_1}{\rho_1} \left[\left(\frac{p_2}{p_1} \right)^{1/2} - 1 \right]$$

$$= -\frac{2(45)144}{0.25} \left[\left(\frac{15}{45} \right)^{1/2} - 1 \right] = 21{,}900 \text{ ft-lb/lb}$$

$$\text{Power} = (\text{work})M = 21{,}900(3.0) = 65{,}700 \text{ ft-lb/sec}$$

$$= \frac{65{,}700}{550} = 119 \text{ hp}$$

EXAMPLE 1·9. Nitrogen flows steadily and frictionlessly through a nozzle at a rate of 0.27 lb/sec. It enters the nozzle at 40 psia, 600 R, with a specific volume of 5.75 cu ft/lb and a velocity of 500 fps. The nitrogen expands within the nozzle according to the relation $pv^{1.4}$ = constant and leaves at 20 psia. The change in elevation between inlet and outlet is negligible. Calculate the cross-sectional area of the nozzle outlet.

Analysis. Since the mass rate of flow is known, the outlet area can be obtained from the continuity equation,

$$A_2 = \frac{Mv_2}{V_2}$$

provided the specific volume and the velocity at the outlet can be found.

The outlet specific volume v_2 can be found from $p_1 v_1^{1.4} = p_2 v_2^{1.4}$ since v_1 and both pressures are known.

In order to find the outlet velocity V_2, let us investigate the suitability of the expression derived from the principles of mechanics,

$$w = -\int_1^2 v\,dp - \frac{V_2^2 - V_1^2}{2g_c} - \frac{g}{g_c}(z_2 - z_1)$$

Since there is no work done on or by a fluid passing through a nozzle, and the elevation change is negligible, the above expression reduces to

$$\frac{V_2^2 - V_1^2}{2g_c} = -\int_1^2 v\,dp$$

V_1 is known and the right-hand side can be integrated because the functional relationship between p and v is known; so V_2 can be found from this expression. The values of V_2 and v_2 which can be found by the methods outlined above can then be used in the continuity equation to give the value of A_2 which is being sought. This analysis thus outlines the method of solution.

Solution. The relation $p_1 v_1^{1.4} = p_2 v_2^{1.4}$ can be solved for v_2:

$$v_2 = v_1 \left(\frac{p_1}{p_2}\right)^{1/1.4} = 5.75 \left(\frac{40}{20}\right)^{1/1.4} = 9.43 \text{ cu ft/lb}$$

Since $pv^{1.4} = C$, work = 0 for flow through a nozzle, and the elevation change is negligible, the expression

$$\frac{V_2^2 - V_1^2}{2g_c} = -w - \int_1^2 v\,dp - \frac{g}{g_c}(z_2 - z_1)$$

reduces to

$$\frac{V_2^2 - V_1^2}{2g_c} = 0 - C^{1/1.4}\int_1^2 p^{-1/1.4}\,dp - 0$$

$$= -p_1^{1/1.4}v_1 \left(\frac{1.4}{1.4 - 1}\right)[p_2^{1-1/1.4} - p_1^{1-1/1.4}]$$

$$= -\frac{1.4}{0.4}p_1 v_1 \left[\left(\frac{p_2}{p_1}\right)^{1-1/1.4} - 1\right]$$

$$= -\frac{1.4}{0.4}(40)144(5.75)\left[\left(\frac{20}{40}\right)^{1-1/1.4} - 1\right] = 20{,}900 \text{ ft-lb/lb}$$

$$V_2 = \sqrt{2g_c(20{,}900) + V_1^2} = \sqrt{2(32.2)20{,}900 + (500)^2}$$

$$= 1263 \text{ fps}$$

The values found for v_2 and V_2 can now be used to find A_2:

$$A_2 = \frac{Mv_2}{V_2} = \frac{0.27(9.43)}{1263} = 0.00202^- \text{ sq ft} = 0.29^+ \text{ sq in.}$$

1·17 Heat

As discussed in Art. 1·11, if two bodies at different temperatures are brought into contact with each other while isolated from all other bodies, they will interact with each other so that the temperature of one or both will change until both bodies are at the same temperature. This interaction between the bodies or systems is the result only of the temperature difference between them and is called *heat*. *Heat is an interaction between a system and its surroundings which is caused by a difference in temperature between the system and its surroundings.* Conventionally, we say that heat is added to a body which becomes hotter or is taken from a body which becomes colder.* The definition above provides a means of *recognizing* the interaction called heat (and particularly provides a means of distinguishing this interaction from the one called work). In addition, we must have some method of *measuring* heat.

Heat can be measured by the use of *standard systems* which can be made to change from one readily recognizable state to another by means of the transfer of heat under specified conditions. The magnitude of the heat transferred is then given by the number of such standard systems which can be made to undergo the specified state change as a result of the interaction. For example, suppose we wish to know how much heat is transferred from a block of steel which cools from the temperature of boiling water at one atmosphere (212 F) to the temperature of freezing water at one atmosphere (32 F). The standard systems we use might be one-pound blocks of ice at 32 F. The steel block can be cooled by being isolated with one such block of ice after another so that each block of ice is melted but the temperature of the resulting liquid is not changed. The number of such standard systems (blocks of ice) so used is a measure of the amount of heat removed from the steel block. Of course, many different kinds of standard systems other than blocks of ice could be used.† (A word of caution is needed here. The conditions under which

---

* Unfortunately, conventional expressions such as "heat is added" and "heat is transferred," which stem from the now discredited caloric theory, tend to give the erroneous impression that heat is a substance. No such difficulty is encountered with the other interaction between systems, work.

† The original definitions of the units of heat, the calorie and the British thermal unit (Btu), were based on standard systems comprised of specified masses of water at specified temperatures. The specified state change in each case was a temperature change of one degree on a particular scale of temperature. The present definitions of the calorie and the Btu are discussed in Art. 2·2.

the standard systems interact with the steel block must be specified and precisely controlled. The blocks of ice, for example, can be made to change state even without heat transfer so the state changes are related to heat transfer only if they are carried out under the same specified conditions in each instance.) The important conclusion is that it is possible to describe certain operations by means of which heat can be measured; hence, heat can be defined operationally.

The widely adopted sign convention for heat is that heat added *to* a system is expressed by *positive* numbers and heat taken *from* a system is expressed by *negative* numbers. Suppose that 10 B of heat is transferred from system A to system B. Following the convention described, we express this as

$$Q_A = -10 \text{ B} \quad \text{or} \quad Q_B = 10 \text{ B}$$

In this textbook, directional subscripts are used for heat just as for work. Where the subscript indicating direction is not used, the usual convention is followed: Q (without a subscript) stands for the net amount of heat *added to* the system to which the term is applied. As an illustration of both the sign convention and the use of directional subscripts, suppose again that heat is transferred from system A to system B in the amount of 10 B. We can express this in the following ways:

$$Q_{\text{in},A} = -10 \text{ B} \qquad Q_{\text{in},B} = 10 \text{ B}$$

$$Q_{\text{out},A} = 10 \text{ B} \qquad Q_{\text{out},B} = -10 \text{ B}$$

$$Q_A = -10 \text{ B} \qquad Q_B = 10 \text{ B}$$

Heat, like work, is an interaction between systems. It is not a characteristic which can be observed while a system is in a particular state. It is not a property of a system. The amount of heat transferred to or from a system during a process cannot be determined from the end states alone. Instead, the amount of heat transferred depends on how the system was changed from one state to another. Heat, like work, is a *path function*.

Occasionally, beginning students in thermodynamics are confused because statements about "the heat in a gallon of gasoline" or "the heat in a radiator" are frequently heard in everyday conversation (conversation in which there is no concern with measurements or with consistency among definitions). The definition of heat used in thermodynamics makes such statements meaningless.

A full understanding of the differences between the two interactions, heat and work, depends on the second law of thermodynamics which is considered in Chapters 6, 7, and 8. Nevertheless, it is well to review at this point the essential difference between them which is established by their definitions: Heat is an interaction caused by a temperature difference between a system and its surroundings; work is done by a system if the sole effect of the system on its surroundings could be reduced to the lifting of a weight.

Consider a system made up of a closed thermally insulated vessel full of air at the temperature of the surroundings with an externally driven paddle wheel in the vessel.* If the paddle wheel is turned by an external motor, the temperature of the system (air) increases. The interaction between the system and its surroundings is the result of the torque exerted on the rotating shaft and is not the result of a temperature difference between the system and its surroundings because (1) the system and surroundings were at the same temperature at the beginning of the process and (2) the vessel is thermally insulated to prevent any interaction resulting from a temperature difference. Thus the interaction is work, not heat. It is unfortunate and misleading that in everyday language it would often be said that the gas was "heated by the paddle wheel" or "heated by friction."

A process in which there is no heat transfer is called an *adiabatic* process. A system which exchanges no heat with its surroundings is called an adiabatic system.

EXAMPLE 1·10.   Referring to the figure, the air, oil, ice, and liquid water within the outer container are all initially at a temperature of 32 F. The outer container is thermally insulated so that no heat can be transferred through it. The weight is allowed to fall, turning the paddle wheel in the oil by means of the pulley. After some time has elapsed, it is observed that the air, oil, ice, and liquid water are again at 32 F but that some of the ice in the inner container has melted. Identify the work done on or by each system and the heat transferred to or from each of the systems which are identified as follows: System *A* is everything within the outer container, system *B* is everything within the inner container, and system *C* is everything within the outer container except system *B*. (System *A* = system *B* + system *C*.)

Solution.   A study of the figure and the problem statement indicates that, as a result of the paddle-wheel action, as the weight falls the temperature of the oil (and the air above the oil) increases. The resulting temperature difference between the oil and the contents of the inner container (system *B*) causes a transfer of heat from the oil into the

* You may justifiably raise an eyebrow at some of the systems chosen for study and may wonder if thermodynamics is concerned only with peculiar systems which a practicing engineer is unlikely to encounter. The reply is that the systems used in proofs and explanations are occasionally unusual because, for the illustration of principles, it is desirable to use systems which involve only one interaction or effect at a time. Sometimes this calls for a highly simplified system (as the paddle-wheel system above), and sometimes it calls for an elaborately controlled system (as the standard systems on page 38, where pressure and temperature were both controlled and interactions with systems other than the steel block were prevented). These systems are chosen because each clearly illustrates some principle or definition; in turn, the application of the principle or definition to some more common or more complex system is then more readily understood.

inner container. This transfer of heat melts some of the ice and causes the temperature of the oil and air to return to 32 F. The interactions involving the various systems are as follows:

System B. Heat: There is a transfer of heat into system B from system C inasmuch as there is an interaction which results from a temperature difference. *Work*: No mechanical work is done on or by system B inasmuch as its interaction with its surroundings involves no motion of the system boundary.

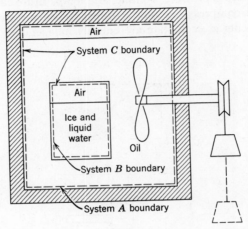

Example 1·10

System A. Heat: No heat is transferred to or from system A because the system is thermally insulated from its surroundings. (Something occurs *within* system A as a result of a temperature difference *within* the system, but with regard to system A this is not heat transfer because heat is an interaction *between a system and its surroundings*.) *Work:* Work is done on system A by means of the shaft which turns the paddle wheel. Notice that, as far as the action of the weight and pulley system external to system A is concerned, the action within system A could be reduced to the lifting of a weight (by removing the oil and replacing the paddle wheel by a weight and pulley arrangement).

System C. Heat: Heat is transferred from system C to system B. No other heat is transferred to or from system C because that part of its boundary which is not common to system B is thermally insulated. *Work:* Work is done on system C by means of the shaft which turns the paddle wheel.

As an additional point of interest, consider system B and its surroundings. After the process described is completed, the temperature of everything outside system B is the same as at the beginning of the process, so the sole effect on the surroundings of system B is the fall of the weight. In Art. 1·13 it was pointed out, however, that an interaction between a system and its surroundings in which the only effect on the surroundings is the *fall* of a body is not necessarily work. In fact, the entire interaction of system B with its surroundings is the result of a temperature difference between the system and its surroundings (even though the temperature difference is zero at both the beginning and the end of the process); so the interaction between system B and its surroundings is only a transfer of heat.

1·18   Point and path functions

Several references have already been made to point functions and path functions. The differences between them will now be discussed.

Consider a system comprised of a gas trapped in a cylinder behind a piston, as shown in Fig. 1·11. Initially, the system is at state 1. At this state 1 the properties pressure, volume, and temperature can be measured. If the gas is then compressed to state 2, the properties can again be measured. The measurements at each state are entirely independent of those made

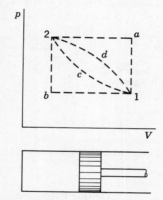

Fig. 1·11   Four possible paths from state 1 to state 2.

at the other state. The change in a property such as pressure is $p_2 - p_1$, and the value of this change depends only on the states 1 and 2; it does not depend on the manner in which the system was changed from state 1 to state 2. For example, the pressure might first have been increased to its final value while the piston was stationary (a constant-volume process) and then held constant while the piston was moved to its final position (a constant-pressure process). This path is shown as 1-a-2 in Fig. 1·11. Three other possible paths connecting states 1 and 2 are shown. The change in any property between state 1 and state 2 is the same for any path, because the value of a property is a characteristic of a system in a given state and is independent of the path followed by the system in reaching that state. A property is a point function.

On a diagram using properties as coordinates, each point represents a particular state of a system; that is, associated with each point on the diagram is a particular value of every property of the system.* Conversely,

* If more than two properties must be specified to define the state of a system, as is often the case, then a two-dimensional diagram is insufficient.

each state of the system can be represented by a single point on the diagram.

Referring again to the system of Fig. 1·11 and supposing that all properties of the system were measured at state 1 and again at state 2, is it possible from these measurements to determine the work done in compressing the gas from state 1 to state 2? The answer is no. Determination of the work done requires more than a knowledge of the end states of the process. To illustrate this, consider that the process is frictionless so that work can be evaluated by $\int p\, dV$. It is readily seen that the value of $\int p\, dV$ is different for each of the four paths shown in Fig. 1·11, and many more paths connecting states 1 and 2 are possible. Thus the amount of work done depends on which path is followed between states 1 and 2. Work is therefore called a path function.

Heat is also a path function, although the demonstration of this fact at this point is more involved than the demonstration that work is a path function.

Notice that there is no such thing as a value of work or of heat at state 1 or at any other state. Work and heat are interactions between systems, not characteristics of systems in particular states.

The mathematical notation for point and path functions and a test which distinguishes between differentials of point functions and those of path functions deserve attention. If x is a function of two independent variables, y and z, this fact is expressed by the notation

$$x = f(y, z)$$

and x is called a *point function*, because at each point on a plane of yz coordinates there is a discrete value of x. The differential dx of a point function x is called an *exact differential*, and

$$dx = \left(\frac{\partial x}{\partial y}\right)_z dy + \left(\frac{\partial x}{\partial z}\right)_y dz$$

This may be written as

$$dx = M\, dy + N\, dz$$

where

$$M = \left(\frac{\partial x}{\partial y}\right)_z \qquad N = \left(\frac{\partial x}{\partial z}\right)_y$$

Then

$$\frac{\partial M}{\partial z} = \frac{\partial}{\partial z}\left(\frac{\partial x}{\partial y}\right) = \frac{\partial^2 x}{\partial z\, \partial y} \qquad \frac{\partial N}{\partial y} = \frac{\partial}{\partial y}\left(\frac{\partial x}{\partial z}\right) = \frac{\partial^2 x}{\partial y\, \partial z}$$

and consequently, since the order of differentiation is immaterial,

$$\frac{\partial M}{\partial z} = \frac{\partial N}{\partial y}$$

In fact, this provides a test for exactness. *A differential in the form $dx = M\,dy + N\,dz$ is an exact differential (hence is the differential of a point function) if and only if*

$$\frac{\partial M}{\partial z} = \frac{\partial N}{\partial y}$$

A proof of this relation can be found in any elementary textbook on differential equations.

For an exact differential dx,

$$\int_1^2 dx = x_2 - x_1$$

where $x_2 = f(y_2, z_2)$ and $x_1 = f(y_1, z_1)$. The value of $\int_1^2 dx$ is independent of the path followed on yz coordinates in going from (y_1, z_1) to (y_2, z_2). For a closed path or cycle the initial and end points are identical; so

$$\oint dx = 0$$

Let G be a path function, a quantity which depends on the path followed in going from point 1 (y_1, z_1) to point 2 (y_2, z_2). For such a quantity *no* relation of the form

$$G = F(y, z)$$

exists, because specifying a value of y and a value of z does not determine a value of G. The notation G_1 or G_2 should not be used, as this implies that there is a particular value of G at point 1 or at point 2, and this is not true. The value of G corresponding to a particular path between points 1 and 2 is therefore not spoken of as a "change" in G, but simply as a value of G for that particular path.

This value of G is equal to the sum of the G values for any number of segments into which the path may be divided. If these segments are taken as being smaller and smaller, the limiting value of G for one segment is δG. The symbol δ is interpreted as meaning "a very small amount of," whereas a corresponding loose interpretation of the differential operator d would be "the difference between two values very close together."

There may be a relationship of the form

$$\delta G = M'\,dy + N'\,dz$$

but, since G is a path function, δG is an *inexact differential* and

$$\frac{\partial M'}{\partial z} \neq \frac{\partial N'}{\partial y}$$

For any path between points 1 and 2, we may write

$$G_{1\text{-}2} = \int_1^2 \delta G$$

however, for a path function,

$$\int_1^2 \delta G \neq G_2 - G_1$$

because (1) a path function cannot be evaluated in terms of end points alone, and (2) there are no values such as G_1 and G_2 which can be assigned to points 1 and 2.

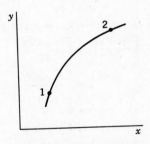

Fig. 1·12 Path on a property diagram.

In order to illustrate a path function other than work or heat, consider the length of a line connecting two points, 1 and 2, on an xy coordinate plane (Fig. 1·12). Let the length of some path connecting 1 and 2 be L. There is no value of L for point 1 nor for point 2, nor is there a single value for points 1 and 2 together. There is, in general, a different value of L for each of the many possible paths between 1 and 2. For any small segment of one of these paths, the limiting relationship is

$$(\delta L)^2 = (dx)^2 + (dy)^2$$

and, for the entire path,

$$L_{1\text{-}2} = \int_1^2 \delta L = \int_1^2 \sqrt{1 + (dy/dx)^2}\, dx$$

This cannot be evaluated unless the relationship between y and x is known, that is, unless the path is specified. Knowledge of the end points alone is insufficient, because L is a path function and $L \neq f(x, y)$.

For a closed path on an xy coordinate plane, notice that

$$\oint dx = 0 \quad \text{and} \quad \oint dy = 0$$

but that

$$\oint \delta L \neq 0$$

EXAMPLE 1·11. For some substances, $pv = BT$, where p, v, T, and B are pressure, specific volume, temperature, and a constant, respectively. The quantities s and I are given by

$$\delta s \text{ or } ds = \frac{dT}{T} - \frac{v\,dp}{T}$$

and

$$\delta I \text{ or } dI = \frac{dT}{T} + \frac{p\,dv}{v}$$

Determine whether each of these quantities is a point function.

Solution. Since in each case the differential is equal to an expression of the form of $M\,dy + N\,dz$, we need only to use the test for exactness

$$\frac{\partial M}{\partial z} \overset{?}{=} \frac{\partial N}{\partial y}$$

In the case of δs or ds, $M = 1/T$, $N = -v/T$, $z = p$, and $y = T$. Then

$$\left[\frac{\partial(1/T)}{\partial p}\right]_T \overset{?}{=} \left[\frac{\partial(-v/T)}{\partial T}\right]_p$$

$$= \left[\frac{\partial(-B/p)}{\partial T}\right]_p$$

$$0 = 0$$

Hence, s is a point function. In the case of I, we have

$$\left[\frac{\partial(1/T)}{\partial v}\right]_T \overset{?}{=} \left[\frac{\partial(p/v)}{\partial T}\right]_v$$

$$0 \neq \frac{B}{v^2}$$

Hence I is not a point function.

EXAMPLE 1·12. Evaluate $\int_A^B dR$ over each of the two paths (1) $y = x^2$, and (2) $y = 3x - 2$ connecting points A (1,1) and B (2, 4) for each case:

$$(a) \quad R = \int (x\,dy + y\,dx)$$

$$(b) \quad R = \int (x\,dy - y\,dx)$$

Solution. (a) For the path $y = x^2$,

$$\int_A^B dR = \int x\,dy + \int y\,dx = \int 2x^2\,dx + \int x^2\,dx$$

$$= 3\int x^2\,dx = x^3 \Big]_{x=1}^{x=2} = 8 - 1 = 7$$

For the path $y = 3x - 2$,

$$\int_A^B dR = \int x\,dy + \int y\,dx = \int 3x\,dx + \int (3x - 2)\,dx$$

$$= \int (6x - 2)\,dx = 3x^2 - 2x \Big]_{x=1}^{x=2} = 8 - 1 = 7$$

The same result for both paths should have been expected because application of the test for exactness shows that $x\,dy + y\,dx$ is exact; hence $R = f(x, y)$ and R has a particular value for each value of x and y. It is readily seen by inspection that $x\,dy + y\,dx$ $= d(xy)$; therefore $R = xy$, and the simplest way to evaluate $\int_A^B dR$ is by

$$\int_A^B dR = R_B - R_A = x_B y_B - x_A y_A = 2(4) - 1(1) = 7$$

No knowledge of any particular path connecting A and B is necessary because R is a point function.

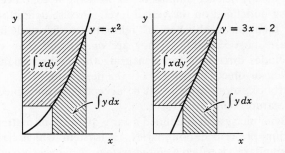

Example 1·12

This particular function allows a simple graphical explanation of its independence of the path chosen between A and B. In each figure, the area between the curve and the x-axis represents $\int y\,dx$. This area is not the same for the two paths. The same is true of the areas between the curves and the y axes which represent $\int x\,dy$. However, the *sum* of the two areas on one figure is the same as on the other figure, so that $\int x\,dy + \int y\,dx$ has the same value for either path.

(*b*) For the path $y = x^2$,

$$\int_A^B dR = \int x\,dy - \int y\,dx = \int 2x^2\,dx - \int x^2\,dx$$

$$= \int x^2\,dx = \frac{x^3}{3}\Big]_{x=1}^{x=2} = \frac{8}{3} - \frac{1}{3} = \frac{7}{3}$$

For the path $y = 3x - 2$,

$$\int_A^B dR = \int x\,dy - \int y\,dx = \int 3x\,dx - \int (3x - 2)\,dx$$

$$= \int 2\,dx = 2x\Big]_{x=1}^{x=2} = 4 - 2 = 2$$

Different results for the two paths should have been expected, since application of the test for exactness to $R = \int (x\,dy - y\,dx)$ shows that $R \neq f(x, y)$. On the figures above it is apparent that the *difference* in areas $\int x\,dy$ and $\int y\,dx$ does depend on the path followed between A and B.

I·19 Summary

Thermodynamics is the science which deals with energy transformations, including heat and work, and the physical properties of substances which are involved in energy transformations. Engineering thermodynamics is the part of the science which pertains to all types of heat engines, turbines, compressors, refrigeration, air conditioning, combustion, and the physical properties of substances used in these applications.

The study of any science should begin with the acceptance of certain terms as being undefined on the verbal level. Precise definitions of other terms must then be established in relation to the undefined terms. Definitions are most valuable if they are *operational*. An operational definition includes directions for measuring the defined quantity or for testing an event or object to see if it fits the definition.

In this textbook, terms which will be accepted as undefined are time, length, temperature, mass, and force.

A thermodynamic system is defined as any quantity of matter or region of space within prescribed boundaries. A system which has no mass crossing its boundaries is called a *closed system*. An *open system* is a region of space within a boundary which mass may cross. Everything outside the system boundary is called the *surroundings*. A closed system which in no way interacts with its surroundings is called an *isolated system*. An *ideal system* is one which can be completely described in terms of a few characteristics.

A *property* is any characteristic of a system which is observable while the system is in any one condition or *state*. Some examples of properties are pressure, temperature, volume, and density.

A *process* is a change in a system from one state to another. The *path* of a process is the series of states through which the system passes during the process. A *cycle* or *cyclic process* is a process or series of processes which returns the system to the state it was in before the process began. The net change in any property of a system which executes a cycle is zero; that is, if x is a property,

$$\oint dx = 0$$

An *intensive property* is one which has the same value for any part of a homogeneous system as it does for the whole system. An *extensive property* is one which has a value for a system equal to the sum of its values for the various parts of the system.

For a fluid in static equilibrium, the relationship between pressure p and elevation z within the fluid is given by the basic equation of fluid statics,

$$dp = -\gamma \, dz \qquad (1·5)$$

where γ is the specific weight of the fluid and z is measured positively upward.

Two bodies are at the *same temperature* or are in *thermal equilibrium* with each other if all properties remain unchanged when the two bodies are brought into conjunction with each other while isolated from all other bodies. Two bodies in thermal equilibrium with a third body are in thermal equilibrium with each other.

Work is an interaction between a system and its surroundings. Work is done by a system on its surroundings if the sole external effect of the interaction could be the lifting of a body. The magnitude of work is the product of the weight of the body lifted and the distance it could be lifted if the lifting of the body were the sole external effect of the interaction. This definition of work includes electrical work, magnetic work, and mechanical work.

Mechanical work is the interaction between a system and its surroundings which is due to the action of a force on a moving boundary of the system, and its magnitude is equal to the product of the force and the displacement of its point of application in the direction of the force. In this book, the term *work* without modifiers will mean mechanical work except in a few cases where the exceptions to the rule are specifically pointed out.

For a frictionless (or quasistatic) process of a closed system comprised of a fluid,

$$\text{Work}_{\text{done by system}} = \int p \, dV \tag{1·7}$$

where p is the pressure of the system and V is its volume.

Steady flow is flow in which all properties at each point within an open system remain constant with respect to time. For steady flow with fluid entering a system at a section 1 and leaving at a section 2, the mass rate of flow M is given by

$$M_1 = M_2 = \frac{A_1 V_1}{v_1} = \frac{A_2 V_2}{v_2} \tag{1·9}$$

in which A is cross-sectional area, V is average velocity across the section, and v is the specific volume of the fluid. This is the continuity equation of steady flow.

For a frictionless steady-flow process, per unit of mass,

$$\text{Work}_{\text{done by system}} = -\int v \, dp - \Delta\left(\frac{V^2}{2g_c}\right) - \frac{g}{g_c} \Delta z \tag{1·10}$$

Heat is an interaction between a system and its surroundings which is caused by a difference in temperature between the system and its surroundings. Heat can be measured by means of standard systems which are changed from one readily recognizable state to another by means of the transfer of heat under specified conditions. An *adiabatic* process is one in which no heat is transferred.

The interactions heat and work are *path functions*. They can be evaluated for a process only if the path of the process is known. Differentials of heat and work are *inexact differentials*. In general,

$$\oint \delta W \neq 0 \qquad \oint \delta Q \neq 0$$

REFERENCES

1·1 D. A. Mooney, *Mechanical Engineering Thermodynamics*, Prentice-Hall, 1953, chapters 1 to 4.

1·2 M. W. Zemansky, *Heat and Thermodynamics*, McGraw-Hill Book Co., 4th ed., 1957, chapters 1 to 3.

1·3 G. N. Lewis and M. Randall, *Thermodynamics and the Free Energy of Chemical Substances*, McGraw-Hill Book Co., 1923, chapters 1 to 3. (The preface of this classic is also interesting.)

1·4 F. W. Sears, *Thermodynamics, the Kinetic Theory of Gases, and Statistical Mechanics*, Addison-Wesley Publishing Co., 2d ed., 1953, chapters 1 and 3.

1·5 J. F. Lee and F. W. Sears, *Thermodynamics*, Addison-Wesley Publishing Co., 1955, chapter 1.

On definitions in general

1·6 S. I. Hayakawa, *Language in Thought and Action*, Harcourt, Brace & Co., 1949, pp. 13–22 and chapters 4 and 10.

1·7 Anatol Rapoport, *Operational Philosopy*, Harper & Brothers, 1954, chapter 1.

PROBLEMS

1·1 Which of the following definitions are operational?

(a) *Potential energy:* energy of a body which is due to the position of the body.

(b) *Kinetic energy:* energy due to the motion of a body.

(c) *Kinetic energy:* energy possessed by a body which is evaluated by $mV^2/2g_c$, where m is the mass of the body, V its velocity, and g_c a dimensional constant.

(d) *Work:* the act of overcoming a resistance through space.

(e) *Work:* work is done by a system when the system acts on its surroundings in such a way that the entire external effect can be reduced to the raising of a weight in the surroundings, and the magnitude of the work done is the product of the weight and the distance the weight is raised.

(f) *Heat:* disordered energy.

(g) *Mass:* the quantity of matter in a body.

(h) *Mass:* a property of matter which can be measured by means of a balance.

(*i*) *Mechanical work*: the interaction between a system and its surroundings which is due to the action of a force at a moving boundary of the system, and its magnitude is equal to the product of the force and the displacement of its point of application in the direction of the force.

1·2 If the specific volume of a gas is 1.7 cu ft/lb, what volume will 3 lb occupy?

1·3 A cylinder having a volume of 2 cu ft contains 20 lb of gas. Determine the specific volume. If 14 lb of gas escape, compute the final specific volume and the final density.

1·4 Two pounds of gas occupy a volume of 14 cu ft. Compute the specific volume in cc/g.

1·5 Determine the pressure in psia units on a rock submerged 80 ft below sea level. Assume that the specific gravity of sea water is 1.025. The barometric pressure is 14.7 psia.

1·6 The absolute steam pressure at entrance and exit for a turbine are 800 and 0.5 psia, respectively. If the barometric pressure is taken as 29.46 in. of mercury, compute the gage pressure for the entering steam and the vacuum gage pressure for the steam at exit from the turbine.

1·7 A vacuum gage reads 25 in. of mercury. Determine the absolute pressure in psia units if the barometer reads 29.7 in. of mercury.

1·8 A mercury manometer at sea level has the same deflection as one at an altitude of 15,000 ft. The temperatures are the same. Which one indicates the greater pressure difference? Explain.

1·9 Convert the following centigrade temperatures to Fahrenheit temperatures: (*a*) −30, (*b*) −10, (*c*) 0, (*d*) 200, (*e*) 1050.

1·10 Convert the following Fahrenheit temperatures to centigrade temperatures: (*a*) −60, (*b*) −40, (*c*) 5, (*d*) 540, (*e*) 2070.

1·11 On the Réaumur temperature scale the ice point is at zero and the steam point is at 80. What is the Réaumur temperature of absolute zero?

1·12 A hoisting engine in a mine is raising a cage weighing 500 lb at a rate of 200 fpm. What horsepower is developed by the engine?

1·13 A 1000-ton train operates at a speed of 60 mph on a level track. If the frictional resistance is 15 lb/ton, determine (*a*) the force required and (*b*) the horsepower developed by the engine.

1·14 A locomotive draws a train at a velocity of 4 mph up a grade which rises 1 ft vertically in each 100 ft measured horizontally. The total weight of the locomotive and cars is 4000 tons. If the frictional resistance is 4 lb/ton, what horsepower is developed by the engine?

1·15 A well hole having a diameter of 2 in. is to be cut into the earth to a depth of 200 ft. Determine the total work required to raise the earth material to the surface if the average weight of 1 cu ft is 115 lb.

1·16 A tank 10 ft long, 7 ft wide, and 6 ft deep is half full of water. How many foot-pounds of work would be required to raise all the water over the top edge of the tank?

1·17 A ½-hp electric motor has nothing attached to its shaft. The motor is operating at 3600 rpm and is connected to a 110-volt power line. What is the power output?

1·18 Calculate the work done on a body having a mass of 10 slugs to accelerate it from a velocity of 400 to 500 fps in (*a*) 10 sec, (*b*) 1 min.

1·19 Calculate the work done in lifting a 7-slug body from an elevation of 640 ft above mean sea level to an elevation of 60 ft higher in (a) 2 min, (b) 10 min.

1·20 Assuming that the gravitational acceleration g varies with altitude h above the earth's surface according to the relationship

$$g = \frac{a}{(b + h)^2}$$

where a and b are constants, sketch a curve of the weight of a given object vs. h, and write an equation for the work done in lifting an object of mass m to an elevation h. Write the equation in terms of m, h, a, b, and g_c.

1·21 Compute the work performed when 4 cu ft of a gas expands to a volume of 9 cu ft under a constant pressure of 200 psia. Draw a pressure–volume diagram for the process.

1·22 A rigid steel tank contains 6 cu ft of oxygen at a pressure of 200 psia. If the pressure is reduced to 180 psia, is any work performed? Assume that the volume of the tank remains constant. Draw a pressure–volume diagram for the process.

1·23 A process occurs for which the pressure changes according to the equation $p = 288V + 900$. In this relation the pressure is expressed in psia units and the volume is expressed in cubic foot units. If the volume changes from 10 to 20 cu ft, compute the work performed.

1·24 Air expands in a cylinder according to the law $pV^{1.4} = C$ from an initial volume of 5 cu ft and pressure of 70 psia to a final volume of 10 cu ft. Compute the work done. The symbol C represents a constant.

1·25 A gas expands according to the law $pV^a = C$, where a and C are constants. Derive a general equation for the work done when the gas expands from an initial absolute pressure and volume of p_1 and V_1 to a final absolute pressure and volume of p_2 and V_2 (a) in a closed system, (b) in a steady-flow system.

1·26 A spherical balloon has a diameter D_1 when the pressure of the gas inside it is p_1 and atmospheric pressure is p_0. The gas is heated, causing the balloon diameter to increase to D_2. The pressure of the gas is proportional to the balloon diameter. How much work is done by the gas? Express your answer in terms of p_1, D_1, and the ratio D_2/D_1. How much work is done on the atmosphere?

1·27 A vapor in a cylinder is compressed frictionlessly from 20 psia and 1 cu ft to 100 psia in such a manner that $pV =$ constant. Sketch the process on pV coordinates, and compute the work done.

1·28 Give a specific example of (a) a closed-system process in which $\int p\, dv = 0$ and work $\neq 0$, and (b) a steady-flow process in which work $= 0$ and $\int v\, dp \neq 0$.

1·29 Consider a nutating disk or "wobble-plate" liquid meter. If the gears of the counter mechanism become hard to turn, will the pressure drop across the meter be affected for a given flow rate?

1·30 Air is compressed in a frictionless steady-flow process from 10 psia, 60 F, and a specific volume of 19.25 cu ft/lb to 15 psia in such a manner that $p(v+5) =$ constant, where v is in cu ft/lb. Inlet velocity is negligibly small, and discharge velocity is 350 fps. The flow rate is 0.45 lb/sec. Calculate the work required per pound of air.

1·31 Derive an expression for the work done in the elastic stretching of a steel wire in terms of modulus of elasticity and strain.

1·32 Consider a liquid flowing through a circular pipe of radius r_0. The velocity is a maximum u_{max} along the pipe axis and zero at the pipe wall. Determine the ratio V/u_{max}, where V is the average velocity at a given section, if the velocity u at any radius r is given by $u = u_{max}(1 - r/r_0)^2$.

1·33 Air with a density of 0.075 lb/cu ft enters a steady-flow system through a 12-in.-diameter duct with a velocity of 10 fps. It leaves with a density of 0.20 lb/cu ft through a 4-in. diameter duct. Determine the outlet velocity and the mass rate of flow.

1·34 In everyday language the noun *heat* and the verb *to heat* are often used in sentences different from those which follow from the definition of heat used in engineering thermodynamics. One type of misuse leads to confusion between an interaction between systems and a property. The other type of misuse leads to a confusion between different types of interactions between systems. Give several examples of each type of misuse which may be heard in everyday conversation.

1·35 For each process and each system listed, indicate whether the work is more than, less than, or equal to zero, and do the same for heat, observing the usual sign convention for work and heat:

(*a*) A coil spring stands on end on a table. A book is placed on the spring, compressing it. Consider as the system (1) the book, (2) the spring, (3) the table.

(*b*) A paddle wheel turned by a motor stirs a liquid in an insulated vessel. Consider as the system (1) the liquid, (2) the paddle wheel.

(*c*) A gas in an insulated cylinder is compressed so that its pressure and temperature both increase. The system is the gas.

(*d*) A steel wire is bent back and forth until it becomes hot to the touch. The system is the wire.

(*e*) Carbon dioxide is compressed in a water-cooled compressor. Steady flow prevails. The system is (1) the carbon dioxide, (2) the cooling water, (3) a section of the compressor cylinder wall.

1·36 Someone has proposed the use of three new thermodynamic quantities: X, Y, and Z. Determine which ones are properties if they are defined as (1) $X = \int (p\,dv + v\,dp)$; (2) $Y = \int (p\,dv - v\,dp)$; and (3) $Z = \int (R\,dT + p\,dv)$, where $R = pv/T = $ constant.

1·37 Evaluate F, G, and H as defined by

$$F = \int (x^2\,dy + y\,dx)$$

$$G = \int [(x - y)\,dy + (y^2 - 2x)\,dx]$$

$$H = \int [2y(x - 2y)\,dx + x(x - 8y)\,dy]$$

over each of the following paths from $x = 0$, $y = 0$, to $x = 1$, $y = 2$: (*a*) $y = 2x$, (*b*) $y = 2x^2$, and (*c*) $y = 2x^{\frac{1}{2}}$.

1·38 Make a list of the ten numbered equations in this chapter. For each one, state the principle involved and the restrictions on its use. Which ones were you familiar with before studying this chapter and which ones are new to you?

CHAPTER 2

The First Law
of
Thermodynamics

Thermodynamics is characterized by a great number and diversity of applications of its few basic principles. One of these basic principles, the first law of thermodynamics, is introduced in this chapter, and several examples of its use are presented. It is shown that the conservation of energy principle follows from the first law of thermodynamics. Further applications of the first law are made throughout the remaining chapters of the book.

2·1　The first law of thermodynamics

It was pointed out in Chapter 1 that, when a closed system passes through a cycle, usually

$$\oint \delta W \neq 0 \quad \text{and} \quad \oint \delta Q \neq 0$$

Many experiments show, however, that *if* the net work of a cycle is zero, then the net heat transfer of that cycle is also zero. Further experiments show that whenever there is a net work input to a closed system during a cycle, there must be a net heat transfer from the system. Conversely, a net work output from a closed system during a cycle is always accompanied by a net heat input. These experimental observations suggest that there is a relationship between work and heat. Let us consider some experiments which might be useful in a search for such a relationship.

Consider a closed system which is comprised of a gas in a rigid vessel fitted with a paddle wheel as shown in Fig. 2·1. If work is done on the gas by means of the paddle wheel (process A), the temperature of the gas will rise. Then heat must be removed from the gas (process B) in order to restore the gas to its initial state. During process A there is work done but no heat transfer; during process B there is heat transferred but no work done. During the complete cycle there is a net work input and a net heat transfer from the system. Even relatively crude experiments with this apparatus show that, as the amount of work input is increased, the amount of heat which must be removed in order to restore the system to its initial state increases proportionately.

Another useful system is a gas which is trapped inside a cylinder fitted with a piston (Fig. 2·2). The piston is a thermal insulator (i.e., heat cannot pass through it) and the cylinder can be surrounded either by thermal insulating material or by liquid baths at various temperatures so that the

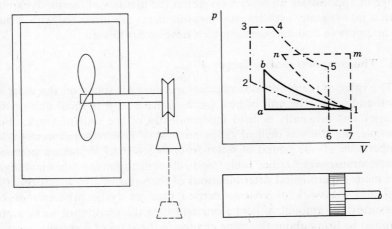

Fig. 2·1   One form of closed system.   **Fig. 2·2**   Three possible cycles
                                                 of a closed system.

transfer of heat to or from the gas can be readily controlled. The work done on or by the gas is determined from measurements of the force on the piston and the displacement of the piston. Many different cycles can be executed by this system. Three possible ones are shown on the pV diagram of Fig. 2·2. The work of the system can be positive, zero, or negative.

Many experiments on systems as shown in Figs. 2·1 and 2·2 and on many other types of systems indicate that, *whenever a closed system executes a cycle, the net work output of the system is proportional to the net heat input.* This conclusion from experiments is known as the first law of thermodynamics and is expressed by*

$$\oint \delta W \propto \oint \delta Q$$

or by
$$\oint \delta W = J \oint \delta Q \qquad (2\text{·}1)$$

* The notation $(\Sigma W)_{\text{cycle}}$ and $(\Sigma Q)_{\text{cycle}}$ is also used.

where J is a proportionality factor whose value depends only on the units selected for W and Q.

The first law of thermodynamics is a far-reaching principle of nature which is induced from the results of many experiments. It cannot be deduced or proved from any other principles of nature. The inductive reasoning process, by which we take the results of a finite number of experiments and extend them to cover all cases, always leaves some room for doubt as to the value of its conclusions. With regard to its truth and range of application, all we can say about the first law of thermodynamics is that many, many experimental measurements are in accord with it and all attempts to find an exception to it have so far failed.

2·2   The proportionality factor *J*

The value of the proportionality factor J depends solely on the units of work and heat. The unit of heat (such as the British thermal unit or the calorie) was originally defined independently of the unit of work. For example, the *Btu* was defined as the amount of heat required to raise the temperature of one pound of water from 59.5 to 60.5 F under a pressure of one atmosphere. James Joule* and subsequently many other investigators made experimental determinations of the value of J by measuring the heat and the work of systems carried through cyclic processes or by measuring the amount of heat alone and then the amount of work alone required to bring about the same change in the state of a system.

The first law of thermodynamics, which directly relates heat and work, makes it possible to *define* the unit of heat in terms of the unit of work or vice versa. Such a definition was proposed in 1929 by the First International Steam Tables Conference and has since been widely adopted by engineers. The 1929 definition of the calorie was in terms of international watt-hours, and conversion from the international electrical units to mechanical units now involves an experimental relationship between the absolute joule and the international joule; therefore the relationship between the Btu and the foot-pound is not entirely independent of experimental measurements.†

* James Prescott Joule (1818–1889) was born into a wealthy family and inherited a large brewery in Manchester, England. His financial independence made it possible for him to devote his life to scientific research, chiefly in the fields of electricity and thermodynamics. He had a much stronger interest in accurate measurements than most of the scientists of his time. His work in thermodynamics included that on the equivalence of work and heat and also some notable contributions regarding the physical properties of gases.

† See E. F. Obert, *Thermodynamics*, McGraw Hill Book Co., 1948, pp. 538–539; or M. W. Zemansky, *Heat and Thermodynamics*, McGraw-Hill Book Co., 4th ed., 1957, pp. 68–70; or J. H. Keenan, "Should the Btu Be Abandoned?" *Heat Power News & Views*, vol. 10, no. 40, December 1955.

The most recent experiments coupled with the 1929 definition give

$$J = 778.165 \text{ ft-lb/B}$$

Throughout this book the approximate value of $J = 778$ ft-lb/B will be used.

Values of J in other units can readily be derived from the above value and the definitions of other units. Some approximate values which are frequently used in connection with the units of power, the horsepower (1 hp $\equiv$ 33,000 ft-lb/min) and the kilowatt (0.746 kw = 1 hp), are

$$1/J = 3413 \text{ B/kwhr} = 2545 \text{ B/hp-hr} = 42.4 \text{ B/hp-min} = 0.707 \text{ B/hp-sec}$$

Since, as a result of the first law, the units of heat and work can be defined in terms of each other, there is no reason why heat and work cannot be measured in the same units. Work and heat can both be measured in Btu's or calories, and heat as well as work can be measured in foot-pounds. It must be understood that any equation expressing a physical relationship must hold regardless of the system of units used for the various quantities in the equation. The only requirement is that the units used be *consistent* and that the proper conversion factors be used in any numerical calculation in order to make them so. When this is recognized, it is unnecessary to write conversion factors as part of an equation. Therefore, the conversion factor J will not be used in connection with work and heat in this book, it being understood that work and heat appearing in the same equation must be expressed in the same units. Thus equation 2·1 becomes

$$\oint \delta W = \oint \delta Q \quad \text{or} \quad \oint (\delta Q - \delta W) = 0 \qquad (2 \cdot 1)$$

EXAMPLE 2·1. Even though a household electric refrigerator is covered by thermal insulating material, there is some transfer of heat from the surrounding room into the refrigerator compartment. In a certain refrigerator, heat is transferred inward through the walls at an average rate of 100 B/hr. A watt-hour meter connected to the motor shows that 6.0 kwhr of electrical work was put into the motor during a 10-day period. What was the average rate of heat transfer away from the refrigerating unit during the 10-day period if all conditions inside the refrigerator are the same at the end of the 10-day period as they were at the beginning of it?

Solution. If all conditions inside the refrigerator are the same at the end of the 10-day period as at the beginning of it, then the closed system comprised of the refrigerator (food compartment and refrigerating unit, including the motor) has undergone one or more complete cycles of operation, and the first law of thermodynamics as stated above can be applied to the system. The only work involved is the 6.0 kwhr of electrical work input to the motor. Heat is transferred into the system through the compartment walls and is transferred from the system by the heat exchanger which is part of the refrigerating unit. Heat is also rejected by the electric motor. Therefore, we integrate

$$\oint \delta Q = \oint \delta W$$

to $Q_{\text{in through walls}} - Q_{\text{out from heat exchanger and motor}} = W$

Rearranging,

$$Q_{\substack{\text{out from heat exchanger} \\ \text{and motor}}} = Q_{\text{in through walls}} + W_{\text{in}}$$

$$= 100 \left[\frac{\text{B}}{\text{hr}}\right](10)[\text{da}](24)\left[\frac{\text{hr}}{\text{da}}\right] + 6.0[\text{kwhr}](3413)\left[\frac{\text{B}}{\text{kwhr}}\right]$$

$$= 24{,}000 + 20{,}478 = 44{,}478 \text{ B}$$

$$\text{Average rate of heat transfer} = \frac{Q}{\text{total time}} = \frac{44{,}478}{10(24)} = 185 \text{ B/hr}$$

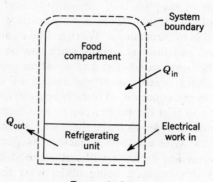

Example 2·1

2·3 The first law for noncyclic processes. Energy.

The first law of thermodynamics as stated above applies only to cyclic processes. We will now extend the application of this principle to non-cyclic processes, that is, to processes which cause a net change in the state of a system. When a closed system undergoes a process which changes it from a state 1 to a state 2, it is usually true that

$$\int_1^2 \delta Q - \int_1^2 \delta W \neq 0$$

or

$$Q - W \neq 0$$

However, since $\oint (\delta Q - \delta W) = 0$, it can be readily shown that the value of $\int_1^2 (\delta Q - \delta W)$ or $(Q - W)$ is the same for any path between states 1 and 2. The proof of this follows:

Consider a closed system which is changed from a state 1 to a state 2 by some process shown as path A on a property diagram such as the pV

diagram of Fig. 2·3. It is then returned to state 1 via path B. The first law states that

$$\oint_{1\text{-}A\text{-}2\text{-}B\text{-}1} (\delta Q - \delta W) = 0$$

or $$\int_{1\text{-}A}^{2} (\delta Q - \delta W) + \int_{2\text{-}B}^{1} (\delta Q - \delta W) = 0 \qquad (a)$$

If C is any other path by which the system could be restored from state 2 to state 1, then it is likewise true that

$$\int_{1\text{-}A}^{2} (\delta Q - \delta W) + \int_{2\text{-}C}^{1} (\delta Q - \delta W) = 0 \qquad (b)$$

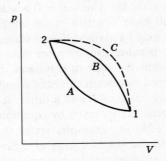

Fig. 2·3   State changes of a closed system.

Comparing equations (a) and (b), we see that

$$\int_{2\text{-}B}^{1} (\delta Q - \delta W) = \int_{2\text{-}C}^{1} (\delta Q - \delta W)$$

Since B and C were *any* two paths between states 2 and 1, it follows that the value of $\int (\delta Q - \delta W)$ is the same for *all* paths between the two states. In other words, the value of $\int (\delta Q - \delta W)$ or $(Q - W)$ depends only on the end states of a process. *Thus $\int (\delta Q - \delta W)$ or $(Q - W)$ is a property.* (This could have been inferred directly from the statement of the first law in the form $\oint (\delta Q - \delta W) = 0$, since if the cyclic integral of any quantity is always zero, that quantity must be a property. The demonstration presented above, however, is generally more satisfying to the beginning student of thermodynamics.) This property is called *stored energy* and is denoted by the symbol E. Thus

$$\Delta E \equiv \int (\delta Q - \delta W) \qquad (2\cdot2a)$$

or $$\Delta E \equiv Q - W \qquad (2\cdot2b)$$

This defining equation for ΔE is generally regarded as a useful statement of the first law.

Since E is a property, its differential is exact, and the differential form of the defining equation is

$$dE = \delta Q - \delta W \qquad (2 \cdot 2c)$$

Only the *change* in the value of E between two states can be evaluated by means of equations 2·2. In fact, thermodynamics provides no information about absolute values of E for any system. It is only the change in E, however, which is important in engineering problems. Consequently, a value of $E = 0$ can be assigned to any particular state of a system. Then from measurements of heat and work during a process which transforms the system to another state, the value of E at the other state can be determined. Since the state for which $E = 0$ is selected arbitrarily, some of the other states will have negative values of E, and some will have positive values. There may be many different states of a system for which E has the same value, because usually more than one property must be specified in order to define the state of a system. For example, one state of a system may be defined by certain values of E and pressure, and another state may have the same value of E and a different value of pressure.

The definition of stored energy given by equations 2·2 is an *operational* definition. Equation 2·2b, for example, states that the number which represents the change in the stored energy of a closed system during any process is obtained by subtracting the net amount of work done by the system from the net amount of heat added to the system. Work and heat have previously been defined operationally.

Because energy is a term in everyday use and most people have (or believe they have) some intuitive grasp of its meaning, nonoperational and less precise definitions are numerous and often satisfy people. For example, the term energy was used in the first article of this book without being defined, and probably very few readers were troubled by the term at that point. Nevertheless, in scientific work where precise meanings are essential, important terms such as energy should be either defined operationally or accepted at the start as verbally undefined.

Since heat and work are related to the stored energy of a system, they are often spoken of as forms of *energy in transition*.* Thus the term *energy* is a general term referring to stored energy (a property of a system) and to heat and work (interactions between systems). This is the reason

---

* Heat and work are often *defined* as energy in transition. Possible definitions are: *Heat* is energy in transition between a system and its surroundings (or between two systems) as a result of a temperature difference between the system and its surroundings (or between the two systems). *Work* is energy in transition between a system and its surroundings by virtue of a force acting through a distance at the system boundary. (For generality, the force acting through a distance must include cases such as an electromotive force acting on a moving charge, etc.)

why the property E has been referred to always as *stored* energy. E is sometimes called internal energy, but we will reserve this name for one particular form of stored energy in conformity with many reference works and published tables of thermodynamic properties.

With heat and work considered as forms of energy in transition, equations 2·2 become statements of the *conservation of energy principle:* The increase in the energy stored in a system is equal to the net transfer of energy into the system. This is equivalent to the statement that energy can be neither created nor destroyed although it can be stored in various forms and can be transferred from one system to another. Thus it is often said that the first law of thermodynamics is the principle (or law) of conservation of energy. (In this book and many others, however, energy is defined by means of the first law, so the law of conservation of energy is a *consequence* of the first law.)

Notice should be taken of the form of the first law as applied to an isolated system. By definition, both work and heat are zero in an isolated system, so that equation 2·2b reduces to

$$\Delta E_{\text{isolated system}} = 0 \qquad (2 \cdot 3)$$

that is, the stored energy of an isolated system must remain constant. This does not mean that there can be no change of state of an isolated system; it does mean that an isolated system can exist only in those states which have the same stored energy as the initial state.

Although stored energy has been defined in terms of work and heat measurements involving a closed system and the first law is established from measurements made on a closed system, the principle of conservation of energy which is a consequence of the first law can be extended to apply to any type of system, open or closed. We shall see later that stored energy is a useful property of open systems as well as of closed systems.

Before looking further into the nature of E, let us summarize the preceding discussion of the first law of thermodynamics as follows:

1. The first law is a generalization based on the results of many experiments. It cannot be deduced from any other physical principles; it is entirely empirical.

2. As a result of the first law, energy can be defined in terms of heat and work, the operationally defined interactions between systems.

3. The first law is stated by any one of the following equations which refer to a closed system:

$$\oint \delta Q = \oint \delta W \quad \textit{cycle} \qquad (2 \cdot 1)$$

$$Q - W = \Delta E \quad \textit{process} \qquad (2 \cdot 2)$$

$$\Delta E_{\text{isolated system}} = 0 \qquad (2 \cdot 3)$$

$$\oint dE = 0 \quad \textit{cycle} \qquad (2 \cdot 4)$$

More precisely, equation 2·1 is the empirical conclusion which we call the first law, equation 2·2 defines stored energy which the first law shows to be a property, and equation 2·3 is a consequence of the first two.

4. Equivalent word statements of the first law are:

(*a*) Whenever a closed system executes a cycle, the net work done by the system is equal to the net heat transfer to the system. (This is the statement closest to the experimental results which support the first law.)

(*b*) The net heat added to a closed system minus the net work done by the system is equal to the increase in the stored energy of the system. (This is the statement most convenient for application to many engineering problems.)

(*c*) The stored energy of an isolated system remains constant. (In a few engineering problems this is a convenient statement for direct application.)

5. One form of the first law is the conservation of energy principle (or the law of conservation of energy): Energy can be neither created nor destroyed although it can be stored in various forms and can be transferred from one system to another.

EXAMPLE 2·2. A system which is comprised of a certain mass of air is contained in a cylinder fitted with a piston. The air expands from a state 1 for which $E_1 = 70$ B to a state 2 for which $E_2 = -20$ B. During the expansion, the air does 60 B of work on the surroundings. Determine the amount of heat transferred to or from the system during the process.

Solution. Applying the first law in the form

$$Q = E_2 - E_1 + W \tag{2·2}$$

to this system,

$$Q = -20 - 70 + 60 = -30 \text{ B}$$

Since Q without subscript stands for heat added to a system, the minus sign of the result indicates that 30 B of heat is transferred from the system. The result can be written also as $Q_{out} = 30$ B.

Notice that in this process heat and work are both taken from the system. The total decrease in the stored energy of the system is equal to the sum of the energy removed as heat and as work.

EXAMPLE 2·3. Determine the final E value of a mass of water which is in an initial state for which $E = 20$ B and then undergoes a process during which 10 B of work is done on the water and 3 B of heat is removed from it.

Solution. Applying the first law to the system comprised of the water, the final amount of stored energy is equal to the initial amount of stored energy plus the energy added as work minus the energy removed as heat.

$$E_2 = E_1 + W_{in} - Q_{out} \tag{2·2}$$

$$= 20 + 10 - 3 = 27 \text{ B}$$

If the first law is applied stated as

$$E_2 = E_1 + Q - W \tag{2·2}$$

the substitution of numerical values (recalling that Q denotes Q_{in} and W denotes W_{out}) would be

$$E_2 = 20 + (-3) - (-10) = 27 \text{ B}$$

2·4   The nature of E

Stored energy E is defined as

$$\Delta E \equiv Q - W \qquad (2·2)$$

This is an operational definition which tells how the change in E of a closed system can be obtained from measurements of heat and work. Since E has been shown to be a property, the question arises as to whether E (or ΔE) values obtained by measurements of heat and work can then be correlated with other properties of a system. There would be several benefits from such a correlation. For one thing, ΔE for any process could then be determined from measurements of other properties at the two end states. This would increase the utility of the first law because, for any system for which E had already been correlated with other properties, it would give an independent method for evaluating ΔE in the relation

$$Q = \Delta E + W \qquad (2·2)$$

Many engineering problems involve the use of equation 2·2 or one of the many special relations which can be derived from it. Often the value of either Q or W is specified for a process. The problem is to find out how much of the other form of transitional energy must be added to or removed from the system in order to bring about a particular change of state. In such a case, the advantage of having E previously correlated with other properties is apparent.

Fortunately, it is possible in certain cases to make the desired correlation between E and other properties. We shall now investigate some of these cases in which the value of ΔE can be determined by measurements of properties of a system at the beginning and the end of a process.

The procedure to be followed in two cases is to consider a system undergoing a process for which heat and work are measurable and during which a limited number of properties change. For each of these two cases the change in stored energy calculated from the heat and work measurements can be easily correlated with properties of the initial and final states of the system.

Potential energy. Consider a system comprised of a body which has its elevation changed while no other property of the body changes. Obviously a change in elevation can be brought about without a transfer of heat. The change in stored energy associated with the change in elevation is then equal to the work done on the body.

$$\Delta E_{\text{change in elevation}} = W_{\text{on body}} = \int_1^2 F \, dz$$

The force required in order to lift the body while producing no other effect on it is equal to the weight of the body, and so the equation above becomes

$$\Delta E_{\text{change in elevation}} = \int_1^2 F \, dz = \int_1^2 (\text{weight}) \, dz = \int_1^2 \frac{mg}{g_c} \, dz$$

where m is the mass of the body and g_c is a dimensional constant with a value dependent only on the units selected for F, m, and g. Usually the variation in g with elevation is negligible, so that

$$\Delta E_{\text{change in elevation}} = \frac{mg}{g_c} \int_1^2 dz = \frac{g}{g_c} m(z_2 - z_1)$$

Experiments show that, when a system undergoes any process, part of the change of stored energy is always attributable to the change in elevation alone, regardless of what other properties may change. This part of the stored energy which is a function of elevation alone is spoken of as a *form* of stored energy and is called potential energy, *PE*. Thus

$$\Delta PE = PE_2 - PE_1 = (\text{weight})(z_2 - z_1) = \frac{g}{g_c} m(z_2 - z_1) \qquad (2 \cdot 4a)$$

The elevation at which the potential energy of a body is zero may be selected arbitrarily. If z_0 is the elevation at which we assign $PE_0 = 0$, and PE is the potential energy at any other elevation, the equation

$$PE - PE_0 = \frac{g}{g_c} m(z - z_0)$$

reduces to

$$PE = \frac{g}{g_c} mz = (\text{weight})z \qquad (2 \cdot 4b)$$

where z is measured from the datum plane at an elevation of z_0. Thus potential energy is often defined as the energy stored in a system* as a

* Strictly speaking, potential energy is stored in the *system* comprised of the earth and the relatively small system under study. A broader and more rigorous definition is: Potential energy is energy stored in a system as a result of gravitational forces between parts of the system. Potential energy changes are evaluated from measurements of work and heat in processes in which parts of the system move relative to each other and no other changes of state occur. When this definition is used, the energy stored in a system comprised of the earth and some other body is a special case which is sometimes referred to as geopotential energy. Throughout this book, "potential energy of a body" will mean "geopotential energy of the system comprised of the earth and the body."

result of its location in the earth's gravitational field, and its magnitude is the product of (1) the weight of the system and (2) the distance between the center of gravity of the system and some arbitrary horizontal datum plane.

Kinetic energy. Consider a system comprised of a body which experiences a change in velocity while its elevation, temperature, volume, and all other properties remain constant. Such a change in velocity can be brought about without heat transfer. Application of the first law then shows that the change in stored energy associated with the change in velocity is equal to the work done on the body in order to accelerate it.

$$\Delta E_{\text{change in velocity}} = W_{\text{on body}} = \int_1^2 F \, dL = \int_1^2 \frac{ma}{g_c} \, dL$$

Noting that $a = dV/d\tau$ and $V = dL/d\tau$, this becomes

$$\Delta E_{\text{change in velocity}} = \frac{m}{g_c} \int_1^2 \frac{dV}{d\tau} \, dL = \frac{m}{g_c} \int_1^2 V \, dV = \frac{m}{2g_c} (V_2^2 - V_1^2)$$

Experiments show that, when a system undergoes any process, part of the change of stored energy is always attributable to the change in velocity alone, regardless of what other properties may change. This part of the stored energy is called kinetic energy, KE. Thus,

$$\Delta KE = KE_2 - KE_1 = m \left(\frac{V_2^2 - V_1^2}{2g_c} \right) \tag{2·5a}$$

It is customary and convenient (but not mandatory) to assign a value of zero kinetic energy to a system with zero velocity relative to some arbitrary frame of reference. When this is done, the kinetic energy of a system in any state is

$$KE = \frac{mV^2}{2g_c} \tag{2·5b}$$

where V is the velocity of the system relative to some specified frame of reference. Thus kinetic energy is defined as the energy stored in a system by virtue of the motion of the system, and its magnitude is given by $mV^2/2g_c$, where the symbols are as previously defined. (Perhaps you have had experience with a system of units in which g_c is numerically unity and in which therefore $KE = \frac{1}{2}mV^2$. Remember that this expression holds only when g_c is unity. See Appendix A.) If not all parts of the system have the same velocity, the kinetic energy is given by

$$KE = \frac{1}{2g_c} \int V^2 \, dm \tag{2·5c}$$

where V is the velocity of any elemental mass dm, and the integration must be carried out over the entire mass of the system. For example, from equation 2·5c it can be shown that the kinetic energy of a solid body rotating about a fixed axis is $I\omega^2/2g_c$, where ω is the angular velocity and I is the moment of inertia of the body about the axis of rotation.

Several other forms of energy can be identified by procedures similar to those used to identify potential and kinetic energies. A form of energy related to magnetic fields can easily be identified, and others related to electrical effects and surface tension effects can be found. Even in the absence of all these effects as well as motion and gravity, a difference in the stored energy of a system can still be discerned by measurements of heat and work. The form of stored energy which is independent of electricity, magnetism, surface tension, motion, and gravity is called *internal energy* and is represented by the symbol U. Thus

$$U \equiv E - KE - PE - \text{(magnetic energy)} - \text{(electric energy)} - \text{(surface energy)}$$

The ease with which internal energy is correlated with other properties of a system depends on the nature of the system. This point is discussed in Chapters 4 and 10.

Although the principles of thermodynamics are independent of any assumptions regarding the structure of matter, it is often helpful to picture the internal energy of a substance, in the absence of chemical or nuclear reactions, as the summation of the kinetic and potential energies of the molecules of the substance. The kinetic energy of molecules is associated with translational, rotational, and vibratory motions of molecules. The kinetic energy of the molecules of a substance increases as the temperature of the substance increases. Molecular potential energy is associated with the attractive forces between molecules. These forces are large in a solid where molecules are close together, smaller in a liquid, and very small in a gas where molecules are separated from each other by distances which are large in terms of molecular dimensions. Molecular potential energy increases as the distance between molecules increases, so it is highest for gases and lowest for solids.

In a process which involves a chemical reaction, the change in the internal energy of a system is related to the changes in the internal structure of molecules, i.e., to changes on the atomic level rather than on the molecular level. Nuclear reactions involve changes on the subatomic level, i.e., changes within the atoms of a substance.* Measurements of only heat

---

* In connection with nuclear reactions and the conversion of matter to energy which has been experimentally verified, the conservation of energy and conservation of mass principles must be generalized to treat matter as a form of energy. This subject is not covered in this book.

and work provide no means of distinguishing among the molecular, atomic, and nuclear levels of energy storage, so all are included under the one category of internal energy.

Thermodynamics provides no information as to absolute values of internal energy; only changes in internal energy can be determined by measurements of heat and work. For convenience, the internal energy of a substance is often assigned the value of zero at some arbitrary reference state just as the potential energy of a body is often assigned the value of zero at some convenient and arbitrary horizontal datum plane.

The total change in the stored energy of a system is equal to the sum of the changes in all of the particular forms of stored energy:

$$\Delta E = \Delta PE + \Delta KE + \Delta U + \Delta(\text{magnetic energy})$$
$$+ \Delta(\text{electric energy}) + \Delta(\text{surface energy}) \qquad (2\cdot6a)$$

In the absence of electricity, magnetism, and surface tension, the stored energy of a system is

$$E = U + KE + PE \qquad (2\cdot6b)$$

If all parts of the system move with the same velocity, and z is the vertical distance of the center of gravity of the system from an arbitrary horizontal datum plane,

$$E = U + \frac{mV^2}{2g_c} + \frac{g}{g_c}mz \qquad (2\cdot6c)$$

Per unit mass of substance, this is written

$$e = u + \frac{V^2}{2g_c} + \frac{g}{g_c}z \qquad (2\cdot6d)$$

2·5 Enthalpy

In many thermodynamic analyses there appears the sum of internal energy U and the product of pressure and volume pV. Because this combination $(U+pV)$ occurs so frequently, it has been given a name, enthalpy (ĕn-thal′pi), and is represented by the symbol H. Since U, p, and V are all properties, this combination of them is also a property. The defining relation is

$$H \equiv U + pV$$

or, per unit mass, $h \equiv u + pv$

It should be noticed that u represents a form of stored energy, but pv does not; therefore, their sum is not a form of stored energy. It will be seen later that in certain applications enthalpy may be treated as energy, but this should not obscure the fact that *enthalpy is simply a useful property defined by an arbitrary combination of other properties and is not a form of energy.*

Since we cannot obtain absolute values of internal energy, we cannot obtain absolute values of enthalpy. Only changes in enthalpy are of importance to us, however.

Internal energy values are often expressed in B/lb_m, whereas typical engineering units for pressure and specific volume give the pv term in $ft\text{-}lb_f/lb_m$. Consequently, careful attention is required when working with numerical values to insure that consistent units are used.

2·6   The first law applied to (stationary) closed systems

A closed system may move, but usually engineering systems analyzed as closed systems do not. Therefore, in this book when the term *closed system* is used and there is no indication to the contrary, it will be assumed that effects of gravity and motion are negligible.* This means that there will usually be no change in the kinetic energy or the potential energy of a closed system. If we also exclude effects of electricity, magnetism, and surface tension, then the total change in the stored energy of the system is the change in internal energy U. Thus the first law applied to a closed system under these conditions becomes

$$Q - W = \Delta U \tag{2·7}$$

or
$$Q - W = U_2 - U_1 \tag{2·7}$$

where the subscripts 1 and 2 refer respectively to the states at the beginning and the end of a process. Notice that equation 2·7 is a special case of equation 2·2. U is internal energy, the form of stored energy which is independent of gravity, motion, electricity, magnetism, and surface tension; E is stored energy in general.

EXAMPLE 2·4.   As a certain quantity of gas expands, it performs 20,000 ft-lb of work while its internal energy decreases by 20 B. Consider the gas as a closed system, and determine the heat transfer of the process.

Solution. There is no indication that forms of stored energy other than internal energy change during this process, so we may apply the first law in the form

$$Q = \Delta U + W$$

and substitute numerical values to obtain

$$Q = -20 + \frac{20,000}{778} = 5.7 \text{ B}$$

(If a negative value were obtained for Q, the conclusion would be that heat is removed from the system during the process.)

* Some engineers use the term "stationary system" or "nonflow system" to designate a closed system which is at rest or in a state of uniform horizontal motion.

EXAMPLE 2·5.   A table of the properties of steam shows that the internal energy and specific volume of steam at 20 psia, 228 F, are 1081.9 B/lb and 20.09 cu ft/lb, respectively. One-half pound of steam initially at this condition in a closed rigid container is heated until its temperature is 440 F and its internal energy is 1158.9 B/lb. Determine the amount of heat added to the steam.

Solution.   The system is the $\frac{1}{2}$ lb of steam. It is a closed system. Applying the first law and noting that no work is done on or by the steam in a closed, rigid container,

$$Q = U_2 - U_1 + W$$
$$= m(u_2 - u_1) + 0$$
$$= \tfrac{1}{2}(1158.9 - 1081.9) = 38.5 \text{ B}$$

EXAMPLE 2·6.   In a cylinder fitted with a piston is trapped 0.02 lb of helium initially at 15 psia with a specific volume of 93.0 cu ft/lb. The helium is compressed frictionlessly in such a manner that $pv^{1.3} = $ constant until its pressure is 30 psia. The internal energy

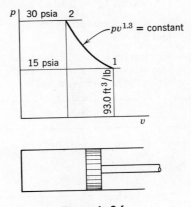

Example 2·6

of helium is given in ft-lb/lb by $u = 1.51pv$, where p is in psfa and v is in cu ft/lb. Determine the heat transfer of the compression process.

Analysis. Q can be found from the first law,

$$Q = U_2 - U_1 - W_{in} = m(u_2 - u_1) - W_{in}$$

if the two terms on the right-hand side can be evaluated. u_1 can be found from $1.51p_1v_1$, and u_2 can be found from $1.51p_2v_2$ after v_2 is found from $p_1v_1^{1.3} = p_2v_2^{1.3}$.

For this frictionless process, work$_{in} = -\int p\, dV = -m\int p\, dv$, and $pv^{1.3} = $ constant is the relation needed between p and v in order to perform the integration.

Solution. v_2 is found from $pv^{1.3} = $ constant $= p_1v_1^{1.3} = p_2v_2^{1.3}$ as

$$v_2 = v_1\left(\frac{p_1}{p_2}\right)^{1/1.3} = 93.0\left(\frac{15}{30}\right)^{0.770} = 54.6 \text{ cu ft/lb}$$

Then

$$u_2 - u_1 = 1.51[p_2v_2 - p_1v_1] = 1.51(144)[30(54.6) - 15(93.0)]\tfrac{1}{778}$$
$$= 67.9 \text{ B/lb}$$

The work input for this frictionless process of a closed system is

$$W_{in} = -\int_1^2 p\, dV = -m\int_1^2 p\, dv = -m\int_1^2 \frac{constant}{v^{1.3}}\, dv$$

$$= -m\int_1^2 \frac{p_1 v_1^{1.3}}{v^{1.3}}\, dv = -p m_1 v_1^{1\cdot3}\left(\frac{1}{-0.3}\right)\left[\frac{1}{v_2^{0.3}} - \frac{1}{v_1^{0.3}}\right]$$

$$= +m p_1 v_1\left(\frac{1}{0.3}\right)\left[\left(\frac{v_1}{v_2}\right)^{0.3} - 1\right] = 0.02(15)144(93.0)\frac{1}{0.3}\left[\left(\frac{93.0}{54.6}\right)^{0.3} - 1\right]$$

$$= 2320 \text{ ft-lb} = 2.98 \text{ B}$$

Substituting the values of Δu and W into the first law formulation

$$Q = m(u_2 - u_1) - W_{in}$$

gives

$$Q = 0.02(67.9) - 2.98 = -1.62 \text{ B}$$

The minus sign indicates that heat was removed from the helium during the compression, because $Q_{out} = -Q = -(-1.62) = 1.62 \text{ B}$.

EXAMPLE 2·7. A mixture of ammonia liquid and vapor is heated slowly at constant pressure until all the liquid has evaporated. Properties of the ammonia at the two end states of the process are given in the accompanying table.

Property	Initial State (1)	Final State (2)
Pressure, psia	50	50
Temperature, F	21.67	21.67
Specific volume, cu ft/lb	2.86	5.71
Enthalpy, B/lb	342.4	618.2

Calculate the amount of heat added per pound of ammonia, assuming that there are no frictional effects within the closed system.

Analysis. The amount of heat added can be found from

$$q = u_2 - u_1 + w \qquad (2\cdot7)$$

by finding the u values from $u_2 = h_2 - p_2 v_2$ and $u_1 = h_1 - p_1 v_1$ and by calculating the work of this frictionless process of a closed system from $work = \int_1^2 p\, dv$. Since $p = constant$, the expression for work is readily integrated to give $p(v_2 - v_1)$ or $(p_2 v_2 - p_1 v_1)$. When this is substituted into equation 2·7, the result is

$$q = u_2 - u_1 + p_2 v_2 - p_1 v_1 = h_2 - h_1$$

By analyzing the problem completely in this manner before beginning numerical calculations, we have saved ourselves the trouble of calculating the internal energy values. A little practice makes it possible to analyze a problem such as this entirely "in one's head," without use of pencil and paper, or perhaps with only sketchy notes on scratch paper. In any event, the problem *solution* which is to be presented to someone else or filed away for later use by the same engineer should be complete and should show each step clearly. The solution based on the above analysis follows.

Solution. The heat added is found from the first law as

$$q = u_2 - u_1 + w \tag{2·7}$$

For a frictionless process of a closed system, $w = \int_1^2 p\, dv$. Making this substitution in equation 2·7 and integrating for this case of $p = \text{constant} = p_1 = p_2$,

$$q = u_2 - u_1 + \int_1^2 p\, dv = u_2 - u_1 + p(v_2 - v_1)$$

$$= u_2 - u_1 + p_2 v_2 - p_1 v_1$$

Noting that $h \equiv u + pv$, we obtain

$$q = h_2 - h_1 = 618.2 - 342.4 = 275.8 \text{ B/lb}$$

2·7 The first law applied to open systems

From the first law or the law of conservation of energy, we can conclude[*] that for any system, open or closed, there is an "energy balance" as

$$\begin{bmatrix} \text{Net amount of energy} \\ \text{added to system} \end{bmatrix} = \begin{bmatrix} \text{net increase in stored} \\ \text{energy of system} \end{bmatrix} \tag{2·8a}$$

With both open and closed systems, energy can be added to the system or taken from it by means of heat and work. In the case of an open system, there is an additional mechanism for increasing or decreasing the stored energy of the system. When mass enters a system, the stored energy of the system is increased by the stored energy of the entering mass. The stored energy of a system is decreased whenever mass leaves the system because the mass leaving the system takes some stored energy with it. If we distinguish this transfer of stored energy of mass crossing the system boundary from heat and work, equation 2·8a becomes

$$\begin{bmatrix} \text{Net amount of} \\ \text{energy added to} \\ \text{system as heat} \\ \text{and all forms of} \\ \text{work} \end{bmatrix} + \begin{bmatrix} \text{stored energy} \\ \text{of mass} \\ \text{entering} \\ \text{system} \end{bmatrix} - \begin{bmatrix} \text{stored energy} \\ \text{of mass} \\ \text{leaving} \\ \text{system} \end{bmatrix} = \begin{bmatrix} \text{net increase} \\ \text{in stored} \\ \text{energy of} \\ \text{system} \end{bmatrix} \tag{2·8b}$$

If we investigate the flow of mass across the boundary of a system, we find that work is always done on or by a system where fluid flows across the system boundary. Therefore, the work term in an energy balance for an open system is usually separated into two parts: (*a*) the work required to push a fluid into or out of the system, and (*b*) all other forms of work.

In order to derive an expression for the work required to push a fluid

---

[*] For a rigorous demonstration, see J. H. Keenan, *Thermodynamics*, John Wiley & Sons, 1941, pp. 32–34.

into or out of a system, consider a system as shown in Fig. 2·4 with fluid entering at section 1 and leaving at section 2. In particular, consider the process by which a volume V_1 of fluid is pushed into the system at section 1. The fluid element of volume V_1 has a cross-sectional area A_1 and a length L_1 as it crosses the system boundary at section 1. The force acting on this element to push it across the system boundary is $F_1 = p_1 A_1$. This force acts through a distance L_1 so that the work done in pushing the element across the system boundary is

$$\text{Work} = F_1 L_1 = p_1 A_1 L_1 = p_1 V_1$$

This is work done on the system by the fluid outside the system, because the effect within the system could be reduced entirely to the lifting of a

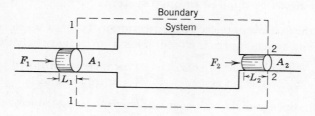

Fig. 2·4   Open system.

weight. In a similar manner, the work performed by the system to push an element of fluid out at section 2 is

$$\text{Work} = p_2 V_2$$

It is seen from this analysis that work must be done in causing fluid to flow into or out of a system. This work is called *flow work*. Other names such as flow energy and displacement energy are sometimes used, but they are not used in this book.*

Per unit mass crossing the boundary of a system, the flow work is pv. If the pressure or the specific volume or both vary as a fluid flows across a system boundary, the flow work is calculated by integrating $\int pv \, \delta m$,

---

* Disagreement on the name used for this quantity results from the fact that the pV term is generally derived as a work quantity; yet it is unlike other work quantities in that it is expressed in terms of a point function. Because it is so expressed, some engineers prefer to group it with stored energy quantities and sometimes speak of it as "transported energy" or "convected energy" instead of work; but it must be remembered that pV can be treated as energy only when a fluid is crossing a system boundary. For a closed system, pV does not represent any form of energy. Incidentally, arguments as to whether pV "really is" flow work or flow energy are fruitless. Both terms are successfully used.

where δm is an infinitesimal mass crossing the boundary. The symbol δm is used instead of dm because the amount of mass crossing the boundary is not a property. The mass within the system is a property, so the infinitesimal change in mass within the system is properly represented by dm.

Since the work term in an energy balance for an open system is usually separated into two parts, (*a*) flow work and (*b*) all other forms of work, the term *work* without modifiers is conventionally understood to stand for all other forms of work except flow work, and the complete two-word name is always used when referring to flow work. In accordance with this convention, we can rewrite equation 2·8*b* to show flow work separately

$$Q - W + \sum_{\substack{\text{mass} \\ \text{entering}}} (pV + E) - \sum_{\substack{\text{mass} \\ \text{leaving}}} (pV + E) = E_f - E_i \quad (2\cdot 8c)$$

where E_f and E_i are respectively the final and initial stored energies of the system. In differential form, where δm is an infinitesimal mass crossing the system boundary,

$$\delta Q - \delta W + [(e + pv)\, \delta m]_{\text{in}} - [(e + pv)\, \delta m]_{\text{out}} = dE \quad (2\cdot 8d)$$

2·8 The first law applied to open systems—steady flow

An open system through which fluid passes under steady-flow conditions is called a steady-flow system. We shall now apply the first law to steady-flow systems.

From the definition of steady flow (Art. 1·15), it is seen that the stored energy of an open system must remain constant as long as steady-flow conditions prevail. Therefore, when the energy balance as written in equation 2·8*b* is applied to a steady-flow system, its right-hand side becomes zero, and we have

$$\begin{bmatrix} \text{Net amount of} \\ \text{energy added to} \\ \text{system as heat} \\ \text{and work} \end{bmatrix} + \begin{bmatrix} \text{stored energy of} \\ \text{mass entering} \\ \text{system} \end{bmatrix} - \begin{bmatrix} \text{stored energy of} \\ \text{mass leaving} \\ \text{system} \end{bmatrix} = 0 \quad (2\cdot 9a)$$

Let us consider a steady-flow system such as shown in Fig. 2·5 which has only two fluid streams crossing its boundary. Fluid enters at section 1 and leaves at section 2. (The system might be an air compressor, a gas turbine, a centrifugal water pump, a fan, a nozzle, or a section of pipe.) Rewriting equation 2·9*a* in terms of symbols already introduced, we have

$$Q + W_{\text{in}} + m p_1 v_1 - m p_2 v_2 + E_1 - E_2 = 0 \quad (2\cdot 9b)$$

where Q = net amount of heat added to the system while an amount of mass m passes through the system

W_{in} = net amount of work, excluding flow work, done on the system during the same time

mp_1v_1 = amount of flow work done on the system by the fluid entering

mp_2v_2 = amount of flow work done by the system on the fluid leaving

(v_1 and v_2 as well as p_1 and p_2 are generally unequal, but for steady-flow conditions the mass of fluid entering must equal the mass of fluid leaving.)

E_1 = stored energy of the fluid entering the system

E_2 = stored energy of the fluid leaving the system

Notice that Q and W may each be either positive or negative.

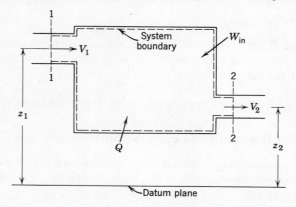

Fig. 2·5 Steady-flow system.

If each fluid stream crossing the system boundary has a uniform velocity and z is the vertical distance of the stream from the horizontal datum plane, then the stored energy of fluid crossing the system boundary is given by

$$E = me = m\left(u + \frac{V^2}{2g_c} + \frac{g}{g_c}z\right) \qquad (2·6c)$$

provided there are no effects of electricity, magnetism, and surface tension. m is the mass of fluid crossing the boundary and is the same for inlet and outlet for a steady-flow system with only one inlet and one outlet. Equation 2·9b may then be written, after rearranging slightly,

$$Q + W_{in} + mp_1v_1 - mp_2v_2 + m\left(u_1 + \frac{V_1^2}{2g_c} + \frac{g}{g_c}z_1\right)$$

$$= m\left(u_2 + \frac{V_2^2}{2g_c} + \frac{g}{g_c}z_2\right) \quad (2·9c)$$

Per unit of mass passing through the system,

$$q + w_{in} + p_1v_1 - p_2v_2 + u_1 + \frac{V_1^2}{2g_c} + \frac{g}{g_c}z_1 = u_2 + \frac{V_2^2}{2g_c} + \frac{g}{g_c}z_2 \quad (2·9d)$$

Using the definition of enthalpy, $h \equiv u+pv$, the energy balance equations above can be shortened. For example, equation 2·9d becomes after a slight rearrangement

$$q + w_{in} = h_2 - h_1 + \frac{V_2^2 - V_1^2}{2g_c} + \frac{g}{g_c}(z_2 - z_1) \quad (2·9e)$$

This is a frequently used form of the energy balance applied to a steady-flow system. It can be written more concisely as

$$q - w = \Delta h + \Delta KE + \Delta PE$$

(Recall the sign convention introduced in Art. 1·13: w stands for work done *by* the system, so that $w_{in} = -w$.) A form of equation 2·9e which is frequently seen is

$$q + h_1 + KE_1 + PE_1 = w + h_2 + KE_2 + PE_2$$

Equations 2·9b through 2·9e are all forms that apply only to steady-flow systems which have a single inlet and a single outlet. Application of equation 2·9a to a steady-flow system with fluid crossing the boundary at several places leads to

$$Q - W = \sum_{\substack{\text{all streams} \\ \text{leaving}}} m(e + pv) - \sum_{\substack{\text{all streams} \\ \text{entering}}} m(e + pv) \quad (2·9f)$$

In the absence of electricity, magnetism, and surface tension effects, we may replace e by $u+V^2/2g_c+(g/g_c)z$. Then the combination $(u+pv)$ can be replaced by h to give a convenient form which is frequently used:

$$Q - W = \sum_{\substack{\text{all streams} \\ \text{leaving}}} m\left(h + \frac{V^2}{2g_c} + \frac{g}{g_c}z\right) - \sum_{\substack{\text{all streams} \\ \text{entering}}} m\left(h + \frac{V^2}{2g_c} + \frac{g}{g_c}z\right)$$

$$(2·9g)$$

Equation 2·9e, which applies to a system with a single inlet and a single outlet, is a special case of equation 2·9g.

In all the above equations where the symbol m appears, it stands for the mass of the fluid. In many engineering applications it is more convenient to use the mass rate of flow M. When this is done, all terms in the energy balance must be on a time basis. Work per unit time is called power P, so equation 2·9g becomes

$$\dot{Q} - P = \sum_{\substack{\text{all streams} \\ \text{leaving}}} M\left(h + \frac{V^2}{2g_c} + \frac{g}{g_c}z\right) - \sum_{\substack{\text{all streams} \\ \text{entering}}} M\left(h + \frac{V^2}{2g_c} + \frac{g}{g_c}z\right)$$

$$(2·9h)$$

The symbol $\dot{Q}$ is used for heat transfer per unit time or rate of heat transfer.

Equation 2·9 has been written above in several forms, and many other arrangements are useful in various applications. You must understand that these are all forms of the same basic relation, equation 2·9a, and it is neither necessary nor advisable to learn the several different forms independently. You should learn and thoroughly understand the relationship expressed by equation 2·9a, and from this relationship you should be able to formulate quickly any of the special forms which may be convenient for a particular application.

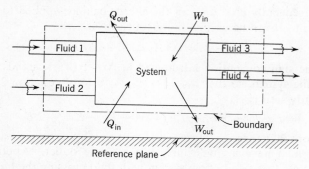

Fig. 2·6   Steady-flow system with mixing of fluid streams.

Notice that the subscripts used in several forms of equation 2·9 (pertaining to steady-flow systems) refer to different sections of the system boundary during the same time interval or at the same instant, whereas the subscripts 1 and 2 used in equations such as

$$Q - W = U_2 - U_1 \qquad (2\cdot7)$$

(pertaining to closed systems) refer to the same mass at different times. The viewpoint used in dealing with steady-flow systems is that of an observer outside the system making simultaneous measurements at all places where mass or energy crosses the system boundary. Another viewpoint for a steady-flow system is that of an observer who travels through the system from inlet to outlet with the flowing fluid and measures the properties of the same mass of material at inlet and outlet. The moving observer viewpoint is not used in this book. It is unsatisfactory in processes involving the mixing of two or more fluid streams as illustrated in Fig. 2·6 because each entering stream loses its identity as it is mixed with or perhaps reacts chemically with another stream. For example, if a stream of methane and a stream of oxygen enter a system and react with each other so that a stream composed of carbon dioxide, carbon monoxide, and water leaves the system, an observer who intended to travel through the system with the methane and measure its properties at inlet and outlet would be faced with an impossible task.

The application of the first law to steady-flow systems is illustrated by the following examples.

EXAMPLE 2·8.   In a steady-flow process, the pressure of a fluid decreased between the entrance and exit of a machine from 200 to 40 psia, the specific volume increased from 3 to 10 cu ft/lb, the internal energy decreased by 40 B/lb, and 10 B/lb of heat was added to the fluid between entrance and exit.   Entrance and exit pipes were at the same elevation, and entrance and exit velocities were 10 and 15 fps, respectively.   Determine the amount of work done on or by the fluid.

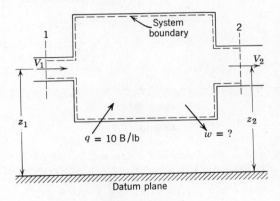

Example 2·8

Solution.   A diagram of the steady-flow system is made first.   Next, the first law is applied to the system in the form of an energy balance solved for work per pound:

$$w = q + u_1 - u_2 + p_1 v_1 - p_2 v_2 + \frac{V_1^2 - V_2^2}{2g_c} + \frac{g}{g_c}(z_1 - z_2) \qquad (2 \cdot 9e)$$

(If a negative value is obtained for w, it will indicate that work is done *on* the system in this process.)   Factoring $(V_1^2 - V_2^2)$ to $(V_1 - V_2)(V_1 + V_2)$ for convenience and substituting numerical values gives

$$w = 10 \left[\frac{B}{lb} \right] 778 \left[\frac{ft\text{-}lb}{B} \right] + 40 \left[\frac{B}{lb} \right] 778 \left[\frac{ft\text{-}lb}{B} \right] + 200 \left[\frac{lb}{in.^2} \right] 144 \left[\frac{in.^2}{ft^2} \right] 3 \left[\frac{ft^3}{lb} \right]$$

$$- 40 \left[\frac{lb}{in.^2} \right] 144 \left[\frac{in.^2}{ft^2} \right] 10 \left[\frac{ft^3}{lb} \right] + \frac{(-5)(25)[ft^2/sec^2]}{2(32.2)[lb_m\text{-}ft/sec^2\text{-}lb_f]} + 0$$

$$= 7780 + 31{,}120 + 86{,}400 - 57{,}600 - \text{negligible} + 0$$

$$= 67{,}700 \ ft\text{-}lb/lb$$

The positive sign indicates that work was performed by the fluid (the system) on the surroundings.

EXAMPLE 2·9.   A compressor requires 5 hp to compress ammonia at a certain rate from 40 psia, 11.7 F, to 135 psia while heat is removed from the compressor by means of water jackets at a rate of 150 B/min. Neglecting changes in potential and kinetic energy, how much is the enthalpy of the ammonia changed per minute?

Solution.   A sketch of the steady-flow system is made first. The enthalpy change

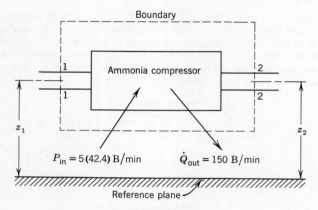

Example 2·9

per minute is the product of the mass rate of flow and the enthalpy change per pound, $M \Delta h$; so an energy balance is written for the system in a form giving $M \Delta h$ explicitly:

$$M \Delta h = M(h_2 - h_1) = M(w_{in} + q - \Delta KE - \Delta PE)$$
$$= P_{in} + \dot{Q} - 0 - 0$$
$$= 5(42.4) + (-150)$$
$$= 212 - 150 = 62 \ \text{B/min}$$

The positive sign indicates that the enthalpy of the ammonia increased. The value 42.4 is a conversion factor: 1 hp = 42.4 B/min.

EXAMPLE 2·10.   Air at 14.7 psia, 70 F ($\rho = 0.0749$ lb/cu ft), is taken into a gas-turbine power plant at a velocity of 400 fps through an opening of 1.2 sq ft cross-sectional area. The air is compressed, heated, expanded through a turbine, and exhausted at 26 psia, 300 F ($\rho = 0.0924$ lb/cu ft), through an opening of 1.0 sq ft cross-sectional area. The power output is 500 hp. The internal energy and enthalpy of the air in B/lb are given by the expressions $u = 0.171T$ and $h = 0.240T$, where T is absolute temperature, degrees Rankine. Calculate the net amount of heat added to the air in B/lb.

Analysis.   A sketch of the steady-flow system is made first. It is sometimes convenient to write on the sketch the values of any physical quantities which are known and which appear to be pertinent. It looks as though we must use an energy balance in order to find q; so an energy balance is written for the system

$$q = w + h_2 - h_1 + \frac{V_2^2 - V_1^2}{2g_c} + \frac{g}{g_c}(z_2 - z_1) \qquad (a)$$

(We could use an energy balance with Δu and Δpv as separate terms instead of using Δh, but the use of Δh will reduce the amount of numerical calculations needed.) Now all that must be done is to evaluate each of the terms on the right-hand side of the equation in order to obtain the value of q. The four terms will be considered in the order in which they appear in the energy balance above.

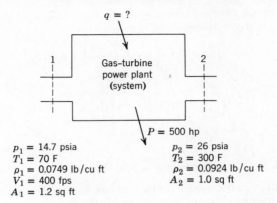

$q = ?$

Gas–turbine
power plant
(system)

1

2

$P = 500$ hp

$p_1 = 14.7$ psia
$T_1 = 70$ F
$\rho_1 = 0.0749$ lb/cu ft
$V_1 = 400$ fps
$A_1 = 1.2$ sq ft

$p_2 = 26$ psia
$T_2 = 300$ F
$\rho_2 = 0.0924$ lb/cu ft
$A_2 = 1.0$ sq ft

Example 2·10

The work output in B/lb can be found from the power output and the mass rate of flow,

$$w = \frac{P}{M} \tag{b}$$

$P = 500$ hp, but the mass rate of flow must be calculated by

$$M = \rho_1 A_1 V_1 \tag{c}$$

and ρ, A, and V at the inlet are all known. Thus equations (b) and (c) together provide the value of w for use in equation (a).

The change in enthalpy can be found from the given relationship, $h = 0.240T$.

The change in kinetic energy requires a knowledge of both V_1 and V_2. $V_1 = 400$ fps, but the value of V_2 must be obtained. Since A_2 and ρ_2 are known, we can use the continuity equation,

$$\rho_2 A_2 V_2 = \rho_1 A_1 V_1 = M$$

ρ_1, A_1, and V_1 are all known, and their product M was found earlier by means of equation (c).

The change in potential energy can be found only if we have some information about the elevations of the inlet and outlet, and we do not have this information. However, if we notice the magnitudes of the other terms in the energy balance and then notice that an elevation change of 778 ft is required to cause a change in potential energy of 1 B/lb, we do not hesitate to assume that the change in potential energy is negligibly small. (An elevation difference of 77.8 ft between inlet and outlet of a gas-turbine plant would be unusually great, and it would correspond to a potential energy change of only 0.1 B/lb.)

Thus our analysis of the problem shows us (1) that we can solve the problem, and (2) the procedure to use in our solution.

An engineer tackling a problem usually analyzes it thoroughly in some manner such as presented above. In a simple problem like this he would not write out all of the words as we have done above, and he might even make the entire analysis so rapidly that unless he pays special attention to his problem-solving technique he would even be unaware that he had made any such analysis. He might outline his analysis in writing in a form such as shown below.

$$q = w + \underbrace{h_2 - h_1} + \left[\frac{V_2^2 - \overset{\vee}{V_1^2}}{2g_c}\right] + \Delta PE$$

$$\longrightarrow \text{negligible}$$

$$\longrightarrow 0.24(\overset{\vee}{T_2} - \overset{\vee}{T_1})$$

$$\longrightarrow w = \frac{\overset{\vee}{P}}{M}$$

$$\longrightarrow V_2 = \frac{M}{\overset{\vee}{A_2}\overset{\vee}{\rho_2}}$$

$$\longrightarrow M = \overset{\vee}{A_1}\overset{\vee}{V_1}\overset{\vee}{\rho_1}$$

The check marks ($\checkmark$) over certain symbols indicate that the numerical values of those quantities are known.

This form of analysis provides a clear outline of the solution. It will be used frequently throughout this book.

Solution.

$$M = A_1 V_1 \rho_1 = 1.2(400)0.0749 = 36.0 \text{ lb/sec}$$

$$w = \frac{P}{M} = \frac{500(0.707)}{36.0} = 9.82 \text{ B/lb}$$

$$V_2 = \frac{M}{A_2 \rho_2} = \frac{36.0}{1.0(0.0924)} = 390 \text{ fps}$$

$$q = w + h_2 - h_1 + \frac{V_2^2 - V_1^2}{2g_c} + \Delta PE$$

$$= w + 0.240(T_2 - T_1) + \frac{(V_2 - V_1)(V_2 + V_1)}{2g_c} + 0$$

$$= 9.82 + 0.240(760 - 530) + \frac{(-10)790}{2(32.2)778} + 0$$

$$= 64.9 \text{ B/lb}$$

EXAMPLE 2·11. Air is compressed in a frictionless steady-flow process from 10 psia, 60 F ($v = 19.2$ cu ft/lb), to 15 psia in such a manner that $p(v+5) = $ constant, where v is in cu ft/lb. Inlet velocity is negligibly small, and discharge velocity is 350 fps. Calculate the work required per pound of air.

Analysis. Applying the first law to this steady-flow system gives an energy balance in the form

$$w_{\text{in}} = q_{\text{out}} + h_2 - h_1 + \frac{V_2^2 - V_1^2}{2g_c} + \frac{g}{g_c}(z_2 - z_1)$$

When we begin to evaluate these terms, we see that the potential energy term is probably negligibly small and we have values for both velocities which appear in the kinetic energy term. There appears to be no way to calculate q or Δh (unless one has already studied Chapter 4!); so we appear to be "stuck." The energy balance written above is valid, but we do not have all the information required in order to solve it for w_{in}. Therefore, we immediately seek some other means of solving the problem. Perhaps we can find w_{in} by means of the expression which is based on the principles of mechanics (Art. 1·16),

$$w_{in} = \int_1^2 v\,dp + \frac{V_2^2 - V_1^2}{2g_c} + \frac{g}{g_c}(z_2 - z_1)$$

We have noted before that we can evaluate the kinetic and potential energy terms. Since we have a functional relationship between p and v, we can integrate $\int v\,dp$, and

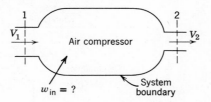

$w_{in} = ?$ System boundary

Example 2·11

so we will be able to determine w_{in}. (The unsuccessful attempt to use the energy balance is shown above as an illustration that no harm is done by making such a "false start" as long as we quickly recognize that we are not on the right track and immediately look for another method of solution.)

Solution.

$$w_{in} = \int_1^2 v\,dp + \frac{V_2^2 - V_1^2}{2g_c} + \frac{g}{g_c}(z_2 - z_1) = \int_1^2 v\,dp + \frac{V_2^2}{2g_c} + 0$$

$$\int_1^2 v\,dp = \int_1^2 \left[\frac{C}{P} - 5\right]dp = C\ln\frac{P_2}{P_1} - 5(p_2 - p_1)$$

$$= p_1[v_1 + 5]\ln\frac{P_2}{P_1} - 5(p_2 - p_1)$$

$$= 10(144)[19.2 + 5]\ln\frac{15}{10} - 5(15 - 10)144$$

$$= 10{,}530 \text{ ft-lb}_f/\text{lb}_m$$

$$w_{in} = 10{,}530 + \frac{(350)^2}{2(32.2)} = 12{,}430 \text{ ft-lb}_f/\text{lb}_m$$

EXAMPLE 2·12.   A mixture of air and water vapor with an enthalpy of 54.1 B/lb enters the dehumidifying section of an air-conditioning system at a rate of 720 lb/hr. Liquid water drains out of the dehumidifier with an enthalpy of 18.0 B/lb at a rate of 16.0 lb/hr. An air–vapor mixture leaves with an enthalpy of 20.1 B/lb. Determine the rate of heat removal from the fluids passing through the dehumidifier.

Solution. After a sketch of the system is made, the first law is applied in the form of an energy balance for steady flow,

$$M_1h_1 = M_2h_2 + M_3h_3 + \dot{Q}_{out}$$

The assumption has been made that changes in kinetic and potential energies are negligibly small. There is no work done. The conservation of mass requires that $M_3 = M_1 - M_2$. Rearranging and substituting numerical values gives

$$Q_{out} = M_1h_1 - M_2h_2 - (M_1 - M_2)h_3$$

$$\dot{Q}_{out} = 720(54.1) - 16.0(18.0) - (720 - 16)20.1$$

$$= 24{,}500 \text{ B/hr}$$

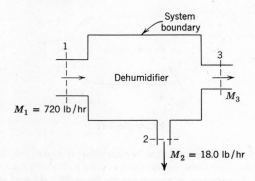

Example 2·12

EXAMPLE 2·13. Brine with a specific gravity of 1.20 enters a pump at 14 psia, 15 F, through a 3-in.-diameter opening and is discharged at 45 psia through a 2-in.-diameter opening. The pump outlet is 3 ft above the inlet. The flow rate is 200 gpm. If the pumping were done frictionlessly, how much power would be required?

Analysis. This is an open system. Steady-flow conditions will be assumed. We can find the power input by multiplying the work per unit mass by the mass rate of flow. In order to find the work, we first consider the use of the first law. As in Example 2·11,

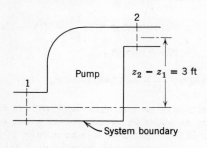

Example 2·13

however, we see that our ignorance of q and Δu stops us.* Therefore, we turn to the relation from mechanics which applies to frictionless steady-flow processes:

$$w_{in} = \int_1^2 v\,dp + \frac{V_2^2 - V_1^2}{2g_c} + \frac{g}{g_c}(z_2 - z_1)$$

Noting that brine is incompressible ($v = $ constant) and that the velocities can be obtained by means of the continuity equation, we see that the work done on the brine can be calculated by this relation.

The flow rate is given in the usual units of gallons per minute, a volume rate of flow. Since the specific gravity is known, the mass rate of flow can easily be obtained.

Solution.

$$M = \text{(volume rate of flow)}\ \rho$$

$$= \frac{200}{60}\left[\frac{\text{gal}}{\text{sec}}\right]\frac{231[\text{in.}^3]}{[\text{gal}]}\frac{[\text{ft}^3]}{1728[\text{in.}^3]}(62.4)1.20\left[\frac{\text{lb}}{\text{ft}^3}\right]$$

$$= 33.4\ \text{lb/sec}$$

$$V_1 = \frac{M}{\rho A_1} = \frac{33.4(4)144}{1.20(62.4)\pi(3)^2} = 9.1\ \text{fps}$$

$$V_2 = \frac{M}{\rho A_2} = \frac{\rho A_1 V_1}{\rho A_2} = \left(\frac{D_1}{D_2}\right)^2 V_1 = \left(\frac{3}{2}\right)^2 9.1 = 20.5\ \text{fps}$$

$$w_{in} = \int_1^2 v\,dp + \frac{V_2^2 - V_1^2}{2g_c} + \frac{g}{g_c}(z_2 - z_1)$$

$$= v(p_2 - p_1) + \frac{(V_2 - V_1)(V_2 + V_1)}{2g_c} + \frac{g}{g_c}(z_2 - z_1)$$

$$= \frac{1}{1.2(62.4)}(45 - 14)144 + \frac{11.4(29.6)}{2(32.2)} + \frac{32.2}{32.2}(3)$$

$$= 59.7 + 5.2 + 3 = 67.9\ \text{ft-lb}_f/\text{lb}_m$$

$$P = Mw_{in} = \frac{33.4(67.9)}{550} = 4.13\ \text{hp}$$

2·9 The first law applied to open systems—general formulations

We have pointed out (in Art. 1·15) that steady flow is a *special case* of the flow through an open system. An open system which has mass crossing its boundaries under any conditions other than those of steady flow is sometimes called a transient-flow system or an unsteady-flow system. The properties of the mass crossing the boundaries may vary with time. The quantity of material in the system may also vary, since the mass of material entering the system may not equal the quantity leaving it.

* But see Prob. 2·18.

Some examples of transient-flow processes are the filling or emptying of any vessel, the flow in the intake and exhaust manifolds of an automobile engine, the flow through an automobile-engine water jacket before the engine parts have reached steady operating temperatures, and the flow through a turbine while the shaft speed or power output is changing.

We have seen (Art. 2·7) that the application of the first law to any open system results in an energy balance in a form such as

$$\begin{bmatrix} \text{Net amount of} \\ \text{energy added to} \\ \text{system as heat} \\ \text{and all forms of} \\ \text{work} \end{bmatrix} + \begin{bmatrix} \text{stored} \\ \text{energy} \\ \text{of mass} \\ \text{entering} \\ \text{system} \end{bmatrix} - \begin{bmatrix} \text{stored} \\ \text{energy} \\ \text{of mass} \\ \text{leaving} \\ \text{system} \end{bmatrix} = \begin{bmatrix} \text{net increase} \\ \text{in stored} \\ \text{energy of} \\ \text{system} \end{bmatrix} \quad (2\cdot8b)$$

It was also shown in Art. 2·7 that the work term in an energy balance for an open system can be separated into two parts: (a) flow work, and (b) all other forms of work. In the general case of an open system, the properties of the mass crossing the system boundary vary with mass or with time. If the variations of p and v with mass crossing the system boundary at some section are known, the flow-work term for that section can be evaluated as $\int_0^{m_1} pv \, \delta m$, where m_1 is the total amount of mass which crosses the boundary there. If the variations of p, v, and the mass rate of flow with time are known, it is more convenient to write the flow-work term for one section as $\int_{\tau_i}^{\tau_f} Mpv \, d\tau$, where τ_i and τ_f are the times at which the process starts (initial time) and ends (final time). In a similar manner, the stored energy of fluid crossing the system boundary can be evaluated as $\int_0^m e \, \delta m$ or as $\int_{\tau_i}^{\tau_f} Me \, d\tau$. Thus the terms in equation 2·8b can be evaluated as follows:

$$\begin{bmatrix} \text{Net amount of energy} \\ \text{added to system as} \\ \text{heat and work} \end{bmatrix} = \begin{cases} Q - W + \sum_{\text{entering}} \int pv \, \delta m - \sum_{\text{leaving}} \int pv \, \delta m \\ \\ Q - W + \sum_{\text{entering}} \int Mpv \, d\tau - \sum_{\text{leaving}} \int Mpv \, d\tau \end{cases}$$

$$\begin{bmatrix} \text{Stored energy of mass} \\ \text{entering system} \end{bmatrix} = \sum_{\text{entering}} \int e \, \delta m = \sum_{\text{entering}} \int Me \, d\tau$$

$$\begin{bmatrix} \text{Stored energy of mass} \\ \text{leaving system} \end{bmatrix} = \sum_{\text{leaving}} \int e \, \delta m = \sum_{\text{leaving}} \int Me \, d\tau$$

$$\begin{bmatrix} \text{Net increase in stored} \\ \text{energy of system} \end{bmatrix} = E_f - E_i$$

where E_i and E_f are respectively the stored energy of the entire system in its initial state and in its final state. If the power input or output of the system is known as a function of time, W may be evaluated as $\int_{\tau_i}^{\tau_f} P \, d\tau$.

For a system with fluid entering only at a section 1 and leaving only at a section 2, equation 2·8b can be written as

$$Q - W + \int (e_1 + p_1 v_1)\, \delta m_1 - \int (e_2 + p_2 v_2)\, \delta m_2 = E_f - E_i \quad (2\text{·}8c)$$

In the absence of electrical, magnetic, and surface tension effects, $e = u + KE + PE$ and $e + pv = h + KE + PE$, so that

$$Q - W + \int \left(h_1 + \frac{V_1^2}{2g_c} + \frac{g}{g_c} z_1\right) \delta m_1 - \int \left(h_2 + \frac{V_2^2}{2g_c} + \frac{g}{g_c} z_2\right) \delta m_2$$

$$= U_f - U_i + \frac{m_f V_f^2 - m_i V_i^2}{2g_c} + \frac{g}{g_c}(m_f z_f - m_i z_i) \quad (2\text{·}8d)$$

It must be remembered that the subscripts i and f denote that the values so marked are for the entire system before and after the process occurs.

The closed system and steady-flow energy balances presented in Arts. 2·3 and 2·8 can be considered as special cases of the general open-system energy balances presented in this article and Art. 2·7.* To illustrate this, let us first rewrite equation 2·8 in differential form:

$$\delta Q - \delta W + (e_1 + p_1 v_1)\, \delta m_1 - (e_2 + p_2 v_2)\, \delta m_2 = dE \quad (2\text{·}8d)$$

For the special case of a *closed system*, $\delta m_1 = \delta m_2 = 0$, and equation 2·8d becomes

$$\delta Q - \delta W = dE \quad (2\text{·}2)$$

which was introduced in Art. 2·3. For the special case of a *steady-flow* system, $dE = 0$, $\delta m_1 = \delta m_2$, and the properties (e, p, v) of the fluids crossing the system boundary do not vary with time. Thus equation 2·8 becomes

$$Q - W + (e_1 + p_1 v_1)m - (e_2 + p_2 v_2)m = 0 \quad (2\text{·}9b)$$

which was introduced in Art. 2·8 for the case of steady flow.

Frequently, moving the boundary of an open system simplifies an energy balance. This is usually true for the flow of a fluid into an open system from a region where the fluid is at rest. As a specific example, consider the flow from the atmosphere into the air compressor shown in

---

* Notice that the closed-system energy balance *can be considered* as a special case of the open-system energy balance, but that to *derive* the closed-system equation from the open-system equation is to reverse the logical structure we have been following. The first law is an inductive conclusion based on observations on *closed systems*. It can then be extended to open systems. Starting from the open-system result and deducing the closed-system energy balance simply reverses the development; so of course it works out, but it proves nothing.

Fig. 2·7. The fluid at section 1 has properties p_1, v_1, h_1, etc. and a velocity V_1. Consider an energy balance between section 1 and some section 0 in the atmosphere where the fluid on its way toward section 1 has a velocity which is very small, $V_0 \approx 0$. Certainly no work is done between 0 and 1. Further, let us neglect ΔPE. Then if we assume that the flow between 0 and 1 is adiabatic and that there is no change in the total amount of energy or mass stored between 0 and 1, the first law gives us

$$h_0 = h_1 + \frac{V_1^2}{2g_c}$$

Thus two terms, enthalpy and kinetic energy at section 1, which appear in an energy balance on the compressor can be replaced by the enthalpy

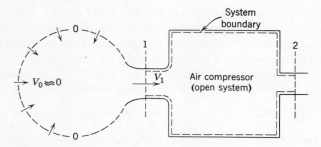

Fig. 2·7 Flow into an open system from an atmosphere at rest.

of the fluid at rest in the surrounding atmosphere. This substitution is often made tacitly. For example, if we are applying the first law to a machine which draws air from a room, we usually make use of the pressure and temperature of the air at rest in the room in evaluating inlet conditions and therefore treat the inlet velocity as being zero. Actually, of course, right at the machine inlet the velocity is greater than zero; but, if we evaluate and use the kinetic energy at that point, then we must use it in conjunction with the enthalpy (which depends on pressure and temperature) at that point, and this will be lower than the enthalpy in the room.

In case you are tempted at this point to memorize some of the many energy balance equations that have been displayed in the last three articles, we repeat: *Learn and understand the relationship*

$$\begin{bmatrix} \text{Net amount of} \\ \text{energy added to} \\ \text{system as heat} \\ \text{and all forms of} \\ \text{work} \end{bmatrix} + \begin{bmatrix} \text{stored} \\ \text{energy} \\ \text{of mass} \\ \text{entering} \\ \text{system} \end{bmatrix} - \begin{bmatrix} \text{stored} \\ \text{energy} \\ \text{of mass} \\ \text{leaving} \\ \text{system} \end{bmatrix} = \begin{bmatrix} \text{net increase} \\ \text{in stored} \\ \text{energy of} \\ \text{system} \end{bmatrix} \quad (2 \cdot 8b)$$

From this, develop any other equations you may need for particular systems and processes.*

EXAMPLE 2·14.   An insulated steel tank with a gas-storage volume of 4 cu ft contains 0.284 lb of air at 14.7 psia, 100 F. The amount of air in the tank is to be increased by connecting the tank to a large compressed air line through which air at 100 psia, 200 F, is flowing. Some of the properties of air are related as follows: $h = 1.4u = 0.24T = 0.0045pv$, where u and h are in B/lb, T is in degrees Rankine, p is in psfa, and v is in cu ft/lb. Assuming that no heat transfer occurs between air in the tank and any part of the surroundings and that conditions are uniform throughout the tank at any instant, compute the final mass and the final temperature of air in the tank. Neglect changes in kinetic and potential energy.

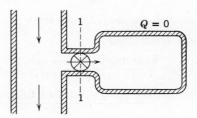

Example 2·14   Open-system analysis.

Solution.   The region within the tank will be considered as the system. Since the quantity of air in the tank varies, this is a transient-flow system. A sketch is made. Since the properties of the air entering the system are constant, they can be tabulated along with the initial and final properties of air in the system as shown in the accompanying table.

	Initial Air in the Tank	Air Flowing into the Tank	Final Air in the Tank
Pressure, psia	$p_i = 14.7$	$p_1 = 100$	$p_f = 100$
Volume, cu ft	$V_i = 4$	....	$V_f = 4$
Mass, lb	$m_i = 0.284$	$m_1 = m_f - m_i$	m_f
Temperature, F	$t_i = 100$ F	$t_1 = 200$ F	t_f

Noting that no work (excepting flow work) is done during the process, we apply the first law to this adiabatic process of a transient-flow system to get the following energy balance:

$$\begin{bmatrix}\text{Stored energy}\\\text{of air initially}\\\text{in tank}\end{bmatrix} + \begin{bmatrix}\text{stored energy of}\\\text{air which flows}\\\text{into tank}\end{bmatrix} + \begin{bmatrix}\text{flow work of}\\\text{air which flows}\\\text{into tank}\end{bmatrix} = \begin{bmatrix}\text{stored energy}\\\text{of air finally}\\\text{in tank}\end{bmatrix}$$

* You may well ask, "If all these equations are not to be learned, why are they in the book?" The answer is that these equations are presented as *samples* of the many that can be obtained from the general energy balance. It is hoped that the study of these samples will help you in developing your own equations to fit the various special cases you encounter.

Neglecting the kinetic and potential energy terms and recalling that u_1, p_1, and v_1 are constant, we can express this energy balance as

$$m_i u_i + m_1(u_1 + p_1 v_1) = m_f u_f$$

$$m_i u_i + (m_f - m_i)h_1 = m_f u_f$$

In this equation there are two unknowns, m_f and u_f. However, another relation between these two variables is given by $1.4u = 0.0045pv$.

$$1.4u_f = 0.0045 p_f v_f = 0.0045 p_f \frac{V_f}{m_f}$$

$$u_f = 0.00321 \frac{p_f V_f}{m_f}$$

Substituting this value of u_f into the energy balance above,

$$m_i u_i + (m_f - m_i)h_1 = 0.00321 p_f V_f$$

$$m_f = \frac{0.00321 p_f V_f - m_i u_i + m_i h_1}{h_1}$$

$$= \frac{0.00321 p_f V_f - m_i(0.24/1.4)T_i + m_i(0.24)T_1}{0.24 T_1}$$

$$= \frac{0.00321(100)144(4) - 0.284(0.24)(560/1.4 - 660)}{0.24(660)}$$

$$m_f = 1.28 \text{ lb}$$

$$T_f = \frac{0.0045}{0.24} p_f v_f = \frac{0.0045 p_f V_f}{0.24 m_f}$$

$$= \frac{0.0045(100)144(4)}{0.24(1.28)} = 844 \text{ R} = 384 \text{ F}$$

(These results and those of the following two solutions are based on the assumption that the tank is filled adiabatically. It is difficult to check these results experimentally because they are affected greatly by heat transfer to the tank wall, even if the outside of the tank is covered by an excellent insulating material. Also, heat transfer from the air to any thermometer placed in the tank will affect the results; yet such a transfer of heat is necessary in order for the thermometer to indicate the temperature of the air.)

Solution with slightly different approach. Some people prefer to start always with an energy balance in differential form such as (for the case of $Q = 0$ and $W = 0$)

$$\begin{bmatrix} \text{Stored energy and} \\ \text{flow work added to} \\ \text{system by entering} \\ \text{mass } \delta m \end{bmatrix} = \begin{bmatrix} \text{increase in stored} \\ \text{energy of system} \\ \text{while mass } \delta m \text{ enters} \end{bmatrix}$$

$$(u_1 + p_1 v_1)\,\delta m_1 = dU$$

$$h_1\,\delta m_1 = dU$$

If m is the mass in the tank, dm is the change in mass in the tank. Since mass enters at only section 1, $\delta m_1 = dm$.

$$h_1\,dm = dU$$

Since $u = 0.00321pv$, then $U = mu = 0.00321pV$, and $dU = 0.00321(V\,dp + p\,dV) = 0.00321\,V\,dp$.

$$h_1\,dm = 0.00321\,V\,dp$$

Integrating, noting that h_1 is constant,

$$h_1(m_f - m_i) = 0.00321\,V(p_f - p_i)$$

$$m_f = m_i + \frac{0.00321\,V(p_f - p_i)}{0.24T_1}$$

Substitution of numerical values gives $m_f = 1.28$ lb, and T_f can then be found as in the first solution.

Alternative solution. This problem can also be solved by the use of a closed-system analysis. Let the system be all the air which finally is in the tank. The system boundary is then an imaginary envelope which encloses all the air in the tank and all the air in the

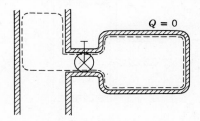

Example 2·14   Closed-system analysis.

pipe line which eventually flows into the tank. No mass crosses this boundary. As air flows from the pipe line into the tank, the volume of that part of the system outside the tank is reduced to zero. Work is done on the system by the surrounding air in the pipe line as the system volume is reduced. Properties of the system before and after the process occurs are listed in the accompanying table.

	Initial Condition	Final Condition
Mass, lb	$m_f = m_i$ in tank $+ (m_f - m_i)$ in pipe	m_f (all in tank)
Internal energy, B	$m_i u_i + (m_f - m_i)u_1$	$m_f u_f$
Volume, cu ft	$V_f + V_1 = m_f v_f + (m_f - m_i)v_1$	$V_f = m_f v_f$

The subscript 1 refers to conditions in the pipe line.

Applying the first law to this system and neglecting changes in kinetic energy,

$$Q + W_{in} + U_i = U_f \qquad (a)$$

The work done on the system is the work done by the surrounding gas in the pipe line to compress that part of the system in the pipe line from a volume of V_1 to a volume of zero. Assuming that *this decrease in volume of the system is brought about frictionlessly* and that *the pressure of that part of the system in the pipe remains constant,*

$$W_{in} = -\int_{V_f + V_1}^{V_f} p\,dV = -p_1\,\Delta V = +p_1 V_1 = p_1(m_f - m_i)v_1$$

Also, the process is adiabatic. Equation (a) becomes

$$0 + p_1(m_f - m_i)v_1 + m_iu_i + (m_f - m_i)u_1 = m_fu_f$$

$$m_iu_i + (m_f - m_i)h_1 = m_fu_f$$

This is the same energy balance obtained in the first solution which was based on an open-system analysis, and so the numerical solution from this point is identical for the open-system analysis and the closed-system analysis.

EXAMPLE 2·15.   A 20-cu-ft well-insulated tank contains initially 3.0 lb of air at 40 psia. (For air, $h = 1.4u = 0.24T = 0.0045pv$, where u and h are in B/lb, T is in degrees Rankine, p is in psfa, and v is in cu ft/lb.) A small valve is opened to let some of the air escape into the atmosphere at 14.7 psia. Assume that conditions are uniform throughout the tank at any instant. Determine the amount of air left in the tank when its pressure has dropped to 20 psia.

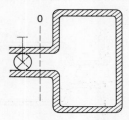

Example 2·15

Solution.   Define the open system as being the region within the tank. A sketch is made. The mass of air remaining in the tank at 20 psia will depend on the temperature, and the temperature will be influenced by the energy removed from the system by means of the outflowing air; so the first step is to set up an energy balance for the system. Since the properties of the air crossing the system boundary vary (unlike the case of Example 2·14), we must start with a differential form of the energy balance. As an infinitesimal mass of air, δm_0, flows out of the system, the mass of air within the system m changes by an amount dm. Since mass δm_0 leaves the system, $\delta m_0 = -dm$. Since $Q = 0$ and $W = 0$,

$$\begin{bmatrix} \text{Decrease in stored energy} \\ \text{of air in tank} \end{bmatrix} = \begin{bmatrix} \text{stored energy of} \\ \delta m_0 \text{ leaving tank} \end{bmatrix} + \begin{bmatrix} \text{flow work of} \\ \delta m_0 \text{ leaving tank} \end{bmatrix}$$

$$-dU = e_0 \, \delta m_0 + p_0v_0 \, \delta m_0 = (e_0 + p_0v_0) \, \delta m_0$$

where a property without a subscript is a property of the air in the tank. Potential energy changes can be neglected. If we locate section 0 just upstream of the small valve opening so that KE_0 is negligibly small, $e_0 = u_0$ and the last equation becomes

$$-dU = (u_0 + p_0v_0) \, \delta m_0$$

Since the properties of the air leaving are the same as those of the air in the tank, $u_0 = u, p_0 = p,$ and $v_0 = v$. Recalling also that $\delta m_0 = -dm$,

$$-dU = -(u + pv) \, dm$$

$$d(mu) = (u + pv) \, dm$$

$$m \, du + u \, dm = (u + pv) \, dm$$

$$m \, du = pv \, dm$$

Specific internal energy can be expressed in terms of pv as

$$u = \frac{0.0045}{1.4} pv \left[\frac{B}{lb_m} \right] = \frac{778(0.0045)}{1.4} pv \left[\frac{ft\text{-}lb_f}{lb_m} \right] = 2.5pv \left[\frac{ft\text{-}lb_f}{lb_m} \right]$$

so that $du = 2.5\, d(pv)$, and the energy balance becomes

$$2.5m\, d(pv) = pv\, dm$$

$$\frac{dm}{m} = 2.5 \frac{d(pv)}{pv}$$

$$\ln \frac{m_f}{m_i} = 2.5 \ln \left(\frac{p_f v_f}{p_i v_i} \right)$$

$$\frac{m_f}{m_i} = \left(\frac{p_f v_f}{p_i v_i} \right)^{2.5} = \left(\frac{p_f V_f m_i}{m_f p_i V_i} \right)^{2.5}$$

But the tank volume is constant, $V_f = V_i$, so

$$\frac{m_f}{m_i} = \left(\frac{p_f}{p_i} \right)^{2.5} \left(\frac{m_i}{m_f} \right)^{2.5}$$

$$\frac{m_f}{m_i} = \left(\frac{p_f}{p_i} \right)^{2.5/3.5} = \left(\frac{20}{40} \right)^{0.714} = 0.609$$

$$m_f = 0.609 m_i = 0.609(3) = 1.83\ lb_m$$

2·10 Heat engines, thermal efficiency; refrigerators, coefficient of performance

A heat engine is a system which receives heat and produces work while executing a cycle. A heat engine may be as simple as a gas confined within a cylinder fitted with a piston or as complex as an entire power plant. Two examples of heat engines are shown schematically in Fig. 2·8. In Fig. 2·8a, a gas trapped in the cylinder is heated at constant pressure (process 1-2), doing work on the piston. Then the gas is cooled while the piston is stationary (process 2-3), there being no work done on or by the gas during this process. Then the piston is moved inward, doing work on the gas in compressing it adiabatically to its final state.

In Fig. 2·8b, heat is added to water in the boiler in order to generate steam which then expands adiabatically through the turbine, doing work. The steam flows from the turbine into the condenser. Heat is removed from the steam in the condenser in order to condense the steam. The liquid leaving the condenser enters a pump which pumps it into the boiler to complete a cycle. Work is done on the liquid flowing through the pump. Even though each of the four pieces of equipment has fluid flowing into and out of it and hence must be treated as an open system, the four pieces of equipment and the connecting piping together always contain the same fluid. No mass enters or leaves this larger system, and so it can be treated as a closed system.

Notice that in each of these heat-engine cycles some heat is rejected from the system. By the first law,

$$\oint \delta W = \oint \delta Q = Q_{in} - Q_{out}$$

where Q_{in} and Q_{out} stand respectively for the *gross* amount of heat added and the *gross* amount of heat rejected. Since Q_{out} in the cycles described

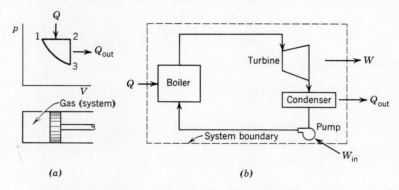

(a)   (b)

Fig. 2·8   Two examples of heat engines.

is not zero, the net work done by the system is less than the gross amount of heat added. In other words, not all the heat added is converted into work. *Thermal efficiency* is defined as that fraction of the gross heat input to a system during a cycle which is converted into net work output, or

$$\eta \equiv \frac{\oint \delta W}{Q_{in}} = \frac{\text{net work output of cycle}}{\text{gross heat added}}$$

Applying the first law,

$$\eta \equiv \frac{\oint \delta W}{Q_{in}} = \frac{Q_{in} - Q_{out}}{Q_{in}} = 1 - \frac{Q_{out}}{Q_{in}}$$

Thus the thermal efficiency of the steam power plant cycle discussed above and shown in Fig. 2·8b is given by either

$$\eta = \frac{W_T - W_{in,P}}{Q_{boiler}} \quad \text{or} \quad \eta = \frac{Q_{boiler} - Q_{out, condenser}}{Q_{boiler}}$$

Notice that thermal efficiency is used only with cycles; there is no such thing as the thermal efficiency of a process.

A system which absorbs heat from some low-temperature part of its surroundings and discharges heat to some other part of its surroundings at a higher temperature while executing a cycle is called a *refrigerator*. In one type of refrigerator, called the vapor-compression type, shown in Fig. 2·9, a vapor is compressed and led into a condenser where it is condensed to a liquid by the removal of heat. The high-pressure liquid refrigerant then passes through an expansion valve into an evaporator where the pressure is low. The temperature of the refrigerant in the

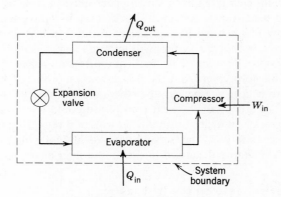

Fig. 2·9 Refrigerator.

evaporator is low enough so that heat can be absorbed from some relatively low-temperature part of the surroundings in order to evaporate the refrigerant. The refrigerant then passes to the compressor to begin the cycle anew. In a household refrigerator, the low-temperature part of the surroundings is the freezer compartment, and the high-temperature part of the surroundings is the air in the room where the refrigerator is operated.

Application of the first law to a refrigeration cycle shows that

$$W_{in} = Q_{out} - Q_{in}$$

The *coefficient of performance* of a refrigerating cycle is defined as the ratio of the heat absorbed from the low-temperature part of the surroundings to the net work input,

$$\beta \equiv \frac{Q_{in}}{-\oint \delta W} = \frac{Q_{in}}{Q_{out} - Q_{in}}$$

Notice that values of the coefficient of performance may be greater or less than one.

Thermal efficiency is an index of performance of heat engines. Coefficient of performance is an index of performance of refrigerators. Neither index is used for a system or cycle other than the one for which it is defined. For example, it is meaningless to speak of "the thermal efficiency of a refrigerator."

2·11   Limitation of the first law

All the relations developed in the preceding sections are used in making an energy accounting for various types of systems. In addition to being able to write an energy balance, an engineer must be able to predict how much of the heat transferred to a system may be converted into useful work, or how much work is required to produce a certain refrigerating effect, or whether or not a system will undergo a specified change. These predictions cannot be made on the basis of the first law alone. For example, it is impossible to predict from the first law alone how much of the heat transferred to a heat engine may be converted into work. As far as the first law is concerned, all the heat transferred could conceivably be converted into work. In order to obtain information regarding these aspects of engineering analysis, the second law of thermodynamics must be employed. This law is discussed in detail in a later chapter.

2·12   Historical note on the first law

The historical approach to the study of a science is usually not the most effective method of study for a person seeking a working knowledge of the science, whether he seeks the working knowledge in order to apply it in the solution of existing problems or in order to use it as a basis for further investigation of the subject. The reason for this is that the development of a science rarely proceeds in an orderly logical manner. The history of a science is usually a story of a few giant strides and many smaller steps in the right direction interspersed with, and nearly obscured by, semiblind groping, mistakes, confusion, misunderstandings, and trips down attractive byroads that turn out to be dead ends.

A science begins to develop as a result of either (1) a practical need for the understanding of certain phenomena so that the behavior of animals or other physical systems can be predicted or controlled, or (2) a curiosity on the part of someone simply to know why things behave as they do. The science grows as hypotheses are formulated, tested, modified, and accepted or discarded. At the same time, the vocabulary of the science is continually modified; for convenience and clarity, definitions of even the basic terms are changed. This is one of the reasons why the study of the "original sources" is often not helpful to a beginning student: he is often confused by the use of terms which have undergone changes in meaning. This is especially true in thermodynamics.

The concept of energy was used in mechanics in the seventeenth century, restricted to what we now call kinetic energy, potential energy, and work. The seventeenth century energy analyses in mechanics were of great value whenever frictional effects could be ignored, but they could not cope with any process in which there was a frictional effect because the relationship involved in a conversion of work to heat was unknown.

The development of the steam engine introduced a number of practical problems regarding the inverse conversion: heat to work. In 1698, Thomas Savery built a steam engine in London for pumping water. Thomas Newcomen built a much-improved engine in 1705, and for three-quarters of a century Newcomen engines were widely used. They were succeeded by the engines of James Watt,* who patented the separate condenser in 1769 as the first of many improvements. The practical need for means to predict and evaluate the performance of these early steam engines stimulated interest in the relationship between work and heat, two concepts which had developed independently. The idea of work had been developed through mechanics. Heat was the subject of an entirely different "science," and the caloric theory, which postulated that heat was an indestructible fluid, was widely accepted.

Origins of the caloric theory have been traced to the Greek philosophers, but the "modern" statement of it was formulated by William Cleghorn in 1779, and the term *caloric* was suggested by Lavoisier in 1787. Though many people today scoff at the caloric theory, it must be said in its defense that it provided adequate explanations for many physical phenomena, and for many years, as apparent exceptions to it were demonstrated, the theory was ingeniously modified to account for these phenomena. (For a discussion of the caloric theory, see reference 2·8 at the end of this chapter.)

Although several people had expressed the belief that the caloric theory

---

* James Watt (1736–1819), Scottish engineer, was trained in his youth as an instrument maker. While serving in this capacity at the University of Glasgow he became interested in the possibility of improving the performance of steam engines. His interest was intensified when he was called on to repair a model of a Newcomen engine. His first patent covered not only a separate condenser but also the condenser air pump, insulation of the engine cylinder, steam jacketing of the cylinder, and the use of steam on both sides of the piston. During the period of his early work on steam engines, Watt also engaged in engineering work pertaining to canals, harbors, and bridges. Watt and Matthew Boulton, a progressive manufacturer and businessman, formed a happy partnership that fully utilized the talents of both men. Engines built by Boulton & Watt, Birmingham, played an important part in the industrial growth of Great Britain during the nineteenth century.

was unsound and that heat might be produced without limit by means of work, the first experimental attack on the caloric theory was made by Count Rumford (Benjamin Thompson)*, beginning in 1787. While directing the manufacture of cannon, Rumford observed that a large amount of heat was evolved from a cannon as it was bored, and that the amount of heat was not directly related to the amount of metal removed or to the size of the chips produced, as would be required by the caloric theory. Experiments showed him that more heat was evolved and more work was required when a dull boring tool was used instead of a sharp one. These and other observations convinced Rumford that the caloric theory was unsound, but his views were not widely accepted. He reported his cannon-boring experiments in 1798 and his demonstration that bodies do not change weight when they are heated or cooled in 1799. Sir Humphry Davy reported in 1799 further experiments on the conversion of work to heat by means such as the rubbing together of two pieces of ice. Still the caloric theory was not generally abandoned, although more people began to question it. Marc Séguin, a French engineer, stated the theory of the equivalence of heat and work in 1839 and performed some experiments in order to support it, but his experiments were not convincing. Julius Robert Mayer, a German physician, stated the theory independently in 1842 and even calculated the mechanical equivalent of heat (the relationship between the foot-pound and the Btu) from data on the specific heat of gases, but he performed no experiments himself. The man who placed the equivalence of heat and work on a sound experimental basis was Joule, who between 1840 and 1849 carefully measured the mechanical equivalent of heat by several methods. His results were published in 1843 and 1849. The law of conservation of energy gained widespread acceptance after the publication in 1848 of a paper in which Hermann Helmholtz, then a surgeon in the Prussian army, clearly showed the applications of the law in several scientific fields.

* Benjamin Thompson (1753–1814) was born in Woburn, Massachusetts. At the age of 14 he is reported to have calculated a solar eclipse with an error of only a few seconds. At 19 he married a wealthy widow and immediately became prominent in Boston social circles. He remained loyal to the Crown when the American Revolution began and in 1776 prudently left Boston for London to become active in the British civil service. Five years later he was involved in a plot to sell British naval information to the French. For eleven years he was in Munich, holding various positions including minister of war and minister of police in the Bavarian government. He was made a count of the Holy Roman Empire and selected the title of Rumford from the name of an American township. His cannon-boring experiments were made while he was in Bavaria. To Rumford's credit are also prison reforms, stove and fireplace improvements, and numerous other items. He was a founder of the Royal Institution of London. To his discredit are several instances of fantastic duplicity and intrigue. His second wife was the wealthy widow of Antoine Lavoisier.

Anyone reading the original papers referred to here or some histories of thermodynamics will perceive that much confusion was caused by the dual use of the term heat: (1) to designate an interaction between bodies and (2) to designate "something" stored in a body. (Expressions such as "the heat in a body" are frequently found.) There was also a confusion of purpose between trying to answer (*a*) the question of what relation heat has to other effects or how it is measured and (*b*) the nebulous question of what heat *is*. An operational approach tells us that the first question can be answered but that the second one cannot.

2·13 Summary

Heat and work were defined operationally and independently of each other in Chapter 1. An empirical relationship between heat and work has been found. As a result of this relationship, stored energy can be operationally defined as

$$\Delta E \equiv Q - W$$

where ΔE is the change in the stored energy of a closed system, Q is the net amount of heat added to the system, and W is the net amount of work done by the system. Also it can be shown that stored energy E is a property.

These facts are generally summarized in a statement of the first law of thermodynamics or the law of conservation of energy. Possible statements are the following:

1. Whenever a closed system executes a cycle, the net amount of heat added to the system during the cycle is equal to the net amount of work done by the system, or

$$\oint \delta Q = \oint \delta W \tag{2·1}$$

2. Energy can be neither created nor destroyed, although it can be stored in various forms and can be transferred from one system to another as heat or work, or

$$\begin{bmatrix} \text{Net amount of} \\ \text{energy added to} \\ \text{system as heat} \\ \text{and all forms} \\ \text{of work} \end{bmatrix} + \begin{bmatrix} \text{stored} \\ \text{energy} \\ \text{of mass} \\ \text{entering} \\ \text{system} \end{bmatrix} - \begin{bmatrix} \text{stored} \\ \text{energy} \\ \text{of mass} \\ \text{leaving} \\ \text{system} \end{bmatrix} = \begin{bmatrix} \text{net increase} \\ \text{in} \\ \text{stored energy} \\ \text{of} \\ \text{system} \end{bmatrix} \tag{2·8b}$$

Many other statements of the first law have been formulated, and several of them are in common use. If any one of the valid statements is accepted as a postulate, all of the others can be deduced from it.

Stored energy may be classified as

1. Potential energy ≡ the energy stored in a system as a result of its location in the earth's gravitational field, its magnitude being the product of (a) the weight of the system and (b) the distance between the center of gravity of the system and some arbitrary horizontal datum plane.

2. Kinetic energy ≡ the energy stored in a system by virtue of the motion of the system, its magnitude being given by

$$\text{Kinetic energy} \equiv \frac{mV^2}{2g_c} \tag{2.5b}$$

where m is the mass of the system, V is its velocity relative to an arbitrary frame of reference, and g_c is a dimensional constant. If not all parts of the system have the same velocity, a more general expression must be used (see equation 2.5c).

3. Internal energy U ≡ the form of energy stored in a system which is independent of gravity, motion, electricity, magnetism, and surface tension. The internal energy of a substance is related to the potential and kinetic energies of the molecules of the substance and to the internal structure of the molecules. In the absence of motion, gravity, electricity, magnetism, and surface tension, $U = E$. In the absence of electricity, magnetism, and surface tension, the stored energy of a system is

$$E = U + \frac{mV^2}{2g_c} + \frac{g}{g_c}mz \tag{2.6c}$$

A useful property formed by the arbitrary combination of other properties is enthalpy, defined as

$$h \equiv u + pv$$

Whenever a fluid flows across the boundary of a system, an amount of work equal to pv is done on the system per unit of mass entering or is done by the system per unit of mass leaving. This work done in pushing fluid across the system boundary is called flow work.

The beginning student of thermodynamics sometimes feels that there are too many equations to learn. Leafing through the pages of a thermodynamics textbook does give the impression that there are many equations printed. Closer inspection, however, shows that many of the equations are simply special forms of a few basic relations. These special forms are included not with the intent that you should learn each of them. They are presented only to show you a few of the many special forms that you can derive yourself from the basic relations in order to apply the basic principles to specific systems and processes. The broad scope of thermodynamics is attested to by the large number and great diversity of applications made of its basic principles. Because the different types of systems to which the basic principles of thermodynamics have been applied are so numerous and because there are so many more as yet untried applications to be made in the future, it would be futile to try to learn all the special forms of the basic relations which have been developed. Instead, an engineer needs a sound understanding of the basic principles, their ranges of application, and their limitations. The best way to achieve this understanding is through practice in the application of the principles to many different situations.

In order to show how few relations (other than definitions) are needed for the solution of the problems in this chapter and the preceding one, formulations of the basic principles for the three types of systems discussed (closed, steady flow, and general open) are tabulated below. These are not

Formulations of Basic Principles

Conditions: Closed System: $\Delta KE = 0, \Delta PE = 0$

Conservation of mass: $m_1 = m_2$

Conservation of energy: $Q = U_2 - U_1 + W$ (2·7)

For *frictionless* processes, an expression for mechanical work:

$$W = \int p\, dV \tag{1·7}$$

Conditions: Open System: one inlet, one outlet

Conservation of mass: $m_f = m_i + m_1 - m_2$

Conservation of energy:

$$Q - W + \int (e_1 + p_1 v_1)\, \delta m_1 - \int (e_2 + p_2 v_2)\, \delta m_2 = E_f - E_i \tag{2·8c}$$

Conditions: Open System, Steady Flow: one inlet, one outlet

Conservation of mass: $M_1 = M_2 = \rho_1 A_1 V_1 = \rho_2 A_2 V_2$ (1·9)

Conservation of energy:

$$q = w + h_2 - h_1 + \frac{V_2^2 - V_1^2}{2g_c} + \frac{g}{g_c}(z_2 - z_1) \tag{2·9e}$$

For *frictionless* processes, an expression for mechanical work:

$$w_{in} = \int v\, dp + \Delta KE + \Delta PE \tag{1·10}$$

in all cases the most general forms. For example, the conservation of mass and conservation of energy equations for steady flow and closed systems are actually special cases of the more general equations for an open system. However, the formulations listed here are convenient starting points in many engineering analyses because they can be readily generalized or restricted as the situation demands. In all cases the symbols and subscripts have been previously defined. In all cases effects of electricity, magnetism, and surface tension are assumed to be negligible.

Thermal efficiency, a performance parameter which applies to heat engine cycles, is defined as

$$\eta \equiv \frac{\oint \delta W}{Q_{in}} = \frac{\text{net work output of cycle}}{\text{gross heat added during cycle}}$$

Coefficient of performance, a performance parameter which applies to refrigeration cycles, is defined as

$$\beta \equiv \frac{Q_{in}}{-\oint \delta W} = \frac{\text{heat absorbed from low-temperature region}}{\text{net work input of cycle}}$$

REFERENCES

2·1   J. H. Keenan, *Thermodynamics*, John Wiley & Sons, 1941, chapters II–IV.
2·2   M. W. Zemansky, *Heat and Thermodynamics*, McGraw-Hill Book Co., 4th ed., 1957, chapter 4.
2·3   D. A. Mooney, *Mechanical Engineering Thermodynamics*, Prentice-Hall, 1953, chapters 5 and 6.
2·4   H. C. Weber and H. P. Meissner, *Thermodynamics for Chemical Engineers*, John Wiley & Sons, 2d ed., 1957, chapters 2 and 5.
2·5   G. J. Van Wylen, *Thermodynamics*, John Wiley & Sons, 1959, chapter 5.
2·6   E. F. Obert, *Thermodynamics*, McGraw-Hill Book Co., 1948, chapter III.

On the historical development of the first law

2·7   P. S. Epstein, *Textbook of Thermodynamics*, John Wiley & Sons, 1937, pp. 27–34.
2·8   Duane Roller, *The Early Development of the Concepts of Temperature and Heat— The Rise and Decline of the Caloric Theory*, Harvard University Press, 1950. (Bibliography included)
2·9   A. E. Bell, "The Concept of Energy," *Nature*, vol. 151, May 8, 1943, p. 519.

PROBLEMS

K NOW WELL

2·1 For each of the following five cases of processes of a closed system, fill in the blanks where possible:

	Q	W	E_1	E_2	ΔE
(a)	10 B	5 B	71 B	+76	15
(b)	10 B	−5 B	60 B		
(c)	25 B	−10 B		−10 B	
(d)		20 B	55 B		17 B
(e)	−10 B			65 B	−20 B

2·2 A closed system passes from state 1 to state 2 while 25 B of heat is added and 35 B of work is done. As the system is returned to state 1, 20 B of work is done on it. What is the heat transfer during process 2-1?

2·3 The internal energy of a fluid in a closed system changes from 500 to 440 B/lb while the fluid performs 30,000 ft-lb/lb$_m$ of work. Compute the heat transfer. (Be sure to state the sign or direction of the heat transfer.)

2·4 During the expansion of 30 lb of gas in a closed system, heat is added to the gas in the amount of 420 B. The internal energy decreases by 1200 B. Compute the work.

2·5 During a process of a closed system, 1000 B of heat is removed and there is a decrease of 200 B in the internal energy. Compute the work.

2·6 Compute the work of a closed-system process during which 50 B of heat is added to the system and the stored energy of the system increases by 300 B.

2·7 An expanding gas does 6000 ft-lb of work while it receives 10 B of heat. Calculate the change in its stored energy.

2·8 During a process 1-2 of a closed system, 200 B of heat is added to the system and the stored energy of the system increases by 150 B. During the return process 2-1 which restores the system to its initial state, 80 B of work is done on the system. Determine the heat transfer of process 2-1.

2·9 During a certain process a closed system does 30 B of work while 10 B of heat is removed. Then the system is restored to its initial state by means of a process in which 4 B of heat is added to it. Determine ΔE for this second process.

2·10 A cylinder with a volume of 2 cu ft contains 0.5 lb of a gas at 20 psia and 50 F. The gas is compressed without friction to 120 psia in such a way that p (in psia) = constant − $100V$. Its final temperature is 20 F. The internal energy of the gas is given by u (in B/lb) = $0.20t$, with t in degrees Fahrenheit. Sketch the process on pV coordinates and compute (a) heat transferred, and (b) enthalpy change per pound.

2·11 In a closed system 0.27 lb of air expands frictionlessly from 30 psia, 140 F, until its volume is doubled. The initial volume is 2.0 cu ft, and the expansion follows the path pV = constant. During the process heat is added to the air in the amount of 28.5 B/lb. Determine the internal energy change of the air in B/lb.

2·12 Air in a cylinder expands frictionlessly against a piston in such a manner that $p^2V =$ constant. Initially the air is at 30 psia, 140 F, has a mass of 0.54 lb, and occupies a volume of 4 cu ft. The final volume is 16 cu ft. Heat is added to the air in the amount of 185 B/lb. Sketch a pV diagram, and determine the change in internal energy per pound of air.

2·13 A gearbox driven by a gasoline engine has an efficiency of 92.0 per cent when its output shaft delivers 120.0 hp at 240 rpm. The gearbox is cooled by means of a fan which blows room air over it. Under these steady operating conditions how much heat is given off by the gearbox? (Use your judgment as to the definition of gearbox efficiency.)

2·14 A closed thermally insulated room contains a household refrigerator. The electric motor of the refrigerator is connected to a 110-volt power line which passes through the wall. If the refrigerator is operated, will the average temperature of the air in the room increase, decrease, or remain constant if the refrigerator door is (a) open, (b) closed?

2·15 Consider an air bubble rising through an open tank of water. Does the size of the bubble change? What are the energy transfers across a boundary which encloses only the bubble? What are the energy transfers across a boundary which encloses all the water and the bubble?

2·16 Occasionally one sees the relation $\delta Q = dU + p\, dV$ referred to as the first law of thermodynamics. Comment on this, stating the restrictions which apply to this equation.

2·17 For a closed system, $\oint \delta Q = \oint \delta W$. Show by an example that this relationship does not hold for an open system.

2·18 Prove that in a frictionless steady-flow process of an incompressible fluid, $q - \Delta u = 0$. Does this mean that such a process is adiabatic?

2·19 Three blocks of steel in a rigid insulated container are initially at different temperatures. As they exchange heat to attain temperature equality, their stored energies change by -260, $+140$, and $+100$ B. Nothing else is in the container except air. Determine ΔE of the air.

2·20 Calculate the amount of work required to accelerate a 3000-lb automobile from rest to a speed of 50 fps on a level highway if there are no frictional effects.

2·21 A certain body has a potential energy of 400 ft-lb relative to datum plane A and a potential energy of -300 ft-lb relative to datum plane B. The body has a mass of 35 lb_m. The local acceleration of gravity is 31.6 ft/sec². What is the relative location of plane A with respect to plane B?

2·22 A body falls freely in a vacuum. Write an energy balance for this process, considering the body as the system and using a stationary frame of reference. Notice that there is a force on the body and the body is moving. Does this mean that work is done on or by the body? If so, with what other system is the work exchanged? If not, what is the meaning of the product of the body weight and the distance moved?

2·23 Comment on this proposal for destroying some energy: A steel coil spring is compressed, and in this manner more energy is stored in it than in the same spring when uncompressed. The compressed spring is held to a constant length by means of a glass thread tied around it and is then submerged in an acid which dissolves the spring but not the thread. Therefore, it is claimed, the energy used to compress the spring is lost and can never be recovered.

2·24 A craft moves in a north-to-south direction at constant speed and constant altitude above sea level. The acceleration of gravity at constant altitude changes with latitude; therefore the weight of the craft itself (excluding the fuel) changes, and consequently its potential energy changes. Explain what is wrong with this reasoning, or explain the energy transformation which is involved.

2·25 Derive an expression for the kinetic energy of a rotating solid body (*a*) from equation 2·5*c*, (*b*) from the work required to put the body in motion.

2·26 Consider two masses in interstellar space. The attractive force between them varies inversely as the square of the distance separating them. How does the potential energy of the two masses vary with that distance?

2·27 Consider a storage battery which has a terminal potential of 12 volts while it delivers a current of 10 amperes for 3 hr. The stored energy of the battery decreases by 1205 B. Determine the heat transfer.

2·28 A d-c electric motor operates steadily at 800 rpm when the torque applied to its shaft is 96 lb-in. It draws a current of 50 amperes at 24 volts. Determine the rate of heat transfer.

2·29 Consider two streams of a liquid flowing through identical circular pipes at the same mass flow rate. The velocity of one is uniform across the pipe cross section, and the velocity of the other varies across the pipe cross-section in such a manner that the velocity u at any radius r is given by $u = u_{max}\left(1 - \dfrac{r}{r_0}\right)^2$, where u_{max} is the velocity at the pipe axis and r_0 is the pipe radius. Determine the ratio of the kinetic energy of the stream with the parabolic velocity distribution to that of the stream with the uniform distribution.

2·30 Derive an expression involving the modulus of elasticity for the change in stored energy of a wire which is stretched adiabatically within its elastic limit. (Be careful with the algebraic sign.)

2·31 Fifty thousand foot-pounds of work is done by each pound of fluid passing through an apparatus under steady-flow conditions. In the inlet pipe which is located 50 ft above the floor, the specific volume is 5 cu ft/lb, the pressure is 100 psia, and the velocity is 100 fps. In the discharge pipe which is 20 ft below the floor, the specific volume is 15 cu ft/lb, the pressure is 20 psia, and the velocity is 600 fps. Heat loss from the fluid is 5 B/lb. Determine the change in internal energy of the fluid passing through the apparatus.

2·32 A steam nozzle is designed to pass 1000 lb of steam per hour. The initial and final pressures are 200 and 2 psia. The initial and final velocities are 500 and 4000 fps. Neglecting heat losses, compute the change in enthalpy.

2·33 A turbine is supplied with 20,000 lb/hr of a fluid. The inlet and exit fluid velocities are 6000 fpm and 24,000 fpm, respectively. If the initial and final enthalpy values are 1260 and 1000 B/lb, respectively, and the heat loss amounts to 140,000 B/hr, compute the power output.

2·34 Air expands through a nozzle from a pressure of 75 psia to a final pressure of 15 psia. The enthalpy decreases by 48 B/lb during the flow of air. If the initial entering velocity and heat-flow terms are neglected, compute the exit velocity.

2·35 An air compressor takes in air at a pressure of 14.4 psia and specific volume of 13.7 cu ft/lb. The discharge pressure and specific volume are 100 psia and 2.74 cu ft/lb. The initial and final internal energy values for the air are 12 and 47 B/lb respectively.

The cooling water around the cylinders removes 33 B/lb of entering air. Neglecting the change in kinetic and potential energy terms, compute the work.

2·36 Steam expands through a nozzle from a pressure of 200 psia to a final pressure of 2 psia. The initial and final enthalpy values are 1289 and 955 B/lb respectively. Neglecting the initial velocity and heat losses, compute the final velocity.

2·37 The supply line to a steam radiator is located 2 ft above the discharge line. Data relative to the steam as it enters follow. The pressure equals 15 psia, the specific volume equals 26.3 cu ft/lb, and the internal energy value is 1077 B/lb. After condensing in the radiator, the steam leaves at a pressure of 15 psia. The specific volume and enthalpy at exit are 0.0167 cu ft/lb and 181 B/lb, respectively. Neglecting the entering and leaving velocities, compute the heat released from the radiator per pound of steam entering.

2·38 Benzene (specific gravity = 0.90) flows through a pump at a rate of 1.8 cfs. The inlet pressure is 10 in. of mercury vacuum. Outlet pressure is 24 psig, and the pump outlet is 3 ft above the inlet. Inlet cross-sectional area is 0.36 sq ft, and outlet area is 0.18 sq ft. The pump operates at 2400 rpm. Calculate the power input.

2·39 The flow rate through a hydraulic turbine is 6 cfs. The pressure of the water is 30.6 psig at the inlet which has a cross-sectional area of 0.50 sq ft. At the outlet, 8 ft below the inlet, the velocity is 2.5 fps, and the pressure is 4 psig. Calculate the power imparted to the turbine by the fluid.

2·40 A gas flows steadily through a machine, entering at 35 psia, 115 F, with a density of 0.091 lb/cu ft and negligible velocity and leaving at 16.7 psia, 40 F, with a density of 0.05 lb/cu ft and a velocity of 500 fps through an opening of 0.4-sq-ft cross-sectional area. As the gas flows through the machine, its internal energy decreases by 30 B/lb and its enthalpy decreases by 40 B/lb. The power output is 400 hp. Determine the heat transfer per pound of gas.

2·41 Calculate the power required by a compressor if air flowing at a rate of 2.0 lb/sec enters at 15.0 psia, 40 F, with a velocity of 200 fps, and leaves at 30.0 psia, 160 F, with a velocity of 400 fps. The enthalpy of the air increases by 28.8 B/lb as it passes through the compressor; its internal energy increases by 20.5 B/lb. Heat transferred from the air to the cooling water circulating through the compressor casing amounts to 8.0 B/lb air.

2·42 Air enters a machine at 14.0 psia, 80 F (ρ = 0.0701 lb/cu ft), with negligible velocity and is exhausted at 14.0 psia, 130 F (ρ = 0.0641 lb/cu ft), with a velocity of 300 fps through an opening having a cross-sectional area of 0.01 sq ft. The enthalpy of the air increases 12.0 B/lb, and its internal energy increases 8.55 B/lb. A blower delivers 1 hp to the air as it passes through the machine. Calculate the heat added to or removed from the air in B/lb.

2·43 A gas flows steadily through a machine while expanding frictionlessly from 60 to 15 psia according to the relation $pv^{1.25} = 32,000$ with p in psf and v in cu ft/lb. The enthalpy decreases 35 B/lb, and the change in kinetic energy is negligible. Calculate the heat transferred in B/lb.

2·44 Air flows through a gas turbine at a rate of 15 lb/sec, entering at 60 psia, 700 F, (u = 201.6 B/lb, h = 281.1 B/lb), and leaving at 15 psia. The net increase in kinetic energy of the air passing through the turbine is 5.0 B/lb. There is no heat transfer. The power output is 1100 hp. Determine the enthalpy of the air at the turbine outlet.

2·45 A gas enters a compressor at 14 psia, 80 F (h = 129 B/lb, u = 92 B/lb, v = 14.3 cu ft/lb) with negligible velocity and is discharged at 70 psia, 500 F (h = 231 B/lb, u = 165 B/lb). The gas leaves the compressor with a velocity of 500 fps. The power input is 3200 hp. The flow rate is 20 lb/sec. Determine the heat transfer in B/lb.

2·46 The power output of a steam turbine is 4000 hp while the steam flow rate is 56,000 lb/hr. Barometric pressure is 29.0 in. of mercury. Determine the amount of heat, in B/lb, added to or removed from the steam passing through the turbine if inlet and exhaust conditions are as listed in the table.

	Inlet	Exhaust
Pressure, psia	200	1
Temperature, F	560	102
Specific volume, cu ft/lb	2.93	331
Velocity, fps	200	500
Internal energy, B/lb	1193	1035
Enthalpy, B/lb	1301	1096

2·47 A blower receives air at $p = 14$ psia, $v = 14.3$ cu ft/lb, $u = 13.6$ B/lb, $V = 10$ fps, and discharges it at $p = 15$ psia, $v = 13.6$ cu ft/lb, $u = 15.5$ B/lb, $V = 50$ fps. Flow is adiabatic and 1500 cfm enters the fan. Calculate the power consumption.

2·48 Carbon dioxide flows steadily through a machine at a rate of 0.5 lb/sec, entering with negligible velocity at 20 psia, 80 F ($u_1 = 67.2$ B/lb, $h_1 = 91.6$ B/lb). Carbon dioxide leaves the machine at 60 psia, 200 F ($\rho_2 = 0.0116$ slug/cu ft, $u_2 = 85.8$ B/lb, $h_2 = 115.6$ B/lb), through an opening which has an area of 0.4 sq in. Power input to the machine is 25 hp. Determine the amount of heat transfer per pound of carbon dioxide.

2·49 Air which has properties such that $h = 1.4u = 0.24T = 0.0045pv$, where u and h are in B/lb, T is in degrees Rankine, p is in psfa, and v is in cu ft/lb, is initially trapped in a well-insulated rigid tank. A paddle wheel in the tank is turned by an external motor, and air is bled from the tank through a small valve to keep the temperature constant at 90 F. Assume that the pressure and temperature are uniform throughout the tank. Determine the mass rate of flow of air out of the tank at an instant when the pressure is 60 psia and the power input is 0.05 hp.

CHAPTER 3

Physical Properties I

Chapter 1 covered several definitions and fundamental concepts. Chapter 2 introduced the first law of thermodynamics and its application to various systems. For the application of the first law to most engineering systems, a knowledge of the physical properties of various substances is required. This chapter and the following two are concerned with some of these physical properties, particularly the relationships among pressure, volume, temperature, and internal energy for various substances.

The study of physical properties could be deferred until after consideration of the second law of thermodynamics. Indeed, such a sequence of topics is nearly always followed in advanced textbooks and is generally a more satisfying sequence to those who have already completed some study of thermodynamics. Also, a more complete presentation of physical property relationships can be made when both the first and second laws are used. Nevertheless, physical properties are made the subject of the next three chapters in order to give you more opportunity to strengthen your grasp on the first law before taking up the second law in Chapter 6.

3·1 Phases of substances: solids, liquids, and gases

It is a matter of everyday experience that substances can exist as solids, as liquids, and as gases. At normal room pressure and temperature, copper is a solid, mercury is a liquid, and oxygen is a gas; but each of these substances can appear in a different *phase* if the pressure or temperature is changed sufficiently.

A *phase* is any homogeneous part of a system which is physically distinct and is separated from other parts of the system by definite bounding surfaces. Ice, liquid water, and water vapor constitute three separate phases of the pure substance H_2O, because each is homogeneous and physically different from the others and each is clearly defined by the boundaries existing between them. At high pressures there are several different forms of ice, each of which constitutes a separate phase because each is clearly distinct from the others and separated from them by definite boundary surfaces. Three solid phases of sulfur can exist at room pressure and temperature. Graphite and diamond are two solid phases of carbon. In general, each solid in a system constitutes a separate phase, since each is homogeneous, physically distinct, and separated from the rest of the system by definite boundary surfaces. A solid solution consists of but a single phase no matter how many substances are involved. A liquid solution constitutes a single phase no matter how many substances are present as long as it is homogeneous. For example, a solution of salt and sugar in water consists of but one phase, even though this one phase consists of three separate constituents: salt, sugar, and water. If additional amounts of salt and sugar are added until the water is unable to dissolve any more, part will remain undissolved (in solid form). Under this condition, three phases will exist: solid salt, solid sugar, and liquid solution. If a liquid contains two distinct layers, two phases exist. For example, under certain concentrations ether and water form two separate layers; each layer is homogeneous and the two are separated by a bounding surface. If a vapor exists above a single- or double-layer liquid system, still another phase is present. A gas or a mixture of gases always constitutes a single phase because the mixture is homogeneous as a result of the intimate mixing of the molecules.

The study of physical properties of substances from the point of view of thermodynamics does not involve considerations of molecular structure and behavior. Nevertheless, some understanding of molecular phenomena is helpful in the study of physical properties, so occasionally in this book explanations based on molecular theory are presented. Let us now consider from the molecular point of view the characteristics of solids, liquids, and gases.

In crystalline solids, the units of the crystal structure are commonly atoms or ions rather than molecules, although molecules in certain types of crystals maintain their identity. In this discussion of solids, the word molecule is used to simplify comparison with liquids and gases. The molecules of a solid are very close together and are arranged in a three-dimensional pattern which is repeated with but minor irregularities throughout the solid. The arrangement of the molecules (or atoms or ions) in a solid is referred to as a *lattice*. In noncrystalline solids, such as glasses, the immediate neighbors of any molecule are generally arranged in a fixed pattern, but the regularity of the pattern does not extend throughout the solid as it does in crystalline solids. Crystalline solids are said to possess long-range order as well as short-range order, whereas noncrystalline solids possess only short-range order. In all solids the molecules are so close together that the forces of molecules on each other (which are repulsive forces at very close spacing and attractive forces when there is a greater separation between molecules*) are large. It is these forces which tend to keep the molecules in fixed positions within the lattice and which give solids their resistance to deformation. The molecules of a solid continually oscillate or vibrate about their equilibrium positions, but the amplitude of this motion is small, so that a molecule is never far from its equilibrium position. The velocity of the molecules during the oscillation depends on the temperature of the solid: The higher the temperature, the higher the velocity. As the temperature of a solid is increased, the molecular velocities and momentum increase until the attractive forces are partially overcome. Then groups of molecules shift position relative to other such groups and the solid becomes a liquid.

In a liquid, the molecular spacing is about the same as in a solid. The molecules are not held in relatively fixed positions, but in regions of molecular dimensions a semblance of crystalline order is retained. That is, each molecule retains an orientation with respect to some of its neighbors that it had in the solid crystalline phase. These small groups of molecules in which remnants of crystalline structure persist are not firmly held in position relative to neighboring groups. For this reason, a liquid in static equilibrium cannot withstand a shearing stress. The presence of a crystalline structure of short-range order in some liquids has been verified by measurements of the scattering of X rays. A number of the macroscopic properties of liquids can be accounted for on the basis of a liquid structure which involves an ordered arrangement of molecules in regions of molecular dimensions. The distances between molecules in a liquid are generally slightly greater than the distances between molecules in the solid phase of the same substance. One of the notable exceptions is water. Water, unlike most substances, expands on freezing, so that the molecular spacing is slightly greater in the solid phase than in the liquid phase.

A gas is composed of molecules which are relatively far apart. There is no regularity or permanence in their arrangement in space, for gas molecules are continually in motion, colliding with each other and rebounding to travel in new directions. For gases of low density, collisions are the only interactions of consequence between molecules, because they are so widely separated that intermolecular forces are small.

Statistical laws exist by which the behavior of great numbers of molecules in a gas may be predicted. It is not possible to study the motion of a single molecule by these laws, just as it is impossible to predict the length

* The force between two molecules a distance r apart is often assumed to be given by the Lennard–Jones equation,

$$F = \frac{a}{r^m} - \frac{b}{r^n}$$

with positive values corresponding to attractive forces. a and b are positive constants. Since the attractive force predominates as r increases, $n > m$.

of life of a given man from the statistical averages established by life insurance companies. Bearing this point in mind, let us look at some numerical values obtained by means of kinetic theory.

In air at normal room conditions, there is a large range of molecular velocities, but an "average" value is about 1600 fps. On the average, a molecule of oxygen or nitrogen in such air travels about 0.0000025 in. between collisions and experiences about 8 billion collisions per second. One cubic inch of normal room air contains about 4.1×10^{20} molecules; but, if this gives the impression that the molecules are jammed together, it should be noticed that the molecules themselves occupy only about 1/1000 of the volume which the gas fills.

In review, this discussion of the molecular picture of solids, liquids, and gases has pointed out that the molecules of a substance are restrained to some extent by the forces which act between individual molecules and groups of molecules. The closer the molecules are grouped together, the greater are the forces between them, and hence they have less freedom of motion. Eldridge (see the reference in Prob. 3·8) has pointed out that the molecules in a gas and in a liquid, respectively, may be compared with life in the country and in a congested city tenement district. In a gas the molecule exists in the wide open spaces where a molecule's a molecule and is more or less free to move about without much interference. In a liquid the molecules are more closely spaced, and their movement is greatly influenced by their neighbors. In a solid the congestion is even greater, and here the freedom of the individual molecule is even less.

3·2 Equilibrium of phases of a pure substance

A *pure substance* is a substance which is chemically homogeneous and fixed in chemical composition. A system comprised of liquid and vapor phases of H_2O is a pure substance. Even if some of the liquid is vaporized during a process, the system will still be chemically homogeneous and unchanged in chemical composition. A mixture may be a pure substance. For example, air is a mixture of (principally) oxygen and nitrogen. In its gaseous phase it may be heated, cooled, compressed, or expanded without undergoing any change in its chemical composition. If it is cooled until part of it liquefies, it is no longer a pure substance, because the liquid will contain a higher fraction of nitrogen than the vapor does and the substance will no longer be chemically homogeneous. A mixture of oxygen and carbon monoxide is a pure substance as long as it remains fixed in composition. If some of the CO combines with some of the O_2 to form CO_2, the system is not considered a pure substance during the process because its chemical composition has changed. A system cannot be treated as a pure substance during any process which involves a chemical reaction.

The state of a pure substance at rest is usually specified completely by the values of two independent properties, provided that there are no electric, magnetic, or surface tension effects. Thus any property of a system comprised of a pure substance is a function of only two independent properties of the system, provided there are no effects of electricity, magnetism, etc. For example, if the pressure and temperature of air are specified, then the values of all other properties of the air such as density, internal energy, enthalpy, viscosity, and thermal conductivity are fixed. If the pressure and density of air are specified, then the temperature and all other properties have fixed values. Care must be exercised to see that the two properties selected to specify a state are *independent* properties. Two properties are independent if either one can be varied throughout a range of values while the other remains constant. It will be pointed out later that, when two phases of a pure substance exist together in equilibrium, the pressure and temperature of the mixture depend only on each other. Consequently, under these conditions pressure and temperature are not independent variables, and values of pressure and temperature do not completely specify the state of the system. Under these conditions it would be necessary to specify pressure and specific volume, pressure and enthalpy, temperature and specific volume, internal energy and temperature, or some other pair of independent variables in order to specify the state of the system completely.

The liquid phase of a substance can exist at many different pressures and temperatures. For example, liquid water at 1 atm (14.7 psia) can exist in equilibrium at any temperature between 32 F and 212 F, inclusive; and liquid water at, say, 60 F can exist in equilibrium under pressures ranging from less than 1 atm to several hundred atmospheres. Likewise, the solid phase of a substance can exist in equilibrium at many different temperatures and pressures, and the gas or vapor phase of a substance also exists under many combinations of pressure and temperature. In short, the pressure and temperature of *any one phase* of a substance can be varied independently over wide ranges. However, when two phases of a pure substance coexist in equilibrium, there is a fixed relationship between their pressure and temperature. At any given pressure there is but one temperature at which a certain two phases will exist together in equilibrium. Conversely, the two phases can coexist in equilibrium at a given temperature only if the pressure is a particular value which corresponds to that temperature. These corresponding values of pressure and temperature are spoken of as the saturation pressure for a given temperature and the saturation temperature for a given pressure.

Generalizing, *saturation conditions* are those conditions under which two or more phases of a pure substance can exist together in equilibrium. Any phase of a substance existing under such conditions is called a *saturated* phase. For example, liquid water and water vapor in equilibrium with each other are spoken of as *saturated liquid* and *saturated vapor*. Ice in equilibrium with liquid or vapor or both is spoken of as a *saturated solid*. The presence of two or more phases is not required in order to have a saturated phase. A phase is saturated even if it exists alone as long as it is at a pressure and a temperature under which two or more phases *could* exist together in equilibrium.

As an illustration of these facts regarding equilibrium of two phases of a pure substance, consider the familiar substance *water*. Liquid water (a single phase) can exist in equilibrium at various temperatures while under a pressure of 14.7 psia. However, it cannot exist at a temperature higher than 212 F while under this pressure. On the other hand, water vapor (a single phase) can exist under a pressure of 14.7 psia only at temperatures of 212 F and higher. The only temperature at which *either* the liquid *or* the vapor phase can exist under a pressure of 1 atm is 212 F. This is also the only temperature at which the two phases can exist *together* in equilibrium at a pressure of 1 atm. Therefore, 212 F is the saturation temperature of water at 14.7 psia. Likewise, 14.7 psia is said to be the saturation pressure of water at 212 F. If the temperature of liquid in a system comprised only of the pure substance water is slowly increased while the pressure is held constant at 1 atm, no vapor will form until the temperature reaches 212 F. Then, no matter how much vapor is formed, as long as both liquid and vapor are present in equilibrium and the pressure is held constant, the temperature will be 212 F. Not until all of the liquid has changed to vapor can the temperature rise above the saturation temperature of 212 F. If liquid water at some pressure other than 14.7 psia has its temperature slowly increased, vapor will form only at some temperature other than 212 F. For liquid–vapor equilibrium, the higher the pressure, the higher the saturation temperature.

A fixed relationship between saturation pressures and temperatures is characteristic of all pure substances. The temperature at which a substance evaporates or condenses (or the temperature at which liquid and vapor phases can coexist in equilibrium) depends only on the pressure of the substance. The relationship between liquid–vapor saturation pressures and temperatures is shown for several substances in Fig. 3·1. These curves are called liquid–vapor saturation curves, vaporization curves, or condensation curves. The upper and lower ends of these curves, known respectively as the critical points and the triple points of the substances, will be discussed later.

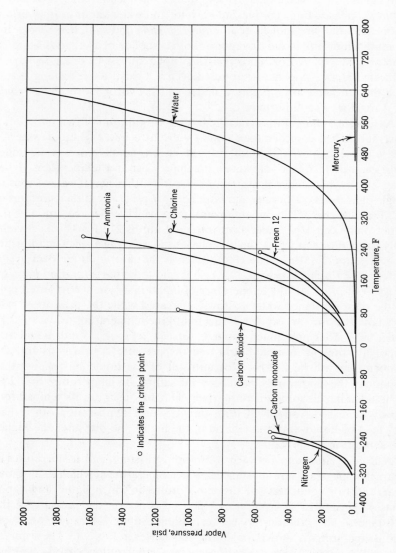

Fig. 3·1 Liquid–vapor saturation curves for several pure substances.

The temperature at which any two phases of a pure substance can coexist in equilibrium is dependent on the pressure. This applies to solid–liquid and solid–vapor equilibrium as well as to the liquid–vapor equilibrium already discussed. Thus the melting or freezing temperature of a substance depends on the pressure, although the variation of this temperature with pressure is usually small. For most substances the freezing temperature increases as the pressure increases, so that the solid–liquid saturation

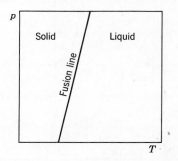

Fig. 3·2   Solid–liquid saturation curve for a substance
which contracts on freezing.

curve or fusion line appears as in Fig. 3·2. For water and other substances which expand on freezing, increasing the pressure lowers the freezing point. This is shown by the familiar laboratory experiment in which a wire weighted at both ends is passed over a cake of ice. The increased pressure caused by the wire lowers the freezing point slightly, causing the ice to melt directly below the wire. The liquid water formed passes above the wire and freezes because the pressure on it is again atmospheric. In this manner the wire will pass completely through the cake of ice which will freeze solid above the wire.

Figure 3·3 shows a pressure-freezing temperature chart for water. At any point on the line, the liquid and solid may exist together in equilibrium. The area to the left of the line represents the solid, and that to the right the liquid. For example, at a pressure of 6000 psia and a temperature of 20 F water can exist only in the solid form, ice. At 6000 psia and 30 F, only liquid water may exist.

For most substances (helium is an interesting exception), there is some pressure below which liquid cannot exist. Below this pressure the solid and vapor phases can coexist in equilibrium, and the relation between pressure and temperature for these solid–vapor saturation states is fixed for each substance. The transformation from a solid to a vapor is known as sublimation; so the solid–vapor saturation line on a pT diagram is

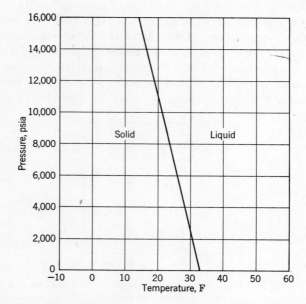

Fig. 3·3 Solid–liquid saturation curve for water. Data from N. E. Dorsey, *Properties of Ordinary Water Substance*, Reinhold Publishing Corp., 1940.

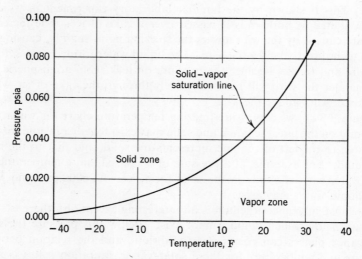

Fig. 3·4 Solid–vapor saturation curve for water. Data from J. H. Keenan and F. G. Keyes, *Thermodynamic Properties of Steam*, John Wiley & Sons, Inc., 1936.

often called a sublimation line. These curves are shown for water and for carbon dioxide in Figs. 3·4 and 3·5. At pressures below 75.1 psia, solid and vapor phases of carbon dioxide can exist but the liquid phase cannot. Therefore, solid carbon dioxide (Dry Ice) at 1 atm sublimes instead of melting. Another familiar example of sublimation is the transformation of moth balls and solid camphor from the solid to the gaseous phase. Ice disappears from a sidewalk during winter weather by the process of sublimation while the temperature remains well below 32 F. (Since the gaseous phase involved in this process is a mixture of air and water vapor,

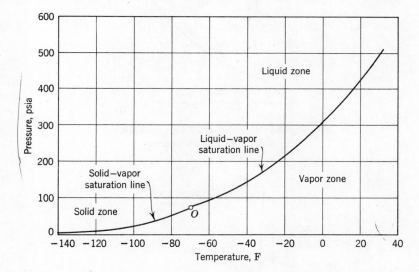

Fig. 3·5   Solid–vapor and liquid–vapor saturation curves for carbon dioxide. Data from H. G. Venemann, *Refrigeration Theory and Application*, Nickerson and Collins Co., Chicago, 1942.

and the solid phase is ice only, this is not a case of equilibrium between phases of a pure substance. This point is discussed further in Chapters 12 and 20.)

3·3   Phase diagrams

A pressure–temperature diagram showing more than one of the saturation lines (liquid–vapor, liquid–solid, solid–vapor, or other) of a pure substance is called a *phase diagram*. A phase diagram for a substance which contracts on freezing (as most substances do) is shown in Fig. 3·6, and Fig. 3·7 is a phase diagram for water. Figure 3·7 is a combination of appropriate parts of Figs. 3·1, 3·3, and 3·4. Any point on a saturation line of a phase diagram represents conditions of pressure and temperature under which two or more phases can coexist in equilibrium. All points

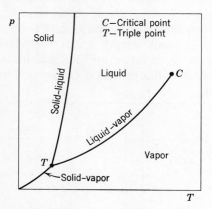

Fig. 3·6 Phase diagram for a substance which contracts on freezing.

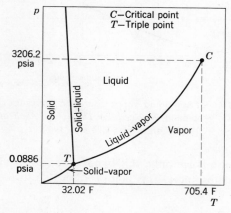

Fig. 3·7 Phase diagram for water (scales distorted).

not on a saturation line represent conditions under which only one phase of the pure substance can exist in equilibrium. Points between the solid–liquid and liquid–vapor lines represent liquid states, and this region of the phase diagram is referred to as the *liquid region*. Similarly, other areas are designated as the *solid region* and the *vapor region*. Liquid existing at a temperature lower than its saturation temperature (or, in other words, at a pressure higher than its saturation pressure) is called a *compressed liquid* or a *subcooled liquid* to distinguish it from a saturated liquid. Thus all points in the liquid region and not on the liquid–vapor saturation line represent states of compressed liquid. Water flowing from a drinking fountain and mercury in an open cup at room temperature are both compressed liquids. In a like manner, a solid at a temperature below its saturation temperature is called a *compressed solid*, and a vapor at a temperature above its saturation temperature is called a *superheated vapor*. These modifiers (compressed, subcooled, superheated) are generally used only in cases where their omission might reasonably mislead a reader into inferring the existence of saturation conditions.

TABLE 3·1
Triple-Point Data

Substance	p, psia	T, F
Ammonia	0.88	−108
Carbon dioxide	75	−70
Helium	0.747	−456
Hydrogen	0.994	−434
Nitrogen	1.86	−346
Oxygen	0.039	−361
Water	0.0886	32.02

The intersection of the vaporization line, fusion line, and sublimation line on a phase (pT) diagram represents the conditions under which three phases can coexist in equilibrium and is called the *triple point* or *triple-phase point*. These conditions are represented by a point only on a pressure–temperature diagram; on other property diagrams they are represented by a line or an area. If there are more than three phases in which a substance can exist, there will be more than one triple point for that substance. For example, at high pressures several solid phases of water other than common ice have been observed, so there are several (at least seven, in fact) triple points of water. References to *the* triple point of water always pertain to the triple point at which liquid, solid, and vapor can exist. Triple-point data for several substances are given in Table 3·1.

In Figs. 3·6 and 3·7 the vaporization line extends from the triple point to a point C known as the *critical point*. At pressures or temperatures higher than the critical-point value, no distinction can be made between liquid and vapor phases. The critical point is discussed in Art. 3·7.

TABLE 3·2
Critical-Point Data

Substance	p, psia	T, F
Ammonia	1639	270
Carbon dioxide	1071	88
Helium	34	−450
Hydrogen	188	−400
Mercury	2646	1649
Nitrogen	493	−233
Oxygen	731	−182
Water	3206	705

3·4 Other property diagrams

Other property diagrams besides the pressure–temperature or phase diagrams are useful in the study of the physical properties of substances and in analyzing various thermodynamic processes. Let us turn our attention first to pv diagrams.

In Fig. 3·8, line a-c, called the saturated liquid line, is a plot of the specific volume of saturated liquid versus pressure. As the pressure increases (and consequently the saturation temperature increases), the specific volume of saturated liquid increases slightly. The volume scale of Fig. 3·8 has been distorted to magnify this increase. The region immediately to the left of the saturated liquid line represents compressed or subcooled liquid states.

The line c-h, called the saturated vapor line, is a plot of the specific volume of saturated vapor versus pressure. As the pressure increases, the specific volume of saturated vapor decreases. The region immediately to the right of the saturated vapor line represents superheated vapor states.

Point c, which is common to the saturated liquid and saturated vapor lines, represents the state at which the specific volume is the same for saturated liquid and for saturated vapor. In fact, there is no distinction between liquid and vapor at this state which is called the *critical point*. On a pressure–temperature diagram, the liquid–vapor saturation line ends at the critical point (see Figs. 3·6 and 3·7) because at higher pressures and temperatures no distinction can be made between liquid and vapor states. There can be no continuation of the line which represents states in which two distinct phases can exist together in equilibrium. There is a question as to whether a substance in a state such as represented by point n in Fig. 3·8 should be called a liquid or a vapor. Arbitrary rules have been established, but it is best simply to recognize the fact that only one phase exists in the region where *n* is located, and this single phase has no properties which characterize it as a liquid instead of a vapor or vice versa. Point *m* represents a state generally referred to as a liquid; point *o* represents a state generally referred to as a gas or vapor; but a transition from state *m* to state *o* or from *o* to *m* can occur with no discontinuities in properties occurring and without any phenomena of boiling or condensation.

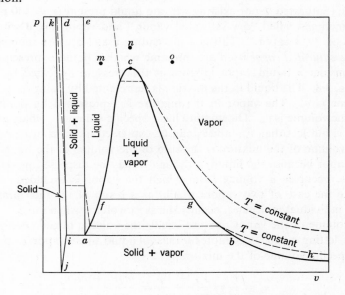

Fig. 3·8   *pv* diagram for a substance which contracts on freezing.

On a *pT* diagram, saturated liquid and saturated vapor at the same pressure (and hence at the same temperature) as well as a mixture of the two phases are represented by the same point. These states are not represented by a single point on a *pv* diagram because the specific volume of saturated vapor is greater than that of saturated liquid at the same pressure, and a mixture of the two phases has a specific volume between these two limiting values. On a *pv* diagram the two-phase mixture states at any pressure therefore lie on a horizontal line between the saturated liquid and saturated vapor lines. The lowest of such lines is the one at the lowest pressure under which liquid can exist. This is the *triple-phase* pressure. The area bounded by this *triple-phase* line (*a-b* in Fig. 3·8), the saturated liquid line (*a-c*), and the saturated vapor line (*c-b*) is called the *wet region*. All states involving mixtures of liquid and vapor are represented by points within this region.

The location of a point in the wet region representing a mixture of liquid and vapor phases depends on the pressure (or temperature) and also on the proportion of liquid and vapor in the mixture. *Quality*, denoted by the symbol x, is defined as the fraction by mass of vapor in a mixture of liquid and vapor. The term quality has no meaning in regard to compressed liquid or superheated vapor states. The limiting values of quality are 0 for the saturated liquid alone and 1.0 or 100 per cent for saturated vapor alone. Saturated vapor existing with no liquid present ($x = 100$ per cent) is sometimes called "dry saturated vapor," and vapor mixed with liquid is called "wet vapor." This is a misleading usage because the properties of *the saturated vapor* itself are the same whether liquid is present or not.

Consider a liquid–vapor mixture at the pressure indicated by line *f-g* in Fig. 3·8. The liquid in the mixture is represented by point *f*; its specific volume is v_f. The vapor in the mixture is represented by point *g*; its specific volume is v_g. The mixture has a specific volume v_x which is greater than v_f but less than v_g; and v_x can be expressed in terms of v_f, v_g, and x. The volume of the mixture is the sum of the volume of the liquid and of the vapor because the liquid, although it may be dispersed in very small drops, occupies a volume from which the vapor is excluded. (This is unlike the case of two vapors which, as a result of the intermingling of their individual molecules, occupy the same volume when mixed. That is, the volume of the vapor mixture equals the volume of each constituent.) Thus, letting m_L and m_V denote the mass of liquid and of vapor, respectively, the specific volume of the mixture is

$$v_x = \frac{V}{m} = \frac{V_L + V_V}{m_L + m_V} = \frac{m_L v_f + m_V v_g}{m_L + m_V}$$

$$= \frac{m_L}{m_L + m_V} v_f + \frac{m_V}{m_L + m_V} v_g$$

Using the definition of quality x,

$$x \equiv \frac{m_V}{m_L + m_V} \quad \text{and} \quad \frac{m_L}{m_L + m_V} = 1 - x$$

and consequently

$$v_x = (1 - x)v_f + x v_g \qquad (3 \cdot 1a)$$

or

$$v_x = v_f + x(v_g - v_f) \qquad (3 \cdot 1b)$$

The difference $(v_g - v_f)$ is denoted by the symbol v_{fg}, so that

$$v_x = v_f + x v_{fg} \qquad (3 \cdot 1b)$$

This shows that, when $x = 50$ per cent, the point representing the state of the mixture is midway between points *f* and *g*; when $x = 20$ per cent, the point is one fifth of the distance along *f-g* from point *f*, and so forth. A physical interpretation of equation 3·1*b* is that the volume of 1 lb of mixture is the volume of 1 lb of saturated liquid plus the increase in volume during the vaporization of x lb of substance. Equation 3·1*b* is generally more convenient for computations than equation 3·1*a*. A form which is convenient for precise computations when x is high is

$$v_x = v_g - (1 - x)v_{fg} \qquad (3·1c)$$

A physical interpretation of equation 3·1*c* is that the volume of 1 lb of mixture is the volume of 1 lb of saturated vapor minus the volume decrease during the condensation of $(1 - x)$ lb of substance.

Saturated liquid at the triple-phase pressure is represented by point *a* in Fig. 3·8, and point *b* represents saturated vapor. The saturated solid at the same pressure (and temperature) is represented by point *i*. Points on the triple-phase line between *i* and *a* represent mixtures of solid and liquid, solid and vapor, or all three phases. Points between *a* and *b* represent solid–vapor, liquid–vapor, or solid–liquid–vapor mixtures.

The saturated solid at pressures higher than the triple-phase pressure is represented by points along the line *i-d*, called the saturated solid line. Liquid at the freezing temperature is represented by points along the line *a-e*. In accordance with the definition of saturation conditions, liquid at the freezing temperature could be called saturated liquid except that this would lead to confusion with liquid at the boiling temperature. Hence the line *a-e* is called the freezing liquid line. Mixtures of solid and liquid are represented by points in the region bounded by lines *a-e*, *i-d*, and *i-a*.

Line *i-j* is also a saturated solid line, but points along it represent states in which the solid can be in equilibrium with a vapor instead of with a liquid. Line *b-h* is likewise an extension of the saturated vapor line and solid–vapor mixtures are represented by points within the area bounded by *j-i-a-b-h*.

Line *j-k* is a plot of the specific volume of the solid versus pressure at some minimum temperature. Figure 3·9 which is discussed below makes this clear.

It must be kept in mind that the volume scale in Fig. 3·8 is very greatly distorted. For all substances the change in volume between points *a* and *b* is many times that between *i* and *a*; and the critical volume v_c is only slightly greater than v_a or v_i.

The broken lines in Fig. 3·8 are lines of constant temperature. Notice that in all two-phase regions constant-temperature lines coincide with constant-pressure lines. The pressure–temperature dependence of saturated phases was discussed in Art. 3·2.

Two-dimensional property diagrams serve adequately in most thermodynamic analyses, but a better picture of the relationship among pressure, specific volume, and temperature of a substance is given by a three-dimensional pvT diagram such as that shown in Fig. 3·9. All equilibrium states of the substance are represented by points on the pvT surface. Figure 3·9 shows the pv and pT diagrams, which have been discussed above, as projections of the pvT surface. Points representing mixtures of two phases all lie in surfaces which have elements perpendicular to the pT plane. Since a straightedge held parallel to the v axis can contact any one of these

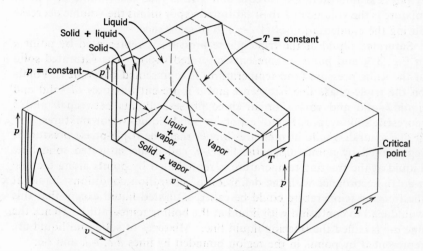

Fig. 3·9 pvT surface for a substance which contracts on freezing.

surfaces all along one of its elements, these are called ruled surfaces. They project into lines on the pT diagram. Various surfaces other than the pvT surface are useful in some types of thermodynamic analyses.

The advantage of a pvT diagram over a two-dimensional diagram is shown by Figs. 3·10 and 3·11 which are for a substance which expands on freezing. Inspection of these figures reveals that point r of the pv diagram can represent solid (r_1), solid–liquid mixture (r_2), or a liquid–vapor mixture (r_3). Point s can represent a solid, a solid–liquid mixture, or a liquid. Thus the various regions on a pv diagram which were easily identified in Fig. 3·8 overlap each other on a pv diagram for a substance which expands on freezing. However, the areas are clearly shown on a pvT diagram, and each point on the pvT surface represents only one state of the substance.

A Tv diagram can also be projected from the pvT surface and is occasionally useful.

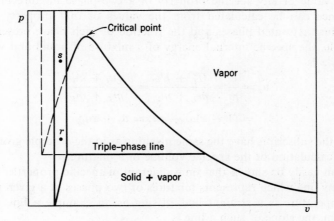

Fig. 3·10 *pv* diagram for a substance which, like water, expands on freezing.

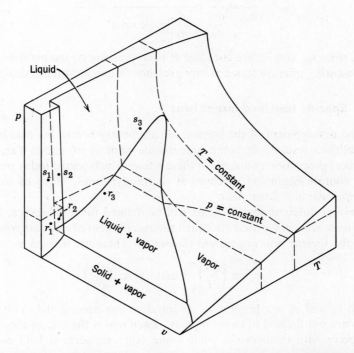

Fig. 3·11 *pvT* surface for a substance which, like water, expands on freezing.

The value of any specific property of a two-phase mixture of a pure substance can be calculated from the values of that property for the individual saturated phases and the fraction of each phase present. For example, the specific internal energy of a mixture of liquid and vapor of quality x is

$$u_x = \frac{U}{m} = \frac{U_L + U_V}{m_L + m_V} = \frac{m_L u_f + m_V u_g}{m_L + m_V}$$

$$= (1 - x)u_f + xu_g = u_f + xu_{fg} \tag{3.2}$$

where the subscripts have the same meaning as in the example given above of the calculation of the specific volume of a mixture.

It can easily be shown that on a diagram of specific properties (u, v, h, etc.) any line which represents mixtures of two phases at a given pressure or temperature is a straight line. Using as an example a line on a uv diagram, the slope of such a line is

$$\frac{du_x}{dv_x} = \frac{\dfrac{du_x}{dx}}{\dfrac{dv_x}{dx}} = \frac{\dfrac{d}{dx}(u_f + xu_{fg})}{\dfrac{d}{dx}(v_f + xv_{fg})} = \frac{u_{fg}}{v_{fg}}$$

and, since u_{fg} and v_{fg} are constant at each pressure or temperature, a line representing mixture states at any pressure or temperature is straight.

3·5 Specific heat and latent heat

The development of the science of calorimetry before the first law was established resulted in some unfortunate choices of names for certain physical properties, and some of these names which persist today occasionally confuse beginning students of thermodynamics. Two of these are *specific heat* and *latent heat*.

Several different specific heats can be defined for a substance, but the two most frequently used are called the *specific heat at constant pressure* c_p and the *specific heat at constant volume* c_v. These are defined as

$$c_p \equiv \left(\frac{\partial h}{\partial T}\right)_p \quad \text{and} \quad c_v \equiv \left(\frac{\partial u}{\partial T}\right)_v \tag{3.3}$$

Both c_p and c_v are properties. In modern engineering thermodynamics they are not defined in terms of heat. Each one is the rate of change of a property with temperature while some other property is held constant. For example, c_p is the slope of a constant-pressure line on an hT diagram of a substance.

The properties c_p and c_v were originally given the name of specific heats because *under certain conditions* they relate the temperature change of a system to the amount of heat added to the system. Let us answer the question, "Just what are the conditions under which $\delta q = c_v \, dT$?" It has been pointed out that the state of a pure substance which is at rest and uninfluenced by electricity, magnetism, etc., is generally determined by any two independent properties. Thus any property of a system comprised of a pure substance is a function of any two independent properties. Using temperature and specific volume as independent properties, we can express the internal energy of the system as

$$u = f(T, v) \qquad (a)$$

Then
$$du = \left(\frac{\partial u}{\partial T}\right)_v dT + \left(\frac{\partial u}{\partial v}\right)_T dv \qquad (b)$$

and, using the definition of c_v,

$$du = c_v \, dT + \left(\frac{\partial u}{\partial v}\right)_T dv \qquad (c)$$

and this relationship is valid for *any process* of a pure substance, provided only that $u = f(T, v)$. For the *special case* of a *constant-volume* process, (c) becomes

$$du = c_v \, dT \qquad (d)$$

Thus, for a pure substance, c_v directly relates *internal energy* changes with *temperature* for a *constant-volume* process. The question now is, "Under what further conditions is *heat* related to *internal energy* changes only?" The answer is seen by noting that the first law as applied to a closed system,

$$du = \delta q - \delta w \qquad (2·7)$$

reduces to
$$du = \delta q$$

for any process in which no work is done, or (since we intend to apply it to a constant-volume process) for any *frictionless constant-volume* process. Therefore, the answer to the original question is that, *for a frictionless constant-volume process,*

$$\delta q = c_v \, dT$$

This relationship was originally the defining equation for c_v which was defined explicitly as

$$c_v = \left(\frac{\delta q}{dT}\right)_{v=\text{const, frictionless}}$$

The definition as given by equation 3·3 is much more concise and less likely to be misinterpreted than this older one. In the same manner, the definition of c_p given by equation 3·3 is superior to

$$c_p = \left(\frac{\delta q}{dT}\right)_{p=\text{const, frictionless}}$$

which was formerly in wide use. It is unfortunate that the name *specific heat* has persisted for these properties, since they are properties which have much more important roles in thermodynamics than simply the roles of coefficients in the calculation of heat transfer under special conditions.

The specific heats as defined by equations 3·3 are sometimes called *instantaneous* specific heats to indicate that they can be evaluated at any one state of a system and to distinguish them from *mean* specific heats which are defined as

$$\overline{c_p} \equiv \left(\frac{\Delta h}{\Delta T}\right)_p \quad \text{and} \quad \overline{c_v} \equiv \left(\frac{\Delta u}{\Delta T}\right)_v$$

Mean specific heats are related to instantaneous specific heats by

$$\overline{c_p} = \frac{\int_1^2 c_p \, dT}{T_2 - T_1} \quad \text{and} \quad \overline{c_v} = \frac{\int_1^2 c_v \, dT}{T_2 - T_1}$$

Notice that these relationships, as well as the defining equations for mean specific heats, involve the specification of a temperature interval, so that a mean specific heat is not a property in the thermodynamic sense because its value does not depend only on the state of the system.

Throughout this textbook, the term *specific heat* without modifiers always signifies *instantaneous* specific heat; *mean* specific-heat values are always so identified.

Latent heat is defined as the magnitude of the difference between the (specific) enthalpy of one phase of a pure substance at saturation conditions and the (specific) enthalpy of another phase of the pure substance at the same pressure and temperature. Letting the subscript i refer to saturated solid, f to saturated liquid, and g to saturated vapor, we distinguish among the various latent heats of a substance as

Latent heat of vaporization, $\quad h_{fg} = h_g - h_f \quad$ (at the same p and T)
Latent heat of fusion, $\qquad\;\; h_{if} = h_f - h_i \quad$ (at the same p and T)
Latent heat of sublimation, $\quad h_{ig} = h_g - h_i \quad$ (at the same p and T)

(It is actually unnecessary to *specify* that the two enthalpy values in each of the three expressions above must be at the same pressure *and* temperature, because, if two saturated phases of a substance are at the same pressure, they must be at the same temperature and vice versa.)

Notice that latent heat as defined here is a property, and its definition does not refer to heat. It has been proposed that h_{fg} be called the *enthalpy of vaporization*, h_{if} the *enthalpy of fusion*, and so forth, but these terms have not been widely adopted. The term *latent heat*, like the term specific heat, evolved from the science of calorimetry which preceded the development of the first law of thermodynamics. This early science was beclouded by a lack of distinction between quantities which are properties and those which are not.

Application of the first law to phase changes of pure substances shows that the latent heat of a substance at a given pressure is the amount of heat which must be added to a unit mass of the substance to cause it to change phase in a *constant-pressure frictionless* process. This was formerly widely accepted as the definition of latent heat. The definition of latent heat in terms of properties is preferred.

The latent heats of a substance are functions of pressure. The latent heat of vaporization usually varies more with pressure than the latent heat of fusion or of sublimation does. A typical variation in the latent heat of vaporization is shown by the *ph* diagram of Fig. 3·12. The distance along a constant-pressure line between the saturated liquid and saturated vapor lines is proportional to h_{fg} for that pressure.

EXAMPLE 3·1.   For a certain substance in the temperature range of 40 to 1800 F and at low pressures,

$$c_p = 0.1 + \frac{100}{T} + \frac{T}{10,000}$$

where c_p is in B/lb-F and T is in degrees Rankine. (Notice that, because the definition of specific heat involves a temperature difference or differential, the units can be interchangeably B/lb-F or B/lb-R. With $T_R = T_F + 460$, we see that $dT_R = dT_F$. This is sometimes explained by saying that the size of a degree is the same on the Rankine and Fahrenheit scales, and so a *change* or *difference* in temperature has the same value on both scales.) Calculate (a) $\overline{c_p}$ between 40 and 1040 F, (b) $\overline{c_p}$ between 40 and 540 F, (c) c_p at 40, 540, and 1040 F, and (d) h at 14.5 psia, 740 F, if $h = 28.0$ B/lb at 14.5 psia, 40 F.

Solution.   (a) From the definition of mean specific heat, we have for the temperature range of 40 F (500 R) to 1040 F (1500 R),

$$\overline{c_p} \equiv \frac{\int_1^2 c_p\, dT}{T_2 - T_1} = \frac{\int_1^2 \left(0.1 + \dfrac{100}{T} + \dfrac{T}{10,000}\right) dT}{T_2 - T_1}$$

$$= \frac{0.1(T_2 - T_1) + 100 \ln (T_2/T_1) + (T_2^2 - T_1^2)/20,000}{T_2 - T_1}$$

$$= 0.1 + \frac{100}{T_2 - T_1} \ln \frac{T_2}{T_1} + \frac{T_2 + T_1}{20,000} \qquad (A)$$

$$= 0.1 + \frac{100}{1500 - 500} \ln \frac{1500}{500} + \frac{1500 + 500}{20,000} = 0.1 + 0.1098 + 0.1$$

$$= 0.310 \text{ B/lb-F}$$

(b) Substituting in equation (A) above the values of $T_1 = 500$ R and $T_2 = 1000$ R, we have

$$\bar{c}_p = 0.1 + \frac{100}{1000 - 500} \ln \frac{1000}{500} + \frac{1000 + 500}{20,000}$$

$$= 0.1 + 0.1386 + 0.075 = 0.314 \text{ B/lb-F}$$

(c) Substituting the proper temperatures into the given expression for c_p,

$$c_{p,40\,F} = 0.1 + \frac{100}{500} + \frac{500}{10,000} = 0.35 \text{ B/lb-F}$$

$$c_{p,540\,F} = 0.1 + \frac{100}{1000} + \frac{1000}{10,000} = 0.30 \text{ B/lb-F}$$

$$c_{p,1040\,F} = 0.1 + \frac{100}{1500} + \frac{1500}{10,000} = 0.317 \text{ B/lb-F}$$

(d) Considering h as a function of p and T,

$$dh = \left(\frac{\partial h}{\partial T}\right)_p dT + \left(\frac{\partial h}{\partial p}\right)_T dp = c_p\, dT + \left(\frac{\partial h}{\partial p}\right)_T dp$$

Letting subscripts 1 and 2 denote the conditions at 14.5 psia, 40 F, and at 14.5 psia, 740 F, respectively,

$$h_2 = h_1 + \int_1^2 dh = h_1 + \int_1^2 \left[c_p\, dT + \left(\frac{\partial h}{\partial p}\right)_T dp \right]$$

Since the pressure is the same at states 1 and 2, the second term in the integrand is zero, so that

$$h_2 = h_1 + \int_1^2 c_p\, dT = h_1 + \int_1^2 \left[0.1 + \frac{100}{T} + \frac{T}{10,000} \right] dT$$

$$= h_1 + 0.1(T_2 - T_1) + 100 \ln \frac{T_2}{T_1} + \frac{T_2^2 - T_1^2}{20,000}$$

$$= 28.0 + 0.1(1200 - 500) + 100 \ln \frac{1200}{500} + \frac{(1200)^2 - (500)^2}{20,000}$$

$$= 28.0 + 70 + 87.5 + 59.5 = 245 \text{ B/lb}$$

EXAMPLE 3·2. One-half pound of a gas is contained at 30 psia, 140 F, in a closed rigid vessel. By means of a paddle wheel, 560 ft-lb of work is done on the gas while 3.0 B of heat is added. During this process, the temperature of the gas rises to 240 F. Calculate $\bar{c}_v$ of the gas.

Solution. The definition of $\bar{c}_v$ is

$$\bar{c}_v \equiv \frac{\displaystyle\int_1^2 c_v\, dT}{T_2 - T_1}$$

and *for a constant-volume process* (see equation d),

$$u_2 - u_1 = \int_1^2 c_v\, dT$$

so that *for a constant-volume process*,

$$\overline{c}_v = \frac{u_2 - u_1}{T_2 - T_1}$$

For a closed system,

$$u_2 - u_1 = \frac{U_2 - U_1}{m} = \frac{Q + W_{\text{in}}}{m}$$

Substituting this value of Δu into the expression above for $\overline{c}_v$,

$$\overline{c}_v = \frac{Q + W_{\text{in}}}{m(T_2 - T_1)} = \frac{3.0 + 560/778}{0.5(240 - 140)} = 0.0744 \text{ B/lb-F}$$

3·6 Phase changes

In order to clarify the nature of phase changes, several processes in which a pure substance changes phase will now be considered and will be represented on six different property diagrams (Fig. 3·12). You should make certain that you can sketch all of these property diagrams from the process descriptions, provided you have data at hand for plotting the saturation lines of the substance. Inspection of Fig. 3·12 shows that the property diagram which is best for showing a particular process depends on the process.

Let us consider first a process in which a pure substance is changed at constant pressure from a compressed liquid (state *a*) to a superheated vapor (state *e*). For all substances, the internal energy of superheated vapor is greater than that of compressed liquid at the same pressure; therefore, energy must be added to the substance during this process. The energy may be added as heat, as work, or as any combination of heat and work. Property diagrams of the process are the same whether the process occurs in an open or a closed system.

As energy is added to the compressed liquid at constant pressure, the temperature of the liquid rises. While liquid is present in equilibrium, the temperature cannot be higher than the saturation temperature which is reached at point *b*. On the Tv diagram of Fig. 3·12, the reciprocal of the slope of line *a-b* is $(\partial v/\partial T)_p$, v times the coefficient of cubical expansion. This property has such low values for liquids that line *a-b* is nearly vertical on a Tv diagram. For water under a pressure of 1 atm specific volume is a minimum at about 39.2 F, and at lower temperatures the coefficient of cubical expansion of the liquid is negative; hence for water below about 39.2 F a constant-pressure line of 1 atm has a negative slope on a Tv diagram.

On the hT diagram, the slope of line *a-b* is $(\partial h/\partial T)_p$, the specific heat at constant pressure. For liquids, c_p varies but slightly with temperature, so line *a-b* is nearly straight on the hT diagram.

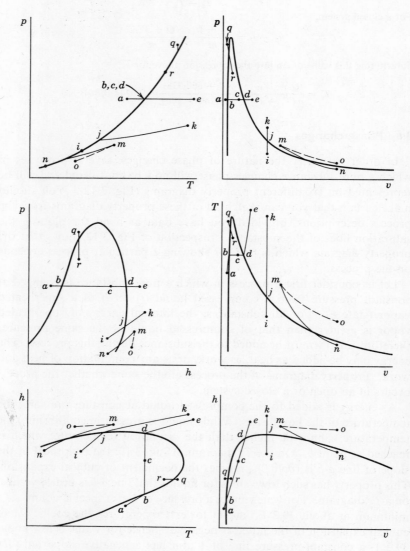

Fig. 3·12 Phase changes on six property diagrams.

After the liquid reaches state b, further energy addition at constant pressure causes some of the substance to evaporate. The vapor thus formed is at the same pressure and temperature as the liquid. The state of this vapor is represented by point d. If only enough energy to vaporize part of the substance is supplied, then the resulting state is a mixture of liquid at state b and vapor at state d. The properties of the mixture are represented by some point c which is located between b and d on any diagram which has a specific property as at least one coordinate. On such a diagram the ratio of the distance b-c to the distance b-d is equal to the quality of the mixture.

In order to evaporate 1 lb of saturated liquid to a saturated vapor at the same pressure, its internal energy must be increased by $u_g - u_f$ or u_{fg}, where the subscripts are as defined in Art. 3·4. The fluid expands during the process. If it is in a closed system, it does some work on the surroundings so that the total energy added to the system is u_{fg} plus an amount equal to the work done by the system. If it is in an open system, any fluid leaving the system does more flow work on the surroundings than an equal amount of fluid entering does on the system so that the total energy added to the system is again greater than u_{fg}.

EXAMPLE 3·3.   One pound of saturated liquid water at 500 psia in a closed system is completely vaporized at constant pressure in a frictionless process. Calculate (a) the amount of heat added and (b) the amount of work done. Properties of the saturated liquid and saturated vapor are as follows:

$$u_f = 447.6 \text{ B/lb} \qquad u_g = 1118.6 \text{ B/lb}$$

$$v_f = 0.0197 \text{ cu ft/lb} \qquad v_g = 0.9278 \text{ cu ft/lb}$$

$$h_f = 449.4 \text{ B/lb} \qquad h_g = 1204.4 \text{ B/lb}$$

Solution.   Analysis of the problem shows that it is possible to solve part (b) first and that this result will be useful in the solution of part (a).

(b) For this frictionless process of a closed system,

$$w = \int_1^2 p \, dv$$

and, since the pressure is constant,

$$w = p \int_1^2 dv = p(v_2 - v_1) = p(v_g - v_f)$$

$$= 500(144)(0.9278 - 0.0197)\tfrac{1}{778} = 84.0 \text{ B/lb}$$

(a) Applying the first law to this closed system,

$$q = u_2 - u_1 + \text{work} = u_g - u_f + \text{work}$$

$$= 1118.6 - 447.6 + 84.0 = 755.0 \text{ B/lb}$$

This result may also be obtained by

$$q = u_2 - u_1 + w = u_2 - u_1 + \int_1^2 p \, dv$$

$$= u_2 - u_1 + p_2 v_2 - p_1 v_1 = h_2 - h_1 = h_g - h_f$$

$$= 1204.4 - 449.4 = 755.0 \text{ B/lb}$$

Notice that because work is done by the system during the vaporization process the amount of heat added is greater than the increase in the internal energy of the system.

EXAMPLE 3·4. One pound of saturated liquid water at 500 psia in a closed system is completely vaporized at constant pressure by the addition of heat while 20 B of work is done on the water by means of a stirrer. Physical properties are tabulated in Example 3·3. Calculate the amount of heat added.

Solution. This process is not frictionless because the action of the stirrer involves fluid shear forces; therefore work $\neq \int p \, dv$. However, if the action of the stirrer is such that the pressure on any boundary of the system which moves so as to change the volume of the system remains uniform and constant, then the work done on this moving boundary (or the work associated with the change in volume of the system) is

$$\text{Work}_{\Delta v} = \int p \, dv = p(v_2 - v_1)$$

and the net work is

$$\text{Work} = \text{work}_{\Delta v} + \text{work}_{\text{stirrer}} = p(v_2 - v_1) + \text{work}_{\text{stirrer}}$$

$$= \frac{500(144)(0.9278 - 0.0197)}{778} + (-20)$$

$$= 64.0 \text{ B/lb}$$

Then, applying the first law,

$$q = u_2 - u_1 + \text{work} = 1118.6 - 447.6 + 64.0$$

$$= 735.0 \text{ B/lb}$$

(This example illustrates that latent heat of vaporization cannot be defined simply as the amount of heat required to change one pound of a saturated liquid to saturated vapor in *any* constant-pressure process. Here, $q = 735 \text{ B/lb} < h_{fg}$.)

EXAMPLE 3·5. Saturated liquid water at 500 psia is completely vaporized at constant pressure in a steady-flow heat exchanger. Calculate the amount of heat added in B/lb. Physical properties are tabulated in Example 3·3.

Solution. Applying the first law to this steady-flow system, noting that no work is done in a heat exchanger, and assuming that changes in potential and kinetic energy are negligible, we have

$$q = h_2 - h_1 + \text{work} + \Delta PE + \Delta KE$$

$$= h_2 - h_1 + 0 + 0 + 0 = h_g - h_f = 1204.4 - 449.4 = 755.0 \text{ B/lb}$$

(Notice that $q = h_{fg}$ *only* when $\text{work} + \Delta PE + \Delta KE = 0$.)

The addition of energy to a saturated vapor at constant pressure causes an increase in its temperature, specific volume, internal energy, and enthalpy as shown by the lines *d-e* in Fig. 3·12. For all substances, $(\partial v/\partial T)_p$ is greater for the vapor than for the liquid at the same pressure and c_p, which is defined as $(\partial h/\partial T)_p$, is lower for the vapor than for the liquid. Thus the relative slopes of lines *a-b* and *d-e* on some of the diagrams can be explained.

Consider now the addition of energy to a liquid–vapor mixture of a pure substance which is held in a closed rigid container and initially has a specific volume greater than the specific volume at the critical point. Such an initial state is represented by point *i* on each diagram of Fig. 3·12. Addition of energy, either as heat or as some form of frictional work such as paddle-wheel work, causes some of the liquid to evaporate as the pressure and temperature increase. At state *j* all of the liquid has been vaporized; only saturated vapor is present. Further addition of energy to the substance in the constant-volume container causes its state to change along line *j-k*.

The expansion of a vapor in a nozzle, a turbine, or an engine is often adiabatic or very nearly so. From any initial state, several adiabatic paths are possible. One such path is shown in Fig. 3·12 as *m-n*. Another is shown as *m-o*. For each of these paths, work is done by the fluid or there is a change in kinetic energy, or both these energy transformations occur.

A *throttling process* is an adiabatic steady-flow expansion in which no work is done and there is no change in kinetic energy. Application of the first law shows that the initial and final enthalpies are the same in a throttling process. Examples of a throttling process are the flow of a fluid through a porous plug and the flow through a pressure-reducing valve. A throttling process in which a phase change occurs is shown by line *q-r* in Fig. 3·12. Notice that this phase change is brought about without the use of heat or work.

In addition to those listed above, many other processes in which phase changes occur are possible and occur in engineering applications.

3·7   The critical point

Reference has already been made to the critical point, the limiting state for the existence of saturated liquid and vapor. The *critical pressure* is the highest pressure under which distinguishable liquid and vapor phases can exist in equilibrium. The *critical temperature* is the highest temperature at which distinguishable liquid and vapor phases can exist in equilibrium. As the critical point is approached from lower pressures and temperatures, the properties of saturated liquid and saturated vapor approach each other.

Therefore, properties such as u_{fg}, h_{fg}, and v_{fg} reach the limiting value of zero at the critical point.

Since the properties, especially density, of liquid and vapor phases of a substance under normal ambient conditions are so different, it is sometimes difficult to visualize conditions under which the two phases are indistinguishable from each other. It is often helpful to consider the following experiment.

If a rigid transparent vessel is filled with a liquid–vapor mixture of a substance in a state represented by point a on Fig. 3·13, all the liquid will in time settle to the bottom of the vessel, and a meniscus can be seen

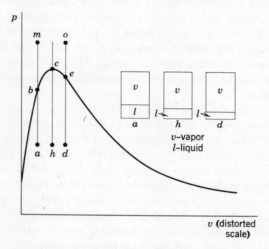

Fig. 3·13 Critical-point experiments.

separating the two phases. If the mixture is then heated, the pressure and temperature will increase. Inspection of Fig. 3·13 shows that the fraction of liquid, as well as the liquid specific volume, will increase, causing the meniscus to rise until it reaches the top of the vessel at point b. During further heating to point m, the vessel contains liquid only. If the vessel had originally been filled with a mixture represented by point d, heating would have caused the evaporation of the liquid, and the meniscus would have fallen until the last bit of liquid in the bottom of the vessel was vaporized as the substance reached the state represented by point e. Further heating to point o would superheat the vapor.

The most interesting case is the one in which the vessel is initially filled with a mixture at state h such that the mixture specific volume v_h is equal to the specific volume at the critical point. As the mixture is heated, it approaches the critical point with the liquid becoming less dense and the vapor becoming more dense. As the critical point is approached, the meniscus fades away because there are no longer two phases present. The single phase which remains may be considered as either a liquid or a vapor, and there is fully as much reason for one designation as for the other.

It appears that the amounts of liquid and vapor initially placed in the vessel must be very carefully controlled (or, in other words, that point *h* must be carefully selected) to insure that constant-volume heating will cause the meniscus to disappear somewhere near the center of the tube instead of rising to the top as the entire sample is liquefied or falling to the bottom as the entire sample is vaporized. Actually experiments show that the meniscus between liquid and vapor phases disappears not only at the critical point but in a region around it where the two phase densities are nearly equal. This means that the disappearance of the meniscus can be demonstrated without making the substance pass exactly through its critical state. Conversely, the critical point cannot be precisely identified by the disappearance of the meniscus. These facts were not anticipated before the performance of such experiments. In fact, the investigation of properties near the critical point offers several eloquent examples of the importance of careful experimentation in conjunction with analytical studies.

3·8   Tables of properties

An equation relating *p*, *v*, and *T* of a substance is called an *equation of state*. The relationships among *p*, *v*, and *T* for some substances are such that they can be represented by fairly simple equations of state, and a few of these are discussed in the next two chapters. Also, it is sometimes possible to express properties such as internal energy and enthalpy as simple functions of one or two of the state properties *p*, *v*, and *T*. Unfortunately, for many substances of importance in engineering the relationships among properties over a wide range cannot be expressed by simple equations. Therefore, the properties of these substances must be determined over the range of interest by measurements supplemented by calculations which insure the self-consistency of interpolated or derived values. The results of these measurements and calculations are then presented in the form of tables or charts.

The properties which are usually tabulated are:

p and *T*, intensive properties, which are directly measurable and usually controllable.

v, which is useful in determining the size of equipment, flow rates, and velocities.

h and *u*, which are useful in applications of the first law (*u* is not used so much as *h* and is frequently not tabulated, but it can always be found by $u = h - pv$).

s (entropy), which is introduced in Chapter 9.

Several other properties are occasionally tabulated, but those listed above are found in all tables of thermodynamic properties. The properties are usually tabulated for the following states:

1. *Saturated liquid*, for which either *p* or *T* is used as the argument or independent variable. Only one argument is needed, because *p* and *T* are dependent on each other for saturation states. (Notice that this does not mean that we can specify the state of a pure substance by only one variable. In addition to the value of pressure or temperature, we must also know the fact that the substance exists in a saturated liquid state.) Complete tables often include one saturation-states table with integral (i.e., whole number) values of pressure and one with integral values of temperature as the argument in order to reduce and simplify the interpolation needed.

2. *Saturated vapor*, these properties usually being given in the same table as the saturated liquid properties.

3. *Superheated vapor*, for which *p* and *T* are used as arguments because *p* and *T* are readily measurable independent variables, and two independent variables are required to specify the state of the substance.

Compressed liquid properties are seldom tabulated. They are functions of temperature and pressure but vary only slightly with pressure. Therefore, the properties of a compressed liquid are approximately equal to the properties of saturated liquid *at the same temperature*. When very high pressures are encountered or a high degree of precision is desired, this approximation may be unsatisfactory. Then the properties needed must be obtained from tables or must be calculated by means of data on specific heats, bulk moduli, and coefficients of expansion. The use of a compressed liquid table for water is illustrated later in this article.

Saturated solid (solid–vapor equilibrium) properties are occasionally tabulated in the same fashion as saturated liquid and vapor properties. Water and carbon dioxide are two substances which are occasionally encountered in solid–vapor equilibrium applications.

Liquid–vapor mixture and *solid–vapor mixture* properties are not tabulated because they can be readily calculated from the quality and the properties of their constituents by means of equations such as 3·1 and 3·2.

It was pointed out in Art. 2·4 that thermodynamics provides no information as to absolute values of internal energy. We are concerned only with *changes* in internal energy. Therefore, the state at which internal energy or enthalpy has a value of zero may be selected arbitrarily. Steam tables generally assign $h = 0$ to saturated liquid at 32 F;* tables for refrigerants often assign $h = 0$ to saturated liquid at -40 F. Other datum temperatures are also used.

Several examples of the use of property tables will now be given. Water or steam is of considerable importance to the engineer by virtue of its widespread use as a working fluid and a heat-transfer medium and its presence in atmospheric air and in the products of combustion of any fuel which contains hydrogen. The tabulation of water properties most widely used in America is *Thermodynamic Properties of Steam*, by Keenan and Keyes (reference 3·4 at the end of this chapter). Many examples and problems in this textbook concern water not only because of the importance of water but also on account of the completeness of the Keenan and Keyes tables which cover a wide range of variables with small tabular differences. Although an abridged table of steam properties is given in the appendix of this textbook, you should have and use a copy of the Keenan and Keyes tables. An engineer who is proficient in the use of steam tables can quickly adjust to the use of any other table of properties, even though its form is somewhat different.

For water, the properties of saturated liquid and vapor are given in Tables A·1 and A·2 of the appendix which are abridged from Tables 1 and 2 of Keenan and Keyes. The primary difference between these two is that Table A·1 is based on integral values of temperature and Table A·2 on integral values of pressure. The first and second columns of Table A·1 (see also Table 3·3, a short version) give the saturation temperature and pressure, respectively. For example, the saturation pressure for 50 F is 0.17811 psia. The other columns of the table are appropriately labeled. The unit for specific volume is cu ft/lb and for (specific) enthalpy B/lb. Values of internal energy are not given in this table, but they can be readily calculated from $u = h - pv$. The table is based on $h_f = 0$ at 32 F. Therefore, u_f at 32 F is negative.

Table A·2 is similar to Table A·1 except that the pressure and temperature columns are interchanged. Also, the column for v_{fg} has been omitted to make room for columns for u_f and u_g.

The data of Tables A·1 and A·2 in conjunction with equations such as equations 3·1 and 3.2 (Art. 3·4) can be used to determine the properties of liquid–vapor mixtures. These mixtures are commonly referred to as "steam," even though they contain liquid.

The properties of superheated steam are presented in Table A·3 of the appendix. The first column shows the pressure and the corresponding

---

* Since the triple-point temperature of water is 32.018 F, saturated liquid cannot exist at 32 F. Nevertheless it is possible and quite convenient to extrapolate saturated liquid properties to 32 F and to use this as the datum temperature.

TABLE 3·3

Water Saturation States: Temperature Table*

(1)	(2)	(3)	(4)	(5)	(6)	(7)	(8)	(9)	(10)	(11)
		Specific Volume			Enthalpy			Entropy		
Temp., F	Abs Press., psia	Sat. Liquid,	Evap.,	Sat. Vapor,	Sat. Liquid,	Evap.,	Sat. Vapor,	Sat. Liquid,	Evap.,	Sat. Vapor,
t	p	v_f	v_{fg}	v_g	h_f	h_{fg}	h_g	s_f	s_{fg}	s_g
32	0.08854	0.01602	3306	3306	0.00	1075.8	1075.8	0.0000	2.1877	2.1877
50	0.17811	0.01603	1703.2	1703.2	18.07	1065.6	1083.7	0.0361	2.0903	2.1264
100	0.9492	0.01613	350.3	350.4	67.97	1037.2	1105.2	0.1295	1.8531	1.9826
200	11.526	0.01663	33.62	33.64	167.99	977.9	1145.9	0.2938	1.4824	1.7762

* Abridged from *Thermodynamic Properties of Steam*, by J. H. Keenan and F. G. Keyes, published by John Wiley and Sons, Inc., 1936.

TABLE 3·4

Water Saturation States: Pressure Table*

(1)	(2)	(3)	(4)	(5)	(6)	(7)	(8)	(9)	(10)	(11)	(12)
		Specific Volume		Enthalpy			Entropy			Internal Energy	
Abs Press., psia	Temp., F	Sat. Liquid,	Sat. Vapor,	Sat. Liquid,	Evap.,	Sat. Vapor,	Sat. Liquid,	Evap.,	Sat. Vapor,	Sat. Liquid,	Sat. Vapor,
p	t	v_f	v_g	h_f	h_{fg}	h_g	s_f	s_{fg}	s_g	u_f	u_g
1.0	101.74	0.01614	333.6	69.70	1036.3	1106.0	0.1326	1.8456	1.9782	69.70	1044.3
5.0	162.24	0.01640	73.52	130.13	1001.0	1131.1	0.2347	1.6094	1.8441	130.12	1063.1
10	193.21	0.01659	38.42	161.17	982.1	1143.3	0.2835	1.5041	1.7876	161.14	1072.2
100	327.81	0.01774	4.432	298.40	888.8	1187.2	0.4740	1.1286	1.6026	298.08	1105.2

* Abridged from *Thermodynamic Properties of Steam*, by J. H. Keenan and F. G. Keyes, published by John Wiley & Sons, Inc., 1936.

saturation temperature in parentheses immediately under the pressure value. The remaining columns give values of v, h, and s for various temperatures at each pressure. Once again, internal energy values may be found by $u = h - pv$. For convenience, the Keenan and Keyes tables give the values of v, h, and s for saturated liquid and vapor on the same pages with the superheated vapor data. Table A·3 does not have this feature.

EXAMPLE 3·6. Ten pounds of steam at 1 psia has a volume of 3000 cu ft. Determine the temperature and the enthalpy per pound.

Solution. From the data given it may not be possible to visualize at once the condition of the steam; hence it will be necessary to refer to Table A·2 of the appendix, which deals with the properties of saturated steam. The specific volume of the steam under consideration equals

$$v = \tfrac{3000}{10} = 300 \text{ cu ft/lb}$$

Reference to the table shows at once that this volume is greater than that for the saturated liquid ($v_f = 0.01614$) and less than that for dry saturated vapor ($v_g = 333.6$). It may be concluded that the steam is a wet vapor ($0 < x < 100$ per cent) at a temperature of 101.74 F which corresponds to the saturation pressure of 1 psia. In order to determine the enthalpy it will be necessary to compute first the quality. This may be accomplished by referring to the relation previously derived (equation 3·1):

$$v_x = v_f + x(v_{fg})$$

Solving for x gives

$$x = \frac{(v_x - v_f)}{(v_g - v_f)} = \frac{300 - 0.01614}{333.6 - 0.01614} = 0.90 \quad \text{or 90 per cent}$$

The enthalpy per pound may be found by

$$h = h_f + x(h_{fg}) = 69.7 + 0.9(1036.3) = 1002.4 \text{ B/lb}$$

EXAMPLE 3·7. Steam at 400 psia has an enthalpy of 600 B/lb. Compute the internal energy.

Solution. The first step is to determine whether the steam is superheated or is a liquid–vapor mixture. To do this, refer to Table A·2, and note that at 400 psia $h_g = 1204.5$ B/lb. The steam under consideration has a lower enthalpy than saturated vapor at the same pressure; therefore it must be a liquid–vapor mixture rather than a superheated vapor. Knowing this, we can compute the internal energy of the steam by finding its quality. Knowing the pressure and the enthalpy, we can find the quality by rearranging

$$h = h_f + x(h_{fg})$$

to give

$$x = \frac{h - h_f}{h_{fg}} = \frac{600 - 424.0}{780.5} = 0.226$$

The internal energy is then given by

$$u = u_f + x(u_g - u_f) = 422.6 + 0.226(1118.5 - 422.6) = 579.8 \text{ B/lb}$$

EXAMPLE 3·8. Determine the enthalpy and specific volume of steam at 1000 psia and 800 F.

Solution. From Table A·2 or A·3 of the appendix, the saturation temperature for a pressure of 1000 psia is 544.61 F. The temperature of the steam under consideration is greater than the saturation temperature; hence it is superheated. Reference to Table A·3 shows the following values for the enthalpy and specific volume:

$$h = 1389.2 \text{ B/lb} \quad \text{and} \quad v = 0.6867 \text{ cu ft/lb}$$

EXAMPLE 3·9. Determine the internal energy of steam at 300 psia and 800 F.

Solution. Since 800 F is higher than the saturation temperature for 300 psia (417.33 F), the steam is superheated. Since internal energy values are not given in the superheated vapor table, it is necessary to calculate u from h, p, and v as follows:

$$u = h - pv = 1420.6 - \frac{300(144)2.442}{778} = 1284.9 \text{ B/lb}$$

EXAMPLE 3·10. Determine the enthalpy of steam at 200 psia, 575 F.

Solution. Since the saturation temperature for a pressure of 200 psia is 381.79 F, the steam under consideration is superheated. Sometimes it is necessary to interpolate between values if available tables are not extensive enough. In Table A·3 of the appendix, values at 200 psia pressure are available only at temperatures of 500 and 600 F. This necessitates making an interpolation on the basis of linear relations between the variables as follows:

$$
\begin{aligned}
p &= 200 \text{ psia} \\
t &= 600 & h &= 1322.1 \\
t &= 575 \\
t &= 500 & h &= 1268.9 \\
\hline
& & & 53.2
\end{aligned}
$$

$$\tfrac{75}{100} \times 53.2 = 39.9$$

The enthalpy value at 575 F and 200 psia is therefore

$$h = 1268.9 + 39.9 = 1308.8 \text{ B/lb}$$

The properties of compressed or subcooled liquid water could be tabulated in the same form as the properties of superheated vapor. However, the compressed liquid table of Keenan and Keyes, a sample of which is shown as Table 3·5, gives for each property (v, h, and s) the *difference* between the value at each compressed liquid state and the value for saturated liquid at the same *temperature*. Notice that for convenience the properties of saturated liquid are given directly under the corresponding temperatures across the top of the table. A property of compressed liquid is obtained by adding the difference value in the body of the table (in the pressure row and the temperature column) to the saturation value of the property which is given beneath the temperature value at the top of the column. It is helpful in using the table to know that the last digit of each difference value corresponds to the last digit of the saturation value given at the top of the column.

A perusal of the compressed liquid table of Keenan and Keyes reveals the magnitude of the error involved at various pressures and temperatures in assuming that the properties of compressed liquid are the same as those of saturated liquid at the same temperature.

TABLE 3·5

Properties of Compressed Liquid Water*

Abs Press., psia (sat. temp., F)		Temperature, F			
		32	200	400	600
	Saturated liquid	p 0.08854	11.526	247.31	1542.9
		v_f 0.016022	0.016634	0.018639	0.023629
		h_f 0	167.99	374.97	617.0
		s_f 0	0.29382	0.56638	0.8131
1000 (544.61)	$(v-v_f)10^5$	−5.7	−5.4	−8.7	—
	$(h-h_f)$	+2.99	+2.21	+0.84	—
	$(s-s_f)10^3$	+0.15	−1.20	−2.00	—
2000 (635.82)	$(v-v_f)10^5$	−11.0	−10.8	−19.5	−32.6
	$(h-h_f)$	+5.97	+4.51	+2.03	−2.5
	$(s-s_f)10^3$	+0.22	−2.39	−4.57	−4.3
3000 (695.36)	$(v-v_f)10^5$	−16.3	−16.0	−30.0	−87.9
	$(h-h_f)$	+9.00	+6.76	+3.33	−6.9
	$(s-s_f)10^3$	+0.28	−3.56	−7.03	−12.4

* Abridged from *Thermodynamic Properties of Steam*, by J. H. Keenan and F. G. Keyes, published by John Wiley & Sons, Inc., 1936.

EXAMPLE 3·11.　Determine the specific volume of water at 3000 psia, 400 F.

Solution.　Since 400 F is lower than the saturation temperature corresponding to 3000 psia, water at 3000 psia, 400 F, is a compressed liquid. From Table 3·5 for a pressure of 3000 psia and a temperature of 400 F, a value of −30.0 is found for $(v-v_f)10^5$; therefore

$$(v - v_f)10^5 = -30.0 \text{ cu ft/lb}$$

Solving for v, the specific volume of the compressed liquid, gives

$$v = v_f - 30.0(10^{-5})$$

The value for v_f is the volume of a saturated liquid at a temperature of 400 F and is 0.018639 cu ft/lb, as shown at the top of the table. Substituting the value for v_f and solving results in

$$v = 0.018639 - 0.000300 = 0.018339 \text{ cu ft/lb}$$

This value shows that water at 400 F in this pressure range is almost incompressible, since the change in volume for a pressure difference of approximately 2750 psia amounts to only about 3 parts in 186.

EXAMPLE 3·12.　Determine the enthalpy of water at 2000 psia, 200 F.

Solution.　It is quickly recognized that this is a compressed liquid state. Reference to Table 3·5 gives

$$h - h_f = 4.51 \text{ B/lb}$$

Then　　　　$h = h_f + (h - h_f) = 167.99 + 4.51 = 172.50 \text{ B/lb}$

EXAMPLE 3·13. Fill in the blanks in the following table for the properties of water. (The given property values are in bold-face type.)

	p, psia	T, F	x, %	v, cu ft/lb	h, B/lb
(a)	30	300	M	14.816	1189.3
(b)	30	250.33	70	9.6273	880.5
(c)	247.31	400	74.9	1.400	994
(d)	1000	690	M	0.600	1318.5
(e)	3000	200	M	0.01647	174.75
(f)	14.696	212	I	I	I
(g)	24.969	240	72.7	11.87	900
(h)	430	700	M	1.53	1361
(i)	3600	350	M	0.01769	327.0
(j)	280	500	M	1.9047	1260

Solution. Values found from the steam tables are inserted in the table above in italics. In a few cases, simple computations similar to those in previous examples were made. *M* denotes *meaningless* and *I* denotes *indeterminate*.

As an example of tables presented in slightly different format from the steam tables, see Tables A·4 and A·5 for ammonia in the appendix. In addition to tables of properties, charts are used for the same purpose. Data can usually be read more rapidly from charts than from tables at some sacrifice in accuracy. Coordinates commonly used for charts of physical properties are enthalpy–entropy, enthalpy–volume, temperature–entropy, and pressure–enthalpy. The use of some of these charts will be discussed following the introduction of the property entropy.

EXAMPLE 3·14. Fill in the blanks in the following table for the properties of ammonia. (The given property values are in bold-face type.)

	p, psia	T, F	x	v, cu ft/lb	h, B/lb
(a)	200	150	M	1.740	671.8
(b)	5.55	−60	15	6.73	67.2
(c)	153	80	I	I	I
(d)	128.4	100	M	2.534	650
(e)	5	−63.11	20.3	10.03	100
(f)	260	130	M	1.22	647.8

Solution. Values found from the ammonia tables in the appendix are inserted in the above table in italics. *M* denotes *meaningless* and *I* denotes *indeterminate*.

EXAMPLE 3·15. Saturated liquid ammonia at 200 psia enters an expansion valve in a refrigerating system and is throttled to 40 psia. What is the state of the ammonia leaving the valve?

Solution. For the flow through a valve, work = 0. Assuming that this is a throttling process as defined in Art. 3·6, $q = 0$ and the change in kinetic energy is negligibly small.

The first law applied to the steady flow through the valve then reduces to

$$h_2 = h_1$$

At the inlet (section 1), the ammonia is saturated liquid, so

$$h_2 = h_1 = h_{f1} = 150.9 \text{ B/lb}$$

This value of enthalpy is greater than h_f and less than h_g at 40 psia; therefore, the ammonia leaving the valve is a liquid–vapor mixture. Its quality is

$$x_2 = \frac{h_2 - h_{f2}}{h_{fg2}} = \frac{150.9 - 55.6}{559.8} = 17.0 \text{ per cent}$$

This indicates that 17 per cent of the ammonia evaporated during the throttling process. The final state is 40 psia, 17 per cent quality.

3·9 Summary

This chapter has dealt, chiefly in a qualitative manner, with some of the physical properties of pure substances. In summary, some of the terms introduced in this chapter are listed or discussed below.

A *pure substance* is a substance which is chemically homogeneous and fixed in chemical composition.

A *phase* is any homogeneous part of a system which is physically distinct and is separated from other parts of the system by definite boundary surfaces.

Two phases of a pure substance can exist together in equilibrium only if their pressure and temperature bear a certain fixed relationship to each other. The corresponding values of pressure and temperature under which two phases can coexist in equilibrium are called the *saturation pressure* and the *saturation temperature*. Any phase existing under these saturation conditions is called a *saturated* phase.

Liquid existing at a temperature lower than the saturation temperature corresponding to its pressure (or, in other words, at a pressure higher than the saturation pressure corresponding to its temperature) is called *compressed liquid* or *subcooled liquid*. Vapor existing at a temperature higher than the saturation temperature corresponding to its pressure (or at a pressure lower than the saturation pressure corresponding to its temperature) is called *superheated vapor* or *gas*.

The condition of pressure and temperature under which three phases of a pure substance can coexist in equilibrium is called the *triple point* or *triple-phase point* of the substance.

For every substance, at low pressures the density of the saturated vapor is much less than that of saturated liquid. As pressure increases, the difference in densities of the two phases decreases until at the *critical pressure* and the *critical temperature* the difference in density between the two phases becomes zero. All other properties also reach the same value for both saturated liquid and saturated vapor as the *critical point* is reached. The critical point is therefore the limiting condition of pressure and temperature under which separate liquid and vapor phases can be distinguished.

Various property diagrams are useful in showing the characteristics of a substance. The pressure–temperature diagram which shows the limiting pressures and temperatures for the existence of the various phases of a substance is called a *phase diagram*. Three-dimensional property diagrams are occasionally used.

The *quality* of a liquid–vapor mixture is defined as the fraction by mass of vapor in a mixture of liquid and vapor. Properties of a liquid–vapor mixture may be found by relations such as

$$v = v_f + x v_{fg}$$

$$h = h_f + x h_{fg}$$

where x is the quality, the subscript f refers to saturated liquid, and the subscript fg refers to the difference between the value of a property for a saturated vapor and for a saturated liquid at the same pressure.

Specific heat at constant pressure c_p and specific heat at constant volume c_v are defined as

$$c_p \equiv \left(\frac{\partial h}{\partial T} \right)_p \quad \text{and} \quad c_v \equiv \left(\frac{\partial u}{\partial T} \right)_v$$

Both c_p and c_v are properties. They are not defined in terms of heat. It can be shown by means of the first law and these definitions of specific heat that for both open and closed systems

$$\delta Q = m c_p \, dT \quad \text{for } \textit{frictionless} \text{ constant-pressure processes}$$
$$\delta Q = m c_v \, dT \quad \text{for } \textit{frictionless} \text{ constant-volume processes}$$

(It is from these special relations that c_p and c_v have been given the name specific heats, even though c_p and c_v are used in many other relations which do not involve heat.)

Latent heat of vaporization is defined as

$$h_{fg} \equiv h_g - h_f$$

where h_g and h_f are the specific enthalpies of saturated vapor and saturated liquid, respectively, at the same pressure.

For many substances the relationships among properties over a wide range cannot be expressed by simple equations. Therefore, the properties of these substances must generally be obtained from tables based on experimental measurements and extensive thermodynamic calculations.

REFERENCES

3·1 M. W. Zemansky, *Heat and Thermodynamics*, McGraw-Hill Book Co., 4th ed., 1957, arts. 11·1 to 11·6.

3·2 F. W. Sears, *Thermodynamics, the Kinetic Theory of Gases, and Statistical Mechanics*, Addison-Wesley Publishing Co., 2d ed., 1953, art. 6·1.

3·3 J. K. Roberts and A. R. Miller, *Heat and Thermodynamics*, Interscience Publishers, 4th ed., 1951, chapters 8 and 9.

For thermodynamic property data

3·4 J. H. Keenan and F. G. Keyes, *Thermodynamic Properties of Steam*, John Wiley & Sons, 1936.

3·5 *Steam Tables*, Combustion Engineering Co., 1940.

3·6 F. O. Ellenwood and C. O. Mackey, *Thermodynamic Charts*, John Wiley & Sons, 2d ed., 1944.

3·7 *Kent's Mechanical Engineers' Handbook*, Power Volume, John Wiley & Sons, 12th ed., 1950.

3·8 *Marks' Mechanical Engineers' Handbook*, McGraw-Hill Book Co., 6th ed., 1958.

3·9 *Handbook of Chemistry and Physics*, Chemical Rubber Publishing Co., published yearly.

3·10 *Chemical Engineers' Handbook*. McGraw-Hill Book Co., 3rd ed., 1950.

PROBLEMS

3·1 Which of the systems described below are comprised of pure substances during the described processes? (The containers and partitions are not parts of the systems.)

(*a*) A tank contains oxygen and nitrogen on opposite sides of a partition. The partition is removed (or punctured).

(*b*) A tank contains nitrogen at 20 psia on one side of a partition and nitrogen at 15 psia on the other side. The partition is removed.

(*c*) Air is contained in a tank. Also within the tank is a covered dish containing water. The cover is removed from the dish.

(*d*) A tank contains liquid water and steam. The tank is cooled so that some of the steam condenses.

3·2 What are the saturation temperatures corresponding to the following pressures for nitrogen: 100, 200, and 400 psia?

3·3 If the pressure is 600 psia, what is the corresponding saturation temperature for chlorine?

3·4 Is it possible to have ice and water at a pressure of 10,000 psia and a temperature of 10 F?

3·5 At what temperature would ice at a pressure of 3000 psia melt?

3·6 Would it be possible to maintain ice at a pressure of 8000 psia and a temperature of 28 F?

3·7 Wet steam at a given pressure has a quality of 90 per cent. If the specific volumes of the saturated liquid and vapor are 0.0235 and 0.2765 cu ft/lb respectively, compute the specific volume of the wet steam.

3·8 It has been suggested that the liquid–vapor saturation curve of a pure substance can be represented by an equation of the form $p = p_0 e^{-\alpha/T}$, where T is absolute temperature and p_0 and α are constants. (Reference: J. A. Eldridge, *The Physical Basis of Things*, McGraw-Hill, 1934, p. 83.) How well does such an equation fit the data for water?

3·9 What are some of the substances besides water which expand on freezing? In what applications is this characteristic important?

3·10 Sketch a phase (pT) diagram for water, and then sketch on this diagram a few lines of (a) constant volume, (b) constant enthalpy.

3·11 On a pv diagram, how many states of a system can be represented by a single point on the triple-phase line?

3·12 Sketch a Tv diagram, and identify the various lines and regions on it for (a) H_2O, (b) CO_2. Show constant-pressure lines for pressures below the triple-phase value, between the triple phase and critical values, and above the critical value.

3·13 A three-phase mixture of H_2O consists of 40 per cent solid, 50 per cent liquid, and 10 per cent vapor by mass. Explain how the point representing this mixture is located on a uv diagram and on a ph diagram.

3·14 Sketch a curve of T vs. u for constant-pressure heating of a substance which passes through solid, liquid, and vapor phases.

3·15 A container of nitrogen leaks at a rate of 0.010 oz in 30 years. What is the average number of molecules escaping per second?

3·16 Show that, for a frictionless constant-pressure process and only for such a process, $q = \int c_p \, dT$ for either a closed system or for a steady-flow system.

3·17 Critical temperature is sometimes defined as the temperature above which the liquid phase of a substance does not exist. Comment on this.

3·18 In the solution of part d of Example 3·1 the statement is made that the second term in $\int_1^2 [c_p \, dT + (\partial h/\partial p)_T \, dp]$ is zero because $p_2 = p_1$. Is it generally true that $\int_1^2 f(x) \, dx = 0$ if $x_2 = x_1$? Explain.

3·19 Using the steam tables, tabulate the following properties of saturated liquid at 100, 300, 500, and 700 F: (a) pressure, (b) specific volume, and (c) enthalpy.

3·20 A closed tank contains 20 cu ft of dry saturated steam at a gage pressure of 140.3 psig. (a) What is its temperature? (b) How many pounds of steam does the tank contain? Barometric pressure equals 14.7 psia.

3·21 Steam at 160 psia has an enthalpy of 1100 B/lb. What is its quality?

3·22 Steam at 380 F contains 3 per cent moisture. What is its specific volume?

3·23 A tank having a volume of 1 cu ft contains 80 per cent saturated water by volume and 20 per cent saturated vapor at a temperature of 80 F. If the liquid and vapor were agitated until thoroughly mixed, what would be the quality of the mixture?

3·24 Determine the enthalpy and specific volume of 1 lb of water at a temperature of 400 F and a pressure of 2000 psia.

3·25 Steam at a pressure of 100 psia is found to have a specific volume of 3.9888 cu ft/lb. Determine the temperature and condition of the steam.

3·26 Steam at a pressure of 200 psia was found to have a specific volume of 2.1736 cu ft/lb. Determine the temperature, enthalpy, and condition of the steam.

3·27 Determine the specific volume and enthalpy of 1 lb of water at a temperature of 200 F and a pressure of 1000 psia.

3·28 Steam at 160 psia and 95 per cent quality is formed from saturated feedwater at 160 F. What is the difference in enthalpy between the two states?

3·29 One pound of water at 180 F is converted into steam at 660 F under 200 psia pressure. How much is the enthalpy changed?

3·30 Steam under 380 psia leaves a boiler carrying 4 per cent moisture. After it passes the superheater, the pressure is unchanged but the temperature has risen to 800 F. What is the difference in enthalpy between the two states? What is the change in specific volume?

3·31 A closed tank contains 200 cu ft of dry saturated ammonia at 80 psia. Compute the enthalpy.

3·32 The enthalpy of sulfur dioxide at a temperature of 60 F equals 160 B/lb. Compute the quality.

3·33 If wet sulfur dioxide vapor at a pressure of 33.45 psia has a quality of 80 per cent, compute the enthalpy per pound.

3·34 The enthalpy of carbon dioxide at a temperature of −40 F equals 70 B/lb. Compute the quality.

3·35 Wet carbon dioxide vapor at a pressure of 652.7 psia has a quality of 87 per cent. Compute the enthalpy per pound.

3·36 If the enthalpy for carbon dioxide is 80 B/lb at a temperature of 50 F, what is the quality?

3·37 The enthalpy of ammonia at a pressure of 160 psia is 707.9 B/lb. Compute the internal energy per pound.

3·38 Determine the enthalpy of ammonia vapor having a quality of 40 per cent at a pressure of 100 psia.

3·39 What are the enthalpy and specific-volume values for ammonia vapor at a pressure and temperature of 120 psia and 250 F, respectively?

3·40 Determine the internal energy per pound for ammonia vapor at a pressure and temperature of 150 psia and 230 F.

3·41 Determine the enthalpy and internal energy for ammonia vapor at a pressure and temperature of 135 psia and 130 F.

3·42 Determine by means of the Keenan and Keyes compressed liquid table the enthalpy of water at 5500 psia, 700 F. Can this value be found in the superheated vapor table? Is water at 5500 psia, 700 F, a compressed liquid or a superheated vapor? Is water at 5500 psia, 750 F, a liquid or a vapor?

3·43 Sketch a pT diagram for liquid water, showing constant-enthalpy lines of $h = 100$ B/lb and $h = 600$ B/lb.

3·44 The Keenan and Keyes steam tables are based on $h_f = 0$ at 32 F. What is the corresponding value of u_f at 32 F?

3·45 Ice at 32 F on the outside of a tube is melted to liquid at 32 F by a transfer of heat from water flowing inside the tube. Water enters the tube at 100 F and leaves at 80 F. Latent heat of fusion of water at 32 F is 143.3 B/lb. (a) How much warm water is needed per pound of ice? (b) Show how the latent heat of fusion given above can be verified from data given in *Thermodynamic Properties of Steam* by Keenan and Keyes (including Table 5).

3·46 Calculate $(\partial u/\partial v)_T$ for steam at 100 psia, 350 F.

3·47 For steam at 400 psia, 520 F, determine from the steam tables approximate values of $(\partial h/\partial T)_p$, $(\partial h/\partial T)_v$, and $(\partial p/\partial T)_v$. Why are the values you obtain approximate? Are these point functions or path functions? Is dh/dT a point or path function?

3·48 A method of obtaining a low pressure in a sealed vessel is to fill the vessel with steam before sealing, seal, and then condense the steam. A vessel having a volume of 2 cu ft is filled with dry saturated steam at 14.7 psia. The vessel is sealed and then chilled to 90 F. (a) What is the final pressure? (b) Sketch pv and pT diagrams of the process, showing saturation lines on each diagram. (c) Calculate the amount of heat added to or taken from the steam.

3·49 The water level in a storage tank 9 ft high is regulated by a float-controlled valve. The water level is indicated by a simple gage glass 8 ft long on the side of the tank. When storing cold water, the gage glass shows that the water level is maintained 8 ft above the tank bottom by the float-controlled valve, but, when hot (200 F) water is in the tank, the gage shows that the same control device maintains the water level 3 in. lower. How do you account for this?

3·50 Three pounds of steam at 200 psia, 90 per cent quality, is heated in a closed-system frictionless process until the temperature is 500 F. Calculate the amount of heat transferred if the process is at (a) constant pressure (b) constant volume.

3·51 Steam at 14.7 psia, 300 F, is contained in a closed rigid vessel which has a volume of 1.0 cu ft. How much heat must be removed in order to lower the steam pressure to 10 psia?

3·52 One tenth of a pound of steam initially dry and saturated at 30 psia is heated in a closed system to a final condition of 40 psia, 400 F. Work done on the steam during the process amounts to 560 ft-lb. Calculate the amount of heat transferred per pound of steam.

3·53 One fifth of a pound of ammonia initially dry and saturated at 70 psia is heated in a closed system to a final condition of 100 psia, 150 F. Work done on the ammonia during the process amounts to 5000 ft-lb. Calculate the amount of heat transferred per pound of ammonia.

3·54 In a closed system, steam initially at 67 psia, 80 per cent quality, expands to 40 psia, 300 F. During the expansion, heat is added to the steam in the amount of 231.0 B/lb. Calculate the work.

3·55 One-half pound of dry saturated steam at 20 psia is heated in a closed rigid container until its temperature is 440 F. Determine the amount of heat added to the steam.

3·56 One tenth of a pound of steam at 14.0 psia, 80 per cent quality, is contained in a rigid thermally insulated vessel. A paddle wheel inside the vessel is turned by an external motor until the steam is at 20 psia. Determine the amount of work done on the steam.

3·57 One tenth of a pound of dry saturated steam at 18.0 psia is contained in a closed rigid tank. Work in the amount of 2.0 B is done on the steam by a paddle wheel while heat is transferred to or from the steam. The final pressure of the steam is 27.0 psia. Sketch a pv diagram of the process, and calculate the heat transferred.

3·58 In a closed system, dry saturated steam at 100 psia is heated in a constant-volume process until its pressure is 174 psia. It is then expanded adiabatically to 100 psia, 700 F, and later cooled to the saturation temperature at constant pressure. Calculate the net work done. State any assumptions made.

3·59 Two tenths of a pound of steam initially dry and saturated at 10 psia (condition 1) is heated at constant pressure until its volume is 9.0 cu ft (condition 2). It is then heated at constant volume until it is at 14.0 psia (condition 3). Calculate the total heat added per pound of steam between conditions 1 and 3.

3·60 (a) Solve Prob. 3·59 for a frictionless steady-flow system. ($v_2 = 45.0$ cu ft/lb and process 2-3 is at constant specific volume.) (b) Is the amount of work done the same in Probs. 3·59 and 3·60?

3·61 Steam enters a turbine with negligible velocity at 1000 psia, 1000 F, and leaves at 1 psia, 10 per cent moisture, with a velocity of 700 fps. The flow rate is 50,000 lb/hr, and the power output is 9300 hp. The cross-sectional area of the exhaust opening is 5.96 sq ft. Determine the heat loss from the steam passing through the turbine in B/lb.

3·62 Steam flows steadily through a turbine at a rate of 2000 lb/hr, entering at 100 psia, 400 F, with negligible velocity and leaving at 1 psia, 90 per cent quality, through an opening of 0.333 sq ft cross-sectional area. The turbine shaft speed is 7000 rpm, and the power output is 150 hp. Calculate the heat transfer in B/lb.

3·63 Steam enters a turbine at 40 psia, 300 F, with negligible velocity and is exhausted at 1.0 psia with a velocity of 500 fps. The flow rate is 40,000 lb/hr, and the turbine power output is 2000 hp. The flow is adiabatic. Determine the quality (if wet) or temperature (if superheated) of the exhaust steam.

3·64 Calculate the throttle temperature required for a steam turbine which is to develop 10,000 kw from a flow rate of 95,000 lb/hr if the steam enters at 600 psia and leaves at 1.0 in. of mercury absolute containing 10 per cent moisture. Assume that there is negligible heat transfer and negligible change in kinetic energy.

3·65 Steam enters a turbine at 400 psia, 600 F, and leaves at 2.0 in. of mercury ($h = 1110$ B/lb). The flow rate is 80,000 lb/hr. If the inlet opening has a cross-sectional area of 0.2 sq ft, what exhaust opening area is required in order to have the change in kinetic energy between inlet and exhaust not more than 1 B/lb?

3·66 One hundred cubic feet per minute of steam at 20 psia and 95 per cent quality enters a compressor and is discharged at 100 psia and 500 F. If the amount of heat transfer is negligible, what is the power consumption of the machine?

3·67 Saturated liquid water at 200 psia is throttled at a steady rate of 300 lb/hr to a pressure of 14.7 psia. What fraction of the water vaporizes during this throttling process? What is the density of the H_2O leaving the throttle valve?

3·68 Steam flows at a rate of 3.59 lb/sec through a tube which has a constant cross-sectional area of 0.05 sq ft. The steam enters at 70 psia, 90 per cent quality, with a velocity of 400 fps, and leaves at 65 psia, 800 F. Calculate the amount of heat added per pound of steam.

3·69 A nozzle discharges steam at 25 psia, 340 F, through an exit area of 1.0 sq in. The flow rate is measured as 0.728 lb/sec. Inlet pressure is 60 psia. Assuming that the flow is adiabatic and that the kinetic energy of the steam at inlet is negligibly small, determine the inlet temperature.

3·70 Ammonia at 20 psia, 90 per cent quality, enters a compressor at a rate of 12 lb/min. Power input to the compressor is 46.7 hp, and heat is removed from the ammonia during compression at a rate of 330 B/min. Discharge pressure is 200 psia. Determine the discharge temperature.

3·71 Carbon dioxide enters a heat exchanger at −40 F, 30 per cent quality, and leaves as dry saturated vapor at the same temperature. Calculate (a) the heat added in

B/lb, and (*b*) the change in internal energy in B/lb. (See the list of references at the end of Chapter 3 for sources of data.)

3·72 Steam at 16 psia containing 60 per cent moisture enters a condenser through a flow area of 0.15 sq ft with a velocity of 700 fps. The condensate leaves at 16 psia, 100 F. Calculate the heat transfer in B/hr.

3·73 Carbon dioxide at −5 F containing 10 per cent moisture enters a condenser through a flow area of 0.05 sq ft with a velocity of 400 fps. The condensate leaves with a low velocity at 281 psia, −15 F. Calculate the heat transfer in B/hr.

3·74 A tank of 10 cu ft volume is half filled with liquid water, and the remainder is filled by vapor. Heat is added until one half of the liquid is evaporated while an automatic valve lets saturated vapor escape at such a rate that the pressure is held constant at 500 psia. Determine the heat transfer.

3·75 Solve Prob. 3·74 for a pressure of 3000 psia.

CHAPTER 4

Ideal Gases

An equation which expresses the relationship among pressure, specific volume, and temperature of a substance is called an *equation of state*. The *pvT* relationship for most substances is quite complex, so that accurate equations of state for wide ranges of pressure and temperature have been developed for only a few substances. Experience shows that gases, particularly those of low molecular weight at low pressure and relatively high temperature, can often be represented by a very simple equation of state, $pv = RT$, where R is a constant for each gas. The relation $pv = RT$ is known as the ideal-gas equation of state. This chapter discusses the ideal-gas equation of state, some of its implications regarding properties other than p, v, and T, and its application to real gases.

4·1 The ideal gas

An ideal gas is defined as one for which the equation of state is

$$pv = RT \qquad (4·1)$$

where R is a different constant for each gas. R is called the *gas constant* for each gas and has units such as ft-lb$_f$/lb$_m$-R or B/lb$_m$-R. R is given by

$$R = \frac{R_u}{M}$$

where R_u is the *universal gas constant* which has the same value for all gases and M is the molecular weight.* The value of R_u expressed in various units is

$$R_u = 1544 \text{ ft-lb}_f/\text{mole-R} = 1.986 \text{ B/mole-R} = 1.986 \text{ cal/g mole-K}$$

---

* Recall that molecular *weight* is a misnomer. Molecular *mass* would be a more accurate name for this quantity which is independent of gravitational effects; but long usage has firmly established the name molecular weight.

TABLE 4·1

R Values for Several Gases

Gas	Molecular Weight M	Gas Constant R, ft-lb$_f$/lb$_m$-R
Acetylene	26.04	59.35
Air	28.966	53.35
Argon	39.944	38.69
Carbon dioxide	44.011	35.11
Carbon monoxide	28.010	55.17
Ethane	30.07	51.40
Helium	4.003	386.2
Hydrogen	2.016	766.53
Methane	16.04	96.35
Nitrogen	28.016	55.16
Oxygen	32.000	48.29

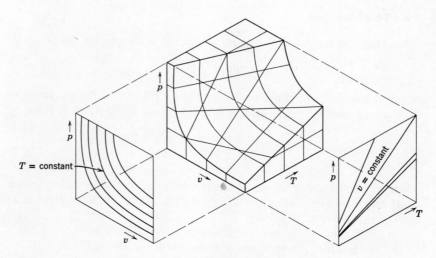

Fig. 4·1 *pvT* surface for an ideal gas.

The ideal-gas equation of state can thus be written in various forms such as

$$pv = RT \qquad pV = NR_uT$$

$$pV = mRT \qquad pV = \frac{mR_uT}{M}$$

$$p = \rho RT \qquad pV = NMRT$$

where N is the number of moles of the gas and the other symbols are as previously defined. R values for several gases are given in Table 4·1.

An ideal gas is a hypothetical substance because we define it simply as a substance which follows the equation of state $pv = RT$. Our definition is not based on any assumption that such a substance actually exists. Historically, the concept of an ideal gas resulted from the work of Boyle, Charles, and Gay-Lussac, but you should remember that they measured properties of real gases. Although both their work and other later work indicate that for real gases at low pressure and relatively high temperature the equation of state is very nearly $pv = RT$, our use of $pv = RT$ for an ideal gas does not depend on the accuracy of any measurements: We *define* an ideal gas as one which follows $pv = RT$.

A pvT surface for an ideal gas is shown in Fig. 4·1.

4·2   Real gases and the ideal-gas equation of state

How closely does $pv = RT$ represent the characteristics of real gases? This is an important question. It is convenient to use such a simple equation of state, but we must know how much accuracy we sacrifice for the convenience. First we give a qualitative answer: Usually $pv = RT$ tends to be more accurate for real gases

1. As molecular weight decreases,
2. As pressure decreases,
3. As temperature increases.

This is a statement of a general trend, but it cannot be relied on in all ranges of pressure and temperature. (Of course, if the pressure of a real gas is decreased at constant temperature to the extent that the molecules are so far apart that we cannot treat the gas as a continuous or homogeneous substance, then the state cannot be described in terms of properties such as p, v, and T and a pvT relation is meaningless.) A complete quantitative answer to the question regarding the accuracy of $pv = RT$ for real gases is given in the next chapter, but at this point it is well to observe, for example, that, for air at room temperature, the error in $pv = RT$ is less than 1 per cent for pressures as high as 400 psia. For air at 1 atm, the error in $pv = RT$ is less than 1 per cent for temperatures as low as -200 F. For hydrogen at 1 atm, the error in $pv = RT$ is less than 1 per cent for temperatures as low as -370 F. For the present let it suffice to say that $pv = RT$ represents the characteristics of many real gases accurately enough for many engineering calculations as long as the gases are at pressures well below their critical pressures and at temperatures well above their critical temperatures. In the next chapter we will investigate this point more thoroughly.

EXAMPLE 4·1.   Compute the pressure of 6 lb of nitrogen at 32 F occupying a volume of 12 cu ft.

Solution.   Assume that nitrogen under these conditions behaves as an ideal gas. Then

$$p = \frac{mRT}{V} = \frac{mR_uT}{VM} = \frac{6[\text{lb}_m]1544[\text{ft-lb}_f/\text{mole-R}]492[\text{R}]}{12[\text{ft}^3]28[\text{lb}_m/\text{mole}]}$$

$$= 13{,}560 \text{ psfa} = 94 \text{ psia}$$

The pressure is low enough so that our assumption that $pv = RT$ holds is reasonable.

EXAMPLE 4·2.   Determine the pressure of hydrogen at 32 F which has a density of 0.00155 slug/cu ft.

Solution.   Assume that the pressure is low enough so that the hydrogen follows the ideal-gas equation of state. Then

$$p = \frac{mRT}{V} = \rho RT = \frac{\rho R_uT}{M}$$

For consistency of units we must express the density ρ in lb_m/cu ft and the molecular "weight" M in lb_m/mole or ρ in slugs/cu ft and M in slugs/mole. We have

$$\rho = 0.00155 \text{ slug/cu ft} = 0.00155(32.2) \text{ lb}_m/\text{cu ft}$$

$$M = 2.016 \text{ lb}_m/\text{mole} = \frac{2.016}{32.2} \text{ slug/mole}$$

Either way, substitution of numerical values gives

$$p = \frac{\rho R_uT}{M} = \frac{0.00155(32.2)1544(492)}{2.016} = 18{,}840 \text{ psfa} = 131 \text{ psia}$$

At 131 psia, 32 F, hydrogen does follow the ideal-gas equation of state so that our assumption is justified.

4·3   The ideal-gas thermometer scale

In Art. 1·12 it was pointed out that different real gases used in constant-volume gas thermometers give results which agree with each other more and more closely as the pressure at any one temperature is reduced. Also, as the pressure of a real gas approaches zero, the gas behaves more and more like an ideal gas. Thus the gas thermometer scale defined by the extrapolation of real gas behavior to the condition of zero pressure is called the ideal-gas thermometer scale. The ideal-gas thermometer scale defined in this manner does not depend on the properties of any one gas but on the properties of gases in general. The defining equation then is

$$\frac{T_2}{T_1} = \left(\frac{p_2}{p_1}\right)_{v=\text{const}, \, p_1 \to 0} \quad \text{or} \quad \frac{T_2}{T_1} = \left(\frac{v_2}{v_1}\right)_{p=\text{const}, \, p \to 0}$$

The ideal-gas thermometer scale can also be defined in terms of the behavior of an ideal gas without reference to a real-gas thermometer. Let an ideal gas be defined as a substance which behaves so that

$$\left(\frac{p_{T2}}{p_{T1}}\right)_{v=\text{const}} = \left(\frac{v_{T2}}{v_{T1}}\right)_{p=\text{const}} \tag{a}$$

where the subscripts $T1$ and $T2$ denote properties measured at temperatures T_1 and T_2. Notice that no scale of temperature nor any numerical value even for T_1 or T_2 is needed in order to define an ideal gas in this manner. Then we can *define* the ideal-gas thermometer scale by either

$$\frac{T_2}{T_1} \equiv \left(\frac{p_{T2}}{p_{T1}}\right)_{v=\text{const}} \quad \text{or} \quad \frac{T_2}{T_1} \equiv \left(\frac{v_{T2}}{v_{T1}}\right)_{p=\text{const}}$$

where the pressures or volumes must be those of a substance which obeys equation (a). The temperature scale or thermometer scale so defined does not depend on the characteristics of any real substance but only on those of a hypothetical substance—an ideal gas. For purposes of practical thermometry, one must then search for a substance which behaves like the hypothetical ideal gas. Such a substance can be identified by its behavior in accordance with equation (a).

The ideal-gas temperature scale depends either on the characteristics of gases in general as their pressure approaches zero or on the characteristics of a hypothetical ideal gas. At this point it still appears that the ideal-gas temperature scale, since it depends on physical properties of some substance or substances, is no better than one based on the expansion of mercury or on the change in electrical resistance of some material. It will be shown in Chapter 8, however, that the ideal-gas scale is equivalent to one that is entirely independent of physical properties.

4·4   Internal energy and enthalpy of ideal gases

From the first and second laws of thermodynamics it can be proved that, for any substance which follows the equation of state $pv = RT$,

$$\left(\frac{\partial u}{\partial v}\right)_T = 0$$

(The proof is given in Example 10·1 which follows the introduction of the second law.) This means that the internal energy of an ideal gas is a function of temperature only, because, as long as T is constant, u is constant. This is an important fact. It is usually referred to as Joule's law because James Prescott Joule conducted a series of experiments which indicated at first that the internal energy of a *real* gas is a function of temperature only. Further work by Joule and others showed that only for an ideal gas is internal energy a function of temperature alone, but Joule's name is usually connected with this fact on account of his original experiments.

If the internal energy of some substance is a function of temperature only, then a process with $q = 0$ and $w = 0$—since the first law would show $\Delta u = 0$—would be a process with $\Delta T = 0$. Thus the interdependence of u and T could be checked experimentally by means of an adiabatic system. However, perfect thermal insulation is not needed, because, if $\Delta T = 0$ and the surroundings are at the initial temperature of the system, there will be no heat transfer because there will be no temperature difference between the system and the surroundings. Thus, to check his hypothesis that $u = f(T)$, Joule submerged two tanks connected by a stopcock in a tank of water. One tank was filled with air at high pressure and the other was evacuated. The air, the tanks, and the surrounding water were allowed to come to the same temperature. Then the stopcock between the tanks was opened to let air pass from one tank to the other. There was of course no work done by the air. Joule observed no change in the temperature of the water bath. From this he concluded that no heat was transferred to or from the air, and hence—since there was also no work done—the internal energy of the air did not change. Since there was no heat exchange between the air and the water, the temperature of the air must have remained constant, even though the volume changed. Thus $(\partial u/\partial v)_T = 0$, and the internal energy of the gas is a function of temperature only.

If in an experiment like Joule's the temperature of the water changes, does this prove that the internal energy of the gas under study is not a function of temperature only? Yes, it does so conclusively. Suppose the water temperature rises. Then there must have been a heat transfer to the water from the gas, and the gas temperature must have risen above that of the water during the expansion process. Since heat was removed from the gas and no work was done, the internal energy of the gas must have decreased. This expansion process is shown as process 1-2 on the uv and Tv diagrams of Fig. 4·2. In order to restore the gas which finally fills both tanks to its initial temperature, heat must be removed. In this constant-volume process, shown as 2-3 in Fig. 4·2, no work is done as heat is removed, and so the internal energy of the gas decreases. Thus, when the gas has been restored to its initial temperature $(T_3 = T_1)$, its internal energy is lower than its initial value $(u_3 < u_1)$. Clearly, the internal energy of a gas which behaves in this manner is not a function of temperature only.

For real gases internal energy is not a function of temperature only, but Joule did not detect a temperature change of the water, because the mass (or, to state the matter completely, the product of mass and specific heat) of the water was so great compared to that of the air that the temperature rise of the water was too small to be detected by his instruments. Joule later ran other experiments with different equipment to show that for real

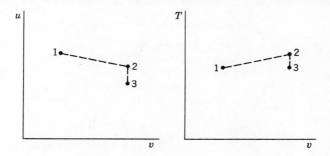

Fig. 4·2   Analysis of Joule's experiment.

gases internal energy is not a function of temperature alone. However, in the ranges of pressure and temperature where $pv = RT$ is sufficiently accurate for real gases, Joule's law holds with the same order of accuracy.

From Joule's law it is easy to establish the relationship between u and T for ideal gases. For any pure substance in the absence of electric, magnetic, and surface tension effects, internal energy is usually a function of any two independent properties. (Recall that a *pure substance* is defined as a substance which is chemically homogeneous and fixed in chemical composition.) For a gas, T and v are certainly independent properties, so we may write

$$u = f(T, v)$$

Then

$$du = \left(\frac{\partial u}{\partial T}\right)_v dT + \left(\frac{\partial u}{\partial v}\right)_T dv$$

Recalling the definition of c_v, we can write

$$du = c_v\, dT + \left(\frac{\partial u}{\partial v}\right)_T dv$$

This equation holds for any process of any pure substance as long as there are no electric, magnetic, or surface tension effects. For an ideal gas, however, Joule's law states that $(\partial u / \partial v)_T = 0$, so that

$$du = c_v \, dT \qquad (4 \cdot 2)$$

for any process of an ideal gas. Since u is a function of T only, then c_v must be a function of T only. For any finite change of state,

$$\Delta u = \int c_v \, dT \qquad (4 \cdot 2)$$

To emphasize that this relationship holds for *all processes* of an ideal gas,

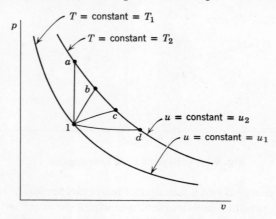

Fig. 4·3   Joule's law: *pv* diagram for an ideal gas.

let us look at the *pv* diagram for an ideal gas shown in Fig. 4·3. In accordance with the equation of state $pv = RT$, the constant-temperature lines are hyperbolas. In accordance with Joule's law, the constant-temperature lines are also lines of constant internal energy. Therefore, $u_a = u_b = u_c = u_d$, and

$$u_a - u_1 = u_b - u_1 = u_c - u_1 = u_d - u_1 = \int_1^2 c_v \, dT \qquad (4 \cdot 2)$$

No matter what path is followed by an ideal gas between a state 1 and any state at a temperature T_2, the change in internal energy per unit mass is given by $\int_1^2 c_v \, dT$. This point troubles many students because they see c_v, which we (unfortunately) call specific heat at constant volume, and then conclude *incorrectly* that equation 4·2 holds only for constant-volume processes. The relationship which *is* restricted to *constant-volume friction-less* processes is $\delta q = c_v \, dT$ (see Art. 3·5). In Fig. 4·3, $q = \int_1^2 c_v \, dT$ only for a frictionless process along the constant volume path 1-*a*. For the other paths shown, q is different for each path. For the *change in internal energy of an ideal gas*, however, the relation $du = c_v\, dT$ applies to *all processes*.

As mentioned earlier, classical thermodynamics does not depend on any assumptions regarding the microscopic structure of matter. Molecules are not considered in classical thermodynamics because their existence has no bearing on the first or second law or on the deductions made from these laws. A consideration of the molecular picture of an ideal gas, however, helps in the understanding of Joule's law. Before discussing molecules, let us first consider a body which has a mass of one pound. At least at some locations on the surface of the earth this body weighs one pound, and the work required to lift it one foot is one foot-pound. Thus, as the body is moved one foot farther from the earth, its potential energy increases by one foot-pound. This same body when 100 miles above the surface of the earth weighs only about 0.95 lb, so only 0.95 ft-lb of work is required to move it one foot farther from the earth. As the body moves farther from the earth, less work is required to move it through each foot of travel because the gravitational force continues to decrease. The condition is approached in which a negligible amount of work is required to move the body farther from the earth. Then the body can be moved through space with only negligible changes in its potential energy. (This does not mean that its potential energy is zero. If we call its potential energy zero when it is at the surface of the earth, its potential energy at any point above the earth is equal to the total amount of work done in lifting it to that point.) Now consider the molecules of an ideal gas. It is the sum of their potential and kinetic energies which comprises the internal energy of the gas. Like the body and the earth we have just discussed, the molecules of an ideal gas are so far from each other that the gravitational forces among them are negligibly small. The distances between molecules are so great that, even if the distances are halved or doubled, there is no appreciable change in the potential energy of the molecules. Thus the internal energy of an ideal gas is independent of the gas volume. When the gas temperature is changed, however, the velocity and the kinetic energy of the molecules change, so the internal energy of an ideal gas is a function of temperature. If the volume and pressure are changed at constant temperature, there is no change in internal energy because (1) molecular potential energy does not change as the spacing of the molecules varies, and (2) molecular kinetic energy does not change as long as the gas temperature is constant. In the light of such reasoning, an ideal gas is sometimes described microscopically as a gas in which there are no gravitational forces among the molecules.

The enthalpy of an ideal gas is also a function of temperature only. By definition, $h \equiv u + pv$, and for an ideal gas this becomes $h = u + RT$.

Both terms on the right-hand side of this equation depend solely on temperature, so h is a function of temperature only. In order to establish the relationship between h and T for an ideal gas, let us start by considering that for any pure substance as long as pressure and temperature are independent properties

$$h = f(p, T)$$

and
$$dh = \left(\frac{\partial h}{\partial T}\right)_p dT + \left(\frac{\partial h}{\partial p}\right)_T dp$$

Recalling the definition of c_p, we can write this as

$$dh = c_p \, dT + \left(\frac{\partial h}{\partial p}\right)_T dp$$

This equation holds for any process of any pure substance in the absence of electric, magnetic, and surface tension effects. For an ideal gas, however, h is a function of T only, so that $(\partial h/\partial p)_T = 0$, and the last expression for dh reduces to

$$dh = c_p \, dT \tag{4.3}$$

for any process of an ideal gas. Since h is a function of T only, then c_p must be a function of T only. For any finite change of state,

$$\Delta h = \int c_p \, dT \tag{4.3}$$

The quantities $\int c_v \, dT$ and $\int c_p \, dT$ which appear in equations 4·2 and 4·3 can be evaluated by three methods. One method is to use the $c_v T$ and $c_p T$ equations presented in the next article so that the integration can be performed analytically. A special case of this procedure is to use a mean value of c_v or c_p. A second method is to perform the integration graphically by means of $c_v T$ or $c_p T$ charts such as those presented in the next article. The third method is to use published tables of u and h versus temperature, a sample of which is given for air in Table A·8 of the appendix. Notice that this is a single-argument (T) table, because u, h, and the other properties which are there tabulated (and which will be introduced later) are functions of temperature only.

In closing this article, let us repeat for emphasis: *For an ideal gas,*

$$du = c_v \, dT \tag{4.2}$$

and
$$dh = c_p \, dT \tag{4.3}$$

for all processes.

EXAMPLE 4·3. Work in the amount of 15,560 ft-lb is required to compress 2 lb of a certain ideal gas ($c_v = 0.18$ B/lb-F throughout the temperature range involved) in a closed system from an initial pressure of 14.1 psia to a final pressure p_2. The temperature increases by 50 F during the compression. Compute the heat transfer.

Solution. For any process of an ideal gas, $\Delta u = \int c_v\, dT$. Since in this instance c_v is constant throughout the temperature range involved, we have

$$\Delta U = m\, \Delta u = m \int_1^2 c_v\, dT = m c_v (T_2 - T_1)$$

Application of the first law to this closed system gives

$$Q = \Delta U + W$$

Substituting the expression shown above for ΔU,

$$Q = m c_v (T_2 - T_1) + W = 2(0.18)50 - \frac{15,560}{778} = -2\,\text{B}$$

The minus sign indicates that heat was removed from the system.

4·5 Specific heats of ideal gases

It has been pointed out that c_p and c_v of ideal gases are functions of temperature only. We should also observe that for ideal gases the difference $(c_p - c_v)$ is a constant. This can be shown by first noting that the definition of enthalpy, $h \equiv u + pv$, gives us for the case of an ideal gas

$$h = u + RT$$

and, since R is constant,

$$dh = du + R\, dT$$

For any process of an ideal gas $dh = c_p\, dT$ and $du = c_v\, dT$, so that

$$c_p\, dT = c_v\, dT + R\, dT$$

$$c_p = c_v + R$$

$$c_p - c_v = R \tag{4·4}$$

The ratio of the specific heats c_p/c_v is designated by k:

$$k \equiv \frac{c_p}{c_v}$$

Combining equation 4·4 and the definition of k gives

$$c_p = \frac{Rk}{k-1} \quad \text{and} \quad c_v = \frac{R}{k-1}$$

Specific heat data for real gases are usually obtained most accurately by

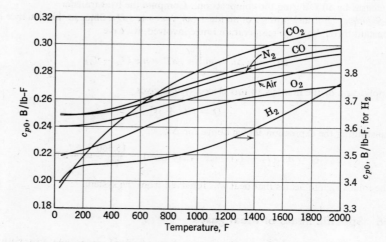

Fig. 4·4 c_{p0} for six gases. Data from *Tables of Thermal Properties of Gases*, National Bureau of Standards Circular 564, 1955.

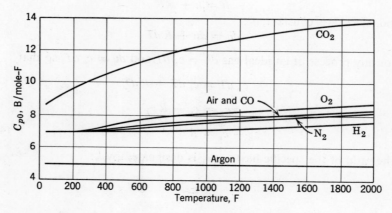

Fig. 4·5 C_{p0} for seven gases. Data from *Tables of Thermal Properties of Gases*, National Bureau of Standards Circular 564, 1955.

spectroscopic methods which will not be discussed here. As pressure decreases, the behavior of real gases approaches that of ideal gases, and so the specific heats of real gases measured at very low pressures are called either the ideal-gas specific heats or the zero-pressure specific heats. The symbols c_{p0} and $c_{v\infty}$ are often used to indicate that the values concerned are those for zero pressure or for very large specific volume. When dealing only with ideal gases, we omit the subscripts 0 and ∞, but we must

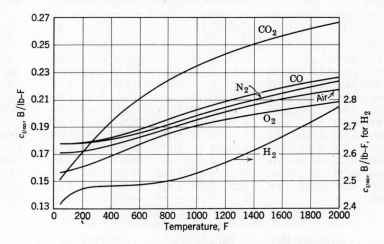

Fig. 4·6 $c_{v\infty}$ for six gases. Data from *Tables of Thermal Properties of Gases*, National Bureau of Standards Circular 564, 1955.

remember that the c_p and c_v values we use for any ideal gas are actually the c_{p0} and $c_{v\infty}$ values for the corresponding real gas.

In Figs. 4·4, 4·5, and 4·6 are presented zero-pressure specific heat data for several gases. Before drawing hasty conclusions from these charts regarding the variation of specific heat with temperature, look carefully at the scales. In particular, notice that a suppressed origin is used, making the variation of specific heat at first glance appear larger than it is.* Specific heat data are also given in Table 4·2.

For ideal gases, changes in internal energy and in enthalpy are represented by areas on c_vT and c_pT diagrams, respectively. An area representing Δh between temperatures T_1 and T_2 is shown in Fig. 4·7. The mean specific

---

* Graphs with suppressed origins make possible larger scales on a given-size sheet of paper so that more accurate reading is possible, but they do have the disadvantage of distortion which is often misleading. Because they exaggerate the variation of one quantity with respect to another, they have been called "gee-whiz graphs." See *How to Lie With Statistics*, by Darrel Huff, W. W. Norton & Co., 1954, chapter 5.

TABLE 4·2

Zero Pressure Specific Heats for Various Gases*
in B/lb-F

Temp., F	Air c_p	Air c_v	Air k	Carbon dioxide, CO_2 c_p	Carbon dioxide, CO_2 c_v	Carbon dioxide, CO_2 k	Carbon monoxide, CO c_p	Carbon monoxide, CO c_v	Carbon monoxide, CO k	Temp., F
32	0.240	0.171	1.401	0.195	0.150	1.300	0.248	0.177	1.400	32
100	0.240	0.172	1.400	0.205	0.160	1.283	0.249	0.178	1.399	100
200	0.241	0.173	1.397	0.217	0.172	1.262	0.249	0.179	1.397	200
300	0.243	0.174	1.394	0.229	0.184	1.246	0.251	0.180	1.394	300
500	0.248	0.179	1.383	0.247	0.202	1.223	0.256	0.185	1.384	500
750	0.255	0.187	1.368	0.266	0.221	1.204	0.264	0.193	1.367	750
1000	0.263	0.194	1.353	0.280	0.235	1.192	0.273	0.202	1.351	1000
1500	0.276	0.208	1.330	0.298	0.253	1.178	0.287	0.216	1.328	1500
2000	0.286	0.217	1.316	0.312	0.267	1.169	0.297	0.226	1.314	2000
3000	0.297	0.229	1.300	0.326	0.281	1.160	0.308	0.237	1.299	3000
4000	0.305	0.236	1.291	0.333	0.288	1.156	0.314	0.243	1.292	4000
5000				0.338	0.293	1.154	0.318	0.247	1.287	5000

Temp., F	Hydrogen, H_2 c_p	Hydrogen, H_2 c_v	Hydrogen, H_2 k	Nitrogen, N_2 c_p	Nitrogen, N_2 c_v	Nitrogen, N_2 k	Oxygen, O_2 c_p	Oxygen, O_2 c_v	Oxygen, O_2 k	Temp., F
32	3.391	2.406	1.409	0.248	0.177	1.400	0.219	0.156	1.397	32
100	3.426	2.441	1.404	0.248	0.178	1.399	0.220	0.158	1.394	100
200	3.451	2.466	1.399	0.249	0.178	1.398	0.223	0.161	1.387	200
300	3.461	2.476	1.398	0.250	0.179	1.396	0.226	0.164	1.378	300
500	3.469	2.484	1.397	0.254	0.183	1.388	0.235	0.173	1.360	500
750	3.483	2.498	1.394	0.261	0.190	1.374	0.245	0.182	1.340	750
1000	3.513	2.528	1.390	0.269	0.198	1.359	0.252	0.190	1.326	1000
1500	3.618	2.633	1.374	0.283	0.212	1.334	0.263	0.201	1.309	1500
2000	3.758	2.773	1.355	0.293	0.222	1.319	0.270	0.208	1.298	2000
3000	4.051	3.066	1.321	0.306	0.235	1.302	0.281	0.219	1.284	3000
4000	4.238	3.253	1.303	0.312	0.241	1.294	0.290	0.228	1.272	4000
5000	4.400	3.415	1.288	0.316	0.245	1.289	0.299	0.237	1.262	5000

* Data from *Tables of Thermal Properties of Gases*, National Bureau of Standards Circular 564, 1955.

heat for a given temperature interval can be obtained from specific-heat–temperature charts by the method illustrated in Fig. 4·8, if we recall from Art. 3·5 that

$$\overline{c_p} \equiv \frac{\int_1^2 c_p \, dT}{T_2 - T_1} \quad \text{and} \quad \overline{c_v} \equiv \frac{\int_1^2 c_v \, dT}{T_2 - T_1}$$

For any process of an ideal gas

$$\Delta h = \overline{c_p} \, \Delta T \quad \text{and} \quad \Delta u = \overline{c_v} \, \Delta T$$

Remember that in general the value of $\overline{c_p}$ or $\overline{c_v}$ is different for each different temperature interval.

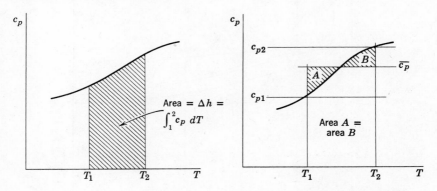

Fig. 4·7 Δh for an ideal gas.   **Fig. 4·8**   Determination of mean specific heat.

Empirical $C_{p0}T$ equations for several gases are given in Table 4·3. These equations can be used for determining C_v values inasmuch as

$$C_v = C_p - R_u \tag{4·4}$$

For the units used in Table 4·3,

$$C_v = C_p - 1.986 \text{ B/mole-R}$$

Since the difference $(c_p - c_v)$ is constant, the ratio c_p/c_v, which is designated by k, varies with temperature. The variation of k with temperature is shown in Fig. 4·9 for six gases.

EXAMPLE 4·4. Compute the amount of heat required to raise the temperature of nitrogen from 100 to 1000 F in a frictionless steady-flow process under a constant pressure of 1 atm.

Solution. For any steady-flow process,

$$q = \Delta h + w + \Delta KE + \Delta PE$$

Since the flow is also frictionless, $w = -\int v\,dp - \Delta KE - \Delta PE$, and so

$$q = \Delta h - \int v\,dp - \Delta KE - \Delta PE + \Delta KE + \Delta PE$$

and, since the pressure is constant, this reduces to

$$q = \Delta h$$

Under the specified conditions of pressure and temperature, nitrogen may be treated as

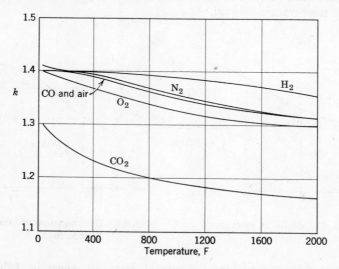

Fig. 4·9 Specific-heat ratio k for six gases. Data from *Tables of Thermal Properties of Gases*, National Bureau of Standards Circular 564, 1955.

an ideal gas. For any process of an ideal gas, $\Delta h = \int c_p\,dT$. Using the $C_p T$ relation from Table 4·3, we have

$$q = \Delta h = \int c_p\,dT = \frac{1}{M}\int C_p\,dT = \frac{1}{28}\int_1^2 \left[9.47 - \frac{3.47(10^3)}{T} + \frac{1.16(10^6)}{T^2} \right] dT$$

$$= \frac{1}{28}\left[9.47(T_2 - T_1) - 3.47(10^3)\ln\frac{T_2}{T_1} - 1.16(10^6)\left(\frac{1}{T_2} - \frac{1}{T_1}\right) \right]$$

$$= \frac{1}{28}\left[9.47(1460 - 560) - 3470\ln\frac{1460}{560} - 1.16(10^6)\left(\frac{1}{1460} - \frac{1}{560}\right) \right]$$

$$= 232 \text{ B/lb}$$

TABLE 4·3
Empirical C_pT Equations for Zero Pressure (Ideal Gases)

Gas	Formula	C_p in B/mole-F; T in degrees Rankine	Approximate Temperature Range of Equation, F
Oxygen	O_2	$C_p = 11.515 - \dfrac{172}{\sqrt{T}} + \dfrac{1530}{T}$	80–4500
Nitrogen and air	N_2	$C_p = 9.47 - \dfrac{3.47(10^3)}{T} + \dfrac{1.16(10^6)}{T^2}$	80–8500
Carbon monoxide	CO	$C_p = 9.46 - \dfrac{3.29(10^3)}{T} + \dfrac{1.07(10^6)}{T^2}$	80–8500
Hydrogen	H_2	$C_p = 5.76 + \dfrac{0.578T}{1000} + \dfrac{20}{\sqrt{T}}$	80–3500
Water vapor	H_2O	$C_p = 19.86 - \dfrac{597}{\sqrt{T}} + \dfrac{7500}{T}$	80–5000
Carbon dioxide	CO_2	$C_p = 16.2 - \dfrac{6.53(10^3)}{T} + \dfrac{1.41(10^6)}{T^2}$	80–4800
Methane	CH_4	$C_p = 4.52 + 0.00737T$	80–1000
Ethylene	C_2H_4	$C_p = 4.23 + 0.01177T$	(−100)–650
Ethane	C_2H_6	$C_p = 4.01 + 0.01636T$	(−60)–650
Gasoline vapors	C_8H_{18}	$C_p = 7.92 + 0.0601T$	(−60)–650
Kerosene	$C_{12}H_{26}$	$C_p = 8.68 + 0.0889T$	(−60)–650

Data from "Empirical Specific Heat Equation Based upon Spectroscopic Data," R. L. Sweigert and M. W. Beardsley, *Georgia School of Technology Engineering Experiment Station Bulletin* 2, 1938.

4·6 Special relations for ideal gases with constant specific heats

Within limited temperature ranges the specific heats of an ideal gas can often be treated as constant without a serious loss of accuracy. When this is done, several relationships among properties are simplified. For example,

$$\Delta u = \int c_v\, dT \quad \text{and} \quad \Delta h = \int c_p\, dT \qquad (4·2,3)$$

become
$$\Delta u = c_v\, \Delta T \quad \text{and} \quad \Delta h = c_p\, \Delta T$$

A type of process which is frequently encountered in thermodynamic analyses is the frictionless adiabatic. Since this process is frequently met, it is worthwhile to establish for it a *pv* relationship for use in integrating $\int p \, dv$ and $\int v \, dp$. Once the *pv* relationship is determined, it can be combined with the equation of state to give the *pT* and *vT* relationships which are also useful. These steps are easily performed for an ideal gas with constant specific heats, so we will now derive the *pv* relationship for a *frictionless adiabatic process of an ideal gas with constant specific heats.*

For a closed system the first law may be written

$$\delta q = du + \delta w$$

If the process is *adiabatic*, this becomes

$$0 = du + \delta w$$

and, if it is also *frictionless*, we have

$$0 = du + p \, dv$$

If the substance is an *ideal gas*,

$$0 = c_v \, dT + p \, dv$$

In order to get a *pv* relation, we must eliminate T. We can do this by use of the ideal-gas equation of state which gives $T = pv/R$ and $dT = (p \, dv + v \, dp)/R$. Thus we have

$$0 = \frac{c_v}{R}(p \, dv + v \, dp) + p \, dv$$

which we rearrange as follows:

$$0 = v \, dp + \left(\frac{R}{c_v} + 1\right) p \, dv = v \, dp + \left(\frac{R + c_v}{c_v}\right) p \, dv$$

$$0 = v \, dp + \frac{c_p}{c_v} p \, dv = v \, dp + kp \, dv$$

$$0 = \frac{dp}{p} + k \frac{dv}{v}$$

Up to this point we have not imposed the restriction of constant specific heats, but now we do so in order to integrate the last expression. Recall that the difference between c_p and c_v is constant (and equal to R), so that a constant k (which equals c_p/c_v) implies constant values of c_p and c_v. Integration gives

$$pv^k = \text{constant} \tag{4.5a}$$

This equation holds for *frictionless adiabatic processes of ideal gases with constant specific heats.* For such a process between states 1 and 2,

$$p_1 v_1^k = p_2 v_2^k \tag{4.5b}$$

Although the derivation above was based on a closed system, the pv relation is the same if the frictionless adiabatic process occurs in an open system. From the ideal-gas equation of state we have

$$\frac{p_1 v_1}{T_1} = \frac{p_2 v_2}{T_2}$$

which when combined with equation 4·5b gives

$$\frac{T_2}{T_1} = \left(\frac{p_2}{p_1}\right)^{(k-1)/k} = \left(\frac{v_1}{v_2}\right)^{k-1} \tag{4·5c}$$

Equations 4·5 are pv, pT, and Tv relations which apply only to a particular type of process of an ideal gas with constant specific heats; they are not equations of state. They involve only two properties at a time. Since for a pure substance there are generally **two** *independent* properties, an equation of state must involve three properties.

For many, but not all, frictionless processes of an ideal gas the pv relation is

$$pv^n = \text{constant} \tag{4·6a}$$

where n is a constant for each process. Any process represented by such an equation is called a *polytropic* process and n is called the *polytropic exponent* for the process. Combining equation 4·6a with the equation of state gives

$$\frac{T_2}{T_1} = \left(\frac{p_2}{p_1}\right)^{(n-1)/n} = \left(\frac{v_1}{v_2}\right)^{n-1} \tag{4·6b}$$

Notice that the frictionless constant-pressure, constant-volume, constant-temperature, and adiabatic processes are special cases of polytropic processes for which the values of n are 0, ∞, 1, and k, respectively. (If the reason for $n = \infty$ in the constant-volume case is not apparent, consider that, when $n = \infty$, $p^{1/\infty} V = \text{constant}$; hence $V = \text{constant}$.) Various polytropic processes are shown on a pV diagram in Fig. 4·10. During a polytropic expansion for which $k > n > 1$, heat is added to the gas but its temperature decreases because the work done by the system exceeds the heat added.

EXAMPLE 4·5. Three pounds of an ideal gas in a closed system is compressed frictionlessly and adiabatically from 14.7 psia, 70 F, to 60 psia. For this gas $c_p = 0.238$ B/lb-F, $c_v = 0.169$ B/lb-F, and $R = 53.7$ ft-lb$_f$/lb$_m$-R. Compute (a) the initial volume, (b) the final volume, (c) the final temperature, and (d) the work.

Solution. (a) The initial volume is computed from the ideal-gas equation of state.

$$V_1 = \frac{mRT_1}{p_1} = \frac{3(53.7)530}{14.7(144)} = 40.3 \text{ cu ft}$$

(b) For this frictionless adiabatic process,

$$V_2 = V_1 \left(\frac{p_1}{p_2}\right)^{1/k} = 40.3 \left(\frac{14.7}{60}\right)^{0.169/0.238} = 14.9 \text{ cu ft}$$

(The value of k is $c_p/c_v = 0.238/0.169 = 1.408$.)

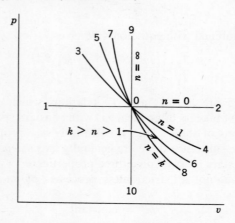

Fig. 4·10 Polytropic processes.

(c) The final temperature can be obtained as

$$T_2 = T_1 \left(\frac{p_2}{p_1}\right)^{(k-1)/k} = 530 \left(\frac{60}{14.7}\right)^{(1.408-1)/1.408} = 798 \text{ R} = 338 \text{ F}$$

or from the ideal-gas equation of state

$$T_2 = T_1 \frac{p_2 V_2}{p_1 V_1} = 530 \left(\frac{60}{14.7}\right) \left(\frac{14.9}{40.3}\right) = 798 \text{ R} = 338 \text{ F}$$

(d) The work done on the gas is computed by means of the first law applied to the closed system and Joule's law for the evaluation of ΔU:

$$W_{\text{in}} = \Delta U - Q = U_2 - U_1 - 0 = mc_v(T_2 - T_1)$$
$$= 3(0.169)(798 - 530) = 136 \text{ B}$$

The work can also be calculated as follows for this frictionless process in which $pV^k = C = p_1 V_1^k = p_2 V_2^k$:

$$W_{\text{in}} = -\int_1^2 p \, dV = -C \int_1^2 V^{-k} \, dV = \frac{-C}{1-k} [V^{1-k}]_1^2 = \frac{p_1 V_1^k}{k-1} [V_2^{1-k} - V_1^{1-k}]$$

$$= \frac{p_1 V_1}{k-1} \left[\left(\frac{V_2}{V_1}\right)^{1-k} - 1\right] = \frac{mRT_1}{k-1} \left[\frac{T_2}{T_1} - 1\right] = m \left(\frac{R}{k-1}\right) [T_2 - T_1]$$

$$= mc_v(T_2 - T_1)$$

Of course, the same result is obtained from $W = \int p \, dV$ as from the first law.

EXAMPLE 4·6.   In a closed system 0.15 lb of air is compressed polytropically from 14.7 psia and a volume of 2 cu ft to a volume of 1 cu ft with a polytropic exponent of 1.3. Compute (a) the final temperature, (b) the work, (c) the change in internal energy, and (d) the heat transfer.

Solution.   (a) The air is initially at a pressure of only 1 atm, so unless its temperature is extremely low the ideal-gas equation of state can be used. Let us check the value of T_1 first of all by means of the ideal-gas equation of state.

$$T_1 = \frac{p_1 V_1}{mR} = \frac{14.7(144)2}{0.15(53.3)} = 530 \text{ R} = 70 \text{ F}$$

At 14.7 psia, 70 F, $pv = RT$ is accurate for air, so we can proceed. The final temperature is

$$T_2 = T_1 \left(\frac{V_1}{V_2}\right)^{n-1} = 530(2)^{0.3} = 652 \text{ R} = 192 \text{ F}$$

(b) As a means of determining work we should first consider the first law, $W_{in} = \Delta U - Q$. Since we know T_1 and T_2, we can compute ΔU, but a method of computing Q is not apparent so it looks as though we cannot determine work by means of the first law. Let us then turn to the expression $W = \int p \, dV$ which holds for frictionless processes of a closed system. Since we know the pV relation for the process in question, we can evaluate $\int p \, dV$ as follows:

$$W_{in} = -\int p \, dV = \frac{-C}{1-n} [V^{1-n}]_1^2 = \frac{-p_1 V_1^n}{1-n} [V_2^{1-n} - V_1^{1-n}]$$

$$= \frac{-p_1 V_1}{1-n} \left[\left(\frac{V_2}{V_1}\right)^{1-n} - 1\right] = \frac{p_1 V_1}{n-1} \left[\left(\frac{V_1}{V_2}\right)^{n-1} - 1\right]$$

$$= \frac{14.7(144)2}{0.3(778)} [(2)^{0.3} - 1] = 4.19 \text{ B}$$

(c) Figure 4·6 shows that, in the temperature range of 70 to 192 F, c_v for air is very nearly constant, so we have for the change in internal energy

$$U_2 - U_1 = m \int_1^2 c_v \, dT = mc_v(T_2 - T_1) = 0.15(0.171)(652 - 530)$$

$$= 3.13 \text{ B}$$

(d) Applying the first law to this closed system,

$$Q = U_2 - U_1 - W_{in} = 3.13 - 4.19 = -1.06 \text{ B}$$

The minus sign indicates that heat was removed from the air.

EXAMPLE 4·7.   A 60-cu-ft tank contains carbon monoxide initially at 20 psia, 100 F. A pump delivers carbon monoxide to the tank, raising the pressure from 20 to 40 psia. As the pump discharge pressure increases, so does the discharge temperature, according to $T = 80p^{0.25}$, where T is in degrees Rankine and p is in psfa. Determine the heat transfer necessary to maintain the temperature of the carbon monoxide in the tank at 100 F.

Solution. A sketch of the pump and tank is first made, and then we define the following symbols:

Subscript i denotes properties of the CO initially in the tank.
Subscript f denotes properties of the CO finally in the tank.
Subscript 1 denotes properties of the CO entering the tank.
m, p, T, u, etc. = the mass, pressure, temperature, internal energy, etc. of CO in the tank at any instant.
m_1 = the mass of CO which has already entered the tank = $m - m_i$.

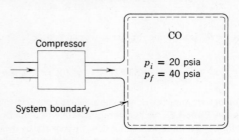

Example 4·7

Consider the space within the tank as the system. This is an open system, and its boundary is the inner surface of the tank. There is no work done and no mass leaves the system; so an energy balance for this open system is

$$\begin{bmatrix} \text{Heat added} \\ \text{to system} \end{bmatrix} + \begin{bmatrix} \text{Stored energy and flow} \\ \text{work of entering mass} \end{bmatrix} = \begin{bmatrix} \text{Increase in stored} \\ \text{energy of system} \end{bmatrix}$$

As an infinitesimal mass δm_1 enters the system, the energy balance formulation is

$$\delta Q + h_1 \delta m_1 = dU$$

$$\delta Q = m\, du + u\, dm - h_1 \delta m_1$$

Since the temperature of the CO in the tank is held constant, u is constant, and therefore $m\, du = 0$.

$$\delta Q = u\, dm - h_1 \delta m_1$$

We must evaluate u and h. Let us see if the temperature range is narrow enough for specific heats to be constant. The pump-discharge (i.e., tank entrance) temperatures for the 20 psia and 40 psia pressure limits are

$$T_{1,\, 20\text{ psia}} = 80 p_1^{0.25} = 80[20(144)]^{0.25} = 585\text{ R} = 125\text{ F}$$

$$T_{1,\, 40\text{ psia}} = 80 p_1^{0.25} = 80[40(144)]^{0.25} = 696\text{ R} = 236\text{ F}$$

Therefore, the temperature range we are concerned with is that of 100 to 236 F. In this range we see from Figs. 4·4 and 4·6 that we can treat the specific heats as constant. (We will use $c_p = 0.250$ B/lb-R and $c_v = 0.179$ B/lb-R.) Thus we have $u - u_0 = c_v(T - T_0)$ and $h - h_0 = c_p(T - T_0)$. For this problem, let $u_0 = 0$ and $h_0 = 0$ when $T_0 = 0$, so that we have $u = c_v T$ and $h = c_p T$. The energy balance now becomes

$$\delta Q = c_v T\, dm - c_p T_1 \delta m_1$$

$$= c_v T\, dm - c_p(80) p_1^{0.25}\, \delta m_1$$

But
$$p_1 = p = \frac{mRT}{v}$$

and
$$\delta m_1 = d(m - m_i) = dm = d\left(\frac{pV}{RT}\right) = \frac{V}{RT} dp$$

Making these two substitutions in the energy balance above,

$$\delta Q = c_v \frac{V}{R} dp - 80 c_p \frac{V}{RT} p^{0.25} dp$$

$$Q = \frac{V}{R} \left\{ c_v \int_i^f dp - \frac{80 c_p}{T} \int_i^f p^{0.25} dp \right\}$$

$$= \frac{V}{R} \left\{ c_v (p_f - p_i) - \frac{80 c_p}{1.25 T} (p_f^{1.25} - p_i^{1.25}) \right\}$$

$$= \frac{60}{55.2} \left\{ 0.179(144)(40 - 20) - \frac{80(0.25)}{1.25(560)} (144)^{1.25} [(40)^{1.25} - (20)^{1.25}] \right\}$$

$$= -344 \text{ B}$$

The minus sign indicates that heat must be removed from the CO.

4·7 The ideal-gas equation of state and kinetic theory

The ideal-gas equation of state can be derived from the kinetic theory of gases. Such a derivation has no bearing on classical thermodynamics, however, because classical thermodynamics neither depends on nor gives us any information on the microscopic structure of matter. This article and the next are included to give a glimpse of the kinetic theory as it explains ideal-gas behavior for two reasons. One is that most engineering students like to have a physical picture of the structure of gases even if it is unnecessary in the logical development of thermodynamics. The other reason is that even a superficial knowledge of kinetic theory helps one to understand why the behavior of real gases differs from that of ideal gases. The following presentation is not rigorous, but it gives an idea of the kinetic theory approach to the behavior of ideal gases.

Let us consider a monatomic gas and make the following assumptions:

1. The gas consists of many, many molecules. In a pure gas, all of the molecules are alike.

2. The molecules are small compared to the average distance between them. That is, the volume occupied by the molecules themselves is a small fraction of the volume of the container which the gas fills.

3. The molecules move about in all directions; all directions of motion are equally probable.

4. The molecules exert no force on each other except when they collide.

5. The laws of macroscopic mechanics (Newton's laws) apply to individual molecules.

6. Collisions of molecules with each other and with the walls of the container are perfectly elastic.

According to the kinetic theory, the pressure exerted by an ideal gas on the walls of a container results from the action of a great number of molecules striking and rebounding from the walls. In order to develop an

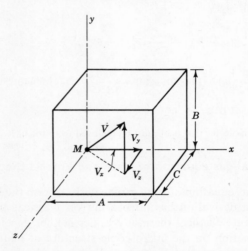

Fig. 4·11   Molecular velocity components.

expression for the pressure, we will consider first the behavior of a single gas molecule. Let this molecule be one of many identical molecules which comprise an ideal gas held in a container of dimensions A, B, and C as shown in Fig. 4·11. The velocity V of the molecule under study has components V_x, V_y, and V_z as shown in Fig. 4·11. When the molecule with this velocity strikes the container wall BC, it rebounds without change in V_y and V_z but with its x component of velocity changed from V_x to $-V_x$. The x component of its momentum changes from $m'V_x$ to $-m'V_x$, where m' is the mass of the molecule. The magnitude of the change in the x component of momentum is $2m'V_x$. The molecule travels the distance A in the time A/V_x if V_x is constant; so it could cross the container in the x direction and return in a time $2A/V_x$. The time between successive collisions with the wall BC is $2A/V_x$, and the number of collisions with wall BC per unit time is $V_x/2A$. The change in x momentum per unit time is the product of the change per collision and the number of collisions per unit time, $2m'V_x(V_x/2A) = m'V_x^2/A$. Thus the force on wall BC is

$$F'_x = \frac{1}{g_c}\frac{d}{dt}(m'V_x) = \frac{1}{g_c}\frac{m'V_x^2}{A}$$

This is the force of just one molecule. The total force on wall BC is the sum of the forces of individual molecules,

$$F_x = \sum \frac{m'V_x^2}{g_c A}$$

All the molecules have the same mass m'; g_c and A are constant; so

$$F_x = \frac{m'}{g_c A} \sum V_x^2$$

Let us define the average V^2 for η molecules as

$$\overline{V_x^2} \equiv \frac{(V_{x1}^2 + V_{x2}^2 + V_{x3}^2 + \cdots)}{\eta} \qquad (a)$$

Then

$$F_x = \frac{m'\eta\overline{V_x^2}}{g_c A}$$

The pressure on wall BC is

$$p_x = \frac{F_x}{\text{area}} = \frac{m'\eta\overline{V_x^2}}{g_c A(BC)} = \frac{m'\eta\overline{V_x^2}}{g_c(\text{vol})} \qquad (b)$$

("vol" is used for volume to avoid confusion between symbols for *volume* and for *velocity*.) If it is assumed that the pressure is the same in all directions and that all directions of velocity are equally probable,

$$p = \frac{m'\eta\overline{V_x^2}}{g_c(\text{vol})} = \frac{m'\eta\overline{V_y^2}}{g_c(\text{vol})} = \frac{m'\eta\overline{V_z^2}}{g_c(\text{vol})} \qquad (c)$$

and therefore

$$\overline{V_x^2} = \overline{V_y^2} = \overline{V_z^2} \qquad (d)$$

Also, since V_x, V_y, and V_z are components of V,

$$V^2 = V_x^2 + V_y^2 + V_z^2$$

and it can be shown that

$$\overline{V^2} = \overline{V_x^2} + \overline{V_y^2} + \overline{V_z^2} \qquad (e)$$

where $\overline{V^2}$ is the average of the squared velocity magnitudes for all molecules and the right-hand terms are defined as $\overline{V_x^2}$ is defined in equation (a).

Combining equations (d) and (e) shows that

$$\overline{V^2} = 3\overline{V_x^2} = 3\overline{V_y^2} = 3\overline{V_z^2}$$

so that equation (c) for the pressure becomes

$$p = \frac{m'\eta\overline{V^2}}{3g_c(\text{vol})}$$

$$p(\text{vol}) = \tfrac{1}{3}\eta m' \frac{\overline{V^2}}{g_c} \tag{f}$$

If we assume the temperature of an ideal gas to be proportional to the kinetic energy of its molecules, we have

$$T = D \frac{m'\overline{V^2}}{2g_c} \tag{g}$$

where D is the factor of proportionality. Combining equations (f) and (g) gives

$$p(\text{vol}) = \frac{2}{3D}\eta T = \left(\frac{2\eta}{3DN}\right)NT \tag{h}$$

where η/N is Avogadro's number, the number of molecules per mole. In equation (h), $2\eta/3DN$ is a constant. If we call it R_u, we have

$$p(\text{vol}) = NR_uT$$

which we recognize as the ideal-gas equation of state.

Following equation (f), we assumed that temperature is proportional to molecular kinetic energy and showed that the ideal-gas equation of state results. Conversely, we could have compared equation (f) with the ideal-gas equation of state and showed that temperature is proportional to molecular kinetic energy because

$$p(\text{vol}) = \tfrac{1}{3}\eta m' \frac{\overline{V^2}}{g_c} \tag{f}$$

and

$$p(\text{vol}) = NR_uT$$

can be combined to give

$$T = \frac{1}{3}\frac{\eta}{NR_u}\frac{m'\overline{V^2}}{g_c} = \frac{2}{3}\frac{\eta}{NR_u}\frac{m'\overline{V^2}}{2g_c} = \text{constant}\frac{m'\overline{V^2}}{2g_c}$$

Using the important physical constant $\mathbf{k}$ which is defined as $\mathbf{k} \equiv NR_u/\eta$ and called Boltzmann's constant, we can write the last equation in a form which is used in the next article:

$$\tfrac{3}{2}\mathbf{k}T = \frac{m'\overline{V^2}}{2g_c} \tag{g}$$

Notice that the average kinetic energy is the same at a given temperature for molecules of any gas. Thus heavier gas molecules have lower mean speeds than lighter molecules at the same temperature.

4·8 Specific heats of ideal gases and kinetic theory

The internal energy of an ideal gas is the sum of molecular kinetic and potential energies. In Art. 4·4 we saw that the molecular potential energy of an ideal gas is constant. Therefore, it can be assigned the value of zero, so that in a monatomic ideal gas where the only molecular motion is translatory we can write

$$U = NMu = \frac{\eta m' \overline{V^2}}{2g_c}$$

The product of molecular weight and specific internal energy Mu is the internal energy per mole of gas. Using equation (g) of the preceding article, we can change this to

$$Mu = \frac{\eta}{N} \tfrac{3}{2} kT = \tfrac{3}{2} R_u T$$

Then the molar specific heat at constant volume is

$$C_v = \left(\frac{\partial Mu}{\partial T}\right)_v = \tfrac{3}{2} R_u$$

The molar specific heat at constant pressure is then

$$C_p = C_v + R_u = \tfrac{3}{2} R_u + R_u = \tfrac{5}{2} R_u$$

and the ratio of specific heats for the monatomic ideal gas is

$$k = \frac{c_p}{c_v} = \frac{C_p}{C_v} = \frac{\tfrac{5}{2}}{\tfrac{3}{2}} = \frac{5}{3}$$

In order to extend this discussion to diatomic molecules, we must introduce the principle of equipartition of energy and the concept of degrees of freedom. By the number of degrees of freedom is meant the number of independent quantities which must be specified to determine the energy of a molecule. For example, a monatomic molecule constrained to move only in the x direction has one degree of freedom because if V_x is specified then the energy can be calculated as $m' V_x^2 / 2g_c$. If the molecule is free to move in any direction, then V_x, V_y, and V_z must be specified, and the molecule has three degrees of freedom. If the moment of inertia of the molecule about the x axis is not zero and the molecule rotates about this axis, then there is rotational kinetic energy and the angular velocity must be specified, adding another degree of freedom. Rotation about other axes adds other degrees of freedom. An important principle in kinetic theory developments is the equipartition of energy principle which states that the total energy of molecules is divided equally among their degrees of freedom. Thus, since the kinetic energy per mole of monatomic molecules which involve translation only (three degrees of freedom) is $3R_uT/2$, the energy per degree of freedom is $\frac{1}{2}R_uT$. The equipartition of energy principle tells us that each additional degree of freedom involves additional energy in the amount $\frac{1}{2}R_uT$ per mole. For f degrees of freedom the internal energy is therefore given by

$$Mu = \frac{f}{2} R_u T$$

Thus

$$C_v = \left(\frac{\partial Mu}{\partial T}\right)_v = \frac{f}{2} R_u$$

$$C_p = C_v + R_u = \frac{f}{2} R_u + R_u = \frac{f+2}{2} R_u$$

and

$$k = \frac{f+2}{f}$$

Consider now a diatomic molecule comprised of two point masses. In addition to translatory kinetic energy, the diatomic molecule may possess rotational kinetic energy by virtue of rotation about the two mutually perpendicular axes which are perpendicular to the line joining the two atoms. Energy of rotation about the axis connecting the atoms is zero because the moment of inertia about this axis is zero for point particles. The atoms may also vibrate along the line connecting them. This involves two additional degrees of freedom because both potential and kinetic energy are involved. (The atoms within a molecule exert forces on each other even though the spacing between molecules is so great that inter-molecular forces are negligible.) Both position and velocity of the atoms must be specified in order to determine the vibrational energy. Thus a diatomic molecule may have seven degrees of freedom: three associated with translation, two with rotation, and two with vibration. However, vibration occurs only at higher temperatures, so that at normal room temperature, for example, a diatomic gas usually has only five degrees of freedom. At very low temperatures rotation ceases; so $f = 3$ for a diatomic gas. Thus for a diatomic gas the kinetic theory as we have discussed it leads us to expect

At low temperatures:	$C_v = \frac{3}{2}R_u$	$C_p = \frac{5}{2}R_u$	$k = \frac{5}{3}$
At intermediate temperatures:	$C_v = \frac{5}{2}R_u$	$C_p = \frac{7}{2}R_u$	$k = \frac{7}{5}$
At high temperatures:	$C_v = \frac{7}{2}R_u$	$C_p = \frac{9}{2}R_u$	$k = \frac{9}{7}$

Such a variation of C_v is shown in Fig. 4·12. The reason for the gradual change shown in Fig. 4·12 is that, as the temperature increases, not all the molecules begin to rotate or vibrate at the same temperature, so that the cumulative effect as more molecules begin to rotate and then to vibrate is a gradual increase in specific heat.

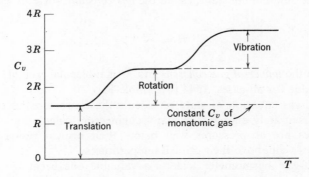

Fig. 4·12 C_v variation based on kinetic theory.

The specific heat values predicted from kinetic theory should be compared with the values presented in Figs. 4·4, 4·5, and 4·6 and in Table 4·2. As a sample comparison, see Table 4·4 which shows good agreement at 32 F for several gases.

TABLE 4·4

Molar Specific Heats of Several Gases
in B/mole-R

Gas	Experimental Values at 14.7 psia, 32 F		From Kinetic Theory (no vibration)	
	C_v	C_p	C_v	C_p
A	2.98	4.96	$\frac{3}{2}R_u = 2.98$	$\frac{5}{2}R_u = 4.97$
He	3.02	5.01	$\frac{3}{2}R_u = 2.98$	$\frac{5}{2}R_u = 4.97$
Air	4.96	6.94	$\frac{5}{2}R_u = 4.97$	$\frac{7}{2}R_u = 6.95$
CO	4.97	6.95	$\frac{5}{2}R_u = 4.97$	$\frac{7}{2}R_u = 6.95$
N_2	4.97	6.95	$\frac{5}{2}R_u = 4.97$	$\frac{7}{2}R_u = 6.95$
O_2	5.00	6.99	$\frac{5}{2}R_u = 4.97$	$\frac{7}{2}R_u = 6.95$

The specific heats of gases with more complex molecules cannot be explained by a simplified approach like the one we have used here.

4·9 Summary

An ideal gas is defined as one for which the equation of state is

$$pv = RT \qquad (4·1)$$

where R is a different constant, called the *gas constant*, for each gas. R is given by

$$R = \frac{R_u}{M}$$

where R_u is the *universal gas constant* and M is molecular weight. R_u has the same value for all gases, 1544 ft-lb$_f$/mole-R.

The ideal-gas equation of state represents the characteristics of many real gases accurately enough for many engineering calculations as long as the gases are at pressures well below their critical pressures and temperatures well above their critical temperatures.

The ideal-gas thermometer scale is a valuable one because it can be shown that it is equivalent to a temperature scale which is entirely independent of physical properties.

From the first and second laws of thermodynamics it can be proved that, for any substance which follows the equation of state $pv = RT$,

$$\left(\frac{\partial u}{\partial v}\right)_T = 0$$

This means that *the internal energy of an ideal gas is a function of temperature only*. This important fact is known as Joule's law. It follows that *for any process of an ideal gas*

$$du = c_v \, dT \qquad (4·2)$$

$$dh = c_p \, dT \qquad (4·3)$$

The specific heats of an ideal gas are functions of temperature only and

$$c_p - c_v = R$$

under all conditions.

Whenever the temperature range is such that the specific heats can be considered as constant,

$$\Delta u = c_v \, \Delta T \quad \text{and} \quad \Delta h = c_p \, \Delta T$$

For a *frictionless adiabatic process of an ideal gas with constant specific heats,*

$$pv^k = \text{constant} \qquad (4·5)$$

where $k \equiv c_p/c_v$. For a process from state 1 to state 2 under the same restrictions

$$\frac{T_2}{T_1} = \left(\frac{p_2}{p_1}\right)^{(k-1)/k} = \left(\frac{v_1}{v_2}\right)^{k-1} \tag{4.5}$$

It must be emphasized that equations 4·5 apply *only* to *frictionless adiabatic processes of an ideal gas with constant specific heats.*

For many, but not all, frictionless processes of an ideal gas the pv relation is

$$pv^n = \text{constant} \tag{4.6}$$

A process which can be represented by such an equation is called a *polytropic* process, and n is called the *polytropic exponent* for the process.

At least for simple molecules, the ideal-gas equation of state and specific heat values can be developed from the kinetic theory of gases.

REFERENCES

4·1 M. W. Zemansky, *Heat and Thermodynamics*, McGraw-Hill Book Co., 4th ed., 1957, chapter 6.

4·2 H. J. Stoever, *Engineering Thermodynamics*, John Wiley & Sons, 1951, arts. 7 to 11 and chapter 4.

4·3 F. W. Sears, *Thermodynamics, the Kinetic Theory of Gases, and Statistical Mechanics*, Addison-Wesley Publishing Co., 2d ed., 1953, chapters 2, 5, and 11.

4·4 J. K. Roberts and A. R. Miller, *Heat and Thermodynamics*, Interscience Publishers, 4th ed., 1951, chapters 1 and 3.

For ideal-gas data

4·5 J. H. Keenan and J. Kaye, *Gas Tables*, John Wiley & Sons, 1948.

4·6 *Tables of Thermal Properties of Gases*, National Bureau of Standards, Circular 564, 1955.

PROBLEMS

4·1 For an ideal gas, is x a property if $x = \int(c/T)\,dT + \int(p/T)\,dv$ and c is a constant?

4·2 A balloon contains 50,000 cu ft of hydrogen at 80 F and 29.0 in. of mercury absolute. Compute the mass of hydrogen in the balloon.

4·3 What volume must be provided in an air receiver to hold 20 lb of air if the pressure is 250 psia and the temperature is 100 F? If the temperature drops to 32 F, what will be the pressure? Assume that the ideal-gas equation of state holds and that the molecular weight of air is approximately 29.

4·4 The density of CO is 0.07704 lb/cu ft at 32 F and 14.7 psia. Using the ideal-gas equation of state, compute the gas constant.

4·5 What volume, in cubic feet, will be required to store 50 lb of air at 250 psia and 70 F? If the air temperature rises to 150 F, what will be the pressure in the storage tank? Assume that the air behaves like an ideal gas.

4·6 A closed tank contains 100 lb of air at a pressure and temperature of 140 psia and 120 F. What amount of air leaks out if the final pressure is 60 psia and the final temperature is 80 F?

4·7 Compute the volume occupied by one mole of CO at a pressure of 14.7 psia and temperature of 190 F.

4·8 Hydrogen gas is to be stored in a cylindrical tank having an internal diameter of 8 in. and a length of 2 ft. If the maximum allowable pressure and temperature are 300 psia and 140 F, how many moles of hydrogen can be stored at the maximum temperature and pressure?

4·9 Three pounds of a certain gas with $c_v = 0.18$ B/lb-F expands adiabatically in a closed system and in so doing performs 10,000 ft-lb of work. The final temperature is 200 F. Compute the initial temperature.

4·10 To compress 5 lb of gas with $c_v = 0.169$ B/lb-F requires 25,000 ft-lb of work while 25 B of heat is removed. Compute the temperature change.

4·11 A gas flows through a nozzle from a pressure of 180 psia to a final pressure of 20 psia. The initial and final specific volume values are 1.277 and 6.09 cu ft/lb respectively. If the initial and final temperatures are 621 and 329 R, respectively, compute the final velocity. Neglect the initial velocity and the heat-loss terms. Assume that the specific heat at constant volume is 0.169 B/lb-F.

4·12 For an ideal gas sketch a pv diagram showing lines of constant T, a Tv diagram showing lines of constant p, and a pT diagram showing lines of constant v. Derive an expression for the slope of each line.

4·13 Prove that for an ideal gas

$$du = \frac{1}{k-1}\,d(pv) \quad \text{and} \quad dh = \frac{k}{k-1}\,d(pv)$$

4·14 Air at 8.0 in. of mercury vacuum, 25 C, is contained in a tank which has a volume of 1.5 cu ft. Barometric pressure is 27.0 in. of mercury, and the local acceleration of gravity is 32.00 ft/sec². Calculate the weight of air in the tank.

4·15 In a building is an elevator shaft 400 ft high. The lower end of the shaft is open so that the air pressure inside the shaft is the same as outside. On a winter day, the outdoor temperature is 0 F and the air inside the shaft is at 80 F. Barometric pressure is 14.7 psia. What is the difference between the air pressure inside the shaft and outside the building at the top of the shaft? State clearly your assumptions.

4·16 A cylinder fitted with a piston contains 0.20 lb of air at 30 psia, 40 F. The air expands frictionlessly and isothermally until its pressure is 15 psia. Calculate the heat transfer.

4·17 Two pounds of air is compressed isothermally in a closed system from 15 psia and 40 F to 45 psia. Calculate (a) work, (b) heat transfer, and (c) change in internal energy.

4·18 A closed rigid tank contains 5 cu ft of air initially at 15 psia, 40 F. Work is done on the air by means of a paddle wheel turned by an external motor, and 20.0 B of heat is added to the air. The final pressure is then 30 psia. Sketch a pV diagram of the process, and calculate the amount of work done on the air during the process.

4·19   Two pounds of nitrogen gas is heated at constant pressure from a pressure and temperature of 100 psia and 100 F to a final temperature of 300 F. Sketch the following diagrams showing the process: $pV, pT, pU, pH, VT, VU, VH, TU, TH, UH$. The first variable listed is to be plotted on the vertical axis.

4·20   One pound of air is compressed isothermally at 100 F from a pressure of 14.7 psia to a final pressure of 300 psia. Sketch the process on the following graphs: $pV, pT, pU, pH, VT, VU, VH, TU, TH$, and UH.

4·21   In a closed system, 2 lb of air is heated at constant pressure from 30 psia, 40 F, to 140 F. On account of a frictional effect, the work output is only 10 B. Calculate the amount of heat added to the air.

4·22   One tenth of a pound of air at 40 psia, 40 F, is trapped inside a vertical cylinder which is fitted at the top with a weighted piston so that the pressure of the air is held constant. There is no heat transfer. A paddle wheel in the cylinder is turned until the volume of the air has increased by 20 per cent. Determine (a) the net amount of work done on the air, and (b) the amount of work done on the air by the paddle wheel.

4·23   Four pounds of air in a closed system expands from 30 psia, 1240 F, to 15 psia, 1100 F, while performing 130 B of work. Calculate the heat transfer.

4·24   A rigid tank having a volume of 6.0 cu ft contains air initially at 15 psia, 40 F. An external motor connected to an impeller inside the tank delivers 0.20 hp to the air in the tank for a period of 3.0 min while heat is removed from the air in the amount of 9.0 B. Calculate the change in internal energy per pound of air in the tank.

4·25   One-half pound of an ideal gas having a molecular weight of 40 is contained at 30 psia, 140 F, in a closed rigid vessel. By means of a paddle wheel 560 ft-lb of work is done on the gas while 3.0 B of heat is added. During this process the temperature of the gas rises to 240 F. Calculate c_v of the gas.

4·26   Two tenths of a pound of an ideal gas with a molecular weight of 40 expands frictionlessly at constant pressure in a closed system from 15 psia, 140 F, to 340 F when 4.9 B of heat is added. Determine c_v.

4·27   A rigid tank having a volume of 20.0 cu ft is filled with an ideal gas at a temperature of 100 F and a pressure of 3000 psfa. The addition of 13.7 B of heat raises the gas temperature to 140 F. The specific heat of the gas at constant pressure is 0.238 B/lb-F. Compute the value of k for the gas.

4·28   One tenth of a pound of air is contained in a cylinder at 15 psia and 40 F. This air is to be compressed to twice its initial pressure and one-half its initial volume. Calculate (a) the net work done on or by the gas, (b) the net heat added to or taken from the gas, and (c) the net change in internal energy if (1) the pressure is first doubled at constant volume, and the volume is then halved at constant pressure, (2) the volume is first halved at constant pressure, and the pressure is then doubled at constant volume.

4·29   An ideal gas at 10 psia, 40 F, fills a closed rigid thermally insulated container. An impeller inside the container is turned by an external motor until the pressure is 14 psia. For this gas in the temperature range involved, $c_p = 0.2 + 0.0001T$ and $c_v = 0.15 + 0.0001T$, where T is in degrees Rankine and c_p and c_v are in B/lb-F. Calculate, in B/lb: (a) the enthalpy change of the gas, and (b) the work done on the gas.

4·30   A certain gas which follows the ideal-gas equation of state and has a molecular weight of 33.1 is heated in a closed rigid tank having a volume of 6.0 cu ft. The gas is initially at 15 psia, 40 F. Calculate the amount of heat which must be added to raise the pressure to 21 psia if specific heats in B/lb-R are given by

$$c_v = 0.200 - \frac{6}{T}$$

$$c_p = 0.260 - \frac{6}{T}$$

with T in degrees Rankine, throughout the temperature range involved.

4·31 One cubic foot of air trapped in a cylinder at 15 psia, 40 F, is compressed until its volume is 0.50 cu ft and its pressure is 25 psia. Calculate the quantities listed below (If there is insufficient information for the calculation of any item, state what additional information is necessary for its determination): (a) total internal energy change of the air, (b) net heat added to the air during the process, (c) net work done by the air during the process.

4·32 Air trapped in a cylinder expands frictionlessly against a piston in such a manner that pV = constant. Initially the air is at 60 psia, 40 F, and occupies a volume of 0.50 cu ft. The local value of g is 31.8 ft/sec². (a) To what pressure must the air expand in order to perform 6000 ft-lb of work? (b) What is the mass of air in the system?

4·33 One cubic foot of argon at 50 psia, 240 F, in a closed system expands frictionlessly until its volume is doubled and its temperature is 35 F. During the expansion, $pV^{1.5}$ = constant. Calculate the heat transfer.

4·34 Carbon dioxide is expanded frictionlessly in a closed system in such a manner that $pV^{1.30}$ = constant from initial conditions of 40 psia, 340 F, V_1 = 2.0 cu ft to a final volume of V_2 = 4.0 cu ft. Calculate (a) the work done, and (b) the heat transferred.

4·35 Consider a rigid vessel 33.9 ft high (inside dimension) which is completely filled with water except for a small bubble of air which is held at the bottom. (The bubble might be held by means of an inverted cup, for example.) The pressure at the top of the water column is 1 atm, so the pressure of the bubble is 2 atm. The bubble is then released. After the bubble reaches the top of the vessel, what is the pressure of the water at the bottom? If two or more equal-size bubbles were initially at the bottom of the vessel, how would the pressure at the bottom vary if they were released one at a time?

4·36 Methane enters a machine at 14.0 psia, 95 F, with a velocity of 30 fps through a cross-sectional area of 0.4 sq ft. It leaves the machine at 32.0 psia, 200 F, through a cross-sectional area of 0.15 sq ft. Heat removed from the methane flowing through the machine amounts to 26.1 B/lb. The flow is steady. Determine the outlet velocity.

4·37 Air enters a gas turbine at 75 psia, 395 F, and leaves at 15 psia, 80 F. Heat removed from the air passing through the turbine amounts to 15 B/lb. The flow rate is 14,000 lb/hr. Calculate the power output if the change in kinetic energy is neglected.

4·38 Air enters a steady-flow system at 25 psia, 400 F, with a velocity of 200 fps through a cross-sectional area of 0.50 sq ft. It leaves at 11.5 psia, 300 F, at the same velocity. The system delivers 20 hp to the surroundings. Calculate the heat transfer in B/lb.

4·39 In a gas-turbine power plant, air is taken in at 14.7 psia, 60 F, at a rate of 40,000 cfm, compressed to 60 psia, heated, and then expanded through a turbine and exhausted at 14.7 psia, 500 F. If the net output of the plant is 3860 hp, calculate the net amount of heat added to the air in B/lb. Neglect changes in kinetic energy.

4·40 A compressor takes in 12,000 cfm of air at 14.0 psia, 80 F, with negligible velocity and discharges air at 30.0 psia, 240 F, through an opening which has a cross-sectional area of 0.25 sq ft. Heat is removed from the air being compressed at a rate of 60 B/min. Determine the power input to the compressor.

4·41 Air is compressed isothermally from 14.0 psia, 40 F, to 70 psia at a rate of 2.0 lb/sec by an ideal compressor. The kinetic energy of the air passing through the compressor increases by 5.0 B/lb. Heat removed from the air amounts to 55.2 B/lb. Determine the power input to the compressor.

4·42 Air is drawn into a multistage centrifugal compressor at 14.0 psia, 40 F, with negligible velocity and is discharged at 40 psia, 300 F, with a velocity of 500 fps through a cross-sectional area of 0.20 sq ft. Power input to the compressor is 1500 hp. Determine the heat transfer in B/lb.

4·43 Air enters a compressor at 15 psia, 40 F, with a velocity of 500 fps through a cross-sectional area of 0.60 sq ft. The air is compressed frictionlessly, steadily, and adiabatically to 30 psia. The discharge velocity is very low. Calculate the power input.

4·44 Six pounds of nitrogen expands frictionlessly and adiabatically in a closed system from 400 psia, 100 F, to 200 psia. Compute the change in internal energy, the change in enthalpy, the work, and the heat transfer.

4·45 Two pounds of air is compressed frictionlessly and adiabatically in a closed system from 15 psia, 70 F, to 150 psia. Compute the change in internal energy, the change in enthalpy, and the work.

4·46 Determine the heat transfer during a polytropic process in which the temperature of air changes from 240 to 40 F and the air does 15,560 ft-lb of work per pound.

4·47 Five cubic feet of gas at 340 F expands polytropically in a cylinder until the temperature is 40 F and the volume is 20 cu ft. Determine the value of n.

4·48 Nitrogen is compressed polytropically in a closed system from 10 psia and a volume of 15 cu ft to 100 psia and a volume of 2 cu ft. Determine the value of n for the process.

4·49 Air enters a nozzle at 100 psia, 340 F, with negligible velocity. It expands adiabatically without friction as it flows through the nozzle and leaves at 50 psia. The nozzle exit area is 0.80 sq in. Calculate the exit velocity.

4·50 Oxygen in a closed system expands frictionlessly and adiabatically from 30 psia, 340 F, to 15 psia. Calculate the work done per pound of oxygen.

4·51 Air at 40 psia, 140 F, enters a nozzle with negligible velocity and expands frictionlessly and adiabatically to 20 psia. The outlet area of the nozzle is 2.54 sq in. Calculate (a) the outlet velocity, and (b) the value of $\int_1^2 v \, dp$ for this process.

4·52 Calculate the power required to compress air frictionlessly and adiabatically from 12 psia, 40 F, to 24 psia, discharging it at an average velocity of 600 fps through a cross-sectional area of 0.5 sq ft. Inlet velocity is negligibly small.

4·53 An ideal centrifugal compressor compresses air polytropically, with $n = 1.35$, at a rate of 5 lb/sec from 15 psia, 40 F, to 45 psia. Inlet velocity is negligibly small while the discharge velocity is 600 fps. Heat is removed from the air being compressed at a rate of 20 B/sec. Calculate the power input.

4·54 An ideal reciprocating compressor draws in 200 cfm of air at 15 psia, 40 F, and compresses it polytropically with $n = 1.35$ to 75 psia. Cooling water which removes heat from the air flows at a rate of 10.2 lb/min and undergoes a temperature rise of 10 Fahrenheit degrees. Calculate the compressor power requirement.

4·55 An ideal centrifugal air compressor takes in 10,000 cfm of air at 15 psia, 40 F, with negligible velocity. It compresses the air polytropically with $n = 1.35$ and discharges it at 30 psia with a velocity of 600 fps. Calculate the power input.

4·56 Air is compressed in a frictionless steady-flow process from 10 psia, 60 F, to 15 psia in such a manner that $p(v+5) =$ constant, where v is in cu ft/lb. Inlet velocity is negligibly small and discharge velocity is 350 fps. Calculate the heat transfer.

4·57 Air flows steadily and frictionlessly through a compressor at a rate of 3.2 lb/sec. At inlet the air is at 10.0 psia, 40 F, and at outlet the air is at 20.0 psia, 247 F. Between inlet and outlet of the system, the air is compressed in such a manner that $pv^2 =$ constant. The inlet area is very large and the outlet area is 0.050 sq ft. Sketch the process on pv and Tv coordinates, and calculate the heat transfer in B/lb.

4·58 A cylinder has an inside cross-sectional area of 100 sq ft and a length of 30 ft. Its top is closed and its bottom open. It is partially submerged in a large body of water with its axis vertical until 2500 cu ft of air is trapped in the cylinder and the water level inside the cylinder is 15 ft below that outside. The air is at 150 F. Neglecting any effects of water vapor in the air, determine the amount of heat which must be removed from the air in the cylinder in order to lower its temperature to 100 F. The water level outside the cylinder remains 10 ft below the top of the cylinder.

4·59 A pound of air which under a pressure of 200 psia occupies a volume of 2 cu ft expands at constant temperature until the volume is doubled. It is then compressed at constant pressure to a volume of 2 cu ft, after which it has its pressure raised to 200 psia at constant volume. Draw approximately to scale the pv diagram for the processes of this closed system. Determine the net change in internal energy for the processes involved. Calculate the net work done and the amount of heat added or abstracted during these processes.

4·60 One pound of air is compressed adiabatically from 15 psia and 14 cu ft to 7 cu ft, then expanded at constant pressure to 14 cu ft, and finally cooled at constant volume until the initial pressure is reached. Sketch the processes on a pv diagram approximately to scale. Shade the area representing the work for the constant-pressure process. Determine the work done, the heat added, and the change in internal energy for the adiabatic process.

4·61 A pound of air occupying 1 cu ft at 200 psia undergoes a change to 2 cu ft at constant pressure, a constant-temperature process to 3 cu ft, an adiabatic change to 2 cu ft, and finally a constant volume process to the original pressure. Draw a pv diagram to approximate scale showing the processes. Compute the work done during the isothermal process, and show the work area by crosshatching on the diagram.

4·62 Compute the amount of heat required to raise the temperature of 6 lb of CH_4 from 500 to 900 F at a constant pressure of 1 atm. What assumption do you make?

4·63 Ethylene is heated under a constant pressure of 1 atm from 100 to 500 F. Compute the heat added.

4·64 Determine the amount of heat which must be added to heat 0.2 lb of carbon dioxide from 100 to 4000 F under a constant pressure of 14.7 psia.

4·65 Starting with the first law as applied to a steady-flow process, prove that $pv^k =$ constant for a frictionless adiabatic process of an ideal gas with constant specific heats.

4·66 Refer to the solution of Example 4;7. Occasionally someone objects to the assignment of $u_0 = 0$ and $h_0 = 0$ when $T_0 = 0$ on the basis that this affects the result.

Carry out the solution with $u = c_vT + K$ and $h = c_pT + K'$, where K and K' are constants, to see how the result is affected. (*Note:* What is the numerical value of $K' - K$?)

4·67   An ideal gas escapes from an insulated tank at a constant low rate of M lb/sec. Derive expressions for the rate of change of pressure and of temperature of the gas in the tank with respect to time in terms of M and the properties of the gas at any instant.

4·68   A tank of volume V contains an ideal gas initially at p_i and T_i. The gas leaks out of the tank through a small opening until the pressure drops to p_f. Heat is added to the gas to keep the temperature constant. Neglect kinetic energy changes. Determine the amount of heat which must be added. Express your answer in terms of quantities included in the following list: $V, p_i, p_f, T_i, m_i, m_f$.

4·69   Air at 100 psia, 40 F, is held in a tank of 20 cu ft volume. Heat is added until the air remaining in the tank is at 240 F while air is bled from the tank to hold the pressure constant at 100 psia. Determine the heat transfer.

4·70   Derive an expression for the amount of heat which must be added to an ideal gas in a tank of volume V in order to increase its temperature from T_i to T_f while gas is bled from the tank to hold the pressure constant.

4·71   Air initially at 14.0 psia, 100 F, is held in an insulated tank having a volume of 10 cu ft. An electric heating element within the tank adds heat at a constant rate of 0.10 B/sec. Air is bled from the tank to hold the pressure constant. Assuming that conditions are uniform throughout the tank at any instant, determine the time required for the air to reach a temperature of 300 F.

4·72   A tank with a volume of 12 cu ft is initially evacuated. Atmospheric air seeps into the tank through a porous plug so slowly that there is ample time for heat transfer to keep the temperature of the air inside the tank equal to the atmospheric temperature of 60 F. Finally the pressure inside the tank is equal to the atmospheric pressure of 14.0 psia. Determine the amount of heat added to or removed from the air in the tank.

4·73   An insulated tank with a volume of 10 cu ft contains oxygen at 14.6 psia, 60 F. It is connected to a large line in which oxygen at 100 psia, 120 F is flowing. Determine the final temperature of oxygen in the tank if the filling process is adiabatic.

4·74   A tank of 100 cu ft volume contains air initially at 100 psia, 100 F. Heat is added at a constant rate of 5 B/sec while an automatic valve allows air to leave the tank at a constant rate of 0.05 lb/sec. What is the temperature of the air in the tank 5 min after the initial condition?

4·75   Refer to Prob. 4·74. Starting from the initial conditions, how long will it take for the air in the tank to reach 380 F?

4·76   Refer to Prob. 4·74. Starting from the initial conditions, what is the pressure of the air in the tank after 10 min?

CHAPTER 5

Real Gases

In Chapter 3 the physical properties of pure substances in general were discussed and the use of tabulated property values was introduced. Chapter 4 dealt with the equation of state and other relations for ideal gases. Now we come to the consideration of real gases which deviate from $pv = RT$ and for which in many cases there are no extensive tables of properties.

As mentioned in Art. 4·2, $pv = RT$ is sufficiently accurate for real gases in many applications. If it is not satisfactory, we must either modify it by means of correction factors or we must use other—and usually more complicated—equations of state. Also, if $pv \neq RT$, specific heats are usually functions of both pressure and temperature so that relations for u and h are not so simple as they are for ideal gases. This chapter concerns the pvT relations for real gases and also presents some data on the specific heats of real gases.

5·1 Compressibility factors

The simplest modification of the ideal-gas equation of state to fit real-gas behavior is the introduction of a compressibility factor Z, which is defined as

$$Z \equiv \frac{pv}{RT}$$

For an ideal gas, obviously, $Z = 1$. For a real gas, Z is a function of pressure and temperature and is usually determined empirically, although principles of both classical thermodynamics and statistical thermodynamics are used in correlating Z with other properties. The value of Z for any state is a direct indication of the error involved in using $pv = RT$ for that state.

Compressibility factor data in the usual form, Z vs. p for various values of T, are given for nitrogen in Fig. 5·1. (The general trend mentioned in Art. 4·2 of increasing accuracy of $pv = RT$ as pressure decreases and temperature increases does not hold for all ranges, and Fig. 5·1 shows this clearly. For example, at 32 F there is less error in $pv = RT$ at 2000 psia than at 1000 psia; and at a constant pressure of 2000 psia the error in $pv = RT$ increases as the temperature increases!)

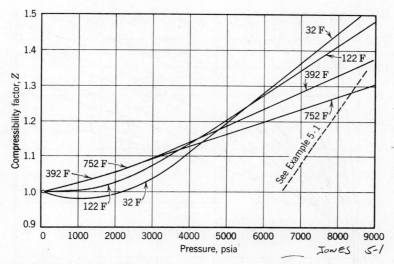

Fig. 5·1 Approximate compressibility factors for nitrogen. Data from E. P. Bartlett, H. L. Cupples, and T. H. Tremearne, *Journal American Chemical Society*, vol. 50, 1928, p. 1275; E. P. Bartlett, H. C. Heterington, H. M. Kvalnes, and T. H. Tremearne, *Journal American Chemical Society*, vol. 52, 1930, p. 1363; and B. F. Dodge, *Chemical Engineering Thermodynamics*, McGraw-Hill Book Co., 1944.

Compressibility factor data are given in a different form for superheated steam in Fig. 5·2. Examination of this chart shows the amount of error involved in the use of $pv = RT$ for steam at various pressures and temperatures.

A few compressibility factor values for four other gases are given in Table 5·1 as an indication of the error involved in using $pv = RT$ without correction.

EXAMPLE 5·1. Determine the pressure in a steel vessel having a volume of 0.5 cu ft and containing 7 lb of nitrogen at 752 F.

Solution. As a first approximation, assume that the ideal-gas equation of state holds; hence the compressibility factor equals 1.

$$p = \frac{ZmRT}{V} = \frac{1(7)1544(1212)}{144(28)0.5} = 6500 \text{ psia}$$

For this pressure and temperature the value for Z is 1.22. Assuming a new value for Z of 1.30 gives

$$p = \frac{1.30(7)1544(1212)}{14(28)0.5} = 8450 \text{ psia}$$

For this pressure and temperature, the value for Z is 1.29. It is evident that the

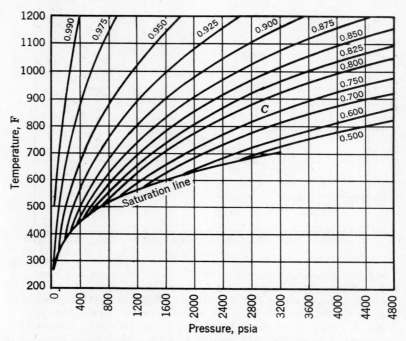

Fig. 5·2 Compressibility factors for superheated steam. Data from G. A. Hawkins and J. T. Agnew, *Combustion*, vol. 16, 1944, p. 46.

pressure is between 6500 and 8450, and very close to 8450; therefore assume that Z equals 1.28. The pressure equals

$$p = \frac{1.28(7)1544(1212)}{144(28)0.5} = 8320 \text{ psia}$$

The value for Z for this pressure and a temperature of 752 F is 1.28; hence by trial the value for p is 8320 psia.

Alternative solution. From the data specified we can write the following relation between p and Z for the state in question:

$$p = \frac{ZmRT}{V} = \frac{Z(7)1544(1212)}{28(0.5)144} = 6500Z \text{ psia}$$

This represents the broken straight line in Fig. 5·1. The intersection of the broken line and the 752 F isotherm gives the desired solution: $p = 8320$ psia and $Z = 1.28$.

TABLE 5·1
Compressibility Factors for Four Gases*

Gas	Pressure atm	psia	−100 F	0 F	200 F	1000 F	2000 F
Argon	1	14.7	0.997	0.999	1.000	1.000	1.000
	10	147	0.970	0.987	0.999	1.003	1.002
	40	588	0.877	0.952	0.995	1.011	1.009
	100	1470	0.690	0.887	0.995	1.029	1.022
Carbon	1	14.7	0.997	0.999	1.000	1.000	1.000
monoxide	10	147	0.973	0.991	1.001	1.004	1.003
	40	588		0.967	1.007	1.017	1.012
	100	1470			1.027	1.044	1.031
Carbon	1	14.7		0.991	0.997	1.000	1.000
dioxide	10	147		0.910	0.974	1.001	1.003
	40	588			0.894	1.006	1.010
	100	1470			0.721	1.018	1.026
Hydrogen	1	14.7	1.001	1.001	1.001		
	10	147	1.007	1.006	1.005		
	40	588	1.028	1.026	1.021		
	100	1470	1.076	1.067	1.052		

* Data from *Tables of Thermal Properties of Gases*, National Bureau of Standards Circular 564, 1955.

Essentially this is the solution of two simultaneous equations involving p and Z. One equation is the one written above from the data on the state in question; the other pZ equation is that of the 752 F isotherm on Fig. 5·1.

EXAMPLE 5·2. Three pounds of nitrogen in a closed system is compressed frictionlessly and isothermally from 4000 psia, 32 F, to 8000 psia. Determine the amount of work required.

Solution. For a closed-system frictionless process,

$$W = \int p \, dV$$

In order to integrate this expression, we must have the relationship between p and V at constant temperature. The pressures involved are too high for the ideal-gas equation to be used accurately, but perhaps we can use $pV = ZmRT$. Z is usually a function of pressure and temperature, but for the constant-temperature path of this process we have simply $Z = f(p)$. Reference to Fig. 5·1 shows that between 4000 psia and 8000 psia the 32 F isotherm is a straight line. Let $Z = a + bp$, and a and b can be determined from

Fig. 5·1. Since we know the pressure limits instead of the volume limits of the compression, let us replace V in the expression for work in terms of p. Thus

$$V = \frac{ZmRT}{p} = \frac{(a + bp)mRT}{p}$$

$$dV = -amRT\frac{dp}{p^2} + 0$$

$$W = \int_1^2 p \, dV = -\int_1^2 \frac{pamRT \, dp}{p^2} = -amRT \ln\frac{p_2}{p_1}$$

a is the $p = 0$ intercept of the 32 F isotherm between 4000 and 8000 psia as it is extended. A measurement on Fig. 5·1 gives $a = 0.78$. (It turns out that we do not have to calculate b.) Thus

$$W = -amRT \ln\frac{p_2}{p_1} = -0.78(3)\frac{1544}{28}(492)\ln\frac{8000}{4000} = -44,000 \text{ ft-lb}$$

The minus sign indicates that work is done on the system.

EXAMPLE 5·3. A closed tank contains 2 lb of nitrogen at 5000 psia and 392 F. Compute the pressure which results if the temperature is lowered to 32 F.

Solution. The mass of nitrogen and the R value are constant; so we can write

$$\frac{p_1 V_1}{Z_1 T_1} = mR = \frac{p_2 V_2}{Z_2 T_2}$$

or

$$p_2 = \frac{p_1 Z_2 T_2}{Z_1 T_1}$$

From Fig. 5·1 the value of Z_1 (at 5000 psia, 392 F) is approximately 1.19. Since the final pressure is unknown, assume that it is 3000 psia, for which $Z_2 = 1.04$. Then

$$p_2 = \frac{p_1 Z_2 T_2}{Z_1 T_1} = \frac{5000(1.04)492}{1.19(852)} = 2520 \text{ psia}$$

For this pressure the compressibility factor is 1.02; hence the assumed pressure is too high. Next assume that the pressure is 2400 psia, for which $Z = 1.01^+$. Then

$$p_2 = \frac{p_1 Z_2 T_2}{Z_1 T_1} = \frac{5000(1.01^+)492}{1.19(852)} = 2460 \text{ psia}$$

This is the approximate final pressure. If greater accuracy is necessary, additional trials and a more precise Zp chart are needed.

5·2   Reduced coordinates

The disadvantage of compressibility factor charts such as Figs. 5·1 and 5·2 is that a separate chart is needed for each gas. It would be convenient if one chart could be used for several gases. One way to do this is by means of the approximation known as the *law of corresponding states.*

According to this law, if any two gases have equal values for the ratio of pressure to critical pressure and equal values for the ratio of temperature to critical temperature, then the ratio of specific volume to critical specific volume is the same for the two gases. The ratios of pressure, temperature, and specific volume to the corresponding critical values are called *reduced coordinates* or *reduced properties*. Reduced pressure, reduced temperature, and reduced specific volume are defined by

$$p_R \equiv \frac{p}{p_c} \qquad T_R \equiv \frac{T}{T_c} \qquad v_R \equiv \frac{v}{v_c}$$

where the subscript R denotes a reduced property and the subscript c denotes a property at the critical point. (Values of p_c and T_c are given in Table 5·2.) In terms of these symbols, the law of corresponding states says that for all gases

$$v_R = f(p_R, T_R)$$

and the function is the same for all gases.

TABLE 5·2

Approximate Critical Constants for Several Gases

Gas	Critical Temperature		Critical Pressure	
	K	R	atm	psia
Air	132.4	238.8	37.2	547.0
Ammonia	405.5	730.1	111.5	1639.0
Argon	151.0	272.2	48.0	705.0
Carbon dioxide	304.1	547.8	72.9	1071.0
Carbon monoxide	134.4	242.2	34.6	508.2
Chlorine	417.0	751.0	76.0	1116.0
Ethane	305.2	549.8	48.8	717.0
Ethylene	282.8	509.5	50.7	745.0
Freon 12	384.7	692.5	39.6	582.1
Helium	5.2	10.0	2.3	33.8
Hydrogen	33.2	60.5	12.8	188.0
Isopentane	460.9	830.0	32.9	483.6
Mercury	1172.0	2109.0	180.0	2646.0
Methyl chloride	416.2	749.7	65.8	967.0
Neon	44.4	79.0	25.9	377.8
Nitrogen	126.0	227.2	33.5	492.5
Oxygen	154.3	278.1	49.7	730.9
Propane	369.9	666.3	42.0	617.0
Sulfur dioxide	430.3	775.0	77.7	1141.0
Water vapor	647.3	1165.4	218.2	3206.2

If the law of corresponding states were accurate, the diagram of Fig. 5·3 which is plotted from data on steam would apply to any gas. Actually, the law of corresponding states is not accurate, so errors in v_R of more than 15 per cent may result from using data on steam for other gases. A second drawback of using a chart like Fig. 5·3 is that accurate data on v_c are scarce, even for substances with very accurately measured values of p_c and T_c.

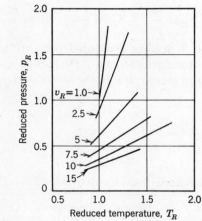

Fig. 5·3 Reduced pressure–temperature chart for superheated steam.

To illustrate the inaccuracy of the law of corresponding states, notice that the left-hand side of

$$v_R = f(p_R, T_R)$$

can be written as

$$v_R = \frac{v}{v_c} = \frac{ZRTp_c}{Z_cRT_cp} = \frac{Z}{Z_c}\left(\frac{T_R}{p_R}\right)$$

so that

$$\frac{Z}{Z_c}\frac{T_R}{p_R} = f(p_R, T_R)$$

and

$$\frac{Z}{Z_c} = \phi(p_R, T_R)$$

Thus it follows from the law of corresponding states that, at the same values of p_R and T_R, all gases have the same value of Z/Z_c. However, at very low values of p_R, $Z = 1$ for all gases; so Z_c must be the same for all gases if the law of corresponding states holds. Experiments show that this is not the case. For example, Z_c is 0.233 for water, 0.279 for carbon dioxide, and 0.305 for hydrogen. Consequently, the law of corresponding

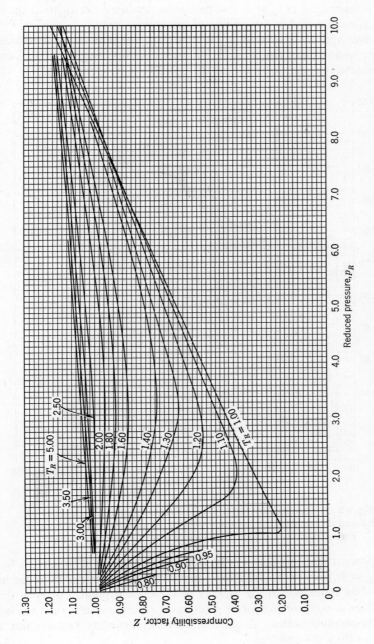

Fig. 5·4 Compressibility factor versus reduced pressure for a series of reduced temperatures (low-pressure range). From B. F. Dodge, *Chemical Engineering Thermodynamics*, McGraw-Hill Book Co., Inc. 1944.

states is inaccurate at least at low pressures. Further investigation shows
that it is most useful in the vicinity of the critical point.

Another approach is based on the observation that at the same reduced
pressure and reduced temperature all gases have approximately the same
compressibility factor, except near the critical point. Symbolically,

$$Z = f(p_R, T_R)$$

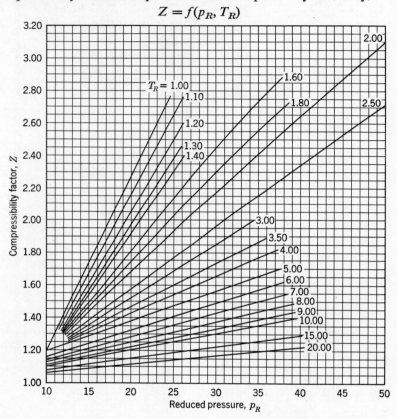

Fig. 5·5 Compressibility factor versus reduced pressure for a series of
reduced temperatures (high-pressure range). From B. F. Dodge, *Chemical
Engineering Thermodynamics*, McGraw-Hill Book Co., Inc. 1944.

It is apparent that this does not hold for the critical point, where $p_R = 1$
and $T_R = 1$, because we have seen above that Z_c is not the same for all
gases. For states not in the vicinity of the critical point, however, this
generalized compressibility factor gives more accurate results than the law
of corresponding states. A generalized compressibility factor chart is
shown in Figs. 5·4 and 5·5.

For helium, hydrogen, and neon, better results are obtained from the Zp_RT_R chart by using a pseudoreduced pressure p_R and a pseudoreduced temperature T_R, defined as

$$p_R \equiv \frac{p}{p_c + 8} \quad \text{and} \quad T_R \equiv \frac{T}{T_c + 14}$$

where p and p_c are in atmospheres and T and T_c are in degrees Rankine. Inspection of Figs. 5·4 and 5·5 shows that this modification influences Z most for values of T_R around 1, regardless of the p_R value, and for values of p_R around 1 when accompanied by a low T_R value, because it is in these regions that the variation of Z with p_R and T_R is the greatest. The use of pseudoreduced pressure and temperature improves the accuracy of the law of corresponding states also.

In the interest of accuracy, generalized compressibility factor data should be resorted to only when compressibility factor data for the particular gas in question are unavailable.

5·3   The van der Waals equation of state

Two assumptions made in developing the ideal-gas equation of state from kinetic theory are: (1) The volume of the molecules themselves is negligible in comparison with the volume occupied by the gas, and (2) the attractive forces between molecules are negligible. An equation of state which fits gases at high densities cannot be developed on the basis of these assumptions.

In 1873, J. D. van der Waals, who was awarded a Nobel prize in 1910, presented an equation of state which takes into account the finite size of the molecules and the attractive forces between them. Van der Waals reasoned that $pv = RT$ would be improved by replacing v by the volume (per unit mass of the gas) of the space between the molecules. If the volume of the molecules themselves is b, then the volume of the space between the molecules per unit mass of gas is $(v-b)$. b is called the covolume, and, since it is the volume occupied by the molecules if they were all jammed together, it is of the same order of magnitude as the specific volume of the liquid. This modification of the ideal-gas equation of state gives us $p(v-b) = RT$. Van der Waals further reasoned that the pressure of a real gas is less than that of an ideal gas at the same temperature and density on account of the attractive forces between molecules, and that this reduction in pressure is proportional to the square of the density or to $(1/v)^2$. Thus the van der Waals equation of state in molar form is

$$p = \frac{R_u T}{v_N - b} - \frac{a}{v_N^2} \tag{5·1}$$

or
$$\left(p + \frac{a}{v_N^2}\right)(v_N - b) = R_u T$$

Notice that the effect of each modification is greatest for states in which v_N is small.

The constants a and b can be evaluated from experimental data. It is found that slightly different values fit the data in various ranges of pressure and temperature; so van der Waals' equation is still only an approximate equation of state for real gases. Values of a and b for use in the van der Waals equation are given in Table 5·3. Care must be exercised to insure homogeneous units.

TABLE 5·3

Approximate Values for the van der Waals Constants

Gas	a, $\dfrac{\text{atm-ft}^6}{\text{mole}^2}$	$\dfrac{\text{psia-ft}^6}{\text{mole}^2}$	b, $\dfrac{\text{cu ft}}{\text{mole}}$
Air	344	5,052	0.587
Ammonia	1,070	15,720	0.596
Argon	346	5,082	0.516
Carbon dioxide	926	13,600	0.686
Carbon monoxide	381	5,598	0.639
Chlorine	1,665	24,460	0.900
Freon 12	2,718	39,950	1.595
Helium	8.57	126	0.372
Hydrogen	62.8	922	0.427
Mercury	5,100	74,900	1.070
Neon	55.4	814	0.282
Nitrogen	346	5,082	0.618
Oxygen	350	5,140	0.510
Sulfur dioxide	1,730	25,420	0.909
Water vapor	1,400	20,580	0.488

If the units for a and b are (atm)(ft^6)/mole^2 and cu ft/mole, the value and units for R_u are 0.729 atm-cu ft/mole-R. If the units for a and b are psia-ft^6/mole^2 and cu ft/mole, the value and units for R_u are 10.71 psia-cu ft/mole-R.

Since accurate pvT data are available for steam, it is possible to make a plot of the data and compare it with plots obtained by the use of the ideal-gas equation of state and the van der Waals equation of state.

The values for the pressure and specific volume of steam at 900 F, as obtained from the steam tables, have been plotted in Fig. 5·6 as curve C.

Values obtained from the van der Waals equation are plotted as curve B. The two curves agree closely. The ideal-gas equation of state was used for plotting curve A. There is a large discrepancy between curve A and curves B and C. Curve D represents the values for water vapor at a

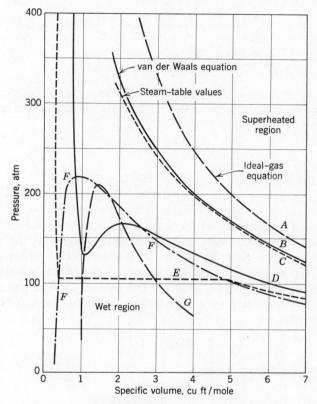

Fig. 5·6 pv diagram for water.

temperature of 600 F as computed by the van der Waals equation. Experimental (steam-table) values are plotted as curve E. These two curves deviate widely. Curve F is the actual saturated liquid and saturated vapor line.

Curve D in Fig. 5·6 is an isotherm for a van der Waals gas. Its shape is certainly peculiar for a constant-temperature line on a pv diagram; yet inspection of the van der Waals equation shows that it is cubic in v and that for some values of T it will have three real roots. Let us investigate this point. First, we can determine the maximum and minimum points of an isotherm by differentiating the van der Waals equation and setting $(\partial p/\partial v)_T$ equal to zero. Thus we have

$$p = \frac{R_u T}{v_N - b} - \frac{a}{v_N^2}$$

$$\left(\frac{\partial p}{\partial v_N}\right)_T = -\frac{R_u T}{(v_N - b)^2} + 2\frac{a}{v_N^3} = 0$$

and $$\frac{R_u T}{(v_N - b)^2} = \frac{2a}{v_N^3}$$

Eliminating T between this last equation and the van der Waals equation gives the equation of the locus of the maxima and minima for the family of isotherms

$$p = \frac{a(v_N - 2b)}{v_N^3}$$

This equation is represented by curve G in Fig. 5·6.

Curve G shows that isotherms at successively higher temperatures have maxima and minima which approach each other until the isotherm which passes through the peak of curve G has neither a maximum nor a minimum but only a point of inflection and a horizontal tangent at the peak of curve G. This is the characteristic of the isotherm which passes through the critical point; so the peak of curve G is the critical point for the van der Waals gas. In order to locate this critical point in terms of the van der Waals constants, we simply find the maximum point of curve G by differentiation,

$$\left(\frac{\partial p}{\partial v_N}\right)_T = -\frac{2a}{v_N^3} + \frac{6ab}{v_N^4} = 0$$

Solving for v_N gives

$$v_{Nc} = 3b$$

If we substitute this value of v_N into the equation of curve G, we have for the pressure at the critical point

$$p_c = \frac{a}{27b^2}$$

Substituting p_c and v_{Nc} into the van der Waals equation gives

$$T_c = \frac{8a}{27R_u b}$$

Isotherms for temperatures higher than $8a/27R_u b$ have no point at which the tangent is horizontal. All isotherms for lower temperatures have maxima and minima, and the portion of each isotherm between the maximum and minimum points does not represent the behavior of any real substance.

The equations above relating p_c, T_c, a, and b show that once the critical pressure and temperature of a substance are known the van der Waals equation can be used as an approximate equation of state.

EXAMPLE 5·4.   Determine by means of the van der Waals equation the pressure of 7 lb of nitrogen at 752 F contained in a vessel having a volume of 0.5 cu ft.

Solution. The molar specific volume is

$$v_N = \frac{V}{N} = \frac{VM}{m} = \frac{0.5(28)}{7} = 2 \text{ cu ft/mole}$$

Obtaining the van der Waals constants a and b from Table 5·3 and substituting values into the van der Waals equation gives

$$p = \frac{R_u T}{v_N - b} - \frac{a}{v_N^2} = \left[\frac{1544(1212)}{2 - 0.618} \right] \frac{1}{144} - \frac{5082}{(2)^2}$$

$$= 9400 - 1270 = 8130 \text{ psia}$$

(Compare this result with the more accurate solution of Example 5·1.)

EXAMPLE 5·5.   Compute the van der Waals constants for steam from the critical pressure and temperature.

Solution. From the steam tables we find the critical pressure and critical temperature to be 3206.2 psia (218.2 atm) and 705.4 F (1164.8 R, to the nearest 0.1 degree), respectively. We then have

$$p_c = 218.2 \text{ atm} = \frac{a}{27b^2}$$

and

$$T_c = 1164.8 \text{ R} = \frac{8a}{27R_u b} = \frac{8a}{27(0.729)b}$$

Solving these two equations for a and b gives

$$a = 1389 \text{ (atm)(ft}^6)/\text{mole}^2$$

$$b = 0.485 \text{ cu ft/mole}$$

5·4   The Beattie–Bridgeman equation of state

Many equations have been proposed since van der Waals presented his pressure–volume–temperature relation. One of these equations, known as the Beattie–Bridgeman equation of state,* is presented here because it has been used for formulating properties of the vapor close to the liquid phase

* Named for James A. Beattie and Oscar C. Bridgeman.

for substances at pressures which are less than the critical pressure. In general, the equation is accurate when the volumes involved are greater than twice the critical volume. The Beattie–Bridgeman equation of state is

$$p = \frac{R_u T(1 - \epsilon)}{v_N^2}(v_N + B) - \frac{A}{v_N^2} \tag{5.2}$$

where

$$A = A_0\left(1 - \frac{a}{v_N}\right)$$

$$B = B_0\left(1 - \frac{b}{v_N}\right)$$

$$\epsilon = \frac{c}{v_N T^3}$$

A_0, a, B_0, b, and c are constants and are given in Table 5·4. ϵ is a function of molar volume and temperature as shown.

EXAMPLE 5·6. Determine by means of the Beattie–Bridgeman equation the pressure of 7 lb of nitrogen at 752 F contained in a vessel having a volume of 0.5 cu ft.

Solution. The molar specific volume as obtained in Example 5·4 is 2 cu ft/mole. Obtaining the Beattie–Bridgeman constants from Table 5·4 and then substituting them

TABLE 5·4

Beattie–Bridgeman Constants

Gas	A_0 atm-ft^6 mole^2	A_0 psia-ft^6 mole^2	a, cu ft mole	B_0 cu ft mole	b, cu ft mole	$c(10^{-4})$, (cu ft-R^3) mole
Air	334	4,910	0.309	0.738	−0.0176	406
A	332	4,880	0.373	0.629	0.0	560
CO	345	5,070	0.419	0.808	−0.111	393
CO_2	1,285	18,890	1.14	1.69	1.16	6,170
H_2	50.7	745	−0.081	0.336	−0.698	4.7
He	5.6	82	0.958	0.224	0.0	0.37
N_2	345	5,070	0.419	0.808	−0.111	393
Ne	54.6	802	0.352	0.330	0.0	9.4
N_2O	1,285	18,890	1.14	1.68	0.116	6,170
O_2	383	5,620	0.411	0.741	0.0674	449

If the units for A_0 are atm-ft^6/mole^2, the value and units for R_u are 0.729 atm-cu ft/mole-R. If the units for A_0 are (psia)(ft^6)/mole^2, the value and units for R_u are 10.71 psia-cu ft/mole-R.

into the form of the Beattie–Bridgeman equation shown as equation 5·2, we have

$$A = A_0\left(1 - \frac{a}{v_N}\right) = 5070\left(1 - \frac{0.419}{2}\right) = 4010 \frac{\text{psia-ft}^6}{\text{mole}^2}$$

$$B = B_0\left(1 - \frac{b}{v_N}\right) = 0.808\left(1 + \frac{0.111}{2}\right) = 0.853 \text{ cu ft/mole}$$

$$\epsilon = \frac{c}{v_N T^3} = \frac{(393)10^4}{2(1212)^3} = 0.001103$$

$$p = \frac{R_u T(1 - \epsilon)}{v_N^2}(v_N + B) - \frac{A}{v_N^2}$$

$$= \frac{1544(1212)(1 - 0.001103)}{(2)^2}(2 + 0.853)\left(\frac{1}{144}\right) - \frac{4010}{(2)^2}$$

$$= 9250 - 1000 = 8250 \text{ psia}$$

(Compare this result with the more accurate solution of Example 5·1 and with the solution based on van der Waals equation, Example 5·4.)

5·5   Virial equations of state

Particularly for the purpose of preparing extensive tables of properties, it is often convenient to have an equation of state in the form

$$\frac{pv}{RT} = A_0 + A_1 p + A_2 p^2 + A_3 p^3 + \cdots$$

or

$$\frac{pv}{RT} = B_0 + \frac{B_1}{v} + \frac{B_2}{v^2} + \frac{B_3}{v^3} + \cdots$$

where the A's and B's are functions of temperature only. These equations are called *virial equations*, and the A's and B's are called *virial coefficients*. Several other forms of virial equations are also used. One of the advantages of virial equations of state is that it is relatively easy to determine the virial coefficients from experimental pvT data.

5·6   Specific heats of real gases

It was pointed out in the preceding chapter that the specific heats of ideal gases are functions of temperature only. The specific heats of real gases are functions of both pressure and temperature. In order to learn when the influence of pressure is greatest, consider first the hT diagram of

Fig. 5·7. This diagram is plotted from data on steam, but diagrams for other substances are similar. Recalling the definition of c_p

$$c_p \equiv \left(\frac{\partial h}{\partial T}\right)_p$$

we see that c_p is equal to the slope of a constant-pressure line on an hT diagram. Notice in Fig. 5·7 the steep slope of the constant-pressure lines

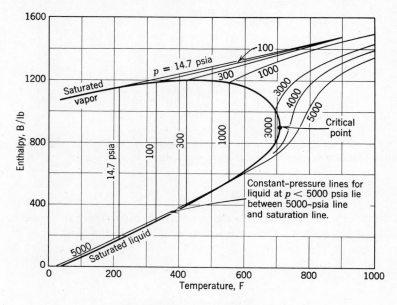

Fig. 5·7 hT diagram for water.

in the vicinity of the critical point. In fact, the constant-pressure line which passes through the critical point is vertical at that point, and so c_p is infinite at the critical point. Notice also that c_p is discontinuous at the saturation line because the slope of a constant-pressure line on an hT diagram changes abruptly there. The plot of c_p vs. T in Fig. 5·8 shows the marked increase in c_p near the critical point. This characteristic can be explained qualitatively in terms of the increase in molecular potential energy required during the expansion of a dense vapor as the temperature is increased at constant pressure. In a less dense vapor, expansion is accompanied by a smaller increase in molecular potential energy because the forces between molecules are smaller. In a liquid the intermolecular forces are high, but there is little increase in molecular potential energy when the temperature is increased at constant pressure because the increase in volume is usually small.

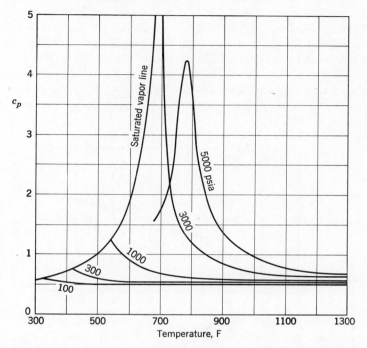

Fig. 5·8 c_p of water. Data from J. H. Keenan and F. G. Keyes, *Thermodynamic Properties of Steam*, John Wiley & Sons, Inc., 1936.

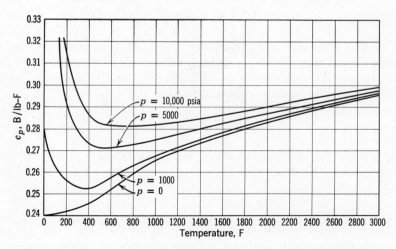

Fig. 5·9 The effect of temperature on c_p of air at various pressures. Data from F. O. Ellenwood, N. Kulik, and N. R. Gay, *Cornell University Engineering Experiment Station Bulletin* 30, 1942.

The increase in c_p near the critical point and the increase in c_p with temperature which is explained by kinetic theory for lower densities together account for the general shape of c_p vs. T curves of real gases at various pressures. Samples of such curves are shown in Figs. 5·9 and 5·10. (The c_{p0} curve of Fig. 5·9 is less accurate than that of Fig. 4·4 which is based on later data.) Pressure has less influence on the value of c_v than it does on the value of c_p. The quantity $(c_p - c_v)$ is not a constant as it is for ideal gases.

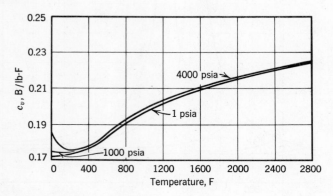

Fig. 5·10 The effect of temperature on c_v of air at various pressures. Data from F. O. Ellenwood, N. Kulik, and N. R. Gay, *Cornell University Engineering Experiment Station Bulletin* 30, 1942.

5·7 Summary

For real gases in many applications the ideal-gas equation of state is sufficiently accurate. When it is unsatisfactory, we must modify it by the use of *compressibility factors*, or we must use other equations of state. A compressibility factor Z is defined as

$$Z \equiv \frac{pv}{RT}$$

For an ideal gas, $Z = 1$. For a real gas, Z is a function of pressure and temperature. The value of Z for any state is a direct indication of the error involved in using $pv = RT$ for that state.

The *law of corresponding states*, which is most accurate in the vicinity of the critical point, states that, if any two gases have equal values for the ratio of pressure to critical pressure and equal values for the ratio of temperature to critical temperature, then the ratio of specific volume to critical specific volume is the same for the two gases. The ratios of pressure, temperature, and specific volume to the corresponding critical values are called *reduced coordinates* or *reduced properties*. By definition,

$$p_R \equiv \frac{p}{p_c} \qquad T_R \equiv \frac{T}{T_c} \qquad v_R \equiv \frac{v}{v_c}$$

where the subscript R denotes a reduced property, and the subscript c denotes a property at the critical point.

Except near the critical point, all gases at the same reduced pressure and reduced temperature have approximately the same compressibility factor. This makes it possible to use a single *generalized compressibility factor* chart of Z vs. p_R at various T_R for all gases.

For some gases the law of corresponding states and the Zp_RT_R chart give more accurate results if empirically determined *pseudoreduced* pressures and temperatures are used instead of the reduced pressures and temperatures as defined above.

Many equations of state have been developed for real gases. One of the most interesting is the van der Waals equation,

$$\left(p + \frac{a}{v_N^2}\right)(v_N - b) = R_u T \tag{5·1}$$

in which a and b are empirically determined constants which are different for each gas.

A more accurate equation of state which involves five constants for each gas is the Beattie–Bridgeman equation,

$$p = \frac{R_u T(1 - c/v_N T^3)}{v_N^2}\left[v_N + B_0\left(1 - \frac{b}{v_N}\right)\right] - \frac{A_0}{v_N^2}\left(1 - \frac{a}{v_N}\right) \tag{5·2}$$

(*a* and *b* in the Beattie–Bridgeman equation are not the same as *a* and *b* in the van der Waals equation.)

The specific heats of a real gas are functions of both pressure and temperature. The influence of pressure on specific heats is greater at lower temperatures.

In conclusion, a word of caution is in order. From this chapter on real gases it must not be inferred that all the gas property information an engineer ever needs has been collected and organized so that it can be found simply by searching the literature. All too often the important problems which engineers face are made more difficult by a dearth of information on some substance, on some particular property of even a common substance, or on the properties of a substance in an extreme pressure or temperature range.

REFERENCES

5·1 B. F. Dodge, *Chemical Engineering Thermodynamics*, McGraw-Hill Book Co., 1944, chapter V.

5·2 J. K. Roberts and A. R. Miller, *Heat and Thermodynamics*, Interscience Publishers, 4th ed., 1951.

5·3 P. J. Kiefer, G. F. Kinney, and M. C. Stuart, *Principles of Engineering Thermodynamics*, John Wiley & Sons, 2d ed., 1954, arts. 11-1 to 11-4.

5·4 E. F. Obert, *Thermodynamics*, McGraw-Hill Book Co., 1948, arts. 7-7 to 7-13.

5·5 L. C. Nelson and E. F. Obert, "Generalized *pvT* Properties of Gases," *Transactions ASME*, vol. 76, 1954, pp. 1057–1066.

5·6 *Tables of Thermal Properties of Gases*, National Bureau of Standards Circular 564, 1955.

PROBLEMS

5·1 Compute the pressure in a tank having a volume of 0.34 cu ft and containing 10 lb of nitrogen at 32 F. Use Fig. 5·1.

5·2 Determine the specific volume of nitrogen under a pressure of 9000 psia and at a temperature of 122 F.

5·3 By means of a compressibility factor, compute the specific volume of superheated steam at a pressure of 1500 psia and 1000 F. The value obtained from the steam tables is 0.539 cu ft/lb.

5·4 Compute the compressibility factor for steam at a pressure of 2000 psia and 900 F. The specific volume under these conditions is 0.3532 cu ft/lb.

5·5 Compute the specific volume of steam at a pressure and temperature of 200 psia and 800 F by means of (*a*) the ideal-gas equation of state, and (*b*) a compressibility factor.

5·6 A closed rigid tank which has a volume of 3.0 cu ft contains nitrogen at 4000 psia, 392 F. Calculate the nitrogen pressure which results when the gas in the tank is cooled to 32 F.

5·7 Compressibility factor has been defined as the ratio of the specific volume of a gas to the specific volume predicted by the ideal-gas equation of state. Does this agree with the definition presented in Art. 5·1?

5·8 Determine the value of Z_c for a van der Waals gas.

5·9 If the values for the reduced pressure and compressibility factor for ethylene are 20 and 1.25, respectively, compute the temperature.

5·10 Compute the specific volume of propane at a pressure of 617 psia and a temperature of 472 F.

5·11 If the compressibility factor and reduced pressure are 0.7 and 1.2, respectively, for isopentane, compute the temperature.

5·12 If the reduced pressure and temperature are 1.5 and 1.22, respectively, for steam, compute the specific volume.

5·13 Compute the specific volume of helium at 541 psia, 200 R.

5·14 Estimate the pressure of nitrogen at a temperature of 122 F if the specific volume is 0.0394 cu ft/lb.

5·15 Compute the specific volume of nitrogen at 1000 atm, 400 F, by means of (a) the ideal-gas equation of state, (b) van der Waals' equation, and (c) reduced coordinates.

5·16 By means of the ideal-gas equation and van der Waals' relation, compute the pressure of 3 moles of sulfur dioxide at 150 F when the total volume is 111 cu ft.

5·17 Compute the critical pressure and the critical temperature for benzene vapor. Assume that $a = 4810$ atm-ft^6/mole^2 and $b = 1.932$ cu ft/mole.

5·18 Compute the pressure of argon for a temperature of 800 F and a specific volume of 0.2 cu ft/lb by means of van der Waals' equation.

5·19 Two pounds of nitrogen at 800 F occupy 90 cu ft. Compute the pressure of the gas according to van der Waals' equation.

5·20 Compute the temperature of a quantity of argon at a pressure of 200 psia and specific volume of 2 cu ft/lb by use of van der Waals' equation.

5·21 The critical temperature and pressure for a hypothetical gas are known to be 380.8 F and 35.5 atm, respectively. Compute the values for van der Waals' constants.

5·22 By means of van der Waals' equation of state, compute the specific volume of nitrogen at 4000 psia, 300 F.

5·23 Develop the following form of van der Waals' equation in terms of the reduced coordinates.

$$\left(p_R + \frac{3}{v_R^2}\right)(v_R - \tfrac{1}{3}) = \tfrac{8}{3}T_R$$

5·24 Compute the pressure of air at 400 F when the specific volume is 0.050 cu ft/lb by means of (a) the ideal-gas equation of state, (b) van der Waals' equation, and (c) the Beattie–Bridgeman equation.

5·25 Compute the pressure of neon for a temperature of 100 F and a specific volume of 0.15 cu ft/lb by means of the Beattie–Bridgeman equation.

5·26 Using the Beattie–Bridgeman equation, compute the pressure exerted by a quantity of air compressed to a volume of 0.008 cu ft at a temperature of 40 F. Before compression, the air occupied a volume of 1 cu ft at 70 F and 14.7 psia.

5·27 Compute the specific volume for nitrogen at 10,000 psia, 200 F, by means of the Beattie–Bridgeman equation of state.

5·28 Compute the heat required to raise the temperature of 1 lb of air from 600 to 1000 F if the pressure is 10,000 psia.

5·29 Compute the heat required to increase the temperature of 1 mole of air from 300 to 700 F at a constant pressure of 5000 psia.

CHAPTER 6

The Second Law

6·1 Limitations of the first law

The first law of thermodynamics expresses a relationship between heat and work and makes possible the definition of stored energy. It can then be extended to give a simple relationship among work, heat, and the change in stored energy of a system. In this form the first law is known as the law of conservation of energy. The first law does not limit the extent of any energy conversion nor does it give any indication as to whether any particular process which may be conceived is possible or not. Yet experience shows that at least one type of desirable energy conversion— heat to work—cannot be carried out completely and also that certain processes which would in no way violate the first law cannot be made to occur. Let us survey these two lessons of experience more closely.

Consider a gasoline engine. Energy stored in the fuel and in the combustion air is delivered to the engine. Energy leaves the engine as work via the drive shaft, as heat, and as stored energy in the exhaust gases. There is also an energy transfer as flow work of the fluids entering and leaving. For economical operation it is desirable to have the work output as great as possible for a given amount of energy input. This means that the energy leaving the engine in the exhaust gases and as heat should be reduced to a minimum. As far as the first law is concerned, these energy losses could be reduced to zero, and the work output would be equal to the energy input. All attempts to obtain such performance from an engine have failed. No matter what ingenious accessories have been used, the complete conversion of fuel energy into work in an engine which operates continuously has not been accomplished. Some energy has always been thrown away either in the exhaust gases or as heat. It is reasonable to ask "Is this necessary?" or "Is there some law of nature which accounts for the limitation on this energy conversion?"

A steam power plant affords another example of a limited conversion of energy stored in fuel into work. Even the best steam power plants require for the production of 100 B of work an energy input of about 250 B. Thus,

for every 100 B of work produced, about 150 B is rejected to the surroundings as some form of energy other than work. Again, the question arises:
"Is this necessary?"

Consider now two blocks of steel at different temperatures which are
enclosed together in a thermally insulated box. Of course, energy will be
transferred from the higher-temperature to the lower-temperature block
as heat, and, if there is nothing inside the box besides the two steel blocks,
the amount of energy lost by the higher-temperature block will be equal
to the amount of energy gained by the lower-temperature block. This is in
accordance with the first law. Just as much in accordance with the first
law, however, would be a process whereby energy was transferred from the
lower-temperature block to the higher-temperature block. This latter
process has never been known to occur, however, so satisfaction of the
first law alone does not insure that a process can occur. As another
example, a spinning flywheel mounted on a shaft between two bearings
will come to rest as a result of friction in the bearings. In this process the
kinetic energy of the flywheel and shaft is reduced to zero while the internal
energy of the bearings, the lubricant, and part of the shaft is increased by
the same magnitude. Energy is conserved. Energy would also be conserved
in the reverse process which would consist of a cooling of the bearings,
lubricant, and parts of the shaft, and the acceleration of the flywheel and
shaft until their kinetic energy equals the decrease in internal energy of
those parts which were cooled. It is common knowledge that this process
does not occur. Although we recognize this intuitively in this simple case,
we naturally wonder if there is some law of nature which will support our
intuition in this case and guide us in more complex cases where intuition
alone will not tell us whether a certain process is possible or not.

These illustrations of the limitations of the first law of thermodynamics
show us the need for another general principle of widespread application:
the second law of thermodynamics.

6·2 The second law of thermodynamics

Studies of questions similar to those in the preceding article in the light
of much experience, including many deliberate experiments, have led to the
formulation of the second law of thermodynamics. This law has been
stated in many different forms, some of which appear to the beginner to
bear no relation whatsoever to the other forms. If any one of the statements of the second law is accepted as a postulate, all the other statements
can then be proved from this starting point; but the statement which is
taken as the starting point cannot be derived from any other law of nature.
Two of the well-known statements of the second law of thermodynamics

are known as the Clausius statement and the Kelvin–Planck* statement.

The Clausius statement may be given as follows: *It is impossible for any device to operate in such a manner that it produces no effect other than the transfer of heat from one body to another body at a higher temperature.* This statement bears close investigation. It does not say that it is impossible to transfer heat from a lower-temperature body to a higher-temperature body. Indeed, this is exactly what a refrigerator does. A refrigerator does not operate, though, unless it receives an energy input, usually in the form of work, from some source other than the two bodies between which it is causing heat to flow. This transfer of energy from the surroundings constitutes an effect other than the transfer of heat from the lower-temperature body to the higher-temperature body. The "no effect" mentioned in the Clausius statement of the second law includes effects within the refrigerating device itself. It is possible to build and operate a device which will absorb heat from a lower-temperature body, reject heat to a higher-temperature body, and produce no other effect in the surroundings. However, this device will itself experience an effect and be in a different state at the conclusion of the process from the one it was in at the beginning. Thus it has produced some effects other than the transfer of heat from one body to another body at a higher temperature and therefore does not violate the Clausius statement. Questions about effects within the device are avoided by having the device operate in a cycle so that it is always returned to its initial state.

The Clausius statement is sometimes given as "Heat cannot of itself pass from a cold to a hot body." This statement requires interpretation. In the words of Planck, "As Clausius repeatedly and expressly pointed out, this principle does not merely say that heat does not flow directly from a cold

---

* Rudolph Julius Emmanuel Clausius (1822–1888) was a German mathematical physicist. After a study of the work of Sadi Carnot (see Arts. 7·6 and 8·1) he presented in 1850 a clear general statement of the second law. He applied the second law and showed the value of the property entropy (see chapter 9) in an exhaustive treatise on steam engines. Although he made significant contributions in the areas of optics, kinetic theory of gases, and electrolysis, he is most famous for his work related to the second law. William Thomson (Lord Kelvin) (1824–1907), one of the outstanding physicists of all time, was for 53 years professor of natural philosophy at the University of Glasgow. In 1851 he presented a paper in which the first and second laws were combined for the first time. In addition to his work in helping to firmly establish the first law and in formulating the second law of thermodynamics, he published papers on geophysics, electricity, magnetism, telegraphy, navigation, and many other branches of science. He invented many instruments for scientific and engineering work. The encouragement which he gave to his students and to other scientists played a large part in scientific advances made by others. Max Planck (1858–1947), professor of physics at the University of Berlin, clarified several concepts in thermodynamics but is best known for his work on radiation in which he laid the foundation of the quantum theory.

to a hot body—that is self-evident, and is a condition of the definition of temperature—but it expressly states that heat can in no way and by no process be transported from a colder to a warmer body without leaving further changes." The form of the Clausius statement given in the preceding paragraph makes this interpretation clear. One advantage of the Clausius statement over many other statements of the second law is that it is one which many people find easy to accept intuitively. A statement which pertains more directly to heat engines is the Kelvin–Planck statement.

The Kelvin–Planck statement of the second law is as follows: *It is impossible for any device to operate in a cycle and produce work while exchanging heat only with bodies at a single fixed temperature.* Notice that the value of the temperature of the bodies in the surroundings is not mentioned. If a device can operate cyclically and produce work while exchanging heat only with bodies at 1000 F, it can be made to do the same thing while exchanging heat only with bodies at, say, 0 F. Application of the first law to a device which violates the Kelvin–Planck statement of the second law (recalling that $\oint dE = 0$) shows that the net work produced would be equal to the net amount of heat received from bodies in the surroundings which are all at the same temperature. Such a device is called a perpetual-motion machine of the second kind. The Kelvin–Planck statement is sometimes paraphrased as "A perpetual-motion machine of the second kind is impossible."

A common version of the Kelvin–Planck statement is: It is impossible for any device operating in a cycle to absorb heat from a single reservoir and produce an equivalent amount of work. The term *reservoir* refers to an *energy reservoir* which is defined as a body or system that a finite amount of energy can be drawn from or added to without causing a change in its temperature. In practice, the atmosphere or the water of a river or lake can serve as an energy reservoir. Thousands of Btu can be discharged to river water by a power plant without appreciably raising the temperature of the river. A furnace atmosphere which is maintained at a constant temperature by the combustion of fuel serves as an energy reservoir in a steam power plant.

The Clausius and Kelvin–Planck statements of the second law are entirely equivalent to each other in their consequences. This equivalence can be demonstrated by showing that the violation of either statement can always be made to result in a violation of the other one. Each case will now be shown.

Referring to Fig. 6·1a, the device marked "Clausius violator" causes heat Q to be transferred from the energy reservoir at T_L to the one at the higher temperature T_H without causing any other effects. This is the kind of device which is impossible according to the Clausius statement. In order to show that the Kelvin–Planck statement can be violated any time the Clausius statement is violated, let a heat engine operate with heat input Q from the reservoir at T_H and with an amount of heat Q_L rejected to the reservoir at T_L. It is a matter of experience that actual heat engines can operate in this manner. Application of the first law shows that the amount of heat rejected Q_L is equal to $(Q - W)$, where W is the work output of the

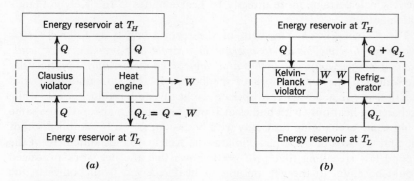

Fig. 6·1 Equivalence of the Clausius and Kelvin–Planck statements of the second law.

heat engine. Since the amount of heat rejected at T_H by the Clausius violator equals the amount absorbed at the same temperature by the heat engine, the operation of the system comprised of these two devices (and bounded by a broken line in Fig. 6·1a) produces no change in the reservoir at T_H. In fact, the reservoir could be eliminated by having the Clausius violator transfer heat directly to the heat engine. Thus the system comprised of the two devices absorbs a net amount of heat $(Q - Q_L)$ from a single reservoir (at T_L), produces work, and produces no other effects. This is a violation of the Kelvin–Planck statement. Thus it is shown that a violation of the Clausius statement can be made to result in a violation of the Kelvin–Planck statement.

The device labeled "Kelvin–Planck violator" in Fig. 6·1b absorbs an amount of heat Q from the reservoir at T_H, produces an equivalent amount of work W, and produces no other effects. This is the kind of device which the Kelvin–Planck statement declares to be impossible. In order to show that the operation of such a device can be made to result in a violation of the Clausius statement, let a refrigerator be used to transfer heat from the reservoir at T_L to the reservoir at T_H. Such a refrigerator can certainly be operated, but some work input is required. Let the refrigerator be driven by the Kelvin–Planck violator. Then see what the system comprised of both devices is doing! It is operating cyclically, causing heat to be transferred from one reservoir to another one at a higher temperature, and producing no other effects. Thus a violation of the Kelvin–Planck statement results in a violation of the Clausius statement. This paragraph and the preceding one therefore show the equivalence of these two statements of the second law of thermodynamics.

Several corollaries will be deduced from the second law. To disprove the second law it is necessary only to disprove any one of its corollaries. As yet, all attempts to do this have failed.

6·3   Perpetual-motion machines

Perpetual-motion machines are sometimes spoken of as being of three kinds. A perpetual-motion machine of the first kind violates the first law by operating in a cycle and producing a greater net work output than the net amount of heat put into the machine. Many such machines have been proposed, and several of them have been patented, but none of these has actually operated as a perpetual-motion machine of the first kind.

As mentioned above, a perpetual-motion machine of the second kind is one which violates the second law by producing work while operating cyclically and exchanging heat only with bodies at a single fixed temperature. Notice that no violation of the first law is involved. No energy is created, but such a device is just as valuable as a perpetual-motion machine of the first kind, because a virtually limitless supply of energy is available in the atmosphere or the oceans for input to such a machine.

Occasionally the name of perpetual-motion machine of the third kind is applied to devices which, once set in motion, continue in motion for an indefinitely long time without slowing down. A spinning top on a frictionless pivot or a spinning flywheel mounted in frictionless bearings is an example of this type of perpetual-motion machine. Notice that it violates neither the first nor the second law of thermodynamics but requires only the elimination of friction. Although no one has succeeded in completely eliminating friction from such devices, it appears that the extent to which friction can be reduced, short of complete elimination, depends only on the time and money available. Notice also that a perpetual-motion machine of the third kind produces no work and would therefore not be so valuable as one of the first or second kind.

6·4   The value of the second law

Why is the second law valuable? What good does it do us? In later chapters we will see that the second law and its corollaries provide means for (1) determining the maximum possible efficiency of a heat engine under various conditions, (2) determining the maximum coefficient of performance of a refrigerator under various conditions, (3) determining whether any particular process we may conceive is possible or not, (4) predicting in which direction a chemical reaction or any other process will proceed, (5) defining a temperature scale which is independent of physical properties, and (6) correlating physical properties.

For example, a few specific questions we will be able to answer after studying the applications of the second law are the following:

1. In a steam power plant, the maximum furnace temperature is 2600 F, and cooling water is available at 60 F. What is the maximum possible thermal efficiency of the steam power plant, no matter how many refinements are included in its design?

2. A refrigerator located in a room where the air temperature is 70 F freezes 10 lb of ice per hour from water initially at 50 F. The refrigerator rejects heat to the air in the room. What is the absolute minimum power requirement of the refrigerator?

3. Air expands adiabatically from 30 psia, 100 F, to 15 psia. What is the lowest possible final temperature?

4. Is it possible to compress air adiabatically from 15 psia, 60 F, to (a) 30 psia, 120 F? (b) 30 psia, 220 F?

5. If carbon dioxide is expanded adiabatically through a nozzle from zero velocity at 40 psia, 100 F, to 15 psia, what is the maximum velocity it can reach?

6. Sixteen pounds of oxygen and 28 lb of carbon monoxide fill a tank. The mixture is heated until it is at 40 psia, 1000 F. To what extent does the reaction $CO + \frac{1}{2}O_2 \rightarrow CO_2$ occur?

7. Is there a limit as to how low a temperature can be attained?

8. Steel expands when heated. When it is stretched adiabatically within the elastic limit, does its temperature increase or decrease?

The answers to questions such as these can be obtained from the second law through a process of deductive reasoning. So that we do not have to reason all the way from the second law itself each time we answer such questions, we carry some of the reasoning through once and establish certain useful definitions and some corollaries of the second law from which we can then begin our reasoning for particular applications. The next chapter does not answer a single one of the questions listed above, but it does establish some of these useful definitions which will help us in answering these questions later.

6·5 Conclusion

The second law of thermodynamics is a far-reaching principle of nature which has been stated in many forms. For engineers, one of the following two forms is usually the most valuable:

The Clausius statement: *It is impossible for any device to operate in such a manner that it produces no effect other than the transfer of heat from one body to another body at a higher temperature.*

The Kelvin–Planck statement: *It is impossible for any device to operate in a cycle and produce work while exchanging heat only with bodies at a single fixed temperature.*

These two statements of the second law and many others are entirely equivalent in their consequences. If any one of them is taken as a starting point, all of the others can be deduced.

CHAPTER 7

Reversible and Irreversible Processes and Cycles

It was mentioned in the preceding chapter that certain processes which can be conceived do not occur. The second law is useful in distinguishing such impossible processes. Of the processes which are possible, some bring about changes in a system and its surroundings which can be completely undone: that is, both the system and the surroundings can be returned to their initial states. Other processes which occur cause changes such that the system and all of its surroundings can never *both* be returned to their initial states! These processes are called reversible and irreversible processes, respectively. One of the reasons why engineers are interested in reversible processes is that for devices which produce work, such as engines and turbines, reversible processes of the working fluid deliver more work than corresponding irreversible processes. Also, refrigerators, compressors, fans, and pumps require less power input when reversible processes are used in place of the corresponding irreversible ones.

This chapter discusses reversible and irreversible processes and also some engine and refrigerator cycles made up of reversible processes.

7·1 Reversible and irreversible processes. Definitions

A process is *reversible* if, after it has occurred, both the system and all the surroundings can by any means whatsoever be returned to the states they were in before the process occurred. Any other process which occurs is *irreversible*.

In order to determine whether the system and surroundings can be returned to their initial states after a process has occurred, it is necessary to apply the second law. The application of the second law for this purpose is illustrated in the following article.

7·2 Reversible and irreversible processes. Characteristics; illustrations

Irreversible processes will be examined before reversible processes for two reasons. First, it is often easier to show the impossibility of meeting the test for reversibility than it is to show a method of meeting it. Second, once certain irreversible occurrences are identified, reversible processes are often recognized simply by the absence of these irreversible events.

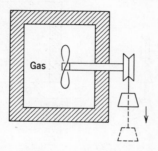

Fig. 7·1   Stirring process.   System changes from state A to state B as the weight drops.

If a process is reversible, then the reverse process—the one which restores both the system and the surroundings to their initial states—is possible. If a process is irreversible, the reverse process is impossible. Determining whether a process is reversible or irreversible is then a matter of determining whether the reverse process is possible or impossible.

One way to prove that a process is impossible is as follows: (1) Assume that the process is possible. (2) Combine this process with other processes, known from experience to be possible, to form a cycle which violates the second law. If such a cycle can be devised, then the assumption of step 1 is false and the process in question is impossible.

Consider the process in which a gas in a closed rigid thermally insulated tank is stirred by a paddle wheel. The system is the gas within the tank. (Assume there is never more than a negligible amount of heat transfer between the gas and the paddle wheel itself.) Let the paddle wheel be turned by the action of a falling weight which turns a pulley on the shaft (see Fig. 7·1). The motion of the paddle wheel is resisted by shearing forces in the gas, and thus work is done on the gas by the paddle wheel. The gas changes from state A to state B. Application of the first law shows that the internal energy of the gas is increased. The temperature of the gas increases.

The question is now: Is this process reversible? If it is reversible, then it is possible to restore both the system and the surroundings to their initial states after the process has occurred. That is, there must be some process which results in the weight's being lifted to its initial position while the internal energy of the gas (and hence its temperature) decreases. The gas changes from state B to state A. No change other than the lowering of the weight was made in the surroundings during the original process; therefore, no change in the surroundings other than the lifting of the

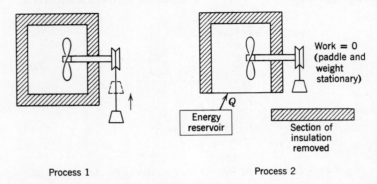

Process 1   Process 2

Fig. 7·2   Process 1: System is changed from state B to state A as the weight is lifted. (Assumed to be possible.) Process 2: System is changed from state A to state B.

weight can be made during the reverse process if it is to result in both the system and the surroundings being returned to their initial states. If this reverse process is possible, then the stirring process is reversible; if this reverse process is impossible, then the stirring process is irreversible. Thus a question equivalent to *Is the stirring process reversible?* is: *Is the reverse process possible?* Let us answer this by first *assuming* that the reverse process *is possible.* Then consider a cycle composed of two processes:

PROCESS 1: the process described above in which the weight is raised as the temperature and internal energy of the gas decrease. (This is the process we have assumed to be possible.) The system changes from an initial state B to state A (see Fig. 7·2).

PROCESS 2: a process in which heat is transferred from some constant-temperature energy reservoir in the surroundings to the gas while the paddle wheel is stationary. (Part of the thermal insulation of the tank must be removed during this process.) This process continues until the gas is brought to its initial temperature T_B. (The energy reservoir must therefore be at a temperature higher than T_B.)

The net results of this cycle are: (1) The system which has executed a cycle is restored to its initial state, and (2) two changes have occurred in the surroundings: (*a*) The weight is at a higher level than it was initially, and (*b*) the amount of energy stored in the energy reservoir has been decreased. Application of the first law shows that the energy decrease of the reservoir equals the energy increase of the weight. Thus the system is a device which operates in a cycle, exchanges heat with a single reservoir, and does work. This is precisely the kind of device which the second law declares to be impossible. Now it is a matter of experience that process 2 is possible; therefore if the cycle is impossible, it must be so because process 1 is impossible. Thus our assumption that process 1 is possible is false: Process 1 is impossible. Since process 1 is impossible, the original stirring process is irreversible. The only alternative is that the second law is false, and a tremendous amount of experience argues against this alternative.

Summarizing the reasoning above, the process considered is the stirring of a gas in a rigid thermally insulated tank. The question is: Is this process reversible? It was shown that the assumption that the process is reversible permits the occurrence of a process which, when combined with a process known to be possible, leads to a violation of the second law. Thus the conclusion is that the assumption is false and the stirring process is irreversible. The following examples show the application of the same line of reasoning to other processes.

EXAMPLE 7·1.   A block initially at rest on an inclined plane slides down the plane and comes to rest at a lower elevation. Is this process reversible?

Solution.   The system is comprised of the block and the plane. During this process, the internal energy of the block and plane increases by an amount equal to the decrease

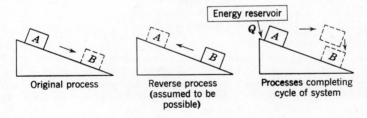

Original process   Reverse process   Processes completing
                     (assumed to be   cycle of system
                     possible)

Example 7·1

in potential energy of the block. At least parts of the block and plane will go to a higher temperature. There is no change in the surroundings. If this process is reversible, the reverse process is possible. The *reverse* process consists of the block being lifted to its initial position while the internal energy of the system (block and plane) is decreased by an amount equal to the increase in potential energy of the block. The temperatures of the block and plane decrease. Since there was no change in the surroundings during the original process, there must be none during the reverse process.

Assume that the reverse process is possible. It can be incorporated into a cycle which violates the second law in the following manner: First, let the reverse process occur, lifting the block from position B to position A and decreasing the internal energy (and temperatures) of the block and the plane. Next, add heat to the system from some energy reservoir in the surroundings to increase the internal energy of the system by the amount it was just decreased. Move the block horizontally off the plane (doing no work) until it is directly above position B. Then lower the block to position B, allowing it to do work equal to its decrease in potential energy. (For example, a weight in the surroundings can be lifted by means of a pulley arrangement.) The system has thus executed a cycle. The net result of this cycle has been to take heat from a single energy reservoir, perform an equivalent amount of work, and produce no other effects.

In accordance with the second law, this cycle is impossible. The heating of the system is possible, and the lowering of the block as it does work is possible; therefore it must be the process in which the block moved from B to A while the system internal energy decreased that is impossible. This is the reverse of the original process in which the block slides down the plane; hence this original process is irreversible.

EXAMPLE 7·2. Demonstrate that the transfer of heat across a finite temperature difference is irreversible.

Solution. *If* the transfer of heat from a body at a temperature T_H to a body at a lower temperature T_L is reversible, then the transfer of heat from the body at T_L to the

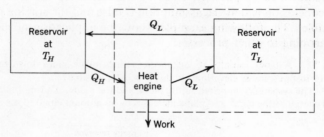

Example 7·2

one at T_H without any other effects is possible. Assume that this transfer of heat from T_L to T_H is possible. Then construct a cycle as follows: (1) Let an amount of heat Q_H be transferred from a reservoir at T_H to a heat engine which operates cyclically, producing work and rejecting an amount of heat Q_L to a reservoir at a lower temperature T_L. It is a matter of experience that this can be done. (2) Then let an amount of heat Q_L be transferred from the reservoir at T_L to the one at T_H in accordance with the assumption that such a process is possible. Since Q_L was added to the low-temperature reservoir in the first process and the same amount of heat was withdrawn from it during the second process, this reservoir has executed a cycle. The heat engine also executed a cycle. Therefore the system enclosed by the broken line on the diagram (and comprised of the heat engine and the reservoir at T_L) has executed a cycle. Notice that during this cycle this composite system has produced work while exchanging heat with a single reservoir. Such a cycle violates the second law. Checking back to see which process of the proposed cycle might actually be impossible and thus prevent the execution of such a cycle, we see that the first process is proved by experience to be possible, and the second process, which we *assumed* to be possible, must actually be impossible. If this process—the transfer of heat from T_L to T_H—is impossible, then the transfer of heat across the finite temperature difference from T_H to T_L must be irreversible.

EXAMPLE 7·3. Demonstrate that the free expansion of a gas is an irreversible process. An example of a free or unrestrained expansion of a gas is the following: An insulated tank is separated into two parts by a partition. A gas is held in the tank on one side of the partition, and on the other side of the partition the tank is evacuated. An opening is then made in the partition, and the gas expands to fill the entire tank. No work is done.

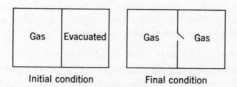

Initial condition   Final condition

Example 7·3

Solution. In order to show that a free expansion is irreversible, we will show that the reverse process is impossible. First, assume that the reverse process is possible. Consider the gas as the system. This reverse process would begin with the gas occupying the entire tank and would result in all the gas on one side of the partition being passed through the partition to the other side against the increasing pressure of the gas. This would occur without any interaction with the surroundings since the free expansion process occurred without any interaction with the surroundings. Consider a cycle made up of three processes: (1) Starting with the gas all on one side of the partition, let part of it expand through an engine and into the other part of the tank until the pressure is

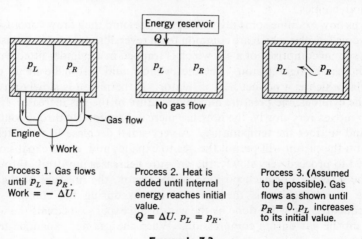

Process 1. Gas flows until $p_L = p_R$. Work $= -\Delta U$.

Process 2. Heat is added until internal energy reaches initial value. $Q = \Delta U$. $p_L = p_R$.

Process 3. (Assumed to be possible). Gas flows as shown until $p_R = 0$. p_L increases to its initial value.

Example 7·3

the same on the two sides of the partition. In expanding through the engine the gas does work so that its internal energy is decreased. (2) Remove part of the tank insulation, and add heat from an external reservoir to the gas until its internal energy is restored to its initial value. (Notice that for a free expansion process $\Delta U = 0$, since during such a process work $= 0$ and $Q = 0$.) (3) Starting with the gas which is now in the condition it would have been in following a free expansion from its initial condition, let the reverse of a free expansion occur to restore the system to its initial state. Thus a cycle is completed.

Inspection of this *cycle* reveals that it results in a production of work while heat is absorbed from a single reservoir. This cycle thereby violates the second law. Reinspection of the cycle reveals that processes 1 and 2 are shown by experience to be possible whereas process 3 is *assumed* to be possible. If the second law is accepted, then the assumption regarding process 3 is false. The reverse of a free expansion is therefore impossible and a free expansion must be irreversible.

By reasoning similar to that used in the preceding examples it can be shown that processes involving mixing,* inelastic deformation of a substance, and certain other effects are also irreversible. A reversible process must therefore involve no

   (a) Friction,
   (b) Heat transfer across a finite temperature difference,
   (c) Free expansion,
   (d) Mixing,
   (e) Inelastic deformation.

Various other effects (such as an electric current flow through a resistance, to name one) are also irreversible but are not listed here. In all cases the test for reversibility involves the application of the second law of thermodynamics.

Let us now examine some reversible processes and then draw conclusions as to some features which are common to all reversible processes. Consider first a system comprised of a gas which is trapped in a cylinder fitted with a frictionless gas-tight piston. Let the cylinder and piston be made of a material which is a perfect heat insulator. If the piston is slowly pushed into the cylinder, the pressure and temperature of the gas increase. If the piston moves very slowly, the pressure increases uniformly throughout the gas, and so does the temperature. A very small decrease in the external force on the piston will permit the gas to expand, and, if the expansion is allowed to proceed very slowly, the pressure decreases uniformly throughout the system. For each position of the piston, the pressure of the gas during the expansion is the same as it was during the compression. Consequently, the work done by the gas during expansion equals the work done on the gas during compression. When the gas has expanded to its initial volume, all the work originally done on the system has been returned to the surroundings as work. There has been no heat transfer. The surroundings have therefore been returned to their initial state. The system has also been returned to its initial state. Thus, after a very slow

* Under very special conditions mixing may be done reversibly. See B. F. Dodge, *Chemical Engineering Thermodynamics*, McGraw-Hill Book Co., 1944, p. 34.

frictionless adiabatic compression is completed, it is possible to restore both the system and the surroundings to their initial states. Consequently the very slow frictionless adiabatic is a reversible process.

If the adiabatic compression is performed by a rapid inward motion of the piston, the process is not reversible. The pressure near the piston face is higher than that elsewhere in the cylinder. A pressure wave is thus initiated, and it travels through the gas until the pressure is again uniform. Then, even if the gas expanded slowly to its initial volume, for each position of the piston the pressure near the piston face is lower than it was during the compression process. The work done during the expansion is therefore less than that done on the gas during compression. Say that the work input to the system during the rapid compression amounts to 10 B and the work output obtained by expanding the fluid to its initial volume is 8 B. At the end of the expansion process, the stored energy of the system is 2 B greater than it was initially; but, since the system volume equals its initial value, the 2 B of excess stored energy cannot be removed *as work* while the system is restored to its initial state. Let 2 B of heat be transferred from the system to the surroundings while the piston is stationary. The system has now been returned to its initial state. Turning our attention now to the surroundings, we see that 10 B of work was taken from the surroundings in order to compress the gas. Perhaps the work was done by the lowering of a weight or the unwinding of a coil spring in the surroundings. Then the system performed 8 B of work on the surroundings to raise the weight part of the way to its initial position or to rewind the spring partially. Then 2 B of heat was transferred to the surroundings. In order for the surroundings to be returned to their initial state, this 2 B of heat must be converted completely into work to raise the weight or wind the spring without causing any other effects. Any device which could perform this conversion would violate the second law; hence we conclude that the system and the surroundings cannot *both* be restored to their initial states. Therefore, the adiabatic compression of the gas during which the pressure is not uniform throughout the gas is irreversible.

A reversible process may be approximated by the elongation or compression of a spring. If a very small load is slowly applied to the spring, the spring will elongate a minute distance. After elongation, if the spring is allowed to contract to its original position, the work performed by the spring as it contracts will be approximately equal to that required to stretch the spring. It is important to note that this process approaches a reversible process only if an infinitesimal force is applied and reduced gradually; otherwise vibrations and other effects will occur which would make the process irreversible.

Another example of a reversible process is the frictionless isothermal process. Consider a gas in a cylinder having a gas-tight frictionless piston and cylinder walls which are perfect conductors of heat. If the temperature of the surroundings is slightly greater than the temperature of the gas, the gas will receive heat from the surroundings and expand, and work will be performed. It is assumed that the process takes place very slowly. If the temperature of the surroundings is reduced to a value slightly less than that of the gas, heat will flow from the gas, and work will be done in compressing it. In this process, minute temperature differentials are to be considered, and the time required for the expansion or compression to occur is extremely long. This type of process fulfills the requirements of a reversible process as the temperature difference between the system and the surroundings approaches zero. Notice that the temperature must be uniform throughout the gas so that only an infinitesimal change in the temperature of the surroundings will cause the surroundings to be at a higher or lower temperature than the entire system.

Next consider a metal cylinder fitted with a frictionless piston and containing a small quantity of water. The cylinder is assumed to be immersed in a *constant-temperature* bath. If the piston is loaded by a weight equal to the product of the area of the piston and the saturation pressure corresponding to the temperature of the bath, the system is in a condition of equilibrium. The force exerted by the vapor pressure of the water in the cylinder is equal to the weight applied to the piston. If the weight applied to the piston is decreased an infinitesimal amount, the water will start to evaporate, thus absorbing heat from the bath. At any instant, if the load is increased to a value infinitesimally greater than the product of the area and saturation pressure at the temperature of the bath, the vapor will start to condense, and heat will flow into the surrounding bath. Thus, by slightly altering the load on the piston, the process may be made to proceed in either direction. As the load differential approaches zero, the process becomes reversible. It is not possible to perform the experiment in the laboratory because of the frictional forces that would be present.

Can the transfer of heat to or from a system be reversible if the temperature of the system varies with time? The answer is yes, provided the temperature of the surroundings also varies with time so that the difference in temperature between the system and the surroundings is never more than an infinitesimal amount.

If heat is transferred from one body to another, the greater the temperature difference between the two bodies, the greater the rate of heat transfer will be. This is true whether the heat is transferred by conduction, convection, or radiation. As the temperature difference between the two bodies is made smaller, the time required to transfer a given quantity of heat increases. As the temperature difference approaches an infinitesimal value, the time required to transfer any finite amount of heat grows toward an infinite value. However, it is only when the temperature difference is infinitesimal (so that the direction of the heat transfer can be changed by an infinitesimal change in the temperature of one of the bodies) that the process can be considered reversible. Thus reversible heat transfer is the limiting case of heat transfer as the temperature difference between two bodies approaches zero.

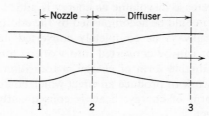

Fig. 7·3   Nozzle and diffuser.

Another example of a reversible process is the steady frictionless adiabatic flow of a fluid through a nozzle. Application of the first law to such a system shows that, as kinetic energy increases in the direction of flow, the enthalpy decreases. If the nozzle is followed by a frictionless diffuser, as shown in Fig. 7·3, the fluid undergoes an increase in enthalpy and a decrease in kinetic energy between sections 2 and 3 and can be discharged in a state 3 which is identical with state 1. Thus after the nozzle process has occurred, it is possible to restore the fluid flowing and all parts of the surroundings to their initial states.

Study of various reversible and irreversible processes such as those just described leads to certain conclusions regarding reversible processes:

1. A reversible process must be such that, after it has occurred, the system and the surroundings can be made to traverse in the reverse order the states they passed through during the original process, with all energy transformations of the original process being reversed in direction but unchanged in form or magnitude.

2. The direction of a reversible process can be changed by making infinitesimal changes in the conditions which control it.

3. During a reversible process, the system and the surroundings must each at all times be in states of equilibrium or infinitesimally close to states of equilibrium; i.e., the process must be quasistatic.

4. A reversible process must involve no friction, unrestrained expansion, mixing, heat transfer across a finite temperature difference, or inelastic deformation.

A reversible process must meet each of the conditions listed. If any one of the conditions listed is not met by a process, the process is irreversible. Thus either these conditions or the definition of a reversible process can be applied to test whether any particular process is reversible.

A test for reversibility which is occasionally useful is the following: If in any process work is used to accomplish some effect which could have been accomplished wholly or in part by heat, the process is irreversible. Consider the stirring of a gas in a closed tank by means of a paddle wheel. Since there is no decrease in volume as energy is added to the system as work, the same effect could be accomplished by the addition of heat to the system. Work can always be completely converted into heat, but the extent to which heat can be converted into work is limited. Therefore, work is the more valuable form of energy in transition. An irreversible process which uses work to produce an effect which could be produced by the less valuable form of energy, heat, is consequently an undesirable process in this respect.

Reversible processes are occasionally spoken of as "maximum work" processes. The reason for this is that, if a system can pass through a given series of states reversibly and also irreversibly, the amount of work done by the system will be greater for the reversible process than for any irreversible process following the same path. If the series of states is such that work must be done on the system (as in the compression of a gas), the reversible process will require a smaller work input than the irreversible one. It is still correct to call the reversible process a *maximum* work process as long as the term work is taken to mean work$_{out}$. Say that the work input for a reversible compression is 8 B and for an irreversible compression is 10 B. Then

$$\text{Work}_{out, rev} = -8 \text{ B} > \text{work}_{out, irrev} = -10 \text{ B*}$$

As an illustration of a system which can be made to pass through the same series of states reversibly and irreversibly, consider a gas which expands reversibly against a piston in a cylinder (see Fig. 7·4a) while heat is added at the same rate at which work is done. The internal energy of the gas consequently remains constant. The same mass of gas at the same initial pressure and temperature might be held in part of a vessel as shown

---

* As a homely example to make this clear, suppose that the statistics for a football game show

	Team *A*	Team *B*
Yards gained, rushing	−5	−20

Although it may be nothing to be proud of, the rushing attack of team *B* was more effective than that of team *B*. In other words, as far as yards *gained* are concerned, −5 > −20.

in Fig. 7·4b. The vessel is thermally insulated and is fitted with many very thin sliding partitions which can be withdrawn in sequence to let the gas expand. Initially all the gas is to the left of the extreme left-hand partition. The rest of the vessel is evacuated. No work is done as the partitions are withdrawn, and no heat is transferred. Consequently the gas expands at constant internal energy. As the number of partitions is increased, the number of equilibrium states through which the system passes increases,

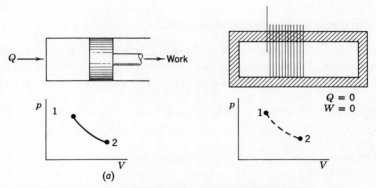

Fig. 7·4 Reversible and irreversible processes through the same equilibrium states.

and the irreversible path approaches more and more closely the reversible path.* Even in the limit of an infinite number of partitions, however, no work is done in the irreversible process; but the work of the reversible process, given by $\int p\, dV$, is greater than zero.

All actual processes which involve finite energy transformations are irreversible. Reversible processes do not occur. One reason they do not occur is that frictional effects cannot be completely eliminated. Nevertheless, reversible processes are extremely useful in the analysis and design of actual processes and devices for several reasons. Reversible processes are useful as standards of comparison or guides to perfection. Reversible processes are often the limiting cases of actual processes as the irreversibilities present in any actual process are reduced further and further. Since many actual processes are difficult to analyze completely, an engineer frequently bases his analysis or design on reversible processes, and then adjusts his results before applying them to the actual process he is working on. This is similar to his use of ideal systems in the analysis or design of

---

* Strictly speaking, even after we locate an infinite number of points on the pV diagram of Fig. 7·4b, the path is not continuous because there are an infinite number of intervals between these points in which the path is not defined!

actual systems. (See Art. 1·7 if you do not remember the discussion of this point.) An engineer uses reversible processes in the same way that he uses point masses, frictionless pulleys, weightless cords, and homogeneous beams: He uses these idealizations to simplify the analysis of actual systems and processes.

Another reason why the concept of reversible processes is important is that it permits the definition of a very useful property called entropy. Entropy is introduced in Chapter 9.

7·3   Internal and external reversibility

A process is irreversible if it involves heat transfer across a finite temperature difference between the system and the surroundings. However, the system behaves during this irreversible process just as though the heat were being transferred to or from it reversibly across an infinitesimal temperature difference. Such a process is said to be *internally reversible* because nothing occurs within the system to make it irreversible, but it is *externally irreversible*.

The frictionless adiabatic and frictionless isothermal processes described in the preceding article are *internally reversible* and *externally reversible*.

A process which involves friction or some other irreversibility within the system and also heat exchange with surroundings at a different temperature is *internally irreversible* and *externally irreversible*.

Calculations of a system's behavior which do not involve any properties of the surroundings are the same for any internally reversible process, whether the process is externally reversible or irreversible. Consequently, from here on in this book, whenever a principle or relation is said to be valid for a reversible process, it is required only that the process be internally reversible. In the few cases where it is required that a process be externally reversible, this additional restriction will be explicitly stated. It is to be understood that any process designated as externally reversible is also internally reversible. (A process *can* be externally reversible and internally irreversible, but no principles or general relationships are formulated for such processes. Therefore, we may always consider external reversibility to be an *additional* restriction instead of an *alternative* restriction.)

7·4   ∫ p dv and ∫ v dp in irreversible processes

In Arts. 1·14 and 1·16 two equations were developed from the principles of mechanics for the work of frictionless processes. Now that the concept of reversibility has been introduced, the restrictions on these equations should be changed from "for frictionless processes" to "for reversible processes" (and this means internally reversible in accordance with the convention established in the preceding article). Thus we have

$$\text{Work} = \int p\, dV \qquad (1\cdot7)$$

for reversible closed system processes and

$$\text{Work} = -\int v\, dp - \Delta KE - \Delta PE \qquad (1\cdot10)$$

for reversible steady-flow processes.

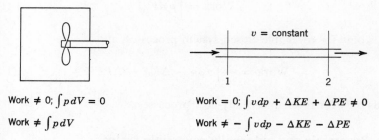

Work $\neq 0$; $\int p\,dV = 0$ Work $= 0$; $\int v\,dp + \Delta KE + \Delta PE \neq 0$

Work $\neq \int p\,dV$ Work $\neq -\int v\,dp - \Delta KE - \Delta PE$

Fig. 7·5   Irreversible processes in closed and steady-flow systems.

Equations 1·7 and 1·10 do not apply to irreversible processes. For many irreversible processes $\int p\, dV$ or $\int v\, dp$ cannot be evaluated because the system is not in equilibrium and there is consequently no single value of p or v which is a property of the system as a whole at any instant. Even for irreversible processes in which $\int p\, dV$ or $\int v\, dp$ can be evaluated, equations 1·7 and 1·10 do not apply. Two illustrations of this point follow.

Consider a system comprised of a gas in a closed rigid vessel. The gas is stirred by a paddle wheel driven externally (see Fig. 7·5). During the stirring process, there is at any instant a variation of pressure from point to point within the vessel. However, the volume of the system is constant so that undoubtedly $\int p\, dV = 0$. Work is delivered to the system by means of the paddle wheel; so work $\neq 0$. Consequently, work $\neq \int p\, dV$, and equation 1·7 does not apply in this case.

As a second illustration, consider the flow of an incompressible liquid through a section of horizontal pipe with a constant cross-sectional area. $\Delta PE = 0$, and $\Delta KE = 0$. No work is done: Work $= 0$. If there is a pressure drop caused by friction, $\int v\, dp \neq 0$. Consequently, work $\neq -\int v\, dp - \Delta KE - \Delta PE$, and equation 1·10 does not apply in this case.

You may ask, "Since $\int p\, dV \neq$ work for an irreversible process of a closed system, what significance does $\int p\, dV$ have for such a process?"

The answer to this question is that $\int p\,dV$ has no significance for an irreversible process except that it is equal to the work that could be done by the system if it passed reversibly through the same series of states. As pointed out in Art. 7·2, the work done by a reversible process is the maximum work for any particular path.

The same answer applies to the question which can be asked regarding $-\int v\,dp - \Delta KE - \Delta PE$ in irreversible steady-flow processes, but it must be added that a dynamic analysis of pipe flow does show some further physical significance of $-\int v\,dp - \Delta KE - \Delta PE$ in this particular application.

Repeating for emphasis,

$$\text{Work} = \int p\,dV \tag{1·7}$$

holds only for reversible closed-system processes, and

$$\text{Work} = -\int v\,dp - \Delta KE - \Delta PE \tag{1·10}$$

holds only for reversible steady-flow processes.

7·5   Reversible and externally reversible cycles

A cycle composed entirely of reversible processes is called a reversible cycle. If all of the processes are externally reversible, the cycle is called an externally reversible cycle.

As an example of a reversible cycle, consider an ideal gas trapped in a cylinder behind a piston. Let the gas expand, reversibly at constant pressure. During this process heat is added to the gas, and the gas does work on the surroundings. Then let heat be removed from the gas while the piston is stationary until the gas reaches its initial temperature. Then let the gas be compressed reversibly and isothermally to its initial state. During the isothermal compression, work is done on the gas, and heat is removed from it. This cycle is shown on a pv diagram in Fig. 7·6a. Since the pressure during the expansion is greater than that during the compression, there is a net work output from this cycle. This work output is represented by the area within the cycle diagram of Fig. 7·6a. Each process of this cycle is reversible. (Recall from Art. 7·3 that this means internally reversible.) The cycle is therefore reversible. In the reversed operation of this cycle, the gas is first expanded reversibly and isothermally, doing work on the surroundings and receiving heat. Then, with the piston stationary, heat is added until the pressure reaches its initial value. The gas is then cooled reversibly at constant pressure to its initial state. Work is done on the gas during this constant-pressure cooling. This cycle is shown in Fig. 7·6b. The net work input to the cycle of Fig. 7·6b equals in magnitude the net work output of the cycle of Fig. 7·6a.

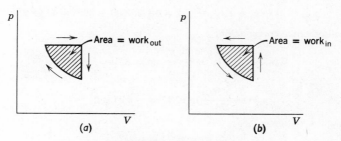

Fig. 7·6 Reversible cycle.

EXAMPLE 7·4. Air in a closed system undergoes a cycle composed of the following three reversible processes: (1) a constant-pressure expansion from 12 psia, 40 F, to 140 F, (2) a constant-volume cooling to 40 F, and (3) an isothermal compression to 12 psia. Determine (a) the energy transfers per pound of air for each process, (b) the thermal efficiency of the cycle, and (c) the energy transfers for each process when air undergoes this cycle in reverse.

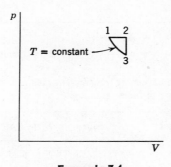

Example 7·4

Solution. (a) Air under conditions such as these behaves as an ideal gas. For the reversible constant-pressure expansion,

$$\text{Work} = \int_1^2 p \, dv = p(v_2 - v_1) = p_2 v_2 - p_1 v_1 = R(T_2 - T_1)$$

$$= \frac{53.3}{778}(600 - 500) = 6.85 \text{ B/lb}$$

Using a constant value of c_v for the limited temperature range involved,

$$u_2 - u_1 = c_v(T_2 - T_1) = 0.1715(600 - 500) = 17.15 \text{ B/lb}$$

Applying the first law,

$$q = u_2 - u_1 + w = 17.15 + 6.85 = 24.00 \text{ B/lb}$$

For the constant-volume cooling, work = 0 and

$$q_{out} = u_2 - u_3 = c_v(T_2 - T_3) = 0.1715(600 - 500) = 17.15 \text{ B/lb}$$

For the isothermal compression,

$$\text{Work} = \int_3^1 p \, dv = \int_3^1 \frac{RT}{v} \, dv = RT \ln \frac{v_1}{v_3} = RT \ln \frac{p_3}{p_1}$$

$$= \frac{53.3(500)}{778} \ln 10/12 = -6.25 \text{ B/lb}$$

Applying the first law,

$$q_{out} = w_{in} + u_3 - u_1 = 6.25 + 0 = 6.25 \text{ B/lb}$$

Presenting the results in tabular form,

Process	q, B/lb	w, B/lb
1-2	24.0	6.85
2-3	−17.15	0
3-1	−6.25	−6.25
Cycle	+0.6	+0.6

(b)

$$\eta = \frac{\oint \delta w}{q_{in}} = \frac{0.6}{24.0} = 2.5 \text{ per cent}$$

(c) For the reversed cycle the energy transfers for each process are equal in magnitude but opposite in sign to those of the original cycle:

Process	q, B/lb	w, B/lb
1-3	6.25	6.25
3-2	17.15	0
2-1	−24.0	−6.85
Cycle	−0.6	−0.6

In order for the cycle described in Example 7·4 and the preceding paragraph to be *externally* reversible, the temperature of part of the surroundings would have to vary during the constant-pressure and constant-volume processes so that heat would be transferred only across infinitesimal temperature differences. If the parts of the surroundings which exchange heat with the system are at constant temperatures, then the cycle must be externally irreversible. The calculations of Example 7·4 are the same, however, whether the processes are externally reversible or externally irreversible. They depend only on the condition that the processes are internally reversible.

Let us look now at a cycle which is externally reversible but exchanges heat with parts of the surroundings at only two fixed temperatures. If heat is exchanged reversibly with bodies at two fixed temperatures T_H and T_L, then heat must be transferred only when the system is at a constant temperature only infinitesimally higher or lower than T_H or T_L. In other

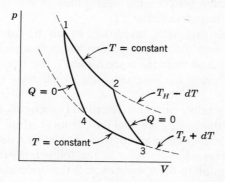

Fig. 7·7 An externally reversible cycle operating between energy reservoirs at T_H and T_L.

words, a system which executes an externally reversible cycle while exchanging heat only with two constant-temperature regions cannot exchange heat with them during any processes except isothermal ones. This means that the processes which are not isothermal must be adiabatic.

As an example of an externally reversible cycle operating between two energy reservoirs at temperatures T_H and T_L, refer to Fig. 7·7, and consider the following cycle executed by a gas in either a closed or a steady-flow system. First, the gas which is at a temperature of (T_H-dT) expands reversibly and isothermally from a state 1 to a state 2. Work is done by the gas, and heat is transferred from the energy reservoir at T_H to the system at (T_H-dT). Since heat is being transferred across an infinitesimal temperature difference, this process is externally reversible. Then the gas expands reversibly and adiabatically from state 2 to state 3, doing work. During this process the temperature of the system drops from (T_H-dT) to (T_L+dT). The gas is then compressed isothermally, rejecting heat to the energy reservoir at T_L. This process, like the heat addition process 1-2, is externally reversible because heat is transferred across only an infinitesimal temperature difference. The isothermal compression progresses until the gas reaches state 4, from which it can be compressed reversibly and adiabatically to state 1 to complete the cycle. During the reversible adiabatic compression process 4-1, the temperature of the system increases from (T_L+dT) to (T_H-dT). The area within the pv diagram of Fig. 7·7 represents the net work of this externally reversible cycle. Since the system executes a cycle, the net change in its stored energy is zero ($\oint dE = 0$). The net effects of this cycle are: (1) Heat is removed from the energy reservoir at T_H, (2) heat is added to the energy reservoir at T_L, and (3) work is produced. Application of the first law shows that the work produced is equal to the difference between the heat added to the system at T_H or (T_H-dT) and the heat rejected at T_L.

Since the cycle is externally reversible, it can be carried out in the opposite direction with the system passing through a sequence of states 1-4-3-2-1, absorbing heat from the reservoir at T_L and rejecting heat to the reservoir at T_H. During the reversed cycle, work must be done on the system.

The externally reversible cycle just described (which can also be executed by substances other than gases) is called the Carnot (kȧr'-nō') cycle in honor of Sadi Carnot,* the French engineer who in 1824 first described it. The Carnot cycle is discussed more fully in the following two articles. The reason for this attention to the Carnot cycle is that no cycle can be devised which is more efficient than a Carnot cycle operating between the same temperature limits. This fact will be demonstrated in Art. 8·1.

7·6 The Carnot cycle

A Carnot cycle can be executed by many different types of systems. The system can be a liquid, a gas, an electric cell, a soap film, a steel wire, or a rubber band, to name just a few. In any case, the operation of a Carnot cycle involves (1) a system, (2) an energy reservoir at some temperature T_H, (3) an energy reservoir at some lower temperature T_L, (4) some means of periodically insulating the system from one or both of the reservoirs, and

---

* Nicholas Leonard Sadi Carnot (1796–1832), member of an illustrious family, studied at the École Polytechnique and was an officer in the French Army Engineers. He was a man of extremely broad interests and was an accomplished athlete. The only paper he published during his lifetime, *Reflections on the Motive Power of Heat*, is one of the milestones of scientific thought. In this paper he originated the use of cycles in thermodynamic analysis and laid the foundations for the second law by describing and analyzing the Carnot cycle and stating the Carnot principle which is discussed in Art. 8·1. He employed the caloric theory in his reasoning, but his conclusions are correct because the second law is a principle which is independent of the first law or of any other "theory of heat." When his paper was first published, many people thought that his analysis and conclusions *depended* on the caloric theory. Consequently, the caloric theory, which had suffered at the hands of Benjamin Thompson and Humphry Davy, was given a new, but short, lease on life. In 1851 Rudolph Clausius and Lord Kelvin showed that there is no dependence of the second law on the caloric theory.

(5) a part of the surroundings which can absorb work and periodically do work on the system.

In order to have a specific example of a Carnot cycle for study, consider a system comprised of a gas (not necessarily an ideal gas—see Example 7·5 for this special case) held in an insulated cylinder fitted with an insulating piston (Fig. 7·8). The insulation I of the cylinder head can be removed so that the cylinder can periodically be placed in intimate contact with the energy reservoir at T_H or the one at T_L.

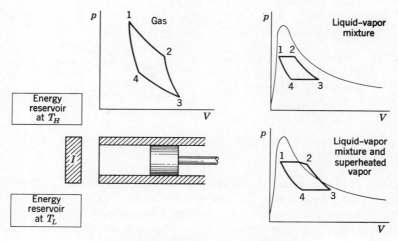

Fig. 7·8   Closed-system Carnot cycle.

Let the cycle begin with the gas in a state 1 as shown on the pV diagram labeled "Gas" in Fig. 7·8. The temperature of the gas is T_H. Then the insulation I is removed from the cylinder, and the cylinder head is placed in contact with the energy reservoir at T_H. The gas expands very slowly, doing work on the surroundings. The temperature of the gas *tends* to decrease, but the flow of the heat from the energy reservoir maintains the gas temperature constant at (T_H-dT). Notice that the transfer of heat is reversible only as long as the temperature difference between the reservoir and the gas is infinitesimal. If the temperature of the gas were to fall lower than (T_H-dT), the process would be externally irreversible. This reversible isothermal process continues until the piston reaches a position 2. The piston is then stopped, holding the gas in state 2, while the cylinder is removed from the reservoir at T_H, and the insulation is put back on the cylinder head. The gas then pushes the piston farther outward as it expands reversibly and adiabatically. Work is done by the gas, and there is no heat input; so the temperature drops. The piston is allowed to move until the gas temperature becomes T_L. The gas is then in state 3. Notice that any heat transfer between the gas and one of the reservoirs while the gas was at a temperature between T_H and T_L would have made the process externally irreversible.

Now, if the piston were to be pushed inward while the cylinder is still completely insulated, the gas would be compressed adiabatically, and its temperature would again rise. If the compression were reversible and

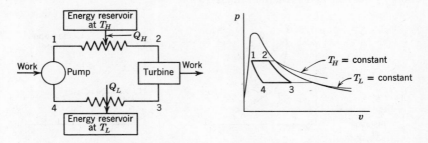

Fig. 7·9 Steady-flow Carnot cycle using a wet vapor as working substance.

adiabatic, the gas would retrace the path between states 3 and 2. Obviously this is not going to help us obtain a net work output from the cycle. Therefore, while the piston is in position 3, the cylinder-head insulation I is again removed, and the cylinder is placed in contact with the low-temperature reservoir. Now, as the piston is pushed inward, the gas temperature *tends* to rise, but heat is transferred from the gas to the cold reservoir at such a rate that the gas temperature remains constant at $(T_L + dT)$. Since the heat is transferred across an infinitesimal temperature difference, the process is externally reversible. This reversible isothermal compression of the gas is continued until a state 4 is reached. State 4 is such that, if the insulation is put back on the cylinder head and the gas is compressed reversibly and adiabatically, its temperature and pressure will increase, and the gas will be returned to state 1. Thus the cycle is completed.

If the working fluid in the cycle just described were a liquid–vapor mixture of some pure substance instead of a gas, the isothermal processes 1-2 and 3-4 would also be constant-pressure processes. During process 1-2, evaporation would occur, and condensation would occur during process 3-4. If all of the liquid were evaporated and the vapor became superheated during the isothermal heat addition, only that part of process 1-2 which occurred with both liquid and vapor present would be a constant-pressure process. pV diagrams for these cases are shown in Fig. 7·8. The important thing to remember is that the heat-addition and heat-rejection processes of the Carnot cycle are always isothermal. For a particular substance, an isothermal process may also be a constant-pressure process or a constant internal energy process, but this characteristic of the substance is merely incidental to the execution of a Carnot cycle. The Carnot cycle requires that the heat-addition and rejection processes be only reversible and isothermal—nothing else.

Figure 7·9 shows a flow diagram and a *pv* diagram for a steady-flow Carnot cycle which uses a liquid–vapor mixture (often called a "wet vapor") as working substance. The reversible isothermal heat-addition process 1-2 is an evaporation which occurs in a heat exchanger where no work is done. The reversible adiabatic expansion during which the temperature of the wet vapor drops from T_H to T_L occurs in a turbine. Heat is rejected from the working fluid in a condenser. No work is done in the condenser. The fluid which leaves the condenser in state 4 is compressed reversibly and adiabatically to its initial state 1 to complete the cycle.

EXAMPLE 7·5. Derive an expression in terms of the reservoir temperatures T_H and T_L for the thermal efficiency of a Carnot cycle using an ideal gas as working fluid. (This problem statement *implies* that the efficiency of this cycle is a function of the temperature limits only, but this fact has not yet been proved. It is proved in Art. 8·1.)

Solution. A schematic diagram of the engine and the reservoirs and a pV diagram of the ideal-gas working fluid are made first.

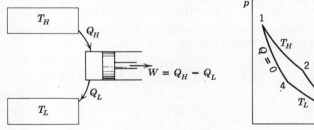

Example 7·5

By the definition of thermal efficiency,

$$\eta = \frac{\oint \delta \text{work}}{Q_{\text{in}}} = \frac{W}{Q_{\text{in}}}$$

Applying the first law to this closed system which executes a cycle,

$$\eta = \frac{\oint \delta \text{work}}{Q_{\text{in}}} = \frac{\oint \delta Q}{Q_{\text{in}}} = \frac{Q_{\text{in}} - Q_{\text{out}}}{Q_{\text{in}}} = 1 - \frac{Q_{\text{out}}}{Q_{\text{in}}} = 1 - \frac{Q_L}{Q_H}$$

where Q_{in} or Q_H and Q_{out} or Q_L stand for the gross or total heat transferred from the reservoir at T_H to the engine and from the engine to the reservoir at T_L, respectively. All the heat added to the working fluid during the cycle is added during the isothermal expansion 1-2, during which the temperature of the working fluid is T_H (or lower than this by only an infinitesimal amount). Applying the first law to the system during the reversible isothermal expansion 1-2,

$$Q_H = U_2 - U_1 + W$$

For an ideal gas, internal energy is a function of temperature only; therefore $\Delta U = 0$ for an isothermal process. Also, for a reversible process of a closed system, $W = \int p \, dV$, so that

$$Q_H = 0 + \int_1^2 p \, dV$$

Substituting for p from the ideal-gas equation of state, and noting that m, R, and T are constant for this process,

$$Q_H = 0 + \int_1^2 \frac{mRT}{V} dV = mRT \int_1^2 \frac{dV}{V} = mRT_H \ln \frac{V_2}{V_1}$$

By the same reasoning,

$$Q_L = U_3 - U_4 - W = 0 - \int_3^4 p \, dV = -mRT_L \ln \frac{V_4}{V_3} = mRT_L \ln \frac{V_3}{V_4}$$

Substituting these values for Q_H and Q_L into the expression obtained above for thermal efficiency,

$$\eta = 1 - \frac{Q_L}{Q_H} = 1 - \frac{mRT_L \ln (V_3/V_4)}{mRT_H \ln (V_2/V_1)} = 1 - \frac{T_L \ln (V_3/V_4)}{T_H \ln (V_2/V_1)}$$

For the reversible adiabatic processes 2-3 and 4-1 of the ideal-gas working substance, at least if the ratio of specific heats is constant,

$$\frac{V_3}{V_2} = \left(\frac{T_2}{T_3}\right)^{1/(k-1)} = \left(\frac{T_H}{T_L}\right)^{1/(k-1)} \quad \text{and} \quad \frac{V_4}{V_1} = \left(\frac{T_1}{T_4}\right)^{1/(k-1)} = \left(\frac{T_H}{T_L}\right)^{1/(k-1)}$$

Thus

$$\frac{V_3}{V_2} = \frac{V_4}{V_1}$$

and

$$\frac{V_3}{V_4} = \frac{V_2}{V_1}$$

so that the expression for thermal efficiency reduces to

$$\eta = 1 - \frac{T_L}{T_H}$$

Before leaving this solution it is well to notice that the thermal efficiency of a Carnot cycle using an ideal gas as a working fluid increases as the ratio of T_H to T_L increases. Writing the efficiency expression as

$$\eta = \frac{T_H - T_L}{T_H}$$

shows that, for a given temperature of either reservoir, the efficiency is increased by increasing the temperature difference between the reservoirs.

7·7 The reversed Carnot cycle

A Carnot cycle operated in reverse is not a heat engine which produces work but is a refrigerator or heat pump. It absorbs heat from a low-temperature reservoir and rejects heat to a high-temperature reservoir. In order to do this, it also absorbs work from the surroundings. In a household refrigerator, heat is absorbed from the refrigerator compartment, heat is rejected to the surrounding air, and an electric motor provides the work input.

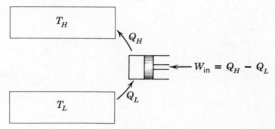

Fig. 7·10   Refrigerator or heat pump.

The working substance of a Carnot refrigerator absorbs heat Q_L during an isothermal process at T_L. Its temperature is then increased adiabatically to T_H. During an isothermal process at T_H, heat Q_H is rejected to the higher-temperature reservoir.   See Fig. 7·10.   The cycle is then completed by an adiabatic process which lowers the temperature of the working substance and returns it to its initial state. All processes are of course externally reversible. Application of the first law shows that

$$\text{Net work}_{\text{in}} = Q_H - Q_L$$

EXAMPLE 7·6.   Derive an expression for the coefficient of performance of a Carnot refrigerator using an ideal gas as working fluid in terms of the reservoir temperatures T_L and T_H.

Solution.   A schematic diagram of the Carnot refrigerator and the reservoirs and a pV diagram of the ideal-gas working fluid are made first.

By the definition of coefficient of performance (Art. 2·10) and application of the first law,

$$\beta = \frac{Q_L}{W_{\text{in}}} = \frac{Q_L}{Q_H - Q_L}$$

Q_L and Q_H can be evaluated by means of the first law, Joule's law, work = $\int p \, dV$, and $pV = mRT$ as in Example 7·5 to give

$$Q_L = Q_{A\text{-}B} = mRT_L \ln \frac{V_B}{V_A}$$

$$Q_H = Q_{\text{out},C\text{-}D} = mRT_H \ln \frac{V_C}{V_D}$$

It can also be shown as in Example 7·5 that

$$\frac{V_B}{V_A} = \frac{V_C}{V_D}$$

so that substitutions in the expression for coefficient of performance give

$$\beta = \frac{mRT_L \ln (V_C/V_D)}{mRT_H \ln (V_C/V_D) - mRT_L \ln (V_C/V_D)} = \frac{T_L}{T_H - T_L}$$

Notice that this is *not* the reciprocal of the efficiency expression obtained in Example 7·5.

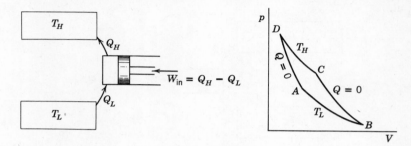

Example 7·6

Before leaving this problem, let us notice some numerical values of β for various reservoir temperatures (recalling that absolute temperatures are used in the expression derived):

T_L, F	T_H, F	β
40	90	10
20	70	9.6
0	50	9.2
−60	70	3.08
−160	70	1.30
−260	70	0.61

7·8   Other externally reversible cycles

The Carnot cycle is not the only externally reversible heat-engine cycle. Two others are known as the Stirling* cycle and the Ericsson* cycle.

* The Reverend Robert Stirling (1790–1878) was the first person to propose the use of regeneration in heat-engine cycles. John Ericsson (1803–1889), Swedish-American engineer and inventor, built a steam locomotive, the *Novelty*, which competed with Stephenson's *Rocket* in 1829. Among his inventions were the revolving naval gun turret, the marine screw propeller, and the steam fire engine. He is well known as the designer and builder of the ironclad *Monitor* used by the United States in answer to the Confederate *Merrimac* during the Civil War. Under Ericsson's supervision the *Monitor* was built in only 126 days.

These warrant consideration here because they both employ the principle of *regeneration* which is used in many modern steam and gas-turbine power plants and elsewhere.

In order for a cycle to be externally reversible and to exchange heat with energy reservoirs at two fixed temperatures, heat can be transferred between the system and the reservoirs only during isothermal processes. However, during nonisothermal processes, it is possible for heat to be

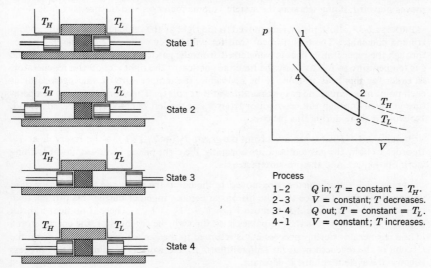

Process	
1-2	Q in; T = constant = T_H.
2-3	V = constant; T decreases.
3-4	Q out; T = constant = T_L.
4-1	V = constant; T increases.

Fig. 7·11   Stirling engine and cycle.

transferred between the system and some regenerative energy-storage device which absorbs heat from the system during part of the cycle and returns the same amount of heat to the system during another part of the cycle. Of course, in order for the operation of the regenerator to be reversible, heat must always be transferred between the system and the regenerator across only an infinitesimal temperature difference.

Figure 7·11 shows a schematic diagram of a Stirling engine and a pV diagram for an ideal-gas working substance. (The engine shown here is not the same physical arrangement as that proposed by Stirling, but the thermodynamic cycle is the same.) The engine consists of a cylinder with a piston at each end. In the middle of the cylinder, between the pistons, is the regenerator. This can be a plug of wire gauze or a porous plug made by holding small metal shot between two wire screens. Assume that the regenerator as a whole is a poor conductor of heat, so that even though a temperature gradient exists across it there will be a negligible amount of heat conducted in the direction of the cylinder axis. The cylinder is completely insulated except for a contact with the hot reservoir at one end and a contact with the cold reservoir at the other end.

Starting with state 1, the cycle proceeds as follows, with each process being externally reversible:

PROCESS 1-2.   Heat is added to the gas at T_H (or, strictly speaking, at T_H-dT) from the reservoir at T_H. During this reversible isothermal process, the left piston moves outward, doing work as the system volume increases and the pressure falls.

PROCESS 2-3.   Both pistons are moved to the right at the same rate to keep the system volume constant. There is no heat transfer with either reservoir. As the gas passes through the regenerator, heat is transferred from the gas to the regenerator, causing the gas temperature to fall to T_L by the time the gas leaves the right end of the regenerator. In order for this heat transfer to be reversible, the temperature of the regenerator at each point must equal the gas temperature at that point. Therefore, there is a temperature gradient through the regenerator from T_H at the left end to T_L at the right end. No work is done during this process.

PROCESS 3-4.   Heat is removed from the gas at T_L (or T_L+dT) to the reservoir at T_L. In order to hold the gas temperature constant, the right piston is moved inward, doing work on the gas, and the pressure increases.

PROCESS 4-1.   Both pistons are moved to the left at the same rate to keep the system volume constant. (Notice that the pistons are closer together during this process than they were during process 2-3, because $V_4 = V_1 < V_2 = V_3$.) There is no heat transfer with either reservoir. As the gas passes back through the regenerator, the energy stored in the regenerator during process 2-3 is returned to the gas, so that it emerges from the left end of the regenerator at the temperature T_H. No work is done during this process because the system volume is constant.

The cycle is thus completed, and it is externally reversible. Notice that the system has exchanged a net amount of heat with only the two energy reservoirs at T_H and T_L.

Figure 7·12 shows a schematic diagram of a steady-flow power plant operating on the Ericsson cycle and a pv diagram for an ideal-gas working fluid. (Ericsson's original engine, of which several models have been built, was a nonflow engine, but the ideal thermodynamic cycle is the same for the steady-flow engine. The steady-flow engine is described here in order to introduce another type of regenerator.) The steady-flow Ericsson engine involves (1) a turbine through which the gas expands isothermally, doing work and absorbing heat from an energy reservoir at T_H, (2) a compressor which compresses the gas isothermally while heat is rejected from the gas at T_L (or T_L+dT) to the energy reservoir at T_L, and (3) a counterflow heat exchanger which is used as a regenerator. In the regenerator, gas from the compressor enters at a temperature of T_L (or T_L+dT) and leaves at a temperature T_H (or T_H-dT). This is process 4-1. The gas from the turbine undergoes process 2-3 by flowing through the regenerator in the

opposite direction. Its temperature drops from T_H to T_L as it rejects heat
to the gas which is undergoing process 4-1. Notice in Fig. 7·12 that the gas
entering the left end of the regenerator (state 4) is at T_L, and so is the gas
which leaves the left end (state 3). Also, the gas leaving the right end
(state 1) is at T_H, and so is the gas which enters the right end (state 2).
Throughout the regenerator there is no more than an infinitesimal temperature difference between the two gas streams at any one section, so that the

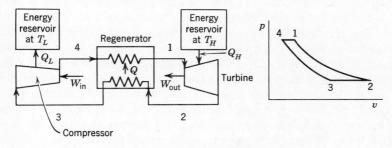

Fig. 7·12 Ericsson engine and cycle.

operation of the regenerator is reversible. (Of course, no actual regenerator
would be designed for an infinitesimal temperature difference because then
a finite amount of heat could not be transferred during a finite period of
time. Remember that reversible heat transfer is the *limiting* case as the
temperature difference is made smaller and smaller.)   All processes of the
Ericsson cycle are externally reversible. The only parts of the surroundings
involved in heat transfer are the two energy reservoirs at T_H and T_L.

The Carnot, Stirling, and Ericsson cycles have been introduced here to
show how an externally reversible cycle can be executed, because the next
chapter introduces some far-reaching consequences of the second law
which involve the performance of externally reversible engines.

7·9   Irreversible processes and molecular disorder

It has been pointed out that, although the principles of thermodynamics
do not depend on any assumptions regarding the existence or behavior of
molecules, occasionally a molecular picture adds to our understanding of
some effect. As an illustration, let us consider briefly a conclusion which
can be deduced from the principles of statistical thermodynamics:
Irreversible processes always result in an increase of molecular disorder.

Consider the sliding of a block along a horizontal plane. Friction
between the block and plane causes the block to come to rest. Energy is
transformed from kinetic energy of the block to internal energy of the

block and plane. Near their rubbing surfaces, the block and plane experience an increase in temperature. This temperature increase shows up on the molecular scale as an increase in molecular velocities, and thus as an increase in kinetic energy of the molecules. The initial kinetic energy of the block can also be considered as kinetic energy of molecules, since all the molecules in the block are initially moving with the block and therefore have a common translatory motion superimposed on their individual oscillations or vibrations. Thus the energy which we speak of as being "transformed" is in the form of kinetic energy of molecules both before and after the transformation occurs. The essential difference is that initially the energy is related to an *ordered* motion of the molecules, whereas finally it is related to a *random* or *disordered* motion. Is the reverse transformation possible? The first law, which requires only conservation of energy, does not prohibit it; but the second law, as discussed earlier in this chapter, leads us to classify the original process as irreversible, so that the reverse transformation is impossible. The transformation which we declare to be impossible is the one which would proceed toward a more highly ordered molecular state. The irreversible process is one which proceeds toward a less ordered (or more disordered) state.

As another example, a paddle wheel stirring a gas imposes an ordered motion on the gas molecules, but this ordered motion is rapidly dissipated into a random motion which is observed as an increase in gas temperature. Our discussion of the second law leads us to believe that the reverse process is impossible: the random molecular motions will not spontaneously become ordered in such a manner as to turn the paddle wheel. But, from the molecular point of view, is such an occurrence absolutely impossible? If the molecules are all in random motion, might there be *some chance* that at some time a sufficient number will be moving in such ways as to turn the paddle wheel? Statistical thermodynamics tells us that such an event *is* possible, but that the probability of its occurrence is *extremely* small—so small that for any calculations or predictions we make we can safely consider the occurrence to be impossible. Thus we can say that the ordered molecular state is a state of extremely low probability and that the disordered molecular state is more probable. Similar reasoning from statistical thermodynamics can be applied to any irreversible process, and the same conclusion is reached in each instance: In an irreversible process, any isolated system proceeds toward more probable states. More probable states are ones of greater molecular disorder.

Remember that this conclusion from statistical thermodynamics cannot be reached from, and has no bearing on, the principles of thermodynamics as presented in this book, because this book is concerned with classical thermodynamics or thermodynamics from the macroscopic point of view.

For purposes of engineering analysis and design, classical thermodynamics is at present more useful than statistical thermodynamics; however, statistical thermodynamics is becoming more and more valuable in explaining certain phenomena and physical properties, and its importance to engineers is increasing rapidly.

7·10 Summary

A *reversible process* is a process such that, after it has occurred, both the system and all the surroundings can be returned to the states they were in before the process occurred. Any other process which occurs is *irreversible*.

One way to prove that a process is irreversible is as follows: (1) Assume that the process is reversible so that the reverse process is possible. (2) Combine this reverse process with other processes, known from experience to be possible, to form a cycle which violates the second law. If such a cycle can be devised, then the assumption of step (1) is false, and the process originally considered is irreversible.

Any process is irreversible if it involves friction, heat transfer across a finite temperature difference, free expansion, mixing, or inelastic deformation.

Reversible processes must be executed very slowly to avoid friction and can involve heat transfer only across infinitesimal temperature differences. Also, a reversible process must be such that, after it has occurred, the system and the surroundings can be made to traverse in the reverse order the states they passed through during the original process, with all energy transformations of the original process being reversed in direction but unchanged in form or magnitude. During a reversible process, the system and the surroundings must each at all times be in states of equilibrium or infinitesimally close to states of equilibrium. The direction of a reversible process can be changed by making infinitesimal changes in the conditions which control it.

Reversible processes actually do not occur in nature. Neither do point masses, frictionless pulleys, weightless cords, and homogeneous beams; but engineers find reversible processes to be just as useful as these other idealizations in analyzing and designing actual systems and processes.

A process is *internally reversible* if all irreversible effects occur outside the system boundary. An *externally reversible* process is internally reversible and also involves no heat transfer across a finite temperature difference.

The relationship derived from the principles of mechanics,

$$\text{Work} = \int p \, dV \qquad\qquad (1·7)$$

holds only for reversible closed-system processes. The analogous relation for steady flow,

$$\text{Work} = -\int v\,dp - \Delta KE - \Delta PE \qquad (1\cdot10)$$

holds only for reversible steady-flow processes.

A cycle composed entirely of reversible processes is called a reversible cycle. If all the processes are externally reversible, the cycle is called an externally reversible cycle. An example of an externally reversible cycle which exchanges heat with energy reservoirs at only two fixed temperatures is the Carnot cycle. A Carnot engine absorbs heat from an energy reservoir at one temperature and rejects heat to an energy reservoir at a lower temperature. Work is produced. The reversed Carnot engine is a refrigerator or heat pump which absorbs heat from the lower-temperature reservoir and discharges heat to the higher-temperature reservoir. Work must be supplied to drive the reversed Carnot engine. The Carnot cycle consists of two isothermal and two adiabatic processes, with all four processes being externally reversible.

Two other externally reversible cycles which operate between two constant-temperature reservoirs are the Stirling cycle and the Ericsson cycle.

REFERENCES

7·1   D. A. Mooney, *Mechanical Engineering Thermodynamics*, Prentice-Hall, 1953.

7·2   J. H. Keenan, *Thermodynamics*, John Wiley & Sons, 1941, chapters VI and VII.

7·3   M. W. Zemansky, *Heat and Thermodynamics*, McGraw-Hill Book Co., 4th ed., 1957, chapters 7 and 8.

7·4   M. Planck, *Treatise on Thermodynamics*, Dover Publications, 3d English ed., part III, chapter I.

PROBLEMS

7·1   Two pounds of air in a closed system expands isothermally from 30 psia, 140 F, to 15 psia. Calculate the amount of heat added if (*a*) the process is reversible, and (*b*) irreversibilities are present which reduce the work to 80 per cent of that produced by the reversible process.

7·2   Comment on the following statement: If in any process work is used to produce an effect which could have been produced by heat, that process is irreversible. (In commenting on such a statement, consider questions such as the following: Is it true, false, meaningless, trivial, important, general?)

7·3   Comment on the following statement: A reversible process, when undone, leaves no history.

7.4 An electric motor doing work receives current from a storage battery. The battery and motor exchange heat with only the atmosphere. Is this a violation of the second law? Explain.

7.5 Man A states that in a reversible isothermal expansion of an ideal gas $\Delta U = 0$ so that the heat added equals the work done. Man B states that such a process violates the second law in that it amounts to a system absorbing heat from a constant-temperature energy reservoir and producing an equivalent amount of work. Resolve this conflict.

7.6 Consider a Carnot engine using air as the working substance. At the beginning of the isothermal expansion, the air is at 80 psia and occupies a volume of 2 cu ft. The pressure and volume at the end of the adiabatic expansion are 20 psia and 6 cu ft. Determine the efficiency of the cycle.

7.7 In a Carnot engine using air as the working fluid, the air is at 75 psia, 200 F, and occupies a volume of 2 cu ft at the beginning of the isothermal expansion. The volume at the end of the isothermal expansion is 4 cu ft. The temperature at the end of the adiabatic expansion is 30 F. Compute (a) the heat added, and (b) the heat rejected.

7.8 A reversed Carnot cycle using air as the working fluid operates between temperature limits of 70 and 400 F. During the isothermal compression, the volume is halved, and the minimum specific volume during the cycle is 2 cu ft/lb. Determine the coefficient of performance and the amount of heat absorbed from the low-temperature region per pound of air.

7.9 Air expands isothermally in a Carnot engine from $V_1 = 1$ cu ft to $V_2 = 3$ cu ft. During the adiabatic expansion process, the enthalpy of the air decreases from 200 to 100 B. Assuming the enthalpy and internal energy of the air to be zero at 0 R, and constant values of $c_p = 0.24$ B/lb-F and $c_v = 0.171$ B/lb-F, compute (a) the efficiency of the engine, (b) the internal energy at the end of the adiabatic expansion, and (c) the pressure at the end of the adiabatic expansion.

7.10 Consider a Carnot engine using air as a working fluid and having an over-all volume ratio of 9. During the isothermal heat rejection which begins with the air at 14.0 psia, 40 F, the volume is decreased to one third of its maximum value. Determine the efficiency of this cycle.

7.11 For a Carnot cycle, is the work of the adiabatic compression equal in magnitude to that of the adiabatic expansion if the working fluid is an ideal gas?

CHAPTER **8**

Some Consequences
of the
Second Law

Many valuable relationships can be deduced from the second law of thermodynamics. Three of these are discussed in this chapter. The first two pertain to the efficiency of reversible engines and are known as the two points of the *Carnot principle*. The third, which follows from the Carnot principle, deals with the establishment of a temperature scale which is independent of the physical properties of any substance.

8·1 The Carnot principle

The following two deductions comprise the Carnot principle:*

I. *No engine can be more efficient than an externally reversible engine operating between the same temperature limits.* We must understand the "temperature limits" of a cycle to be the temperatures of the two energy reservoirs with which the system exchanges heat.

II. *All externally reversible engines operating between the same temperature limits have the same efficiency.*

We shall now prove these two statements by showing that a violation of either one results in a violation of the Kelvin–Planck statement of the second law.

Referring to Fig. 8·1a, some engine designated as engine X and an externally reversible engine R operate between the same temperature limits. As a first step in proving that no engine can be more efficient than an externally reversible engine operating between the same temperature limits, let us *assume* that engine X has a higher efficiency than the externally reversible engine. Then for the same amount of heat Q_H supplied to each engine, $W_X > W_R$ and $Q_{LX} < Q_{LR}$. (For this discussion we drop our sign

---

* The Carnot principle is also called the *Carnot theorem* or the *Carnot theorem and corollary*.

convention and let Q and W stand for absolute values.) Now let the externally reversible engine be reversed to operate as a refrigerator as shown in Fig. 8·1*b*. The reversed engine rejects heat Q_H to the energy reservoir at T_H and requires a work input of W_R. Since the magnitude of W_R is less than the work output W_X of engine X, engine X can drive the reversed engine and still deliver work in the amount $(W_X - W_R)$ to other parts of the surroundings. The reversed engine is rejecting heat in the amount Q_H to the reservoir at T_H, and engine X is absorbing the same amount of heat from this reservoir. Therefore, there is zero net exchange of heat with the reservoir, and it could in fact be eliminated by having the

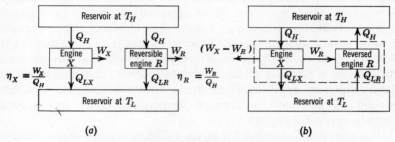

(a)   (b)

Fig. 8·1 Proof of the Carnot principle.

reversed engine discharge heat directly into engine X. Now look at the system which is comprised of engine X and the reversed engine together and which is enclosed by the broken line in Fig. 8·1*b*. See what it is doing. It is operating cyclically, exchanging heat with a single reservoir (the one at T_L), and producing work. This is precisely what the Kelvin–Planck statement of the second law declares to be impossible. Consequently our assumption that $\eta_X > \eta_R$ must be false. *Conclusion:* No engine can be more efficient than an externally reversible engine operating between the same temperature limits.

To prove the second point of the Carnot principle, let both of the engines in Fig. 8·1*a* be externally reversible engines. Assume that their efficiencies are different so that their work outputs are different for the same amount of heat input. Then reverse the less efficient engine. The more efficient engine can drive the reversed engine and have some work left over, even though a net amount of heat is drawn from only one reservoir. This is the same absurdity* that we reached earlier when we

* If the result does not appear absurd to you, recall that the single reservoir could be the atmosphere, the ocean, or the water of a river or lake. The engine and reversed engine together comprise a device which could draw energy only from one of these sources and convert it into work continuously while producing no other effects. What a marvelous device this would be! Do you believe that such a device is possible?

made a false assumption. We must conclude that our assumption that two externally reversible engines operating between the same temperature limits can have different efficiencies is false. *Conclusion:* All externally reversible engines operating between the same temperature limits have the same efficiency.

8·2   The efficiency of reversible engines

The second point of the Carnot principle means that the efficiency of any externally reversible engine depends only on the temperatures of the reservoirs with which it exchanges heat. The efficiency does not depend on the working substance. For given temperature limits, an externally reversible engine operating on air has the same efficiency as one operating on steam or any other substance. This means that, if we can determine the efficiency of an externally reversible engine operating on any particular substance as a function of its temperature limits, then this functional relationship must apply to all externally reversible engines. The same equation for efficiency in terms of temperature limits applies to all externally reversible engines.

It was shown in Example 7·5 that, for a Carnot engine using an ideal gas as working substance and operating between reservoir temperatures of T_H and T_L,

$$\eta = 1 - \frac{T_L}{T_H}$$

where T_H and T_L are temperatures on the ideal-gas absolute temperature scale. In accordance with the second point of the Carnot principle, then, the efficiency of *any* externally reversible engine operating between the temperature limits T_H and T_L is given by

$$\eta = 1 - \frac{T_L}{T_H} \tag{8·1}$$

where T_H and T_L are temperatures on the ideal-gas absolute temperature scale. It is shown in the next article that these are the same as temperatures on what is known as the absolute thermodynamic temperature scale.

8·3   The thermodynamic temperature scale

In Art. 1·12 the shortcoming of any temperature scale defined in terms of the physical properties of a substance was mentioned.* Now we know

---

* As shown in Art. 4·3, the ideal-gas temperature scale does not depend on the properties of any one gas, but it does depend either on the characteristics of gases in general or on the characteristics of a hypothetical substance—an ideal gas. Which of

that (1) the efficiency of externally reversible engines is a function of temperature only, and (2) efficiency involves only heat and work and can therefore be measured independently of properties. In view of these two facts, perhaps a temperature scale can be defined by the relationship

$$\eta_{\text{externally reversible}} \equiv \frac{W}{Q_{\text{in}}} = f(T_H, T_L)$$

As a matter of fact, this can be done, and the procedure is discussed in the following paragraphs. A temperature scale which is independent of the properties of substances is called a thermodynamic temperature scale.

First, let us make clear just what we mean by "defining a temperature scale" and why we must do it. We are not trying to define temperature, because we accept it—along with mass, length, and time—as being verbally undefined. When we define a temperature scale, we specify a method for assigning numerical values to various temperatures.

From childhood you are used to reading thermometers—usually mercury-in-glass or alcohol-in-glass—to get numbers for different temperature levels; so, when part way through a thermodynamics course you are told that we must define a temperature scale, your reaction may well be: "What's wrong with the one we've been using?" Let us answer this question partly by considering an experiment. Take four liquid-in-glass thermometers which do not have scale markings on their stems and which are filled with four different liquids. Call them thermometers A, B, C, and D. Put all four of them in a container with a mixture of air-saturated water and ice at 1 atm pressure. After the thermometers have reached equilibrium with the mixture, put a mark on each stem at the level where the liquid in the thermometer stands. Label this mark 32. Then put all four thermometers into a container with a mixture of liquid water and steam at 1 atm. After the thermometers have reached equilibrium with this mixture, put a mark on each stem at the level where the liquid in the thermometer stands. Label this mark 212. Now we have four thermometers which agree exactly with one another at two temperatures. (We say

---

the two it depends on is a matter of point of view. Still another point of view—that there is no ideal-gas temperature scale but that T in $pv = RT$ is by definition an absolute thermodynamic temperature—is mentioned in Art. 10·8. These three points of view are not in conflict in the sense that one is right and the other two are wrong. Each one is part of a different logical structure or a different philosophy of thermodynamics. If you go into more advanced study of thermodynamics, you may come to believe, as some people do, that one point of view is much to be preferred over the others. If you are interested chiefly in the applications and results of thermodynamic analysis, you will be happy to know that all three points of view lead to the same results. After all, there are many recipes for delicious chocolate cake. Some people are interested in recipes and prefer this one or that one over all the rest; other people just enjoy the result.

that the thermometers have been calibrated at two points.) Divide the stem of each thermometer into 180 equal divisions between the two marks labeled 32 and 212. These intermediate marks can be labeled 33, 34, 35, $\cdots$, 211. Next put all four thermometers into a bath of warm water which is at a uniform temperature. After all the thermometers have reached equilibrium with the bath, read them. Suppose (and this is quite possible) that A

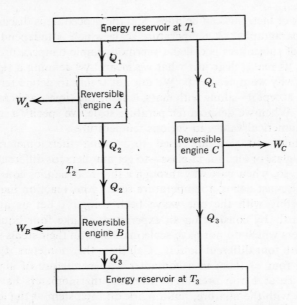

Fig. 8-2 Schematic arrangement of externally reversible engines.

reads 122, B reads 124, C reads 123, and D reads 121. What is the temperature of the bath? There is no reason to select the reading of one thermometer as being "better" than that of another. (For that matter, there is no reason to select a liquid-in-glass thermometer in preference to an electrical-resistance thermometer or a thermocouple.) You may say, "Well, why not arbitrarily establish one of these thermometers as a standard and thereby define a temperature scale?" This looks like a good suggestion (provided you can get other people to adopt the same thermometer as a standard), but as we use such a scale in scientific work we will be annoyed by some features of it. There may be a question as to whether this scale should be used below the freezing point or above the boiling point of the thermometer liquid. Also, we will find certain quantities (such as the efficiency of externally reversible engines) which are functions of temperature only, but the functional relationship is not quite the same for different temperature

ranges. Certain other difficulties will also arise. Thus we find the answer
to the question of what is wrong with the thermometer scale we use in
everyday life. It is all right for indicating when we should wear an overcoat
or when an automobile engine is too hot; but as a scientific tool we need
some other means of assigning numerical values to different temperatures,
and that is what we mean by saying that we must "define a temperature
scale."

Consider three externally reversible engines operating as shown in Fig.
8·2. Engines A and C each absorb heat in the amount Q_1 from the
reservoir at T_1. Engine C rejects heat Q_3 to the reservoir at T_3. Engine A
rejects heat Q_2 at a constant temperature T_2 to engine B. Engine B rejects
heat to the reservoir at T_3, and the amount rejected must be Q_3, the same
amount that engine C rejects. This must be true because engines A and B
taken together constitute an externally reversible heat engine operating
between the same temperature limits as engine C; so engines A and B
taken together must have the same efficiency as engine C. Since the heat
input to engines A and B combined is the same as the heat input to engine
C, the heat rejected must be the same.

By the Carnot principle, the efficiency of an externally reversible engine
is a function of its operating temperature limits only,

$$\eta = \frac{W}{Q_{\text{in}}} = \frac{Q_{\text{in}} - Q_{\text{out}}}{Q_{\text{in}}} = 1 - \frac{Q_{\text{out}}}{Q_{\text{in}}} = 1 - \frac{Q_L}{Q_H} = \phi(T_H, T_L)$$

Therefore,
$$\frac{Q_H}{Q_L} = \psi(T_H, T_L)$$

For engines A, B, and C this is

$$\frac{Q_1}{Q_2} = \psi(T_1, T_2) \tag{a}$$

$$\frac{Q_2}{Q_3} = \psi(T_2, T_3) \tag{b}$$

$$\frac{Q_1}{Q_3} = \psi(T_1, T_3) \tag{c}$$

The product of equations (a) and (b) is

$$\frac{Q_1}{Q_3} = \frac{Q_1}{Q_2}\frac{Q_2}{Q_3} = \psi(T_1, T_2) \cdot \psi(T_2, T_3) \tag{d}$$

Combining equations (c) and (d),

$$\psi(T_1, T_3) = \psi(T_1, T_2) \cdot \psi(T_2, T_3) \tag{e}$$

Look closely at this equation. The left-hand side is a function of T_1 and T_3 only; therefore the right-hand side must be a function of T_1 and T_3 only. The value of T_2 does not affect the value of the product on the right-hand side. This tells us something about the form of the function ψ. In order to satisfy this condition, the function ψ must have the form

$$\psi(T_1, T_2) = \frac{f(T_1)}{f(T_2)}$$

$$\psi(T_2, T_3) = \frac{f(T_2)}{f(T_3)}$$

where f is another function. Substituting into equation (e) gives

$$\psi(T_1, T_3) = \psi(T_1, T_2) \cdot \psi(T_2, T_3) = \frac{f(T_1)}{f(T_2)} \cdot \frac{f(T_2)}{f(T_3)} = \frac{f(T_1)}{f(T_3)}$$

Substituting now into equation (c) gives

$$\frac{Q_1}{Q_3} = \frac{f(T_1)}{f(T_3)}$$

which tells us much more than equation (c) does regarding the dependence of Q_1/Q_3 on the reservoir temperatures. This is as far as deductive reasoning will take us. The second law thus requires *only* that

$$\frac{Q_H}{Q_L} = \frac{f(T_H)}{f(T_L)} \tag{8·2}$$

for any externally reversible engine. The function $f(T)$ can be chosen arbitrarily to define a temperature scale which is independent of the physical properties of any substance. Such a temperature scale is called a thermodynamic temperature scale. As proposed by Lord Kelvin, we can let $f(T) = T$ so that a thermodynamic temperature scale is *defined* by

$$\frac{Q_H}{Q_L} = \frac{T_H}{T_L} \tag{8·3}$$

On this scale, which is often called the Kelvin scale, the ratio of two temperatures is equal to the ratio of the amounts of heat transferred between an externally reversible heat engine and two reservoirs at these temperatures.

A characteristic of the Kelvin or absolute thermodynamic temperature scale is that negative temperatures are impossible. Recall that in our discussion of externally reversible engines and in equation 8·3, Q_H and Q_L stand respectively for heat added to the engine at T_H and rejected from the engine at T_L. Therefore, if an externally reversible heat engine operates with Q_H absorbed from a reservoir at T_H and if T_L is negative, then we see from

$$\frac{Q_H}{Q_L} = \frac{T_H}{T_L} \qquad (8·3)$$

that Q_L must be negative; that is, heat must be absorbed by the engine from the reservoir at T_L. Since the energy removed from the reservoir at

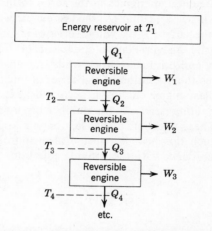

Fig. 8·3 Schematic arrangement of externally reversible engines used in discussing the Kelvin temperature scale.

T_L can always be replaced just by transferring heat from the reservoir at T_H to the one at T_L, the reservoir at T_L could operate cyclically, and it and the engine together would constitute a device which absorbed heat from the reservoir at T_H and produced an equivalent amount of work while operating cyclically. Thus the existence of a negative absolute thermodynamic temperature would make possible a violation of the second law.

In order to define zero on the Kelvin scale or absolute zero temperature, consider a series of reversible engines as shown in Fig. 8·3. One engine absorbs heat Q_1 from the energy reservoir at T_1. It rejects heat Q_2 at a temperature T_2 to another reversible engine which in turn rejects heat Q_3 at a temperature T_3 to another reversible engine and so forth. Let the temperatures be selected so that the same amount of work is done by each engine. Thus

$$W_1 = W_2 = W_3 = \cdots$$

and

$$Q_1 - Q_2 = Q_2 - Q_3 = Q_3 - Q_4 = \cdots$$

and application of the defining equation of the Kelvin scale (equation 8·3) shows that

$$T_1 - T_2 = T_2 - T_3 = T_3 - T_4 = \cdots$$

That is, the engines in the series do equal work when the temperature differences across them are equal.

As more engines are added to the series, the total work output increases. By the first law, the total work output cannot exceed Q_1. In the limiting case where there are enough engines in the series to make the total work output $(W_1 + W_2 + W_3 + \cdots)$ equal Q_1, the last engine will reject zero heat. The last engine in the series (or the whole series of engines taken together) is then violating the Kelvin–Planck statement of the second law by operating cyclically and producing work while exchanging heat with only one reservoir. Thus the operation of the series of engines with zero heat rejection from the last engine cannot be accomplished, although it can be approached as a limiting case. As the number of engines in the series is increased and the heat rejection of the last engine approaches zero, the temperature at which this heat is rejected also approaches zero on the Kelvin scale in accordance with the defining equation

$$\frac{Q_H}{Q_L} = \frac{T_H}{T_L}$$

Absolute zero temperature may be defined as follows: *If an externally reversible heat engine operates between two energy reservoirs, absorbing a constant heat input from the hotter reservoir, and the temperature of the colder reservoir is successively lowered, the amount of heat rejected decreases. As the amount of heat rejected approaches zero, the temperature of the colder reservoir approaches absolute zero.* Notice that this definition makes no mention whatsoever of the physical properties of any substance either at absolute zero or at any other temperature. Also, the second law alone does not lead to the conclusion that it is impossible for the temperature of any system to be absolute zero. (This conclusion is in the realm of the third law of thermodynamics and is not discussed in this book.)

The Kelvin or thermodynamic temperature scale is not completely defined until the "size" of the degree is fixed. This is usually done by assigning the difference in temperature between freezing water and boiling water at 1 atm the numerical value of 100 centigrade degrees or 180 Fahrenheit degrees. Calling the temperature of the ice point T_i and the temperature of the steam point T_s, we have

$$T_s - T_i = 180 \text{ Fahrenheit degrees}$$

The other equation involving T_s and T_i is the one for an externally reversible engine operating between these two temperatures,

$$\frac{Q_s}{Q_i} = \frac{T_s}{T_i}$$

If we could build an externally reversible engine and operate it between reservoirs maintained at temperatures T_s and T_i, measurements of Q_s and Q_i (or of Q_s and work or of work and Q_i) would show that

$$\frac{Q_s}{Q_i} = 1.3661$$

This is equal to the ratio of T_s/T_i; so we now have two equations

$$T_s - T_i = 180 \quad \text{and} \quad \frac{T_s}{T_i} = 1.3661$$

which can be solved for T_s and T_i. With $T_s - T_i = 180$ degrees, the resulting scale is the absolute Fahrenheit scale which is also called the Rankine scale; with $T_s - T_i = 100$ degrees, the resulting scale is the absolute centigrade scale which is also called the Kelvin scale. Thus the designation *Kelvin scale* is used for two different things: (1) the absolute thermodynamic centigrade scale and (2) any absolute thermodynamic scale which is established in accordance with equation 8·3.

Fortunately, it is unnecessary to operate an externally reversible engine in order to determine numerical values on the thermodynamic temperature scale or in order to establish the relationship between this scale and various other ones. Several relations between absolute thermodynamic temperatures and other properties of substances are now known.* One of these we should observe now. From the definition of thermal efficiency and the first law, we can write for any heat engine.

$$\eta = \frac{W}{Q_{in}} = \frac{Q_{in} - Q_{out}}{Q_{in}} = 1 - \frac{Q_{out}}{Q_{in}}$$

From the definition of the thermodynamic temperature scale, which depends on the second law, we can write for any externally reversible heat engine operating between reservoirs at T_H and T_L

$$\frac{Q_{out}}{Q_{in}} = \frac{Q_L}{Q_H} = \frac{T_L}{T_H}$$

* See, for example, J. H. Keenan, *Thermodynamics*, John Wiley & Sons, 1941, chapter XXI.

Therefore, the efficiency of any externally reversible heat engine operating between reservoirs at T_H and T_L is

$$\eta = 1 - \frac{T_L}{T_H} = \frac{T_H - T_L}{T_H} \qquad (8 \cdot 1)$$

where T_H and T_L are temperatures on the absolute thermodynamic scale. But this same equation was given for this efficiency in the preceding article, and the temperatures were specified as being on the ideal-gas absolute temperature scale. The conclusion is that the ideal-gas absolute temperature scale agrees identically with the absolute thermodynamic temperature scale.

In practice, highly accurate temperature measurements are made on the international temperature scale which has been adopted by interested people in many nations as an accurately reproducible scale without the use of complicated gas thermometers. The international scale is defined by (1) assigning values to certain accurately reproducible temperatures such as boiling and melting points, (2) specifying the type of thermometer to be used in each range of the scale, and (3) specifying the interpolation formula to be used for each thermometer between the assigned values. The international scale was established to agree with the thermodynamic scale and it does so very closely.

EXAMPLE 8·1. Determine the heat input to a Carnot engine which operates between 900 and 60 F and produces 100 B of work.

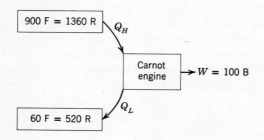

Example 8·1

Solution. Applying the first law and the definition of the absolute thermodynamic temperature scale to this engine, we have two simultaneous equations:

$$Q_H - Q_L = W$$

$$\frac{Q_H}{Q_L} = \frac{T_H}{T_L}$$

Solving these for Q_H,

$$Q_H - Q_H \frac{T_L}{T_H} = W$$

$$Q_H = \frac{W}{1 - T_L/T_H} = \frac{100}{1 - 520/1360} = 165 \text{ B}$$

(Notice that the last equation is the same as $Q_H = W/\eta$.)

EXAMPLE 8·2. Compute the power required to drive a reversed Carnot engine if 100 B/min is absorbed from the cold region and the isothermal processes occur at 500 and 32 F.

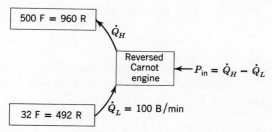

Example 8·2

Solution. The power input is the difference between the rate at which heat is rejected and the rate at which heat is absorbed. The rate of heat rejection can be found by

$$\dot{Q}_H = \dot{Q}_L \frac{T_H}{T_L} = 100 \,(960/492) = 195 \text{ B/min}$$

and then $P_{in} = \dot{Q}_H - \dot{Q}_L = 195 - 100 = 95 \text{ B/min} = 2.24 \text{ hp}$

8·4 Summary

No engine can be more efficient than an externally reversible engine operating between the same temperature limits. The "temperature limits" of a cycle are the temperatures of the two energy reservoirs with which the system exchanges heat.

All externally reversible engines operating between the same temperature limits have the same efficiency.

These two italicized statements are called the two points of the *Carnot principle.*

A temperature scale which is entirely independent of the physical properties of any substance is called a *thermodynamic temperature scale.* The most commonly used absolute thermodynamic temperature scale is one that was proposed by Kelvin and is defined by the relationship

$$\frac{T_H}{T_L} = \frac{Q_H}{Q_L} \tag{8·3}$$

where T_H and T_L are the temperatures of the energy reservoirs between which an externally reversible engine operates when it absorbs heat Q_H from the hotter reservoir and rejects heat Q_L to the colder reservoir. The ideal-gas absolute temperature scale agrees identically with the absolute thermodynamic temperature scale.

Negative absolute temperatures are impossible. The question of whether the temperature of any system can be lowered to absolute zero on the thermodynamic temperature scale cannot be answered by the second law alone.

It must be remembered that the relationship

$$\frac{Q_H}{Q_L} = \frac{T_H}{T_L} \tag{8.3}$$

applies only to externally reversible engines operating between reservoirs at T_H and T_L. *The efficiency of any externally reversible engine operating between temperatures of T_H and T_L is given by*

$$\eta = 1 - \frac{T_L}{T_H} = \frac{T_H - T_L}{T_H}$$

REFERENCES

8·1 D. A. Mooney, *Mechanical Engineering Thermodynamics*, Prentice-Hall, 1953, arts. 8-1 and 8-2.

8·2 J. H. Keenan, *Thermodynamics*, John Wiley & Sons, 1941, chapter VIII.

8·3 M. W. Zemansky, *Heat and Thermodynamics*, McGraw-Hill Book Co., 4th ed., 1957, chapter 9.

8·4 P. J. Kiefer, G. F. Kinney, and M. G. Stuart, *Principles of Engineering Thermodynamics*, John Wiley & Sons, 2d ed., 1954, chapter 6.

PROBLEMS

8·1 Refer to Fig. 8·1. Demonstrate the Carnot principle by letting one of the initial assumptions be that $Q_{LX} = Q_{LR}$.

8·2 Prove that no refrigerator can have a higher coefficient of performance than an externally reversible refrigerator operating between the same temperature limits.

8·3 Prove that all externally reversible refrigerators operating between the same temperature limits have the same coefficient of performance.

8·4 It is possible for an actual engine to be more efficient than a Carnot engine. Explain this.

8·5 Prove from the Clausius statement or the Kelvin–Planck statement the following, which is known as the Carathéodory statement of the second law: In the vicinity of any state of a substance there are some states which cannot be reached (from the state first mentioned) by adiabatic processes alone.

8·6 Lowering the temperature at which a heat engine rejects heat increases its efficiency. A steam power plant usually rejects its heat to water from a river, lake, or ocean; so would it be advisable to cool the water first by means of a refrigeration system driven by the power plant? Explain.

8·7 When Sir Isaac Newton established the first numerical temperature scale, would it have been possible to assign numbers so that temperatures of colder bodies were represented by larger numbers? (This means that a man in England stepping outdoors in January might turn up his coat collar and say, "Brrr, the temperature is really getting up there today.") If impossible, state why. If possible, do you see any objections?

8·8 Upon learning that a temperature of 0.0014 K has been reached in a cryogenic laboratory, someone states that the scientists "practically reached absolute zero." Comment on this statement.

8·9 Referring to Fig. 8·2, demonstrate that $Q_1/Q_3 = f(T_1)/f(T_3)$ without making reference to any heat engines except A and B.

8·10 Someone has paraphrased the first law of thermodynamics as "You can't get something for nothing" and the second law as "You can't get as much as you thought you could." Someone else has suggested "You can't win" and "You can't even break even." Do these appear to you to be apt paraphrases? Explain.

8·11 Comment on the validity of the following as a statement of the second law: Heat cannot be converted into work unless there is a temperature difference.

8·12 Prove whether the following statement is true or false: A closed system cannot execute a cycle while receiving heat from a single energy reservoir.

8·13 Refer to the footnote on page 251. To what extent can it be proved that the device as described is impossible?

8·14 A Carnot engine develops 10 hp and at the same time rejects 40,000 B/hr at 70 F. Compute the temperature of the source or hot body.

8·15 A Carnot engine operates between a source at 1200 F and a receiver at 70 F. If the output of the engine is 100 hp, compute the heat supplied, the heat rejected, and the efficiency of the engine.

8·16 A Carnot engine operates between a source at 800 F and a receiver at 100 F. If 200 B are rejected each minute to the receiver, compute the power output.

8·17 The efficiency of a Carnot engine discharging heat to a cooling pond at 80 F is 30 per cent. If the cooling pond receives 800 B/min, what is the power output of the engine? What is the temperature of the high-temperature source?

8·18 A Carnot engine receives 15 B/sec from a source at 900 F and delivers 6000 ft-lb/sec of power. Determine (a) the efficiency, and (b) the temperature of the receiver.

8·19 A Carnot engine produces 5 hp while operating between temperatures of 400 and 100 F. Find the heat absorbed from the source by the medium per minute.

8·20 A Carnot engine receives 102,000 B/hr from a source at 540 F and rejects 75,700 B/hr to a cold body. At what temperature is the cold body?

8·21 A Carnot engine works between a hot body at 1000 F and a cold body at 80 F. For each 100 B absorbed from the source, compute (a) the heat rejected, and (b) the work developed by the engine.

8·22 A Carnot engine receives 8 B from a source at 500 F and during the cycle performs 3500 ft-lb of work. What is the temperature of the cold body?

8·23 A Carnot engine containing 8 lb of air has at the beginning of the expansion stroke a volume of 10 cu ft and a pressure of 220 psia. The exhaust temperature is 40 F. If 8 B of heat is added during the cycle, find (a) the efficiency of the engine, and (b) the work of the cycle.

8·24 A heat engine operating on the Carnot cycle produces 10,000 ft-lb of work while operating between temperature limits of 500 and 40 F. Determine the efficiency.

8·25 If 100 B represents the net output for a Carnot engine operating between 100 and 300 F, how much heat must be absorbed from the source and how much rejected to the receiver?

8·26 A Carnot engine reversed is used as an ice machine; it operates between 32 and 84 F. How many pounds of ice will it produce per hour if the power input is 2 hp? (Latent heat of fusion of ice is 144 B/lb.)

8·27 A reversed Carnot engine is used as a refrigerating machine for removing 6000 B/min from a cold storage room at −5 F. Heat is discharged to a hot body at 70 F. Compute the power required to operate the reversed engine.

8·28 A Carnot heat pump is used for heating a building. The outside air at 22 F is the cold body, the building at 72 F is the hot body, and 200,000 B/hr is required for heating. Find (a) heat taken from the outside per hour, and (b) power required.

8·29 A reversed Carnot engine operates between 100 and 40 F. If 400 B/min is to be removed from the cold body, calculate the power required.

8·30 A reversed Carnot engine operating between 0 and 100 F rejects 40,000 B/hr to the receiver at 100 F. Compute the power required to operate the machine.

8·31 A Carnot refrigerator is used to make ice. Freezing water at 32 F is the cold body, and heat is rejected from the system to a river at 70 F. What is the work required to freeze 100 lb of ice? (Latent heat of fusion of ice is 144 B/lb.)

8·32 A reversed Carnot engine absorbs 400 B/min from a source at a temperature of −10 F. If heat is rejected at 90 F, compute the coefficient of performance.

8·33 A reversed Carnot engine operating between 40 and 100 F delivers 100,000 B/hr to the hot body. Compute the coefficient of performance.

8·34 A Carnot engine using wet steam as the working fluid operates between temperature limits of 300 and 100 F. Sketch a pv diagram of the cycle. For a work output of 100 B, calculate the amount of heat rejected from the working fluid at the lower temperature.

8·35 A Carnot refrigerator using wet steam as a working fluid removes 10,000 B/hr from a region at 40 F. The highest pressure reached by the working fluid is 10 psia. Sketch a pv diagram of the cycle. Calculate the power input to the refrigerator.

8·36 A Carnot refrigerator is to be used to remove 400 B/hr from a region at −60 F and discharge heat to the atmosphere at 40 F. The Carnot refrigerator is to be driven by a Carnot engine operating between an energy reservoir at 1040 F and the atmosphere at 40 F. How much heat must be supplied, in B/hr, to the Carnot engine at 1040 F?

8·37 Solve Prob. 8·36 with the Carnot engine rejecting heat to the region at −60 F instead of to the atmosphere. The refrigerator must then absorb 400 B/hr plus the heat rejected by the engine.

8·38 A Carnot cycle uses 0.2 lb of steam as a working fluid. At the beginning of the isothermal expansion the working fluid is at 200 psia, 20 per cent quality. At the end of the isothermal expansion, the steam is dry and saturated. During the isothermal compression the steam is at 10 psia. Calculate (a) the efficiency of the cycle, and (b) the amount of work done per cycle.

8·39 A reversed Carnot cycle uses 0.2 lb of steam as working fluid. At the beginning of the isothermal expansion, the steam is at 0.5 psia, 30 per cent quality; at the end of the isothermal expansion, the steam is dry and saturated. Heat is rejected at 240 F. Determine (a) the change in internal energy of the steam during the isothermal expansion, and (b) the work input per cycle.

8·40 Describe precisely the steps involved in executing a Carnot cycle using a rubber band as the working substance and water at 32 F and water at 140 F as the energy reservoirs. Sketch a force–length diagram.

8·41 Sketch a curve of Carnot refrigerator coefficient of performance versus low temperature for a fixed heat-rejection temperature.

8·42 Sketch a curve of Carnot cycle efficiency versus heat source temperature for a fixed heat-rejection temperature.

CHAPTER **9**

Entropy

The first law of thermodynamics leads to the definition of a very useful property which we call stored energy E. The term *energy* is used in everyday conversation, often in the same sense as in engineering and science. Consequently, you were familiar with the term before meeting it in the study of thermodynamics, and this familiarity may even have helped you to gain an understanding of the nature of stored energy as rigorously defined by the first law.

The second law also leads to the definition of a very useful property. This property is called entropy (ĕn′trō-pĭ) S. Unlike energy, the term *entropy* is not used in everyday conversation. It is not mentioned in most high school physics courses nor in many college introductory physics courses. Consequently, entropy is probably an unfamiliar term. Furthermore, it is defined in terms of a mathematical operation, and no direct physical picture of it can be given. For these reasons, you may find at first that the concept of entropy is somewhat nebulous. In order to gain an understanding of entropy, you should study its uses and keep asking the questions, "What is it used for?" and "How is it used?" If you are looking for a physical description as an answer, the question "What *is* entropy?" is fruitless. (Recall that the development of the first law was impeded by the question, "What *is* heat?" and it was only when attention was turned to the question, "How is heat related to work and other effects?" that progress was made toward the understanding of heat.) Consequently, this chapter not only introduces entropy but also discusses several of its uses. You will see that every subsequent chapter in this book except one makes use of the property entropy.

9·1 The property entropy

One way to prove that some quantity is a property is to show that the cyclic integral of the quantity is always zero. Physically, this means that, if a system executes a cycle, the quantity is always returned to its initial value when the system is returned to its initial state. The value of the quantity thus depends only on the state of the system. This is true for all properties and for properties only. We will now prove that $\oint_{\mathrm{rev}} \dfrac{\delta Q}{T} = 0$ and that therefore $\displaystyle\int_{\mathrm{rev}} \dfrac{\delta Q}{T}$ is a property. This is the property called entropy S, so that the definition of entropy (or entropy change) is

$$\Delta S \equiv \int_{\mathrm{rev}} \frac{\delta Q}{T} \qquad\qquad (9\cdot 1a)$$

As a first step in the proof we will show that any reversible process can be approximated by a series of reversible adiabatic and isothermal

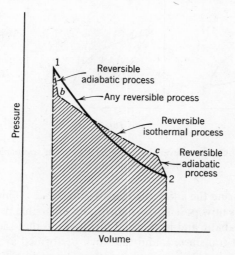

Fig. 9·1 Simulating any reversible process by a series of reversible adiabatics and reversible isothermals.

processes. For example, the reversible process represented by line 1-2 in Fig. 9·1 may be approximated by a series of reversible adiabatic and isothermal steps as shown by 1-*b*, *b*-*c*, and *c*-2, provided that the individual steps are so chosen that the area under curve 1-2 is equal to that under 1-*b*-*c*-2. Of course, the greater the number of adiabatic and isothermal steps, the closer the series of lines will approach the original reversible process. For purposes of discussion, the two adiabatic lines and the one isothermal line will suffice. Consider a closed system. Since the areas under the two curves are made equal, the work terms $\int p\, dv$ will be the same; hence

$$W_{1\text{-}2} = W_{1\text{-}b\text{-}c\text{-}2}$$

Applying the first law,

$$Q_{1\text{-}2} = U_2 - U_1 + W_{1\text{-}2}$$

and

$$Q_{1\text{-}b\text{-}c\text{-}2} = U_2 - U_1 + W_{1\text{-}b\text{-}c\text{-}2}$$

Since the initial and final internal energy (property) values are the same regardless of the path and the steps are so selected that the work terms are equal,

$$Q_{1\text{-}2} = Q_{1\text{-}b\text{-}c\text{-}2}$$

In other words, the heat transferred during the reversible process 1-2 is the same as that transferred during the isothermal change *b-c*, since no heat

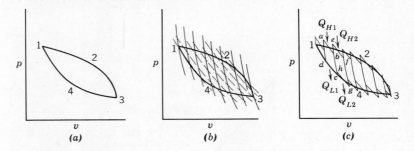

Fig 9·2 Simulating a reversible cycle by a series of reversible adiabatics and reversible isothermals.

is transferred during the adiabatic steps 1-*b* and 2-*c*. This is a significant fact, because it is now possible to replace any reversible process by a series of reversible adiabatic and isothermal processes so that the internal energy change, the heat transferred, and the work performed are the same.

A system (for example, a gas) at state 1 as shown in Fig. 9·2*a* is assumed first to undergo a reversible process 1-2-3 and then to proceed along the reversible path 3-4-1 to the initial state 1. These processes form a cycle. The first step in this proof is to replace the original processes by a series of reversible adiabatic and isothermal lines as shown in Fig. 9·2*b* in a manner similar to that previously described. These various adiabatic (solid) and isothermal (dashed) lines may then be connected so as to represent a number of Carnot cycles, as shown in Fig. 9·2*c*. For the Carnot cycles *a-b-c-d* and *e-f-g-h*.

$$\frac{Q_{H1}}{T_{H1}} = \frac{Q_{L1}}{T_{L1}}$$

$$\frac{Q_{H2}}{T_{H2}} = \frac{Q_{L2}}{T_{L2}}$$

where the temperatures are the temperatures of the system during the isothermal processes. In order to simplify previous developments, both Q_H and Q_L were considered positive (or it could be said that only absolute values were used). Actually the heat rejected Q_L should be opposite in sign to the heat added Q_H; hence, by using the sign convention of positive for heat absorbed and negative for heat rejected, the preceding equations become

$$\frac{Q_{H1}}{T_{H1}} + \frac{Q_{L1}}{T_{L1}} = 0$$

$$\frac{Q_{H2}}{T_{H2}} + \frac{Q_{L2}}{T_{L2}} = 0$$

From these relations it is apparent that the summation of all the ratios of heat transfer to absolute temperature for *all* the Carnot cycles equals zero, or

$$\left(\frac{Q_{H1}}{T_{H1}} + \frac{Q_{L1}}{T_{L1}}\right) + \left(\frac{Q_{H2}}{T_{H2}} + \frac{Q_{L2}}{T_{L2}}\right) + \cdots = 0$$

It is possible to simplify the summation expression by employing Q to represent heat transfer and T the absolute temperature at which the heat is transferred. Hence for the cycle,

$$\Sigma \frac{Q}{T} = 0$$

If the number of Carnot cycles is greatly increased, the stepped path approximates more closely the actual processes. Finally, as the number of Carnot cycles becomes very large, the summation of the Q/T terms becomes equal to the integral of $\delta Q/T$; hence the preceding equation becomes

$$\oint_{\text{rev}} \frac{\delta Q}{T} = 0$$

From this result alone *we can conclude that* $\int_{\text{rev}} \frac{\delta Q}{T}$ *is a property.* However, it may be worthwhile to demonstrate once again* that $\oint_{\text{rev}} \frac{\delta Q}{T} = 0$ means that the value of $\int_{\text{rev}} \frac{\delta Q}{T}$ for any process depends only on the end states and not on the path followed in going from one state to another.

* It was demonstrated in Art. 2·3 that $\oint(\delta Q - \delta W) = 0$ leads to the fact that the value of $\int(\delta Q - \delta W)$ depends only on the end states of a process.

Consider two equilibrium states 0 and 1 for a system as shown in Fig. 9·3. The path 0-a-1 is a reversible* path from state 0 to state 1. Paths 1-b-0 and 1-c-0 are any other two reversible paths between state 1 and state 0. Two cycles may be considered: 0-a-1-b-0 and 0-a-1-c-0, for which the cyclic integral is zero. In each cycle the cyclic integral may be represented as two integrals.

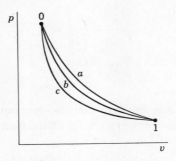

Fig. 9·3   Reversible paths.

Cycle 0-a-1-b-0:
$$\oint \frac{\delta Q}{T} = \int_{0\text{-}a}^{1} \frac{\delta Q}{T} + \int_{1\text{-}b}^{0} \frac{\delta Q}{T} = 0$$

and

Cycle 0-a-1-c-0:
$$\oint \frac{\delta Q}{T} = \int_{0\text{-}a}^{1} \frac{\delta Q}{T} + \int_{1\text{-}c}^{0} \frac{\delta Q}{T} = 0$$

Subtracting these two expressions gives

$$\int_{1\text{-}b}^{0} \frac{\delta Q}{T} - \int_{1\text{-}c}^{0} \frac{\delta Q}{T} = 0$$

Transposing and rearranging results in

$$\int_{0}^{1\text{-}b} \frac{\delta Q}{T} = \int_{0}^{1\text{-}c} \frac{\delta Q}{T}$$

Since b and c are *any* two reversible paths between states 0 and 1, it follows that the value of $\int \frac{\delta Q}{T}$ is the same for *all* reversible paths between the two states. In other words, the value of $\int_{\text{rev}} \frac{\delta Q}{T}$ depends only on the end states of any process. The notation "rev" on the integral sign indicates that the

* Remember the convention that *reversible* without a modifier means *internally reversible*.

integration must be carried out along some *reversible* path connecting the two states.

This property $\int_{\text{rev}} \dfrac{\delta Q}{T}$ is called entropy and is denoted by the symbol S. Thus

$$\Delta S \equiv \int_{\text{rev}} \frac{\delta Q}{T} \tag{9·1a}$$

This is an operational definition. It tells us how to obtain numbers for ΔS, even though the operations prescribed are "pencil and paper" operations. Notice that we actually define the *change in entropy* ΔS instead of entropy S, just as we earlier defined ΔE instead of E. In engineering work it is usually only the *change* in S which is important; so a value of $S = 0$ can be assigned to any particular state of a system arbitrarily. Once this is done, the entropy at any other state x is given by

$$S_x = S_0 + \int_0^x \frac{\delta Q}{T}$$
$$\text{rev}$$

where state 0 is the one for which $S = S_0 = 0$.

Because S is a property, ΔS between two states is the same, no matter what path, reversible or irreversible, is followed as a system changes from one state to the other. Equation 9·1a states, however, that the numerical value for ΔS must be obtained by integrating $\int \dfrac{\delta Q}{T}$ along *some reversible* path. Examples of this calculation are given in the next article.

$\left(\text{If } \int \dfrac{\delta Q}{T} \right.$ is integrated along *irreversible* paths between two states, it is found that in general a different numerical value is obtained for each path; that is, $\int_{\text{irrev}} \dfrac{\delta Q}{T}$ is not a property. In fact, it can be shown that $\oint_{\text{irrev}} \dfrac{\delta Q}{T} < 0$. The general statement, $\oint \dfrac{\delta Q}{T} \leq 0$, where the equality holds for reversible cycles and the inequality for irreversible ones is useful in some thermodynamic analyses and is known as the *inequality of Clausius.* $\Big)$

The definition $\Delta S \equiv \displaystyle\int_{\text{rev}} \dfrac{\delta Q}{T}$ holds for any closed system or any fixed quantity of matter, just as the definition $\Delta E \equiv \int(\delta Q - \delta W)$ does. To determine a general expression for ΔS of an open system, consider any open system as in Fig. 9·4 (where for convenience only one inlet and one outlet are shown). Let the mass δm_1 entering the open system have a specific entropy s_1. Let this mass come from an open system A which might be in the particular form shown in Fig. 9·5. System A exchanges no heat with the surroundings, and the only work done on system A by the surroundings is equal to the flow work delivered to the open system as mass δm_1 crosses the boundary. (Notice that this restriction on system A does not restrict the generality of the open system's behavior at all.) The entropy change of A, as mass δm_1 is transferred to the open system, is $-s_1 \, \delta m_1$. Let the mass leaving the open system go to a system B which behaves in the same manner as system A. The entropy change of B is then $s_2 \, \delta m_2$. Since there is no heat transfer to systems A and B, the heat transfer

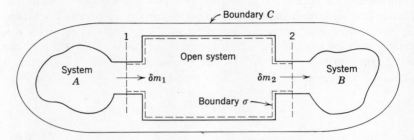

Fig. 9·4 Entropy change of an open system.

to closed system C is the same as that to open system σ. Thus for the closed system enclosed in boundary C,

$$dS_C = \left(\frac{\delta Q}{T}\right)_{\text{rev}, C} = \left(\frac{\delta Q}{T}\right)_{\text{rev}, \sigma}$$

where T is the temperature of that part of the system to which heat is transferred. (Recall that the temperature throughout an open system is generally not uniform.) Then, since entropy is an extensive property,

$$dS_C = dS_\sigma + dS_A + dS_B$$

and

$$dS_\sigma = dS_C - dS_A - dS_B$$

$$dS_\sigma = \left(\frac{\delta Q}{T}\right)_{\text{rev}, \sigma} + s_1 \, \delta m_1 - s_2 \, \delta m_2 \qquad (9·1b)$$

This is the general expression for dS of an open system. Notice that, for steady flow, $dS_\sigma = 0$ and $\delta m_1 = \delta m_2$, so that equation 9·1b becomes

$$0 = \left(\frac{\delta Q}{T}\right)_{\text{rev}, \sigma} - (s_2 - s_1) \, \delta m$$

For steady flow, $\displaystyle\int_{\text{rev}} \frac{\delta Q}{T}$ for the system is the same as $\displaystyle\int_{\text{rev}} \frac{\delta Q}{T}$ for the mass flowing through the system. The integration can then be performed between the entering and leaving states of the fluid, and we have

$$s_2 - s_1 = \int_{1}^{2} \frac{\delta q}{T} \bigg|_{\text{rev}}$$

which agrees with the definition of Δs which holds for any fixed mass, including a mass which is moving through an open system.

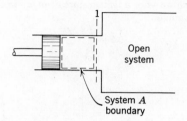

Fig. 9·5   Possible form of system A in Fig. 9·4.

9·2 Calculation of entropy changes

In order to calculate ΔS between any two states of a substance, select any reversible path connecting the two states, and integrate along that path. Some examples of this procedure follow.

EXAMPLE 9·1.   Calculate the change in entropy of 1 lb of helium which is heated reversibly at constant pressure from 18 psia, 80 F, to 200 F in a closed system. c_p is constant at 1.25 B/lb-F.

Solution A. ΔS can be calculated from the defining equation

$$\Delta S \equiv \int_{1}^{2} \frac{\delta Q}{T} \bigg|_{\text{rev}} \tag{9·1a}$$

by evaluating the integral along any reversible path between the end states. Let us use the reversible constant-pressure path which the system actually follows. We must find a relationship between δQ and dT in order to integrate. This can be done by the following steps in which each step is explained, or the restriction imposed is stated, by the words in parentheses:

$$\begin{aligned}
\delta Q &= dU + \delta W && \text{(first law, closed system)} \\
&= dU + p\,dV && \text{(reversible process)} \\
&= dU + d(pV) && \text{(constant pressure)} \\
&= d(U + pV) = dH && \text{(definition of } H\text{)} \\
&= mc_p\,dT && \text{(ideal gas)}
\end{aligned}$$

(Of course, it might have been recalled directly that for a *reversible constant-pressure process* $\delta Q = mc_p \, dT$.) Making this substitution for δQ,

$$\Delta S = \int_1^2 \frac{mc_p \, dT}{T}$$

$$\Delta S = mc_p \ln \frac{T_2}{T_1} = 1(1.25) \ln \frac{660}{540} = 0.251 \text{ B/R}$$

(Notice that the units of c_p may be either B/lb-F or B/lb-R, as explained in Example 3·1, but the units of entropy change should be B/R and not B/F because the definition of ΔS involves *absolute* temperature—not a temperature change—in the denominator.)

Solution B. Let us evaluate

$$\Delta S = \int_{\substack{1 \\ \text{rev}}}^2 \frac{\delta Q}{T}$$

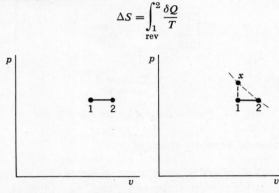

Example 9·1

over some reversible path other than the constant-pressure path. (There is no reason to choose any other path in this case except to illustrate that the same result will be obtained.) Let us choose a path as shown on the diagram which consists first of a reversible constant-volume heating from the initial state 1 to the final temperature. Call this state for which $V = V_1$ and $T = T_2$ state x. The second part of the reversible path is a reversible isothermal process from state x to state 2. Since ΔS is the same for all paths between states 1 and 2, we have

$$\Delta S = \int_{\substack{1 \\ \text{rev}}}^2 \frac{\delta Q}{T} = \int_{\substack{1 \\ \text{rev}}}^x \frac{\delta Q}{T} + \int_{\substack{x \\ \text{rev}}}^2 \frac{\delta Q}{T}$$

Applying the first law and noting that 1-x and x-2 are reversible processes,

$$\Delta S = \int_1^x \frac{dU}{T} + \int_x^2 \frac{dU + p \, dV}{T}$$

Since the system is comprised of an ideal gas,

$$\Delta S = \int_1^x \frac{mc_v \, dT}{T} + \int_x^2 \frac{0 + p \, dV}{T} = \int_1^x \frac{mc_v \, dT}{T} + \int_x^2 \frac{mR \, dV}{V}$$

Assuming c_v and R to be constant,

$$\Delta S = mc_v \ln \frac{T_x}{T_1} + mR \ln \frac{V_2}{V_x}$$

Noting that $T_x = T_2$, $V_x = V_1$, and $V_2/V_1 = T_2/T_1$,

$$\Delta S = mc_v \ln \frac{T_2}{T_1} + mR \ln \frac{T_2}{T_1} = m(c_v + R) \ln \frac{T_2}{T_1}$$

$$= mc_p \ln \frac{T_2}{T_1}$$

This, as expected, is the same expression that was obtained in solution A by integrating $\int \frac{\delta Q}{T}$ along the reversible constant-pressure path.

EXAMPLE 9·2.   Calculate the change in entropy per pound of helium which is heated reversibly at constant pressure from 18 psia, 80 F, to 200 F in a steady-flow system.

Solution.   Entropy is a property. For a pure substance, entropy is a function of any other two properties. Since here the initial pressure and temperature and the final pressure and temperature are the same as in Example 9·1, the entropy change must be the same. The fact that the helium in one case is in a closed system and in the other case is in a steady-flow system makes no difference. If we had not realized this, we might have calculated Δs as follows:

The first law applied to a steady-flow system gives an energy balance which, in differential form, is

$$\delta q = dh + dKE + dPE + \delta w$$

For a reversible steady flow process

$$\delta w = -v\,dp - dKE - dPE$$

so that

$$\delta q = dh + dKE + dPE - v\,dp - dKE - dPE$$

and for a constant-pressure process, $v\,dp = 0$ so that

$$\delta q = dh$$

For a steady-flow system, $dS_\sigma = 0$ and $\delta m_1 = \delta m_2$; so the expression for dS of an open system,

$$dS_\sigma = \left(\frac{\delta Q}{T}\right)_{\text{rev},\sigma} + s_1\,\delta m_1 - s_2\,\delta m_2 \qquad (9\cdot1b)$$

becomes

$$dS_\sigma = 0 = \left(\frac{\delta Q}{T}\right)_{\text{rev},\,\sigma} + (s_1 - s_2)\,\delta m$$

$$s_2 - s_1 = \int_1^2 \frac{\delta q}{T}\bigg|_{\text{rev}} = \int_1^2 \frac{dh}{T} = \int_1^2 \frac{c_p\,dT}{T}$$

and, for a constant c_p of 1.25 B/lb-F (or 1.25 B/lb-R),

$$\Delta s = c_p \ln \frac{T_2}{T_1} = 1.25 \ln \frac{660}{540} = 0.251 \text{ B/lb-R}$$

(Notice that this is the entropy change of the helium flowing through the system, not that of the system itself. From the definition of steady flow, $\Delta S_{\text{system}} = 0$.)

EXAMPLE 9·3.   Air expands irreversibly from 30 psia, 340 F, to 15 psia, 240 F. Calculate Δs, assuming that c_p and c_v are constant over a wide range of temperature with values of 0.24 B/lb-F and 0.171 B/lb-F respectively.

Solution.   First we notice that no indication is given as to whether the air is in a closed system or is flowing into, out of, or through an open system; but this lack of information is of no consequence because entropy is a property and is determined for a pure substance such as air by any two independent properties, regardless of the motion or position of the system. p and T are known at each of the end states. We also notice that the path between the two end states is not specified. Again this lack of information is of no consequence because entropy is a property: The change in entropy depends only on the end states and not on the path connecting them.

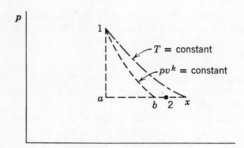

Example 9·3

Calculate Δs for any process, reversible or irreversible, by evaluating $\int \dfrac{\delta q}{T}$ along *any* *reversible* path connecting the same end states. Three of the possible reversible paths between the end states 1 and 2 are those shown passing through states a, b, and x on the pv diagram. [In order to sketch the pv diagram approximately to scale, it is noted that $v_2/v_1 = p_1 T_2/p_2 T_1 = 30(700)/15(800) = 1.75$ and $v_b/v_1 = (p_1/p_2)^{1/k} = (2)^{1/1.403} = 1.64$.] The evaluation of $\int \dfrac{\delta q}{T}$ for each of these reversible paths is illustrated below, and of course we expect to obtain the same value in each case.

Path 1-a-2: a reversible constant-volume process followed by a reversible constant-pressure process.

$$\Delta s = \int_{1-a}^{2} \frac{\delta q}{T} \bigg|_{\text{rev}} = \int_{1}^{a} \frac{\delta q}{T} \bigg|_{\text{rev}} + \int_{a}^{2} \frac{\delta q}{T} \bigg|_{\text{rev}} = \int_{1}^{a} \frac{c_v \, dT}{T} + \int_{a}^{2} \frac{c_p \, dT}{T}$$

$$= c_v \ln \frac{T_a}{T_1} + c_p \ln \frac{T_2}{T_a} = c_v \ln \frac{p_2}{p_1} + c_p \ln \frac{v_2}{v_1}$$

$$= 0.171 \ln 0.5 + 0.24 \ln 1.75 = -0.1185 + 0.1343 = 0.0158 \text{ B/lb-R}$$

Path 1-b-2: a reversible adiabatic process followed by a reversible constant-pressure process.

$$\Delta s = \int_{1-b}^{2} \frac{\delta q}{T} = \int_{1}^{b} \frac{\delta q}{T} + \int_{b}^{2} \frac{\delta q}{T} = 0 + \int_{b}^{2} \frac{c_p \, dT}{T} = c_p \ln \frac{T_2}{T_b}$$
$$\text{rev} \qquad \text{rev} \qquad \text{rev}$$

$$= c_p \ln \frac{v_2}{v_b} = c_p \ln \frac{v_2/v_1}{v_b/v_1} = 0.24 \ln \frac{1.75}{1.64} = 0.0158 \text{ B/lb-R}$$

Path 1-x-2: a reversible isothermal process followed by a reversible constant-pressure process.

$$\Delta s = \int_{1-x}^{2} \frac{\delta q}{T} = \int_{1}^{x} \frac{\delta q}{T} + \int_{x}^{2} \frac{\delta q}{T} = \frac{1}{T_1} \int_{1}^{x} \delta w + \int_{x}^{2} \frac{c_p \, dT}{T} = \frac{1}{T_1} \int_{1}^{x} p \, dV + c_p \ln \frac{T_2}{T_x}$$
$$\text{rev} \qquad \text{rev} \qquad \text{rev} \qquad \text{rev}$$

$$= \frac{RT_1}{T_1} \int_{1}^{x} \frac{dv}{v} + c_p \ln \frac{T_2}{T_1} = R \ln \frac{v_x}{v_1} + c_p \ln \frac{T_2}{T_1}$$

$$= R \ln \frac{p_1}{p_2} + c_p \ln \frac{T_2}{T_1} = \frac{53.3}{778} \ln \frac{30}{15} + 0.24 \ln \frac{700}{800}$$

$$= 0.0475 - 0.0320 = 0.0155 \text{ B/lb-R}$$

(The three results agree within the accuracy of the data used. Notice that (1) there is a loss in accuracy when the difference is taken in the last step, and (2) the values of R, c_p, and c_v which are used are not self-consistent to a degree which warrants more precise calculation. Remember that $c_p - c_v = R$ and $k \equiv c_p/c_v$.)

So far in this chapter the property entropy has been defined and some examples of entropy change calculations have been given, but no answer has been given to the question, "Of what value is entropy?" The next few articles answer this question.

9·3   Entropy as a coordinate

The definition of entropy

$$\Delta S \equiv \int_{\text{rev}} \frac{\delta Q}{T} \quad \text{or} \quad dS = \left(\frac{\delta Q}{T} \right)_{\text{rev}} \tag{9·1a}$$

can be rearranged as

$$Q_{\text{rev}} = \int T \, dS \quad \text{or} \quad \delta Q_{\text{rev}} = T \, dS \tag{9·2}$$

to show that the heat transfer of a reversible process is represented by an area on a diagram which uses absolute temperature and entropy as coordinates. Figure 9·6 shows the path on a TS diagram of a reversible process 1-2. The area beneath the path is $\int_{1}^{2} T \, dS$; so it represents the heat transferred to the system during the reversible process. If the process is reversed so as to proceed from state 2 to state 1, then the heat transferred to the system is

$$Q = \int_2^1 T \, dS$$

For the same path, $\int_1^2 T \, dS$ and $\int_2^1 T \, dS$ are equal in magnitude but opposite in sign; likewise the area beneath the curve is the same for both directions of the process, but in one case the area represents a negative quantity.

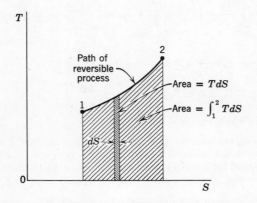

Fig. 9·6 *TS* diagram of a reversible process.

The relation

$$q_{\text{rev}} = \int T \, ds \qquad\qquad (9\cdot2)$$

is in some respects analogous to the relations

$$w_{\text{rev}} = \int p \, dv \qquad\qquad (1\cdot7)$$

and

$$w_{\text{rev}} + \Delta KE + \Delta PE = -\int v \, dp \qquad\qquad (1\cdot10)$$

Each of these three equations relates heat or work to an area on a property diagram. Equation 1·7 applies only to a closed system and equation 1·10 applies only to a steady-flow system; but equation 9·2 applies to either type of system.

Temperature–entropy diagrams are frequently used in the analysis of processes and cycles because for reversible processes areas on the diagrams represent heat transfer. Another commonly used diagram is the enthalpy–entropy diagram. Areas on the *hs* diagram have no significance, but entropy is still a useful coordinate because the ideal process which we often try to approximate in actual machines is the reversible adiabatic process. Since a reversible adiabatic process must be a constant-entropy or *isentropic* process,* such a process is represented by a vertical line on any diagram which has entropy on the abscissa. Enthalpy is a convenient coordinate

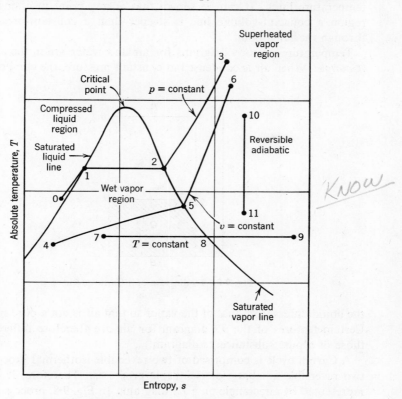

Fig. 9·7   *Ts* diagram for liquid and vapor.

because for many processes in steady-flow systems enthalpy change is equal to the work done, the heat transferred, or the change in kinetic energy.

Temperature–entropy diagrams on which two and three phases of a substance are represented are shown in Chapter 10. At present, let us look at a *Ts* diagram which shows only the liquid and vapor phases of some substance (Fig. 9·7).

* If you do not see why a reversible adiabatic process is a constant-entropy process, refer to the definition of entropy.

The saturation line, which represents saturated liquid states to the left of the critical point and saturated vapor states to the right of the critical point, can be plotted by taking the s_f and s_g values from a table of properties. Of course, in the two-phase-mixture region or "wet-vapor" region of a pure substance, constant-pressure lines coincide with constant-temperature lines. It can be shown that at any point in a single-phase region a constant-volume line is steeper than a constant-pressure line through the same point.

Temperature–entropy diagrams for air and water are in the appendix. (*Caution:* When air is condensed at constant pressure, the composition of

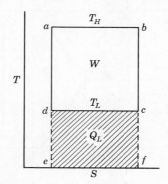

Fig. 9·8 *TS* diagram of a Carnot cycle.

the liquid differs from that of the vapor so that air is not a pure substance. Certain features of the *Ts* diagram for air are therefore different from those of a pure substance *Ts* diagram.)

A Carnot cycle is comprised of two reversible isothermal processes and two reversible adiabatic or isentropic processes. Therefore, it is always represented by a rectangle on a *TS* diagram. In Fig. 9·8, process *a-b* is the reversible isothermal heat addition at T_H. The area *a-b-f-e-a* beneath line *a-b* represents the heat added Q_H. Since process *b-c* is a reversible adiabatic process, the area beneath line *b-c* must be zero. Process *c-d* is the reversible isothermal rejection of heat Q_L to the energy reservoir at T_L. Q_L is represented by the area *c-d-e-f-c*. The cycle is completed by means of the reversible adiabatic process *d-a* which returns the system to its initial state *a*.

The area *a-b-c-d-a*, being the difference between area *a-b-f-e-a* (representing Q_H) and area *c-d-e-f-c* (representing Q_L), represents ($Q_H - Q_L$) or the work done by the cycle. Areas on a *TS* diagram represent heat transfer for all reversible processes of a substance, but they represent work only for reversible cycles, because for any cycle of a given quantity of substance

$$\oint \delta W = \oint \delta Q$$

The area beneath the path of an irreversible process on a TS diagram has no significance. Certainly it does not represent heat transfer because

$$Q_{\text{irrev}} \neq \int T \, dS*$$

As a reminder that the area beneath an irreversible process path has no significance, such paths are often shown as broken lines. Also, the exact

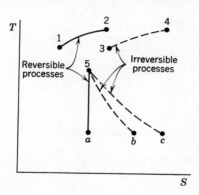

Fig. 9·9   Reversible and irreversible processes on a TS diagram.

path of an irreversible process between two states is frequently unknown or cannot be represented on a property diagram because the system may not be in an equilibrium state at all times. This is another reason for showing irreversible processes as broken lines on TS diagrams as illustrated in Fig. 9·9.

EXAMPLE 9·4.   Dry saturated steam at 118 psia undergoes a reversible isothermal expansion in a closed system until its pressure is 74 psia. Calculate the work done per pound of steam.

Analysis.   A Ts diagram is made first. As we sketch the diagram, we note that (1) the process is reversible so that the area beneath the path represents heat transfer, and (2) the path is a simple one on the Ts diagram: a horizontal line.

---

* It can be shown rigorously that $Q_{\text{irrev}} < \int T \, dS$. As *an example* that $Q_{\text{irrev}} \neq \int T \, dS$, consider a gas stirred by a paddle wheel inside a closed rigid thermally insulated vessel. The gas goes from state 1 to state 2. A reversible process between the same two end states would be a constant-volume heating, so that $S_2 > S_1$ and $\int_1^2 T \, dS \neq 0$. Yet the paddle-wheel process occurs in an insulated vessel so that $Q = 0$. Therefore, for this irreversible process

$$Q \neq \int T \, dS$$

Since we are looking for the value of work, let us apply the first law to the system:

$$w = u_1 - u_2 + q$$

State 1 is specified in the problem statement. For state 2 we know the pressure p_2 and the temperature, $T_2 = T_1 = T_{sat.,118\ psia}$. Therefore we have enough information to obtain the two internal energies from the steam tables. For this reversible isothermal process, $q = \int_1^2 T\,ds = T(s_2 - s_1)$ and since both end states are specified, this expression can be evaluated.

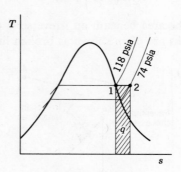

Example 9·4

Solution. In accordance with the analysis above, the following are from the steam tables:

<table>
<tr><td align="center">State 1</td><td align="center">State 2</td></tr>
<tr><td>$T_1 = 339.99\ F \approx 340\ F$</td><td>$T_2 = T_1 \approx 340\ F$</td></tr>
<tr><td>$u_1 = u_g = 1107.4\ B/lb$</td><td>$u_2 = h_2 - p_2 v_2$</td></tr>
<tr><td>$s_1 = s_g = 1.5891\ B/lb\text{-}R$</td><td>$= 1200.1 - \dfrac{74(144)6.202}{778}$</td></tr>
<tr><td></td><td>$= 1115.2\ B/lb$</td></tr>
<tr><td></td><td>$s_2 = 1.6506\ B/lb\text{-}R$</td></tr>
</table>

Applying the first law to the system,

$$w = u_1 - u_2 + q$$

and, for the reversible isothermal process,

$$w = u_1 - u_2 + \int_1^2 T\,ds = u_1 - u_2 + T(s_2 - s_1)$$

$$= 1107.4 - 1115.2 + 800(1.6506 - 1.5891) = 41.4\ B/lb$$

EXAMPLE 9·5. Ammonia is compressed reversibly and adiabatically at a steady rate of 5 lb/min from 40 psia, 80 per cent quality, to 200 psia. Determine the power input to the ammonia.

Analysis. For a steady-flow process, $P = Mw$. Work can be found from the first law or steady-flow energy balance

$$w_{in} = h_2 - h_1 + \Delta KE + \Delta PE - q$$

which for an adiabatic process and no change in kinetic or potential energy becomes

$$w_{in} = h_2 - h_1$$

h_1 can be found from $h_1 = h_{f1} + x_1 h_{fg1}$. In addition to the pressure at the discharge, we know that $s_2 = s_1$ for the *reversible adiabatic* process. The Ts diagram helps us to see that, if s_2 is greater than s_g at 200 psia, the ammonia discharged is superheated, but, if s_2 is less than s_g at 200 psia, the ammonia discharged is wet. If the discharge is superheated, h_2 can be obtained from the tables by using p_2 and s_2; if the discharge is wet,

$$h_2 = h_{f2} + x_2 h_{fg2} \quad \text{and} \quad x_2 = \frac{s_2 - s_f}{s_{fg}}$$

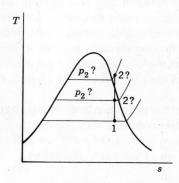

Example 9·5 Analysis.   **Example 9·5** Solution.

Solution.   Referring to the ammonia tables in the appendix,

$$h_1 = h_{f1} + x_1 h_{fg1} = 55.6 + 0.80(559.8) = 503.4 \text{ B/lb}$$
$$s_2 = s_1 = s_{f1} + x_1 s_{fg1} = 0.1246 + 0.80(1.1879) = 1.0749 \text{ B/lb-R}$$

The value of s_2 is less than s_{g2}, so the ammonia is wet at discharge.

$$x_2 = \frac{s_2 - s_f}{s_{fg}} = \frac{1.0749 - 0.3090}{0.8666} = 0.884$$
$$h_2 = h_{f2} + x_2 h_{fg2} = 150.9 + 0.884(481.8) = 576.8 \text{ B/lb}$$

Applying the first law, recalling that $q = 0$, and assuming that $\Delta KE + \Delta PE = 0$,

$$w_{in} = h_2 - h_1 = 576.8 - 503.4 = 73.4 \text{ B/lb}$$

and the power input is

$$P_{in} = Mw_{in} = \frac{5(73.4)}{42.4} = 8.65 \text{ hp}$$

9·4   A useful relationship among properties

Entropy is defined by

$$\Delta s \equiv \int_{rev} \frac{\delta q}{T} \tag{9·1a}$$

From the first law, for any closed system which passes through equilibrium states and for which the only type of work that can be done reversibly is that evaluated as $\int p\, dv$, $\delta q_{\text{rev}} = du + p\, dv$.* Therefore,

$$\Delta s = \int \frac{du + p\, dv}{T}$$

or

$$ds = \frac{du + p\, dv}{T}$$

If the relationship among p, v, T, and u is known, this expression can be integrated to give the change in entropy between any two equilibrium states. Since entropy is a property (and thus a point function), Δs must be the same for any process, reversible or irreversible, between two given states. Also, the relation holds for a fluid flowing through an open system as well as for a closed system because entropy is a function of properties such as p, v, T, and u and is independent of the position or state of motion of the system.

It is well to repeat that the integration of the right-hand side of equation 9·1a must be performed for some reversible process between the end states. However, for an infinitesimal section of any path, $(du + p\, dv)$ is equal to δq for a *reversible* process along that section of the path. Therefore,

$$ds = \frac{du + p\, dv}{T}$$

holds for any process, provided that the path of the process is one which a reversible process can follow. In essence, this means that the path must connect equilibrium states. Also, it is implied in such an equation that there is a continuous functional relationship among the properties. For our purposes we will meet this implied condition by restricting our use of the equation to pure substances. (If a chemical reaction occurs, entropy can change even though internal energy and volume are held constant; so obviously the equation does not apply. This point is treated in Chapter 14.)

The fact that this equation for ds applies to irreversible state changes as well as to reversible ones is an important but elusive point; so it is worth restating in different words for emphasis. Consider two states of a pure substance infinitesimally close to each other. The substance may go from one of these states to the other by many different processes, some reversible

---

* The relation $\delta q_{\text{rev}} = du + p\, dv$ holds also for a steady-flow system as shown by

$$\delta q = du + d(pv) + d(KE) + d(PE) + \delta w$$

which for a reversible process is

$$\delta q_{\text{rev}} = du + p\, dv + v\, dp + d(KE) + d(PE) - v\, dp - d(KE) - d(PE)$$
$$= du + p\, dv$$

Notice, however, that for the steady-flow system $p\, dv \neq \delta w$.

and some irreversible. Entropy is a property, however; so its change must be the same for all processes between the same two states. Since the change in entropy for (at least) any reversible process is given by

$$ds = \frac{du + p\,dv}{T}$$

it follows that this equation gives the change in entropy between the two states for any and all processes.

This equation can be rearranged as

$$T\,ds = du + p\,dv = dh - v\,dp \qquad (9\cdot3)$$

and it will be seen that this is a convenient form. *Conclusion: The relations*

$$T\,ds = du + p\,dv \qquad (9\cdot3)$$

$$T\,ds = dh - v\,dp \qquad (9\cdot3)$$

are valid for any process of a pure substance in the absence of electricity, magnetism, and surface tension, the only restriction being that the integration can be performed only between equilibrium states. Equations 9·3 are useful relationships among the properties of pure substances and are not restricted to any particular process. They are often referred to as the "*T ds* equations."

Notice the differences among the restrictions which apply to the following four equations.

(a) $\delta q = du + \delta w$ This is a statement of the first law, applicable to any closed system.

(b) $\delta q = du + p\,dv$ This is a statement of the first law, restricted to reversible processes of a closed system.* By comparison with (a), $p\,dv = \delta w$.

(c) $T\,ds = du + \delta w$ This is a statement combining the first and second laws and is restricted to reversible processes of a closed system. By comparison with equation (a), $T\,ds = \delta q$.

(d) $T\,ds = du + p\,dv$ This is a relationship among properties (p, v, T, s, u) *valid for all processes between equilibrium states*. It is based on the first and second laws, but in itself it is a statement of neither. In general, $T\,ds \neq \delta q$ and $p\,dv \neq \delta w$. (By comparison with equation (a) it is seen, in fact, that for a closed system, $T\,ds = \delta q$ *only* when $p\,dv = \delta w$, and vice versa.)

---

* This equation can also be applied to frictionless processes of a fluid flowing through an open system, but then $p\,dv \neq \delta w$.

To illustrate the difference between equations (a) and (d), consider the system comprised of a gas trapped in a closed rigid thermally insulated vessel fitted with a paddle wheel so that work can be done on the gas. Let the paddle wheel be turned by an external motor. Notice that $p \, dv = 0$ but $\delta w \neq 0$, and $\delta q = 0$ but $T \, ds \neq 0$. Equation (a), the first law, reduces to

$$0 = du + \delta w$$

Equation (d), the $T \, ds$ equation, reduces to

$$T \, ds = du + 0$$

Equations (b) and (c) do not apply because they are restricted to reversible processes.

You should learn equations 9·3 because they are useful in a number of ways. For one thing, they provide a means of calculating the change in entropy of a system if the relationship among p, v, T, and u is known. For example, equations 9·3 can be easily integrated for an ideal gas so that it is unnecessary to learn any special equations for the entropy change of an ideal gas. Many other useful results can be derived from these equations.

EXAMPLE 9·6.   Air expands irreversibly from 30 psia, 340 F, to 15 psia, 240 F. Calculate Δs, assuming that c_p and c_v are constant over a wide range of temperature with values of 0.24 B/lb-F and 0.171 B/lb-F, respectively.

Solution.   Assuming that air under the stated conditions behaves as an ideal gas,

$$T \, ds = du + p \, dv \tag{9·3}$$

becomes $T \, ds = c_v \, dT + p \, dv$

and $$\Delta s = \int_1^2 ds = \int_1^2 \frac{c_v \, dT}{T} + \int_1^2 \frac{p \, dv}{T} = \int_1^2 \frac{c_v \, dT}{T} + \int_1^2 \frac{R \, dv}{v}$$

Integrating, for constant values of c_v and R,

$$\Delta s = c_v \ln \frac{T_2}{T_1} + R \ln \frac{v_2}{v_1} = c_v \ln \frac{T_2}{T_1} + R \ln \frac{p_1 T_2}{p_2 T_1}$$

$$= 0.171 \ln \frac{700}{800} + \frac{53.3}{778} \ln \frac{30(700)}{15(800)} = 0.0158 \text{ B/lb-R}$$

Alternative solution.   Using in similar fashion the relation

$$T \, ds = dh - v \, dp \tag{9·3}$$

we have $T \, ds = c_p \, dT - v \, dp$

and $$\Delta s = \int_1^2 ds = \int_1^2 \frac{c_p \, dT}{T} - \int_1^2 \frac{v \, dp}{T} = c_p \ln \frac{T_2}{T_1} - R \ln \frac{p_2}{p_1}$$

$$= 0.24 \ln \frac{700}{800} - \frac{53.3}{778} \ln \frac{15}{30} = 0.0155 \text{ B/lb-F}$$

(The results agree to within the accuracy of the data used.)   See how much simpler the calculation of Δs is when the "$T \, ds$ equations" are used than when Δs is calculated from its definition as in Example 9·3.

EXAMPLE 9·7.   Determine s_{fg} for ammonia at 20 F if $h_{fg} = 553.1$ B/lb.

Solution.   For the calculation of an entropy change at constant pressure, which is what s_{fg} is, the relation

$$T\,ds = dh - v\,dp \tag{9·3}$$

simplifies to

$$T\,ds = dh$$

Since s_{fg} is also an entropy change at constant temperature, this equation can be integrated as

$$\Delta s = \frac{\Delta h}{T}$$

$$s_{fg} = \frac{h_{fg}}{T} = \frac{553.1}{479.7} = 1.153 \text{ B/lb-R}$$

EXAMPLE 9·8.   Determine for an ideal gas the slope of (*a*) a constant-pressure line and (*b*) a constant-volume line on a *Ts* diagram.

Solution.   For an ideal gas, the *T ds* equations

$$T\,ds = dh - v\,dp \tag{9·3}$$

$$T\,ds = du + p\,dv \tag{9·3}$$

become

$$T\,ds = c_p\,dT - v\,dp$$

$$T\,ds = c_v\,dT + p\,dv$$

For a constant-pressure process, the last term of the first equation is zero. For a constant-volume process, the last term of the second equation is zero. The desired slopes can consequently be obtained readily as

$$\text{Slope of constant-pressure line} = \left(\frac{\partial T}{\partial s}\right)_p = \frac{T}{c_p}$$

$$\text{Slope of constant-volume line} = \left(\frac{\partial T}{\partial s}\right)_v = \frac{T}{c_v}$$

Since $c_p > c_v$, the slope of a constant-pressure line is less than that of a constant-volume line *at the same temperature.* You can see now that the general form of these lines is as shown in the figure.

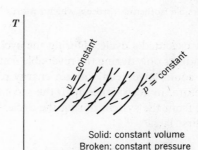

Solid: constant volume
Broken: constant pressure

Example 9·8

9·5 The increase of entropy principle

The property entropy often provides a means of determining if a process is reversible, irreversible, or even possible. This application of entropy is based on the *principle of the increase of entropy* which states that *the entropy of an isolated system always increases or, in the limiting case of a reversible process, remains constant with respect to time.* In mathematical form,

$$\left(\frac{dS}{d\tau}\right)_{\text{isolated system}} \geq 0$$

or, with the understanding that time is the independent variable, this statement is usually written

$$\Delta S_{\text{isolated system}} \geq 0 \tag{9·4}$$

The inequality holds for irreversible processes; the equality holds for reversible processes.

Since an isolated system is one which in no way interacts with its surroundings, this principle may at first appear to be severely restricted in application. However, you will see that a judicious selection of boundaries often makes it possible to work with isolated systems. A proof of the increase of entropy principle follows.

A system can always be made to go from one state to another by a series of reversible adiabatic and reversible isothermal processes. (See Art. 9·1.) In fact, two states of a system can always be connected by one reversible adiabatic process and one reversible isothermal process. Let any closed system undergo an adiabatic process from a state 1 to a state 2 as shown in Fig. 9·10. Now the system can be restored to state 1 by means of

PROCESS 2-*a*: a reversible adiabatic process which restores the system to its initial temperature, followed by

PROCESS *a*-1: a reversible isothermal process which restores the system to its initial state.

The system has now executed a cycle. During the cycle it could exchange heat with its surroundings only during the reversible isothermal process *a*-1. This heat exchange could have been with an energy reservoir at constant temperature. Therefore, in accordance with the second law, there can be no net work output from the system during the cycle; that is, $\oint \delta W \leq 0$. Then applying the first law,

$$\oint \delta Q = \oint \delta W$$

we see that $\oint \delta Q \leq 0$: Either (1) heat was removed from the system during process a-1, or (2) the cycle was completely adiabatic so that state a was identical with state 1. Consequently,

$$S_1 - S_a \leq 0 \tag{a}$$

where the equality holds if the reversible adiabatic process 2-a alone returned the system to state 1, state a and state 1 being identical. This could be the case only if the original adiabatic process 1-2 had been reversible. For process 2-a,

$$S_a - S_2 = 0 \tag{b}$$

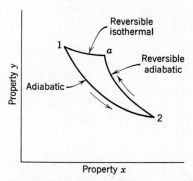

Fig. 9·10   Proof of the increase of entropy principle.

For the cycle,

$$\Delta S = (S_2 - S_1) + (S_a - S_2) + (S_1 - S_a) = 0 \tag{c}$$

Comparison of equations (a), (b), and (c) shows that

$$S_2 - S_1 \geq 0$$

where the equality holds only if the adiabatic process 1-2 is reversible. Recalling that process 1-2 was an adiabatic process of any closed system, we have shown that in general,

$$\Delta S_{\text{adiabatic closed system}} \geq 0$$

This is one statement of the principle of the increase of entropy: *The entropy of an adiabatic closed system always increases or, in the limiting case of a reversible process, remains constant.* The independent variable is understood to be time.

An isolated system has already been defined as a system which in no way interacts with its surroundings. Therefore, every isolated system is (at least) an adiabatic closed system, and we can conclude that

$$\Delta S_{\text{isolated system}} \geq 0 \tag{9·4}$$

Thus another statement of the principle of the increase of entropy is: *The entropy of an isolated system always increases or, in the limiting case of a reversible process, remains constant.* The independent variable is understood to be time. This statement is actually less general than the one which refers to an adiabatic closed system, because an isolated system is a special case (work = 0) of an adiabatic closed system. Nevertheless, this is a convenient and widely used form of the increase of entropy principle.

The increase of entropy principle provides another criterion of reversibility in addition to those listed in Art. 7·2. For any process of an isolated system if the entropy of the system remains constant, the process

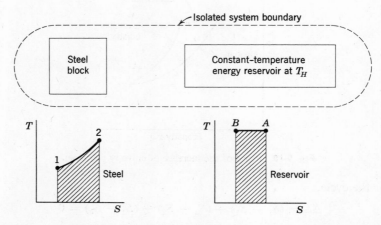

Fig. 9·11   Transfer of heat across a finite temperature difference.

is reversible; if the entropy of the system increases, the process is irreversible. The entropy of an isolated system cannot decrease.

Consider the heating of a block of steel from a temperature T_1 to a temperature T_2. Heat is supplied from a constant-temperature reservoir (perhaps steam condensing at constant pressure) at T_H. T_H is greater than T_2. Neither the block nor the reservoir is an isolated system, but the block and the reservoir taken together do constitute an isolated system. Since the transfer of heat from the reservoir to the block across a finite temperature difference is irreversible, the entropy of the isolated system increases. The entropy increase of the block is greater in magnitude than the entropy decrease of the reservoir. This can also be seen from the TS diagrams of Fig. 9·11. Since the heating of the block and the cooling of the reservoir are *internally* reversible, the amount of heat transferred is represented by the area beneath the path on each TS diagram. The two areas must be equal; so the lower temperature of the block requires that $|\Delta S_{\text{block}}| >$ $|\Delta S_{\text{reservoir}}|$ and thus $\Delta S_{\text{isolated system}} > 0$.

A Carnot cycle which is modified by having an irreversible adiabatic expansion is shown on a TS diagram in Fig. 9·12a. A Carnot cycle modified by having an irreversible adiabatic compression is shown in Fig. 9·12b. In each case the entropy of the system during the irreversible adiabatic process must increase. In each case the heat supplied is represented by the area beneath path 1-2, and the heat rejected is represented by the area beneath path 3-4. Remember that an area bounded in part by the path of an irreversible process has no significance.

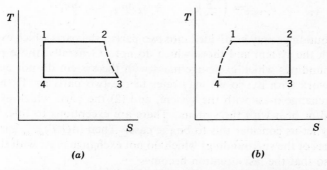

(a)   (b)

Fig. 9·12 Carnot cycles modified by irreversible adiabatic processes.

An isolated system can always be formed by including any system and its surroundings within a single boundary. Sometimes the original system which is then only a part of the isolated system is called a *subsystem*. Since a system and its surroundings include, by definition, everything which is affected by the process, the combination is sometimes called the *universe*, so that the increase of entropy principle is stated as

$$\Delta S_{\text{universe}} \geq 0$$

where $$\Delta S_{\text{universe}} = \Delta S_{\text{system}} + \Delta S_{\text{surr}}$$

Recall that we defined the surroundings as everything outside the system boundary but that the term is usually restricted to things outside the system which in some way affect the behavior of the system. Consequently, the term *universe* generally refers to everything which is involved in a process and need not include things which have no effect on the process.

Now we must show how the increase of entropy principle can be applied to an open system. An isolated system can always be formed by including within one boundary an open system and its surroundings. Denoting the properties of the open system by the subscript σ, we then have

$$dS_{\text{isolated system}} = dS_\sigma + dS_{\text{surr}} \geq 0 \qquad (a)$$

As shown in Art. 9·1,

$$dS_\sigma = \left(\frac{\delta Q}{T}\right)_{\text{rev},\sigma} + s_1 \, \delta m_1 - s_2 \, \delta m_2 \qquad (b)$$

where δm_1 is the mass entering the open system, and δm_2 is the mass leaving it. Likewise, for the surroundings of the open system (which constitute another open system),

$$dS_{\text{surr}} = \left(\frac{\delta Q}{T}\right)_{\text{rev,surr}} + s_2 \, \delta m_2 - s_1 \, \delta m_1$$

The surroundings may be divided into two parts: the parts which exchange mass with the system and those which do not. Generally, those parts of the surroundings which exchange mass with the system do not exchange heat or work with it; so we may refer to the two parts as (1) the parts which exchange mass with the system, and (2) the parts which exchange work and/or heat with the system. There are exceptions to this, but for simplicity let us consider this to be the case. Then $(\delta Q/T)_{\text{rev,surr}}$ is dS for those parts of the surroundings which do not exchange mass with the open system, so that the last equation becomes

$$dS_{\text{surr}} = dS_{\text{surr which exchange no mass with system}} + s_2 \, \delta m_2 - s_1 \, \delta m_1 \qquad (c)$$

The surroundings which exchange no mass with the system may exchange work and heat with it. Any part of the surroundings which exchanges only work with the system *can*, as far as the behavior of the system is concerned, operate reversibly and adiabatically so that its entropy change will be zero. Therefore, the entropy change of the surroundings which exchange no mass with the system is simply the entropy change of the surroundings which exchange heat with the system, and equation (c) can be written

$$dS_{\text{surr}} = dS_{\text{surr which exchange heat with system}} + s_2 \, \delta m_2 - s_1 \, \delta m_1 \qquad (c)$$

Making these substitutions from equations (b) and (c) in equation (a), we have *for any open system,*

$$\left(\frac{\delta Q}{T}\right)_{\text{rev},\sigma} + dS_{\text{surr which exchange heat with system}} \geq 0$$

For *steady flow, $dS_\sigma = 0$,* so that equation (a) becomes

$$dS_{\text{surr}} \geq 0$$

or $\qquad dS_{\text{surr which exchange heat with system}} + s_2 \, \delta m - s_1 \, \delta m \geq 0 \qquad (9·5)$

A frequently encountered special case in engineering is the adiabatic steady-flow process. The increase of entropy principle shows that

$$\Delta s_{\text{matter passing through adiabatic steady-flow system}} \geq 0$$

(Remember that ΔS for a steady-flow system itself, which is a region in space in which the properties at each point remain constant, is zero for all processes.) Some possible adiabatic compression and expansion paths for steadily flowing fluids are shown on Ts diagrams in Fig. 9·13.

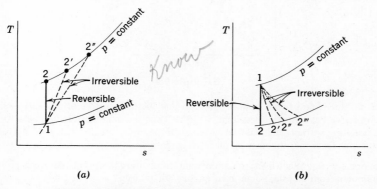

(a)   (b)

Fig. 9·13   Reversible and irreversible adiabatic processes.

EXAMPLE 9·9.   Air enters a turbine at 75 psia, 395 F, and leaves at 15 psia, 80 F. Heat removed from the air passing through the turbine amounts to 15 B/lb. The flow rate is 14,000 lb/hr. Is the process reversible?

Solution.   Consider the steady-flow system to be the region bounded by the turbine casing. Then, per pound of air flowing through the turbine,

$$\Delta s_{\text{air passing through system}} + \Delta s_{\text{surr which exchange heat with system}} \geq 0 \qquad (9·5)$$

If the equality holds, the process is reversible; if the inequality holds, the process is irreversible. For the air,

$$\Delta s = \int_1^2 ds = \int_1^2 \frac{dh}{T} - \int_1^2 \frac{v\,dp}{T} = \int_1^2 \frac{c_p\,dT}{T} - \int_1^2 \frac{R\,dp}{P}$$

Assuming c_p to be constant,

$$\Delta s = c_p \ln \frac{T_2}{T_1} - R \ln \frac{p_2}{p_1} = 0.24 \ln \frac{540}{855} - \frac{53.3}{778} \ln \frac{15}{75}$$

$$= -0.110 + 0.110 = 0.00$$

Heat is removed from the air passing through the turbine, so heat is added to the surroundings; therefore, the entropy of the surroundings increases. Thus

$$\Delta s_{\text{air passing through system}} = 0.00 \text{ B/lb-R}$$

and $$\Delta s_{\text{surr which exchange heat with system}} > 0$$

so that the sum of these two quantities is greater than zero, and the process consequently must be irreversible. (Notice that, even though no information is available on the temperature of the surroundings, it is reasonable to assume that the temperature of the air

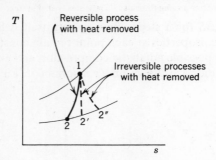

Example 9·9

in the turbine is never greater than 395 F so that the temperature of the surroundings which receive heat must be less than 395 F. Thus the extreme minimum Δs for the surroundings can be calculated and turns out to be much greater than 0.00 B/lb-R, in case anyone fears that the next significant figure might upset our conclusion.)

EXAMPLE 9·10. What is the minimum final temperature for the adiabatic compression of ammonia from 30 psia, 90 per cent quality, to 200 psia?

Solution. For an adiabatic compression, the entropy of the ammonia must increase if the process is irreversible and remain constant if the process is reversible. Sketching reversible and irreversible processes on a Ts diagram shows that the minimum final

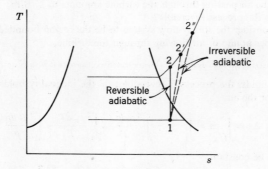

Example 9·10

temperature is reached by means of the reversible process. It is therefore only necessary to determine the final temperature for a reversible adiabatic or isentropic process.

$$s_2 = s_1 = s_f + x s_{fg} = 0.0962 + 0.90(1.2402) = 1.2124 \text{ B/lb-R}$$

Since s_2 is greater than s_g at 200 psia, the final condition (2) must be one of superheated ammonia. Referring to the superheated ammonia table, it is seen that for $p = 200$ psia and $s = 1.2124$ B/lb-R, the temperature is 124 F. This is the minimum possible final temperature for an adiabatic compression.

EXAMPLE 9·11.   Is an adiabatic expansion of air from 25 psia, 140 F, to 15 psia, 40 F, possible?

Solution.   For all possible adiabatic expansions, the entropy of the air must increase or, in the limiting case of a reversible adiabatic expansion, remain constant. For the end states specified,

$$\Delta s = \int_1^2 ds = \int_1^2 \frac{dh}{T} - \int_1^2 \frac{v\, dp}{T} = \int_1^2 \frac{c_p\, dT}{T} - \int_1^2 \frac{R\, dp}{P}$$

Assuming that the specific heats are constant,

$$\Delta s = c_p \ln \frac{T_2}{T_1} - R \ln \frac{p_2}{p_1} = 0.24 \ln \frac{500}{600} - \frac{53.3}{778} \ln \frac{15}{25}$$

$$= -0.0087 \text{ B/lb-R}$$

Since the adiabatic process considered would result in a decrease in entropy, it is impossible.

One of the most valuable uses of the increase of entropy principle is in connection with predicting the direction in which a chemical reaction will proceed. A reaction can never proceed in such a direction as to cause the entropy of the universe to decrease. This point is discussed in Chapter 13 in connection with combustion reactions.

9·6   Available and unavailable energy

As an introduction to the definition and discussion of available and unavailable energy, let us consider two questions and their answers. First, suppose an energy reservoir at 1000 R gives up 1000 B of heat. If the surrounding atmosphere, which is the coldest energy reservoir in the surroundings, is at 500 R, how much of this heat can be converted into work by devices which are not permanently changed, that is, which operate cyclically?* We answer this question by noting that the maximum work can be obtained by the use of an externally reversible engine (such as a Carnot, Stirling, or Ericsson engine) which receives the 1000 B at 1000 R and rejects heat at the temperature of the atmosphere, 500 R. The efficiency of such an engine is 50 per cent, so the answer to the question is that 500 B of the 1000 B given up by the reservoir can be converted into work, and this maximum amount of work can be obtained by the use of an

---

* We confine our attention to devices which operate cyclically in order to make certain that no part of the work produced results from the depletion of the stored energy of the devices.

externally reversible engine as shown in Fig. 9·14a. For the second question, suppose that the 1000 B is transferred from the reservoir at 1000 R to a reservoir at 800 R. Then, after this transfer of heat has been made, and with the atmosphere still at 500 R, how much of the 1000 B can be converted into work by cyclically operating devices? In answering this question we first note that the 1000 B stored in the reservoir at 800 R can be supplied to an externally reversible engine as in Fig. 9·14b at 800 R but at no higher temperature. The efficiency of such an engine is $1 - T_{\text{low}}/T_{\text{high}} = 1 - 500/800 = 37.5$ per cent; so the answer to this second

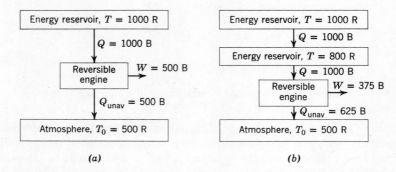

(a)   (b)

Fig. 9·14   Different amounts of available energy from the same amount of heat.

question is that a maximum of 375 B of the 1000 B originally obtained from the reservoir at 1000 R and then transferred to the 800 R reservoir can be converted into work. Yet this same 1000 B as removed from the reservoir at 1000 R could have been converted to the extent of 500 B into work if it had not first been transferred to the reservoir at 800 R.

Such questions and their answers are important in engineering. For example, suppose that 1000 B of heat is added to an engine and a certain amount of work is actually performed. In evaluating the performance of the engine, it is helpful to know how much of the heat added could have been converted into work by an externally reversible engine (or how much of it could *not* have been converted into work *even* by an externally reversible engine). Or we may wish to know how much of the heat rejected by an actual engine could be converted into work by an externally reversible engine.

For another example of the type of question we want to answer, consider a steam power plant. For each 1000 B of energy input to the plant, suppose that 100 B is converted into work, 750 B is rejected as heat to the cooling water, and 150 B is carried away by the stack gases. Which is the more serious loss—the 750 B to the cooling water or the 150 B in the stack gases? Obviously, one is five times as big as the other in terms of energy quantities, but is it five times as valuable? It certainly is not, because usually only a very small fraction of the heat rejected to cooling water could be converted into work even by an externally reversible engine, while perhaps a third of the energy carried away by the stack gases could be converted into work. So in the evaluation of energy rejected by a system the question is not simply how much is rejected but how much of that rejected could be converted into work? This question can always be

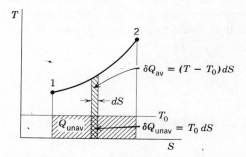

Fig. 9·15   Available and unavailable parts of heat transferred.

answered by considerations of availability and irreversibility which will be introduced in Chapter 11, but in many cases it can be answered more readily by means of similar concepts—available energy and unavailable energy—which we will now define.

Available energy is defined as that part of the heat added to or taken from a system which could be converted into work by means of an externally reversible engine. Unavailable energy is defined as that part of the heat added to or taken from a system which could not be converted into work even by an externally reversible engine. Using the symbols Q_{av} and Q_{unav} for available energy and unavailable energy and Q for the total amount of heat added to a system, $Q = Q_{av} + Q_{unav}$. In the light of these definitions we could determine operationally the available and unavailable parts of the heat removed from a system by transferring the heat to one or more externally reversible engines which reject heat to the atmosphere at T_0 and then measuring the amount of work done by these engines or the amount of heat rejected to the atmosphere by them.

For a Carnot engine which receives heat Q_H at T_H and rejects heat at T_0, the lowest temperature in the surroundings, the available and unavailable parts of Q_H are the same as the work done and the heat rejected.

If heat Q is added to a system in a reversible process such as 1-2 in

Fig. 9·15, we can determine the available and unavailable parts by imagining that each small fraction of the heat δQ is added instead to a Carnot (or other externally reversible) engine at some temperature T. T varies from T_1 to T_2, but each Carnot engine receives so little heat that it operates between essentially constant temperature limits of T and T_0. The available and unavailable portions of δQ are represented by the areas $(T-T_0)\,dS$ and $T_0\,dS$ in Fig. 9·15 for any one of these engines. In order to add all of the heat Q to Carnot engines at the same temperatures at which the original system absorbs heat, an infinite number of Carnot engines is required because only an infinitesimal amount of heat can be added to each engine at constant temperature. The available and unavailable parts of the heat Q are respectively the sums of δQ_{av} and of δQ_{unav} for all of the engines. Thus

$$Q_{unav,1\text{-}2} = \int_1^2 T_0\,dS = T_0(S_2 - S_1)$$

$$Q_{av,1\text{-}2} = \int_1^2 (T - T_0)\,dS = \int_1^2 T\,dS - T_0(S_2 - S_1) = \int_1^2 T\,dS - Q_{unav}$$

The *available* part of heat transferred can be represented by an area on a TS diagram only for reversible processes. It can be proved, however, that when heat is added to or taken from a system, causing it to undergo any process, reversible or irreversible,

$$Q_{unav} = T_0\,\Delta S \tag{9·6}$$

so that the *unavailable* part of heat transferred can always be represented by an area on a TS diagram.

An interesting approach to the unavailable part of the heat added to a system undergoing an *irreversible* process is the following: Let heat be added to a system, causing it to change irreversibly from state 1 to state 2 (Fig. 9·16a). How much of the heat added cannot be converted into work? To make sure that any work produced results from a conversion of the heat added and not from depleting the stored energy of the system, let us return the system to its initial state 1. In selecting the processes which we will add to the process 1-2 in order to complete a cycle, we realize that the maximum work output will be obtained if the heat rejected by the system while being restored to state 1 is a minimum. Some reflection on this indicates that the minimum amount of heat is rejected if the cycle is completed by means of a reversible adiabatic expansion to T_0 (process 2-*a* in Fig. 9·16b), a reversible isothermal heat rejection (process *a-b*), and a reversible adiabatic compression (process *b*-1) to state i. All of the heat rejected during this cycle is rejected in process *a-b* at the temperature of the atmosphere; so none of it can be converted into work, even by the use of a Carnot engine. Recalling that this is the *minimum* amount of heat which can be rejected in completing the cycle, it is therefore the unavailable portion of the heat added to the system in process 1-2. Its magnitude is $T_0 \, \Delta S$. This is an illustration of the general conclusion that, when heat is added to or taken from a system, causing it to change from a state 1 to a state 2, the unavailable portion of the heat transferred to or from the system is given by

$$Q_{\text{unav}} = T_0(S_2 - S_1) \qquad\qquad (9\cdot6)$$

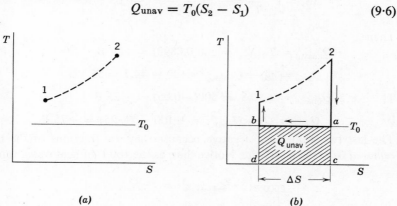

(a)   *(b)*

Fig. 9·16   Unavailable part of the heat added in an irreversible process.

T_0, the temperature of the atmosphere, is often called the *sink temperature* because an energy reservoir such as the atmosphere or the water of a river or lake which is used chiefly for absorbing heat from other systems is called a sink. T_0 is also referred to as the *lowest temperature in the surroundings*. This actually means the lowest temperature of an energy reservoir to which appreciable quantities of heat may be rejected.

A numerical illustration may be helpful at this point. Consider the transfer of 100 B of heat from a reservoir at 2000 R to 2 lb of a gas initially at 25 psia, 1000 R, in a closed tank. For the gas, let $c_v = 0.20$ B/lb-R throughout the temperature range involved. The lowest temperature in the surroundings is 500 R. Let us determine how much of the heat removed from the reservoir is available and unavailable and how much of that absorbed by the gas is available and unavailable. In Fig. 9·17 the *TS* diagrams for the reservoir and for the gas are shown together. Since for each system (reservoir and gas) the process can be internally reversible, the area beneath the *TS* diagram path 1_r-2_r equals the area beneath 1_g-2_g because in each case the area represents the 100 B of heat transferred.

After finding $T_{g2} = 1250$ R from $Q = \Delta U_g = mc_v(T_{g2} - T_{g1})$, we can find ΔS_g and ΔS_r by

$$\Delta S_g = \int_1^2 \frac{\delta Q}{T} = \int_1^2 \frac{dU}{T} = \int_1^2 \frac{mc_v\, dT}{T} = mc_v \ln \frac{T_2}{T_1}$$
$$\text{rev}$$

$$= 2(0.2) \ln \frac{1250}{1000} = 0.0893 \text{ B/R}$$

$$\Delta S_r = \int_1^2 \frac{\delta Q}{T} = \frac{Q}{T} = \frac{-100}{2000} = -0.05 \text{ B/R}$$
$$\text{rev}$$

Then

$$Q_{\text{unav},g} = T_0\, \Delta S_g = 500(0.0893) = 44.7 \text{ B}$$

$$Q_{\text{av},g} = Q - Q_{\text{unav},g} = 100 - 44.7 = 55.3 \text{ B}$$

$$Q_{\text{unav},r} = T_0\, \Delta S_r = 500(-0.05) = -25 \text{ B}$$

$$Q_{\text{av},r} = Q - Q_{\text{unav},r} = -100 - (-25) = -75 \text{ B}$$

The last two values are negative because they are fractions of the heat *removed from* the reservoir. Notice that, as the 100 B of heat was given up

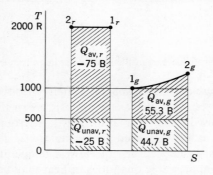

Fig. 9·17   Heat transfer across a finite temperature difference.

by the reservoir at 2000 R, 75 B of it could have been converted into work by an externally reversible engine; but, as the heat was absorbed by the gas at a temperature varying from 1000 to 1250 R, only 55.3 B of it could have been converted into work. Thus 19.7 B ($= 75 - 55.3$) has been made unavailable for conversion into work by the irreversible transfer of heat across a finite temperature difference.

Notice that available energy and unavailable energy are not properties of a system. They are fractions of the heat which is transferred to or from a system.

The first law is the basis for "energy accounting" procedures in which heat, work, and stored energy are compared and balanced. The second law makes possible the division of heat into available and unavailable energy and thus adds valuable information to an energy balance. It shows that something more than just the quantity of energy is important. As an illustration of this, consider two quantities of heat, Q_C and Q_D, rejected by vapors which condense at constant temperature. $Q_C = -1000$ B, and vapor C condenses at 500 F; $Q_D = -1000$ B and vapor D condenses at 200 F. The lowest temperature in the surroundings is 60 F. The amount of heat rejected is the same in each case; but the available part of Q_C is

$$Q_{av,C} = Q_C - Q_{unav,C} = Q_C - T_0\,\Delta S_C = Q_C - T_0\frac{Q_C}{T_C}$$

$$= -1000 - 520\frac{-1000}{960} = -458 \text{ B}$$

and the available part of Q_D is

$$Q_{av,D} = Q_D - Q_{unav,D} = Q_D - T_0\,\Delta S_D = Q_D - T_0\frac{Q_D}{T_D}$$

$$= -1000 - 520\frac{-1000}{660} = -212 \text{ B}$$

More than twice as much ($458/212 = 2.16$) work can be obtained from the 1000 B rejected by vapor C as can be obtained from the 1000 B rejected by vapor D. This available energy accounting shows clearly that the equal amounts of energy rejected by C and D are not equal in all respects.

EXAMPLE 9·12. Dry saturated steam at 118 psia undergoes a reversible isothermal expansion in a closed system until its pressure is 74 psia. (This is the same process that was considered in Example 9·4) The lowest temperature in the surroundings is 0 F. How much of the heat added per pound is available energy?

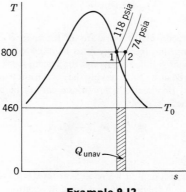

Example 9·12

Solution. Since the process is reversible,

$$q = \int_1^2 T \, ds$$

and, since it is isothermal, integration gives

$$q = \int_1^2 T \, ds = T(s_2 - s_1) = 800(1.6506 - 1.5891) = 49.2 \text{ B/lb}$$

The unavailable part of this heat is given, as always, by $q_{unav} = T_0 \, \Delta s$:

$$q_{unav} = T_0(s_2 - s_1) = 460(1.6506 - 1.5891) = 28.3 \text{ B/lb}$$

The available part is then

$$q_{av} = q - q_{unav} = 49.2 - 28.3 = 20.9 \text{ B/lb}$$

EXAMPLE 9·13.   A closed rigid thermally insulated tank contains 2 lb of air initially at 20 psia, 40 F (state 1). The lowest temperature in the surroundings is 40 F. An impeller in the tank is driven by an external motor and stirs the air until its temperature becomes 140 F (state 2). After this process is completed, how much of the energy which was added can be reconverted into work?

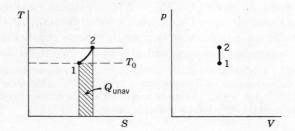

Example 9·13

Solution.   In order to reconvert to work any of the energy which was added to the system by means of the impeller, the energy must be removed from the system. All the energy added by the impeller will be removed if the system is returned to its initial state of 20 psia, 40 F. This can be done by removing the insulation from the tank and removing heat. The fractions of this heat which can and cannot be converted into work by externally reversible engines are given by

$$Q_{av} = Q - Q_{unav}$$

$$Q_{unav} = T_0 \, \Delta S$$

As for the *cooling* process, notice that it proceeds from state 2 to state 1 so that $\Delta S = S_1 - S_2$ and $\Delta U = U_1 - U_2$. Applying the first law and assuming that the air behaves as an ideal gas with constant c_v,

$$Q = U_1 - U_2 = mc_v(T_1 - T_2) = 2(0.171)(40 - 140) = -34.2 \text{ B}$$

$$\Delta S = S_1 - S_2 = \int_2^1 \frac{dU}{T} + \int_2^1 \frac{p \, dV}{T} = mc_v \ln \frac{T_1}{T_2} + 0$$

$$= 2(0.171) \ln \tfrac{500}{600} = -0.0624 \text{ B/R}$$

$$Q_{\text{unav}} = T_0 \, \Delta S = 500(-0.0624) = -31.2 \text{ B}$$

$$Q_{\text{av}} = Q - Q_{\text{unav}} = -34.2 - (-31.2) = -3.0 \text{ B}$$

Of the 34.2 B added to the system as work done by the impeller, 31.2 B cannot and 3.0 B can be reconverted into work by means of an externally reversible engine. (The values of Q_{av} and Q_{unav} obtained are negative because during the cooling process each is a fraction of the heat *removed* from the system.)

EXAMPLE 9·14.   One tenth of a pound of air in a closed system is carried through a cycle composed of four reversible processes: process 1-2 is an isentropic compression of the air from 14.0 psia, 40 F, to one-sixth its initial volume; process 2-3 is a constant volume heating until $T_3 = 1500$ R; process 3-4 is an isentropic expansion to the initial volume; and process 4-1 is a constant-volume cooling to the initial state. The lowest temperature in the surroundings is 40 F. Assume that the specific heats are constant at their 40 F values. Make an energy accounting and an available energy accounting for the cycle as a whole.

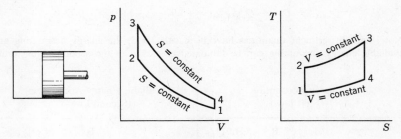

Example 9·14

Solution. First a sketch of the system and pV and TS diagrams are made. Analysis of the problem shows that the temperatures at the various states must be known. The two which are not given above can be readily found by use of the ideal-gas equation of state and the pv, vT, or pT relationship for an isentropic process of an ideal gas with constant specific heats:

$$T_2 = T_1 \left(\frac{V_1}{V_2}\right)^{k-1} = 500(6)^{0.4} = 1025 \text{ R}$$

$$T_4 = T_3 \left(\frac{V_3}{V_4}\right)^{k-1} = T_3 \left(\frac{V_2}{V_1}\right)^{k-1} = 1500 \left(\frac{1}{6}\right)^{0.4} = 732 \text{ R}$$

We determine the gross heat added and the gross heat rejected by applying the first law to processes 2-3 and 4-1 of the closed system.

$$Q_{2\text{-}3} = U_3 - U_2 + W = mc_v(T_3 - T_2) + 0 = 0.1(0.171)(1500 - 1025) = 8.12 \text{ B}$$

$$Q_{4\text{-}1} = U_1 - U_4 + W = mc_v(T_1 - T_4) + 0 = 0.1(0.171)(500 - 732) = -3.97 \text{ B}$$

Then the net work of the cycle is given by the first law as

$$W = \oint \delta W = \oint \delta Q = Q_{2\text{-}3} + Q_{4\text{-}1} = 8.12 - 3.97 = 4.15 \text{ B}$$

Of the heat added in process 2-3, the unavailable and available parts are

$$Q_{\text{unav,2-3}} = T_0(S_3 - S_2) = T_0 \int_{\substack{2 \\ \text{rev}}}^{3} \frac{\delta Q}{T} = T_0 \int_{\substack{2 \\ \text{rev}}}^{3} \frac{mc_v\, dT}{T} = T_0\, mc_v \ln \frac{T_3}{T_2}$$

$$= 500(0.1)0.171 \ln \tfrac{1500}{1025} = 3.25 \text{ B}$$

$$Q_{\text{av,2-3}} = Q_{2\text{-}3} - Q_{\text{unav,2-3}} = 8.12 - 3.25 = 4.87 \text{ B}$$

Notice that $(S_4 - S_1) = (S_3 - S_2)$, so that the unavailable part of $Q_{2\text{-}3}$ is equal in magnitude to the unavailable part of $Q_{4\text{-}1}$. Thus

$$Q_{\text{av,4-1}} = Q_{4\text{-}1} - Q_{\text{unav,4-1}} = -3.97 - (-3.25) = -0.72 \text{ B}$$

Now that all pertinent quantities have been calculated, the energy accounting and available energy accounting can be tabulated as shown in the accompanying table.

	Energy Accounting (First Law)			Available Energy Accounting (Second Law)		
		B	% of $Q_{2\text{-}3}$		B	% of $Q_{\text{av,2-3}}$
Energy in: $\quad Q_{2\text{-}3}$		8.12	100	Available energy in: $\quad Q_{\text{av,2-3}}$	4.87	100
Energy out: $\quad W$ $\quad Q_{4\text{-}1}$		4.15 3.97	51.1 48.9	Available energy out: $\quad W$ $\quad Q_{\text{av,4-1}}$	4.15 0.72	85.2 14.8

Only the *net* work is tabulated because the exchange of work is probably made with only one part of the surroundings, whereas the $Q_{2\text{-}3}$ and $Q_{4\text{-}1}$ are tabulated separately because they involve different parts of the surroundings. The results are shown graphically in the accompanying figure.

$$Q_{av} = 4.87 \text{ B}$$

$$W = 4.15 \text{ B}$$

Energy in,

$$Q_{2\text{-}3} = 8.12 \text{ B}$$

$$Q_{av} = 0.72 \text{ B}$$

Energy out,

$$Q_{out,\,4\text{-}1} + W = 8.12 \text{ B}$$

$$Q = 3.97 \text{ B}$$

$$Q_{unav} = 3.25 \text{ B} \qquad Q_{unav} = 3.25 \text{ B}$$

Discussion. It is clear that the second-law analysis gives information which changes greatly the picture obtained from the first-law analysis alone. The first-law analysis or energy accounting shows that 51.1 per cent of the gross heat input to the cycle is converted into work. From the first-law analysis *alone*, one might conclude that it would be possible through various improvements nearly to double the work output obtainable from a cycle with a heat-input process like 2-3. The second-law analysis, however, shows that 85.2 per cent of the gross available energy added in process 2-3 is converted into work by this cycle; so that, no matter what improvements are made in the cycle (as long as the heat-addition process 2-3 is unchanged), the work output can be increased by only about 17 per cent $[(100-85.2)/85.2) = 17.4$ per cent]. The first law shows that 48.9 per cent of the gross heat input is rejected by the cycle as heat, but the second law shows that, of the available energy added, only 14.8 per cent is wasted. Of the heat rejected by the cycle, only $0.72/3.97 = 18.1$ per cent is available energy; the remaining 81.9 per cent could not be converted into work even by an externally reversible engine rejecting heat only at T_0.

In this cycle 3.25 B of the heat input is unavailable energy, and 3.25 B of the heat rejected is unavailable energy. There is no increase in unavailable energy because all processes are reversible. If one or more of the processes were irreversible, the unavailable energy rejected by the cycle would be greater than that added.

9·7 Helmholtz (A) and Gibbs (G) functions *Know case 1*

Enthalpy was introduced as a derived property, being defined as the sum of U and pV. Many other derived properties could be defined by such arbitrary combinations of other properties, but there is no justification for such derived properties unless they are useful. Two derived properties which are quite useful in some areas of thermodynamics are the Helmholtz or A function and the Gibbs* or G function which are defined as

$$A \equiv U - TS \quad \text{or} \quad a \equiv u - Ts \tag{9·7a}$$

$$G \equiv H - TS \quad \text{or} \quad g \equiv h - Ts \tag{9·8a}$$

* Josiah Willard Gibbs (1839–1903) received from Yale University in 1863 the first Ph.D. in engineering awarded in America. After further study in Europe he became professor of mathematical physics at Yale and held that position until his death. He made significant contributions in several fields, but a single paper, "On the Equilibrium of Heterogeneous Substances," places him in the first rank among scientists. Because the value of this contribution can be appreciated only by those with an understanding of thermodynamics, the name of this man who was one of the outstanding scientists of all time is virtually unknown to the general public.

The differential of the A function is

$$dA = dU - T\,dS - S\,dT$$

which becomes

$$dA = -p\,dV - S\,dT \qquad (9{\cdot}7b)$$

upon substitution from $T\,dS = dU + p\,dV$. For a constant-temperature process,

$$dA = -p\,dV \quad \text{or} \quad A_1 - A_2 = \int_1^2 p\,dV$$

Thus the decrease in A equals the amount of work done by a closed system during a reversible isothermal process.

Consider a closed system which is initially and finally at the temperature T_0 of the atmosphere around it and exchanges heat only with the atmosphere. (During the process the system temperature may differ from T_0. For example, the system might be compressed or expanded adiabatically so that its temperature changes and then exchange heat with the atmosphere until its temperature is again T_0.) The maximum amount of heat which can be transferred to the system is $T_0(S_2 - S_1)$, so that the maximum work output of the system is given by

$$W_{\max} = U_1 - U_2 + Q_{\max} = U_1 - U_2 + T_0(S_2 - S_1)$$

$$= U_1 - T_0 S_1 - (U_2 - T_0 S_2) = A_1 - A_2$$

Thus a more general conclusion than the one in the last paragraph is that, *if a closed system passes from one state to another at the same temperature while exchanging heat only with the surroundings at that temperature, the maximum work which can be produced during the process is equal to the decrease in A of the system.* This conclusion is not restricted to systems comprised of pure substances, so it may be applied, for example, to a process involving a chemical reaction.

Part of the work done by a closed system may be done in pushing back the atmosphere if the system expands. (See Art. 1·14.) This part of the work is $p_0(V_2 - V_1)$, where p_0 is atmospheric pressure and V_1 and V_2 are the initial and final volumes of the system. If useful work means that work done in addition to pushing back the atmosphere,

$$W_{\text{useful}} = W - p_0(V_2 - V_1)$$

and the maximum useful work if the system exchanges heat only with the surroundings at T_0 is

$$W_{\max\,\text{useful}} = U_1 - U_2 + T_0(S_2 - S_1) - p_0(V_2 - V_1)$$

$$= U_1 + p_0 V_1 - T_0 S_1 - (U_2 + p_0 V_2 - T_0 S_2)$$

and, if $p_2 = p_1 = p_0$,

$$W_{\text{max useful}} = H_1 - T_0 S_1 - (H_2 - T_0 S_2) = G_1 - G_2$$

Conclusion: If a closed system passes between two states, in each of which it is at the pressure and temperature of the surrounding atmosphere, and exchanges heat only with the atmosphere, the maximum useful work (i.e., work done on systems other than the atmosphere) which can be produced during the process is equal to the decrease in G of the system. The conditions specified are met by a system undergoing a chemical reaction in an open vessel.

Differentiating the G function,

$$dG = dH - T\,dS - S\,dT = V\,dp - S\,dT \qquad (9\cdot8b)$$

For a constant-temperature process,

$$dG = V\,dp \quad \text{or} \quad G_1 - G_2 = -\int_1^2 V\,dp$$

Thus the decrease in G equals the amount of work done by a steady-flow system in a reversible isothermal process in which $\Delta KE = \Delta PE = 0$. A more general conclusion can be reached by considering a steady-flow process for which $\Delta KE = \Delta PE = 0$, $T_1 = T_2 = T_0$, and the system exchanges heat only with the surrounding atmosphere at T_0. The maximum work output is

$$W_{\text{max}} = H_1 - H_2 + Q_{\text{max}} = H_1 - H_2 + T_0(S_2 - S_1)$$
$$= H_1 - T_0 S_1 - (H_2 - T_0 S_2) = G_1 - G_2$$

Conclusion: If a substance enters and leaves a steady-flow system at the temperature of the surrounding atmosphere and exchanges heat only with the atmosphere, the maximum work which can be produced is equal to the decrease in G of the substance.

As an example of the use of the G function, suppose we determine the G value for the air and fuel entering a gasoline engine and for the products of combustion after they are cooled to atmospheric temperature. The difference between these values is the maximum amount of work that can conceivably be obtained from this particular flow of air, fuel, and products.

The A function (or Helmholtz function) and the G function (or Gibbs function) have both been called free energy, and consequently some confusion between them exists in the literature. The symbols A, Ψ, and F have been used for A; and G, Z, and F (again!) have been used for G. Consequently, you must be careful when you encounter the name free energy or the symbol F in the literature. Neither is used in this book.

The two properties A and G have been introduced here simply as examples of useful properties which, like entropy, can be defined as a consequence of the second law. We will make use of them in Chapters 10 and 14.

9·8 Uses of entropy

The introduction to this chapter pointed out that searching for a general physical picture of entropy is fruitless. Instead of trying to answer the question "What *is* entropy?," you should concentrate on the questions "What is it used for?" and "How is it used?" Let us review some of the uses of entropy which have already been discussed.

(*a*) *Entropy is used as a convenient coordinate.* (1) The ideal process in many machines and flow passages is a constant-entropy process. (2) On a temperature–entropy diagram the area beneath the path of a reversible process represents the heat transfer of the process. By leafing through the remaining pages of this book you will see how frequently diagrams with entropy as a coordinate are used.

(*b*) *Entropy is used in the calculation of heat transfer in reversible processes,* $Q_{\mathrm{rev}} = \int T \, dS$. This is of limited practical value because, in most cases where $\int T \, dS$ can be integrated, sufficient data are available for the calculation of Q by means of the first law.

(*c*) *Entropy is used to tell whether a process is reversible, irreversible, or impossible.* This use is based on the increase of entropy principle, $\Delta S_{\mathrm{isolated\ system}} \geq 0$, where the equality holds only for reversible processes.

(*d*) *Entropy is useful in the correlation of physical property data.* This use is based on the relations $T \, ds = du + p \, dv = dh - v \, dp$ and on the definitions of a and g. Further illustrations of it will appear in later chapters.

(*e*) *Entropy is used in the calculation of unavailable energy,* $Q_{\mathrm{unav}} = T_0 \, \Delta S$. A more general use in this connection is presented in Chapter 11.

9·9 Entropy and probability

It was stated earlier that a conclusion from statistical thermodynamics is that in an irreversible process an isolated system proceeds toward more probable states or, in other words, toward states of higher probability. In this chapter we have seen that a conclusion of classical thermodynamics is that during an irreversible process an isolated system proceeds toward states of higher entropy. A natural question is whether there is any direct relationship between probability and entropy. The answer to this question is yes. Before looking at this relationship, let us see what is meant by the probability of a state.

The most frequently used illustration begins with the consideration of a box which is divided into two equal parts by a half-partition. See Fig. 9·18. Let there be a marble in the box, but the box has been shaken so that the marble is as likely to be on one side of the partition as on the other. There are two possible configurations or arrangements. Then the probability that the marble is in side X of the box is 1/2. The probability that the

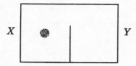

Fig. 9·18   System which can exist in either one of two states.

marble is in side Y of the box is also 1/2. (Since it is a certainty that the marble is somewhere in the box, the probability that it is in either side X or side Y is 1.)   Now consider the case of two marbles, called A and B, in the box.   There are four possible, and equally probable, arrangements as follows:

Arrangement	Marbles in X	Marbles in Y
1	A and B	None
2	A	B
3	B	A
4	None	A and B

The probability of each arrangement is 1/4 because there are four possible arrangements.   If the marbles cannot be distinguished from each other, arrangements 2 and 3 are identical.   We say that arrangements 2 and 3 produce the same state: the state in which there is one marble in each side of the box.   Therefore, only three states are possible:

State	Number of Marbles in X	Number of Marbles in Y	Probability
a	2	0	1/4
b	1	1	1/2
c	0	2	1/4

State b has a probability of 1/2 because two out of the four possible arrangements result in state b. The probability of state a is 1/4 because only one out of the four possible arrangements results in this state. The same is true of state c. Since there are no states other than a, b, or c possible, the sum of the probabilities of these three states is 1. For four marbles in the box there are 16 possible arrangements which can produce five different states, and their probabilities can be calculated as shown below.

Number of Marbles in X	Number of Marbles in Y	Probability
4	0	1/16
3	1	1/4
2	2	3/8
1	3	1/4
0	4	1/16

If we go now to n marbles, we see that the probability of having all n marbles in X is $(1/2)^n$. In other words, the state in which all marbles are in one side of the box is a state of low probability. The probability of having r marbles out of n in side X (i.e., the number of combinations of n things taken r at a time, divided by the total number of arrangements) is

$$\frac{n(n-1)(n-2)\cdots(n-r+1)}{r!(2)^n}$$

Let us now extend our consideration from a few marbles to many molecules of a gas which are free to move from one side of the box to the other. The opening in the partition can be very small in comparison with the size of the box and still permit enormous numbers of molecules to pass back and forth. It is assumed that any molecule is equally likely to be in side X or side Y. The probabilities of uniform and nearly uniform distributions of n molecules are shown in Table 9·1. It is seen that even for as few as 1000 molecules the probability of an appreciable departure from an equal distribution is very small. (Note that one cubic inch of air at normal room conditions contains more than 4×10^{20} molecules.) Any state in which the molecules are unequally distributed is a state of lower probability than one in which they are more nearly equally distributed. Having thus looked into the meaning of the probability of a state, we still face the question, "How is this related to entropy?"

In seeking the relationship between entropy and probability, let us first recall that entropy is an extensive property, so that, if systems A and B are combined to form system C,

$$S_C = S_A + S_B$$

TABLE 9·1

Probabilities of Some Distributions of Molecules

Number of Molecules, n	Number of Combinations of Molecules, 2^n	Number of Combinations in Which Number of Molecules (r) in X Is			Fraction of Combinations in Which Number of Molecules in X Is		
		$0.5n$	$0.49n$ to $0.51n$	$0.45n$ to $0.55n$	$0.5n$	$0.49n$ to $0.51n$	$0.45n$ to $0.55n$
2	4	2			0.500		
4	16	6			0.375		
6	64	20			0.313		
8	256	70			0.273		
10	1024	252			0.246		
20	1.049×10^6	0.1848×10^6		0.5207×10^6	0.176		0.496
40	1.100×10^{12}	0.1378×10^{12}		0.6272×10^{12}	0.125		0.570
100	1.2676×10^{30}	0.1009×10^{30}	0.2987×10^{30}	0.9238×10^{30}	0.0796	0.236	0.729
200	1.6069×10^{60}	0.0905×10^{60}	0.4439×10^{60}	1.3862×10^{60}	0.0563	0.276	0.863
1000	1.0715×10^{301}	0.0270×10^{301}	0.5282×10^{301}	1.0700×10^{301}	0.0252	0.493	0.9986

On the other hand, the probability of the state of the combined system is

$$\mathcal{P}_C = \mathcal{P}_A \cdot \mathcal{P}_B^*$$

These conditions are satisfied by letting

$$S = C \ln \mathcal{P}$$

because then

$$S_C = S_A + S_B = C(\ln \mathcal{P}_A + \ln \mathcal{P}_B) = C \ln \mathcal{P}_A \mathcal{P}_B = C \ln \mathcal{P}_C$$

Thus the change in entropy of a system which passes from a state 1 to a state 2 is

$$S_2 - S_1 = C \ln \frac{\mathcal{P}_2}{\mathcal{P}_1}$$

where $\mathcal{P}_2$ and $\mathcal{P}_1$ are the probabilities of the final and initial states, respectively, and C is a constant.

As an example, consider an ideal gas which undergoes a free expansion in a closed system until its volume is doubled, $V_2 = 2V_1$ (see Fig. 9·19). From the reasoning above, the probability that all n molecules of the gas would be in the half the enclosure called V_1 just after the partition is opened is $(1/2)^n$. This is the probability of the initial state.

$$\mathcal{P}_1 = \left(\frac{1}{2}\right)^n$$

---

* For example, consider two semipartitioned boxes, each with ends labeled X and Y and each containing one marble. What is the probability that the Y ends of both boxes are empty? The probability that the Y end of one box is empty is $1/2$; the probability that the Y end of the other box is empty is $1/2$; the probability that the Y ends of both boxes are empty is $(1/2) \cdot (1/2) = 1/4$. (This is the same as determining the probability of flipping a coin twice and getting a specified result on each flip.)

For a final equilibrium state, the distribution of molecules throughout the total volume V_2 is very nearly uniform so that the probability of the final state is very nearly 1.

$$\mathscr{P}_2 = (1)^n = 1$$

The constant C for this case is NR_u/n, where N is the number of moles of gas, R_u is the universal gas constant, and n is the number of molecules in the system. Then

$$S_2 - S_1 = \frac{NR_u}{n} \ln \frac{1}{(1/2)^n} = \frac{NR_u}{n} \ln (2)^n = NR_u \ln 2 = NR_u \ln \frac{V_2}{V_1}$$

and this is the same expression for ΔS that we obtain from classical thermodynamics.

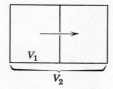

Fig. 9·19   Free expansion of a gas.

When a solid is melted or a liquid is vaporized, there is a change toward a less ordered molecular state or an increase in the "randomness" of molecular motions and configurations. Such processes serve as additional illustrations of the relationship between entropy increase and the increase in molecular disorder.

In addition to the relationship between entropy and probability just discussed, such a relationship has been introduced into communication theory. No more than a mention of this is made here because even an elementary discussion must cover a scheme for the quantitative measurement of information, and this by itself requires a considerable amount of exposition. Suffice to say that the concept of entropy is important in several areas outside the scope of classical thermodynamics.

9·10   Summary

From the second law it can be shown that

$$\Delta S \equiv \int_{rev} \frac{\delta Q}{T} \tag{9·1a}$$

is a property. This property is called entropy. It is actually the *change* in entropy which is defined by equation 9·1a, but in engineering work we are usually concerned only with entropy changes rather than with absolute values of entropy.

ΔS between any two states of a system can be calculated by integrating $\int \dfrac{\delta Q}{T}$ along any reversible path between the two states. It is usually easier, however, to calculate ΔS from the equations

$$T \, dS = dU + p \, dV \tag{9·3}$$

$$T \, dS = dH - V \, dp \tag{9·3}$$

which can be developed from the first and second laws and which apply to any system changing from one equilibrium state to another in the absence of electrical, magnetic, and surface tension effects. These equations are also useful in correlating the physical properties of substances.

The heat transfer of any reversible process is given by

$$Q_{\text{rev}} = \int T \, dS \tag{9·2}$$

Consequently, the heat transfer of any reversible process is represented as an area on a TS diagram. Entropy is also useful as a coordinate in conjunction with other properties besides temperature.

Whether a process is reversible, irreversible, or even possible can be determined by the *increase of entropy principle:*

$$\Delta S_{\text{isolated system}} \geq 0 \tag{9·4}$$

in which the equality applies to reversible processes. Application of this principle to a steady-flow system results in

$$\sum_{\text{out}} ms - \sum_{\text{in}} ms + \Delta S_{\text{surr which exchange heat with steady-flow system}} \geq 0 \quad (9·5)$$

Available energy is defined as that part of the heat added to or taken from a system which could be converted into work by an externally reversible engine rejecting heat at the lowest temperature in the surroundings. *Unavailable energy* is that part of the heat which could not be converted into work by such an engine. Thus

$$Q = Q_{\text{av}} + Q_{\text{unav}}$$

It can be shown that for any process the unavailable part of the heat transferred is

$$Q_{\text{unav}} = T_0\,\Delta S \tag{9.6}$$

where T_0 is the lowest temperature in the surroundings and ΔS is the entropy change of the system.

Two properties which are quite useful, particularly in processes involving chemical reactions, are the Helmholtz function or A function, defined as

$$A \equiv U - TS \tag{9.7}$$

and the Gibbs function or G function, defined as

$$G \equiv H - TS \tag{9.8}$$

For a closed system passing from one state to another at the same temperature while exchanging heat only with the surroundings at that temperature, the decrease in A of the system is equal to the maximum work which can be produced during the process. For a closed system passing between two states, in each of which it is at the pressure and temperature of the surrounding atmosphere, while exchanging heat only with the atmosphere, the decrease in G of the system is equal to the maximum useful work which can be produced during the process. Useful work is defined as the total work minus the work done on the surrounding atmosphere. The decrease in G of a substance which enters and leaves a steady-flow system at the temperature of the surrounding atmosphere and exchanges heat only with the atmosphere is equal to the maximum work which can be produced during the process.

In addition to its uses in classical thermodynamics which are listed here, the concept of entropy has proved to be valuable in several other fields.

REFERENCES

9·1 D. A. Mooney, *Mechanical Engineering Thermodynamics*, Prentice-Hall, 1953, chapter 8.

9·2 J. H. Keenan, *Thermodynamics*, John Wiley & Sons, 1941, chapter VIII.

9·3 M. W. Zemansky, *Heat and Thermodynamics*, McGraw-Hill Book Co., 4th ed., 1957, chapter 10.

9·4 G. J. Van Wylen, *Thermodynamics*, John Wiley & Sons, 1959, chapter 7.

9·5 F. W. Sears, *Thermodynamics, the Kinetic Theory of Gases, and Statistical Mechanics*, Addison-Wesley Publishing Co., 2d ed., 1953, chapter 8.

9·6 G. N. Lewis and M. Randall, *Thermodynamics and the Free Energy of Chemical Substances*, McGraw-Hill Book Co., 1923, chapters X and XI.

9·7 V. W. Young, *Basic Thermodynamics*, McGraw-Hill Book Co., 1952, chapter 6.

9·8 E. F. Obert, *Thermodynamics*. McGraw-Hill Book Co. 1948, chapter 5.

PROBLEMS

9·1 A closed system can go from a state A to a state B by means of several different adiabatic paths. Is the work the same for all paths? Explain.

9·2 Is $\displaystyle\int_{rev} \frac{\delta w}{p}$ a property?

9·3 Prove that the minimum work input to a refrigerator which cools a rigid body from atmospheric temperature T_0 to a lower temperature T_L is $W_{in} = T_0(S_0 - S_L) + U_L - U_0$, where S and U are properties of the body being cooled.

9·4 Prove that for any process of a closed system $\Delta S \geq \displaystyle\int \frac{\delta q}{T}$.

9·5 Ten pounds of air in a closed system expands reversibly with constant entropy from 40 psia, 140 F, to 20 psia. Calculate the work done per pound of air.

9·6 Air flowing through a compressor at a rate of 12 lb/sec is compressed isentropically from 15 psia, 40 F, to 30 psia. The kinetic energy of the air is increased by 3.0 B/lb. Calculate the power input to the air.

9·7 Steam flows isentropically through a turbine from 200 psia, 500 F, to an exhaust pressure of 2 in. Hg abs. The flow rate is 10,000 lb/hr. Calculate the power output, assuming $\Delta KE = 0$.

9·8 Calculate the work required per pound of steam which is compressed reversibly and adiabatically in a steady-flow system from 100 psia, 330 F, until its density is doubled. Kinetic energy changes are negligible.

9·9 Steam is supplied to a turbine at 200 psia, 600 F, and exhausted at 14.7 psia. Assume reversible adiabatic flow. To what pressure must the incoming steam be throttled in order to reduce the work per pound to two thirds of that obtained without throttling? Assume that the flow through the turbine is still reversible adiabatic and that the exhaust pressure is unchanged.

9·10 An ideal gas is heated at constant volume from state 1 to state 2, expanded isothermally to state 3, expanded adiabatically to state 4 which is at the same pressure as state 1, and then restored to state 1 by a constant-pressure process. All four processes are reversible. (a) Sketch pv and Ts diagrams of the cycle. (b) State whether each of the following quantities is greater than zero, less than zero, equal to zero, or of indeterminate sign: $\oint \delta Q, \oint \delta w, \oint du, \oint ds$.

9·11 A vapor in a closed system passes through a cycle comprised of three processes: isentropic expansion 1-2, constant-pressure cooling 2-3, and constant-volume heating 3-1. Sketch pv and Ts diagrams for the cycle if state 1 is superheated vapor and (a) states 2 and 3 are also superheated, (b) states 2 and 3 are "wet vapor" states.

9·12 In a closed system, steam expands reversibly from a dry saturated condition at 100 psia to a dry saturated condition at 10 psia in such a manner that the process is represented by a straight line on a Ts diagram. Determine the work per pound of steam.

9·13 A heat engine utilizing air as the working fluid completes its cycle in three steps as follows: process 1-2: adiabatic compression from $T_1 = 100$ F to $T_2 = 300$ F; process 2-3: isothermal expansion at 300 F; process 3-1: $dT/ds = $ constant. Assuming each step in the cycle to be reversible, compute the efficiency of the engine.

9·14 A fluid passing through a steady-flow system can be heated reversibly from state 1 to state 2 in either of two ways. In one case, $T = a+bs$; in the other case, $T = c+es^2$. a, b, c, and e are constants. In which case is the heat transfer greater?

9·15 Sketch Ts, pv, Tv, ph, hs, and hv diagrams of a Carnot cycle using as a working fluid (a) an ideal gas, (b) a liquid–vapor mixture.

9·16 In a reversible isothermal process, 100 B/lb of heat is added to a closed system comprised of water which is initially saturated liquid at 400 F. Determine the work done during this process.

9·17 Dry saturated steam at 118 psia enters a steady-flow system and is expanded reversibly and isothermally to 74 psia. There is no change in kinetic energy. The flow rate is 2.0 lb/sec. Sketch the process on a Ts diagram, and calculate the amount of work done per pound of steam.

9·18 In a reversible steady-flow process, steam initially at 40 psia, 340 F, undergoes an isothermal expansion to 35 psia. Sketch a Ts diagram for the process. If no work is done, calculate the change in kinetic energy of the steam in B/lb.

9·19 In a closed system, dry saturated steam at 100 psia is heated in a constant-volume process until its pressure is 174 psia. It is then expanded isothermally to 100 psia, and finally cooled to the saturation temperature at constant pressure. All processes are reversible. Calculate the net work done.

9·20 Fifty pounds of water at 40 F and 80 lb of water at 180 F are mixed in an insulated vessel under a constant pressure of 1 atm. Determine the entropy change of the system comprised of the 130 lb of water.

9·21 State the conditions under which each of the following equations is true:

$$\oint T\,ds = -\oint v\,dp$$

$$\oint T\,ds = \oint p\,dv$$

9·22 A Carnot engine operates between a source at 800 F and a receiver at 100 F. If 200 B is transferred to the receiver each minute, compute the changes in entropy per unit time for the system and the universe for the isothermal expansion.

9·23 A reversed Carnot engine operates between temperature limits of 70 and 120 F. Sketch the cycle on a Ts diagram, and indicate the areas that represent the heat transferred from the reservoir at 70 F and the work input. If 100 B is absorbed from the reservoir at 70 F, compute the change in entropy of the system for the isothermal compression process.

9·24 An engine operates on a slightly modified Carnot cycle between constant temperature limits of 500 and 100 F. During the isothermal expansion the entropy of the system changes 0.3 B/R for 2 lb of the working substance. Owing to fluid friction, an increase in entropy of 0.01 B/R occurs during the adiabatic expansion. Sketch the cycle on a Ts diagram. Compute heat added, heat rejected, and work performed. Also determine the efficiency of the cycle. Determine heat added, heat rejected, and work performed, and the efficiency on the basis that the adiabatic expansion is reversible.

9·25 An engine operates in accordance with a Carnot cycle except that, owing to fluid friction, the entropy increases slightly during the adiabatic expansion. The constant operating temperature limits are 240 and 100 F. During the isothermal expansion

50 B/min is added. The increase in entropy for the system during the adiabatic expansion is 5 per cent of the entropy change for the isothermal expansion process. Sketch the cycle on a Ts diagram. Compute the power output of the engine.

9·26 A refrigerating machine patterned after a reversed Carnot cycle operates between -10 and 90 F; 10,000 B is to be removed each hour from the cold room at -10 F. One expansion process is an irreversible adiabatic process which causes an entropy increase for the system of 10 per cent of the total entropy change for the reversible isothermal expansion. Draw a sketch on a Ts diagram, and show by area the heat absorbed at -10 F. Compute the power required.

9·27 Ten pounds of nitrogen is cooled in a closed tank from 500 to 100 F. The initial pressure is 400 psia. Compute the changes in entropy, internal energy, and enthalpy.

9·28 Fifty cubic feet of air at 80 F and 14 psia is compressed isothermally to 10 cu ft. Is the entropy of the air increased or diminished, and by how much?

9·29 The entropy of 4 lb of air decreases 0.4 B/R during a constant-temperature process at 270 F. If the original pressure was 120 psia, compute (a) the work done, and (b) the final volume.

9·30 One pound of air is heated at constant volume from 140 F and 50 psia to 540 F, compressed adiabatically to 200 psia, and then cooled under constant-volume conditions to 240 F. Determine the change in entropy of the air for the individual steps and for the complete series of steps.

9·31 A pound of air which is under a pressure of 200 psia occupying a volume of 2 cu ft undergoes a constant-pressure change until the volume is doubled. The pressure is reduced to 100 psia under constant-volume conditions, after which it is compressed isothermally to its original volume. Compute the total change in entropy of the system for the three steps.

9·32 One-half pound of air at 15 psia, 140 F, is contained in a closed rigid thermally insulated vessel. A paddle wheel inside the vessel is turned by an external motor until the pressure is 20 psia. Sketch pv and Ts diagrams for this process, and calculate the change in entropy of the air.

9·33 Air initially at 25 psia, 40 F, has its volume doubled while its temperature rises to 200 F. Calculate, if possible, the change in enthalpy, the change in internal energy, the change in entropy, the work done, and the heat transferred.

9·34 One tenth of a pound of air in a closed system is compressed irreversibly from 15 psia, 40 F, to 30 psia. During the process 1.7 B of heat is removed from the air, and the work done on the air amounts to 2.6 B. Determine the entropy change of the air.

9·35 Air in a closed system is heated reversibly from 15.0 psia, 40 F, to 17.92 psia, 240 F, in such a manner that $dT/ds =$ constant. (a) Calculate the work done per pound of air. (b) Sketch a large accurate Ts diagram for the process, showing lines of constant pressure for 15 and 17.92 psia. Show also some constant-volume lines. (c) Sketch a large accurate pv diagram for the process. (You may wish to support your sketches by some calculations proving that you have shown the correct shapes or slopes.)

9·36 Prove that the constant-pressure lines in the wet region of an hs diagram for steam are straight. Also prove that they are or are not parallel.

9·37 In Example 9·8 it is shown that for an ideal gas $(\partial T/\partial s)_p = T/c_p$ and $(\partial T/\partial s)_v = T/c_v$. Show that these relations are true for any pure substance.

9·38 Derive the following expressions for an ideal gas with constant specific heats:

$$s_2 - s_1 = c_p \ln \frac{T_2/T_1}{(p_2/p_1)^{(k-1)/k}}$$

$$s_2 - s_1 = c_v \ln \frac{p_2}{p_1} + c_p \ln \frac{v_2}{v_1}$$

9·39 (a) In a closed system, a gas undergoes a cycle made up of the following processes: 1-2, reversible isothermal compression; 2-3, reversible constant-volume heating; 3-4, reversible constant-pressure expansion; 4-1, reversible adiabatic expansion. Sketch pv and Ts diagrams, and state whether each of the following quantities is positive, zero, negative, or indeterminate in sign: $\oint \delta W$, $\oint \delta Q$, $\oint dS$, $\oint dU$, $\oint dH$. (b) Repeat part (a) with process 4-1 changed to an irreversible adiabatic expansion.

9·40 Air is compressed irreversibly from 15 psia, 40 F, to 30 psia, 240 F. (a) Calculate Δs of the air. (b) Give all the information you can on the numerical value of the entropy change of the surroundings per pound of air.

9·41 Is an adiabatic expansion of steam from 60 psia, 300 F, to 14.7 psia, quality, reversible, irreversible, or impossible? State the quality limits for for irreversible, and for impossible adiabatic expansions between 60 psia, 14.7 psia.

9·42 Dry saturated sulfur dioxide at -10 F is compressed adiabatically in a steady-flow process. What is the minimum final temperature? Is it the closed-system adiabatic compression?

9·43 Is an adiabatic expansion of air from 40 psia, 140 F, to 20 psia, 80 F, Prove your answer. What is the lowest possible final temperature for an a expansion of air from 40 psia, 140 F, to 20 psia? What is the maximum possi... temperature?

9·44 A turbine operating on air has inlet conditions of 30 psia, 200 F, and an exhaust pressure of 15 psia. If the expansion is adiabatic and $\Delta KE = 0$, is an exhaust temperature of 40 F possible? Is it possible if $\Delta KE \neq 0$?

9·45 One-half pound of air in a closed system expands from 40 psia, 240 F, to 20 psia, 80 F, producing 8.0 B of work. During this process, the entropy of the surroundings increases by 0.0114 B/R. (a) Calculate the heat transfer. (b) Is the process reversible? Prove your answer.

9·46 One pound of air in a closed system expands from 60 psia, 1040 F, to 15 psia. During the process, the entropy change of the surroundings is 0.0713 B/R. Determine the minimum temperature possible for the air in the system.

9·47 Can a system undergo an isentropic process which is not reversible and adiabatic? Explain. Can an isolated system undergo an isentropic process which is not reversible and adiabatic?

9·48 Heat is transferred from a furnace at a constant temperature of 2540 F to water which is evaporating at a constant temperature of 540 F. The lowest temperature in the surroundings is 90 F. For each 1000 B transferred, how much of the energy would be available if it were absorbed by a fluid at 2540 F? How much of the energy is available as it is received by the water at 540 F? Show these quantities as areas on a TS diagram.

9·49 Consider the transfer of heat from an energy reservoir at 540 F to 5 lb of air initially at 15 psia, 140 F, trapped in a closed, rigid tank. Heat is transferred until the temperature of the air is 340 F. The temperature of the surroundings is 40 F. (a) How much heat is transferred? (*b*) How much of the energy removed from the reservoir is available energy? How much is unavailable? (*c*) How much of the energy added to the air in the tank is available energy? How much is unavailable?

9·50 For each 1000 B supplied to a power plant, 600 B is rejected to the atmosphere at 80 F from the working fluid which is condensed at a constant temperature of 90 F, and 200 B of heat is rejected to the atmosphere from working fluid at 800 F. The work output is 200 B. Determine the maximum amount of work which might be obtained from (*a*) the heat rejected from the fluid at 90 F and (*b*) the heat rejected from the fluid at 800 F.

9·51 A closed rigid container holds dry saturated steam at 17.0 psia. Heat is added until the pressure becomes 32.0 psia. How much of the heat added is available energy if the sink temperature is 32 F?

9·52 Ten pounds of air (the system) is cooled at a constant pressure of 20 psia from 300 to 100 F. Sink (surroundings) temperature is 100 F. All the heat removed is dissipated to the surroundings. How much of the heat removed from the air is available energy? Calculate the entropy change of the system and of the universe. By how much does the total energy of the universe change?

9·53 Air flows reversibly and at constant pressure through a steady-flow system at a rate of 1.4 lb/sec. It enters at 20 psia, 100 F, and leaves at 300 F. The lowest temperature in the surroundings (the sink temperature) is 40 F. Calculate, per pound of air, (*a*) the heat added to the air, (*b*) the work done on or by the air, and (*c*) the amount of heat added to the air which is available energy.

9·54 In a steady-flow reversible process with no change in potential or kinetic energy, a gas is cooled at a constant pressure of 20 psia from 340 to 140 F. The sink temperature is 40 F. For this gas, in the temperature range involved, $c_p = 0.2 + 0.0001T$ and $c_v = 0.15 + 0.0001T$, where T is in degrees Rankine and c_p and c_v are in B/lb-F. Sketch a Ts diagram and calculate, in B/lb, (*a*) the amount of heat removed from the gas, (*b*) the entropy change of the gas, and (*c*) the amount of heat removed from the gas which is unavailable energy.

CHAPTER 10

Physical Properties II

In Chapters 3, 4, and 5 physical properties and phase transformations were discussed in terms of relationships among p, v, T, u, and h—properties which are defined independently of the laws of thermodynamics or are defined by means of the first law. Now that the second law and the resulting properties s, a, and g have been introduced, we can greatly extend our study of physical property relationships.

Engineers are interested in physical property relationships for several reasons. One reason pertains to the selection of materials or substances to perform various functions. For example, just as the materials used for the various parts of an automobile engine are selected on the basis of their strength, hardness, ductility, cost,* and so forth, the fluids used in household refrigerators, nuclear reactor cooling circuits, and air-conditioning systems are selected on the basis of other properties.

Often the data which an engineer needs on a particular property of a substance are not available. In such cases a knowledge of general property relationships such as those discussed in this chapter may permit him to calculate the needed properties from data on other properties. Occasionally an engineer finds that for some substance he needs data outside the range of available data. He can make extrapolations much more reliably if he is familiar with certain characteristics of substances in general. If the paucity of data on some substance is so restrictive that some experimental measurements must be made, a knowledge of general property relationships is essential in organizing the experimental program to give the needed information with the required accuracy and with the least expenditure of time and money. Indeed, the cost of preparing the extensive tables of properties which are now available for many substances would be prohibitive if it were not possible to gain much information from a relatively small amount of data.

This chapter deals with properties of pure substances. Mixtures of variable composition are treated in Chapters 12, 14, and 20.

---

* Cost of course is not a property in the sense that the others listed are, but it is well to remember that it is a pertinent factor which the engineer must always consider.

10·1   The Maxwell* equations

The following four equations which were introduced earlier are valid, at least for pure substances in the absence of electricity, magnetism, and surface tension, for any process between equilibrium states:

$$du = T\,ds - p\,dv \qquad (9\cdot3)$$

$$dh = T\,ds + v\,dp \qquad (9\cdot3)$$

$$da = -p\,dv - s\,dT \qquad (9\cdot7b)$$

$$dg = v\,dp - s\,dT \qquad (9\cdot8b)$$

Since u, h, a, and g are properties, du, dh, da, and dg are exact differentials. Therefore,

$$\left(\frac{\partial T}{\partial v}\right)_s = -\left(\frac{\partial p}{\partial s}\right)_v \qquad (10\cdot1)$$

$$\left(\frac{\partial T}{\partial p}\right)_s = \left(\frac{\partial v}{\partial s}\right)_p \qquad (10\cdot2)$$

$$\left(\frac{\partial p}{\partial T}\right)_v = \left(\frac{\partial s}{\partial v}\right)_T \qquad (10\cdot3)$$

$$\left(\frac{\partial v}{\partial T}\right)_p = -\left(\frac{\partial s}{\partial p}\right)_T \qquad (10\cdot4)$$

These four equations are called the *Maxwell equations*. They are important in the correlation of properties of pure substances because they relate entropy to the directly measurable properties pressure, specific volume, and temperature.

Many other relations among properties can be derived from equations 9·3, 9·7b, and 9·8b. For example, taking u as a function of s and v, we have

$$du = \left(\frac{\partial u}{\partial s}\right)_v ds + \left(\frac{\partial u}{\partial v}\right)_s dv$$

Comparing this with equation 9·3,

$$du = T\,ds - p\,dv \qquad (9\cdot3)$$

* James Clerk Maxwell (1831–1879), a member of a wealthy Scottish family, received his formal education at the University of Edinburgh and Cambridge University. He was professor of physics and astronomy at King's College, London (1860–68), and in 1871 became the first professor of experimental physics at Cambridge University. He made scientific contributions in many areas, including mechanics, optics, electricity and magnetism, kinetic theory of gases, and thermodynamics.

and noting that ds and dv are independent, we can equate the coefficients of ds and dv to give

$$\left(\frac{\partial u}{\partial s}\right)_v = T \qquad \left(\frac{\partial u}{\partial v}\right)_s = -p \qquad (10\cdot5)$$

Treating the expressions for dh, da, and dg similarly, we obtain

$$\left(\frac{\partial h}{\partial s}\right)_p = T \qquad \left(\frac{\partial h}{\partial p}\right)_s = v \qquad (10\cdot6)$$

$$\left(\frac{\partial a}{\partial v}\right)_T = -p \qquad \left(\frac{\partial a}{\partial T}\right)_v = -s \qquad (10\cdot7)$$

$$\left(\frac{\partial g}{\partial p}\right)_T = v \qquad \left(\frac{\partial g}{\partial T}\right)_p = -s \qquad (10\cdot8)$$

You do not have to memorize equations 10·1 through 10·8 because they are so easy to derive from equations 9·3, 9·7b, and 9·8b, which you should know or be able to derive quickly. Many other relations among the eight variables p, v, T, s, h, u, a, and g can be derived from equations 10·1 through 10·8.* Some of these will be used later in this chapter.

Some interesting conclusions can be drawn directly from the Maxwell equations and equations 10·5 to 10·8. For example, from the second of equations 10·6,

$$\left(\frac{\partial h}{\partial p}\right)_s = v \qquad (10\cdot6)$$

we conclude that, since v is always positive, in any isentropic process the enthalpy of a substance is decreased if the pressure is decreased. Notice also that, for any system for isentropic processes,

$$\Delta h = \int v\, dp \qquad (s = \text{constant, only})$$

An important fact is that this conclusion in no way depends on any equation of state.

Let us look at another example of a conclusion drawn from the Maxwell equations. The density of water under a pressure of 1 atm is a maximum at about 39.2 F. In other words, the specific volume is a minimum at this point, so that $(\partial v/\partial T)_p = 0$. The fourth Maxwell equation, equation 10·4, then shows that $(\partial s/\partial p)_T = 0$. Thus, at the temperature of maximum

* See P. W. Bridgman, "A Complete Collection of Thermodynamic Formulas," *Physical Review*, vol. 3, 1914, for a systematic compilation which is ingeniously arranged so that millions (!) of relations can be obtained directly from less than one hundred tabulated relations.

density, entropy is independent of pressure. This means that constant-pressure lines in the liquid region of a Ts diagram for water coincide with each other and cross the saturation line at around 39.2 F as shown in Fig. 10·1. Point M in Fig. 10·1 can represent either compressed liquid at 16 psia or a low-quality mixture of liquid and vapor at some pressure lower than the saturation pressure for 39.2 F.

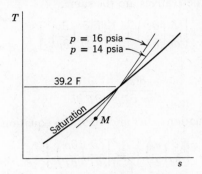

Fig. 10·1   Constant-pressure lines for compressed liquid water.

The first of equations 10·5,

$$\left(\frac{\partial u}{\partial s}\right)_v = T \tag{10·5}$$

can be written as

$$\left(\frac{\partial u}{\partial T}\right)_v \left(\frac{\partial T}{\partial s}\right)_v = T$$

Recalling the definition of c_v, we have

$$c_v \left(\frac{\partial T}{\partial s}\right)_v = T$$

or

$$\left(\frac{\partial T}{\partial s}\right)_v = \frac{T}{c_v} \tag{10·9}$$

Thus the slope of a constant-volume line on a Ts diagram is equal to T/c_v for any substance. This was shown in Example 9·8 to be true for an ideal gas, but here we see that the conclusion is independent of any equation of state.

The Maxwell equations provide a simple proof that the specific heats of an ideal gas are functions of temperature only. The third Maxwell equation is

$$\left(\frac{\partial s}{\partial v}\right)_T = \left(\frac{\partial p}{\partial T}\right)_v \tag{10·3}$$

and we have just shown that

$$\left(\frac{\partial s}{\partial T}\right)_v = \frac{c_v}{T} \tag{10.9}$$

As long as s is a continuous function of T and v, and the derivatives are also continuous, the order of differentiation is immaterial and the "mixed" second-order partial derivatives are the same,

$$\left[\frac{\partial}{\partial v}\left(\frac{\partial s}{\partial T}\right)_v\right]_T = \left[\frac{\partial}{\partial T}\left(\frac{\partial s}{\partial v}\right)_T\right]_v \tag{a}$$

This is usually written

$$\frac{\partial^2 s}{\partial v\, \partial T} = \frac{\partial^2 s}{\partial T\, \partial v}$$

Substituting from equations 10.3 and 10.9 into equation (a),

$$\left[\frac{\partial}{\partial v}\left(\frac{c_v}{T}\right)\right]_T = \left[\frac{\partial}{\partial T}\left(\frac{\partial p}{\partial T}\right)_v\right]_v$$

$$\left(\frac{\partial c_v}{\partial v}\right)_T = T\left(\frac{\partial^2 p}{\partial T^2}\right)_v$$

For an ideal gas, $pv = RT$, and therefore $(\partial^2 p/\partial T^2)_v = 0$. Thus

$$\left(\frac{\partial c_v}{\partial v}\right)_T = 0$$

which indicates that c_v is a function of temperature only. In a similar manner it can be shown that c_p of an ideal gas is a function of temperature only, although this is unnecessary because it is even easier to show that, if either c_p or c_v of an ideal gas is a function of temperature only, then so is the other.

Let us now see how the Maxwell equations help in the evaluation of entropy from data on the directly measurable properties pressure, specific volume, temperature, and specific heats. For a pure substance entropy is a function of any two of the properties: p and v, p and T, or v and T. Two partial derivatives involving s are associated with each of the three pairs of measurable properties, making a total of six:

$$\left(\frac{\partial s}{\partial p}\right)_v, \quad \left(\frac{\partial s}{\partial v}\right)_p; \qquad \left(\frac{\partial s}{\partial p}\right)_T, \quad \left(\frac{\partial s}{\partial T}\right)_p; \qquad \left(\frac{\partial s}{\partial v}\right)_T, \quad \left(\frac{\partial s}{\partial T}\right)_v$$

If we can express each of these derivatives in terms of p, v, T, and other readily measurable properties, we will have complete information on the entropy of any substance for which we have data on the other properties.

The third and fifth derivatives can be evaluated from pvT data by means of two Maxwell equations alone:

$$\left(\frac{\partial s}{\partial p}\right)_T = -\left(\frac{\partial v}{\partial T}\right)_p \qquad \left(\frac{\partial s}{\partial v}\right)_T = \left(\frac{\partial p}{\partial T}\right)_v$$

The last derivative can be evaluated as

$$\left(\frac{\partial s}{\partial T}\right)_v = \frac{c_v}{T} \tag{10·9}$$

as shown in the paragraph before last; and it can be shown in similar fashion (starting from the first of equations 10·6) that the fourth derivative can be evaluated as

$$\left(\frac{\partial s}{\partial T}\right)_p = \frac{c_p}{T} \tag{10·10}$$

The specific heats c_p and c_v are readily measurable properties. The two remaining derivatives can be expressed as

$$\left(\frac{\partial s}{\partial p}\right)_v = \left(\frac{\partial s}{\partial T}\right)_v \left(\frac{\partial T}{\partial p}\right)_v = \frac{c_v}{T}\left(\frac{\partial T}{\partial p}\right)_v$$

and

$$\left(\frac{\partial s}{\partial v}\right)_p = \left(\frac{\partial s}{\partial T}\right)_p \left(\frac{\partial T}{\partial v}\right)_p = \frac{c_p}{T}\left(\frac{\partial T}{\partial v}\right)_p$$

Thus we have obtained from the Maxwell equations a complete description of the entropy variation of a pure substance in terms of data on p, v, T, c_p, and c_v.

Notice that only *derivatives* of entropy have been expressed in terms of pvT data, so that entropy values can be obtained only by integration. The integration introduces arbitrary functions or "constants of integration" which cannot be evaluated from pvT data alone. The same difficulty is experienced in trying to evaluate u, h, a, or g from pvT data alone. On the other hand, inspection of equations 10·5 through 10·8 shows that at least some properties can be completely evaluated by differentiation alone, and thus no arbitrary functions will be involved if we start with data on certain groups of properties. For example, if we have complete uvs data, we determine p and T by

$$p = -\left(\frac{\partial u}{\partial v}\right)_s \qquad T = \left(\frac{\partial u}{\partial s}\right)_v \tag{10·5}$$

Then
$$h \equiv u + pv = u - \left(\frac{\partial u}{\partial v}\right)_s v$$

$$a \equiv u - Ts = u - \left(\frac{\partial u}{\partial s}\right)_v s$$

$$g \equiv h - Ts = u - \left(\frac{\partial u}{\partial v}\right)_s v - \left(\frac{\partial u}{\partial s}\right)_v s$$

Thus we can evaluate p, T, h, a, and g completely from uvs data alone. The uvs relation for a substance,

$$f(u, v, s) = 0$$

is called a *characteristic function*. A characteristic function is one from which all properties of a substance can be obtained by differentiation alone, so that no arbitrary functions which require supplementary data for their evaluation are introduced. Other characteristic functions are

$$f(h, p, s) = 0$$

$$f(a, v, T) = 0$$

$$f(g, p, T) = 0$$

As noted earlier, $f(p, v, T)$ is not a characteristic function. Unfortunately, the formulation of the properties of a substance cannot be started from a characteristic function because in none of them are all three properties directly measurable. The usefulness of the characteristic functions lies in the fact that once any one of them is formulated for a substance, all properties can then be determined without the use of additional data.

EXAMPLE 10·1. Joule's law states that for an ideal gas $(\partial u/\partial v)_T = 0$. Prove this.

Solution. We must express $(\partial u/\partial v)_T$ in terms of p, v, and T and their derivatives so that we can evaluate it from $pv = RT$. Notice that equation 10·5 is an expression for $(\partial u/\partial v)_s$. $(\partial u/\partial v)_T$ can be expressed in terms of $(\partial u/\partial v)_s$ and other quantities by (see Appendix B for derivation)

$$\left(\frac{\partial u}{\partial v}\right)_T = \left(\frac{\partial u}{\partial v}\right)_s + \left(\frac{\partial u}{\partial s}\right)_v \left(\frac{\partial s}{\partial v}\right)_T$$

The three derivatives on the right-hand side can be expressed as

$$\left(\frac{\partial u}{\partial v}\right)_s = -p \tag{10·5}$$

$$\left(\frac{\partial u}{\partial s}\right)_v = T \tag{10·5}$$

$$\left(\frac{\partial s}{\partial v}\right)_T = \left(\frac{\partial p}{\partial T}\right)_v \tag{10·3}$$

so that
$$\left(\frac{\partial u}{\partial v}\right)_T = -p + T\left(\frac{\partial p}{\partial T}\right)_v$$

For an ideal gas, $pv = RT$ and $(\partial p / \partial T)_v = R/v$.

$$\left(\frac{\partial u}{\partial v}\right)_T = -p + T\frac{R}{v} = -p + p = 0$$

10·2　The Clapeyron equation

As an example of the use of the Maxwell equations in correlating physical properties, we will now derive the Clapeyron equation which indicates clearly certain property relationships during phase changes of a pure substance.

For two phases of a pure substance existing together in equilibrium, pressure and temperature are dependent only on each other. Therefore $(\partial p / \partial v)_T = 0$, so that the general expression

$$\frac{dp}{dT} = \left(\frac{\partial p}{\partial T}\right)_v + \left(\frac{\partial p}{\partial v}\right)_T \frac{dv}{dT}$$

reduces to
$$\frac{dp}{dT} = \left(\frac{\partial p}{\partial T}\right)_v$$

Also, if s' and v' represent the properties of one phase and s'' and v'' those of the other phase,

$$\left(\frac{\partial s}{\partial v}\right)_T = \frac{s'' - s'}{v'' - v'}$$

Thus the third Maxwell equation

$$\left(\frac{\partial p}{\partial T}\right)_v = \left(\frac{\partial s}{\partial v}\right)_T \qquad (10\cdot3)$$

becomes, for the case of two phases of a pure substance coexisting in equilibrium,

$$\frac{dp}{dT} = \frac{s'' - s'}{v'' - v'} \qquad (a)$$

The equation
$$T\,ds = dh - v\,dp \qquad (9\cdot3)$$

for the case of a phase change at constant pressure (and, consequently, at constant temperature) becomes

$$T(s'' - s') = (h'' - h') \qquad (b)$$

The quantity $(h'' - h')$ is the latent heat of the phase transformation. Combining equations (a) and (b),

$$\frac{dp}{dT} = \frac{h'' - h'}{T(v'' - v')} \tag{10.11}$$

This equation is called the Clapeyron equation and is useful because it relates three readily measurable properties: the slope of the saturation

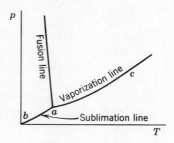

Fig. 10·2   Phase diagram for water.

pressure–temperature line, the latent heat, and the change in volume during a phase transformation. Thus it can be used in checking the consistency of measurements or for obtaining information on one of these properties from data on the other two.

We have noticed earlier (Art. 3·2) that the freezing temperature of water decreases as the pressure increases. We have also noted the unusual behavior of water in expanding as it freezes. Now we see that these two characteristics are related by the Clapeyron equation as it applies to the liquid–solid transformation:

$$\frac{dp}{dT} = \frac{h_f - h_i}{T(v_f - v_i)} = \frac{h_{if}}{T v_{if}}$$

Since $h_{if} > 0$ and for water $v_{if} < 0$, the slope of the fusion line on a phase (pT) diagram must be negative. We already knew this about water from independent observations; but the Clapeyron equation now permits us to generalize: The freezing temperature of *any* substance which expands on freezing is lowered as the pressure is increased.

Because the latent heats h_{fg} and h_{ig} and the volume changes v_{fg} and v_{ig} are all positive for all substances, the sublimation and vaporization curves have positive slopes on the phase diagrams of all substances.

EXAMPLE 10·2.   Show that on a phase diagram for water the sublimation line and the vaporization line do not have the same slope at the triple point (i.e., that in Fig. 10·2 line *a-c* is not simply a continuation of line *b-a*).

Solution. We must prove that dp/dT has different values at the triple point for lines *b-a* and *a-c*. The difference between the slopes can be evaluated by means of the Clapeyron equation as follows:

$$\left(\frac{dp}{dT}\right)_{b-a} - \left(\frac{dp}{dT}\right)_{a-c} = \frac{s_{ig}}{v_{ig}} - \frac{s_{fg}}{v_{fg}}$$

At the triple point, $s_{ig} = s_{if} + s_{fg}$ and $v_{ig} = v_{if} + v_{fg}$, so that the difference in slopes is

$$\left(\frac{dp}{dT}\right)_{b-a} - \left(\frac{dp}{dT}\right)_{a-c} = \frac{(s_{if} + s_{fg})v_{fg} - s_{fg}(v_{if} + v_{fg})}{v_{fg}(v_{if} + v_{fg})}$$

$$= \frac{s_{if}v_{fg} - s_{fg}v_{if}}{v_{fg}(v_{if} + v_{fg})}$$

Since v_{if} is very small compared with v_{fg} while s_{if} is smaller than s_{fg} to a lesser degree, this reduces to approximately

$$\left(\frac{dp}{dT}\right)_{b-a} - \left(\frac{dp}{dT}\right)_{a-c} \approx \frac{s_{if}}{v_{fg}}$$

Both quantities included in the right-hand side are positive, so the slope of the sublimation line is greater than that of the vaporization line at the triple point.

EXAMPLE 10·3.   The following data are obtained from the steam tables.

Saturation Temperature, F	Saturation Pressure, psia	Specific Volume	
		Liquid v_f, cu ft/lb	Vapor v_g, cu ft/lb
195	10.385	0.01660	37.09
196	10.605	0.01661	36.37
197	10.830	0.01661	35.66

Compute the approximate latent heat value at 196 F.

Solution. Assuming a linear variation between temperature and pressure for the temperatures specified, the latent heat may be found from the Clapeyron equation:

$$h_{fg} = v_{fg}T\frac{dp}{dT} = \frac{(36.37 - 0.017)656}{778}\frac{(10.830 - 10.385)144}{(197 - 195)} = 985 \text{ B/lb}$$

The steam table value is 980.4 B/lb.

10·3   The Joule–Thomson coefficient

A useful property of substances which, like specific heats, is defined as a partial derivative is the Joule–Thomson coefficient μ:

$$\mu \equiv \left(\frac{\partial T}{\partial p}\right)_h$$

Its importance stems partly from the fact that it can be measured more accurately and more readily than can certain other useful properties that can be directly related to it.

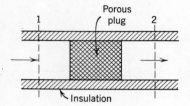

Fig. 10·3 Schematic diagram of apparatus for measuring Joule–Thomson coefficient.

In order to measure the Joule–Thomson coefficient of a liquid or a gas, the fluid is allowed to expand steadily through a porous plug as shown schematically in Fig. 10·3. (The plug may be made of steel wool, for example.) The plug and adjacent piping are thermally insulated; so $q = 0$.

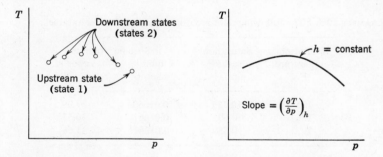

Fig. 10·4 (*a*) Data from Joule–Thomson expansions, and (*b*) the resulting constant-enthalpy line.

There is no work done, and the changes in potential and kinetic energy can be made negligibly small. The first law as applied to any steady-flow system,

$$q + u_1 + \frac{V_1^2}{2g_c} + \frac{g}{g_c} z_1 = u_2 + \frac{V_2^2}{2g_c} + \frac{g}{g_c} z_2 + w + p_2 v_2 - p_1 v_1 \quad (2 \cdot 9)$$

becomes for this system

$$u_1 + p_1 v_1 = u_2 + p_2 v_2$$

or

$$h_1 = h_2$$

The inlet pressure and temperature (p_1 and T_1) are held constant. The downstream pressure is held at several different values successively, and at each of these T_2 is measured. Then T_2 is plotted against p_2 as in Fig. 10·4*a*.

Each of the plotted points represents a state for which the enthalpy is equal to h_1. If enough measurements are made, we can pass a curve through the points and with reasonable confidence label the curve a constant-enthalpy line, (Fig. 10·4b). The slope of this line at any point is $(\partial T/\partial p)_h$, the Joule–Thomson coefficient. In order to obtain the Joule–Thomson coefficient at various pressures and temperatures it is necessary to use several combinations of initial pressure and temperature, each combination providing a different constant h line as shown in Fig. 10·5. Values of the Joule–Thomson coefficient for two gases are given in Fig. 10·6.

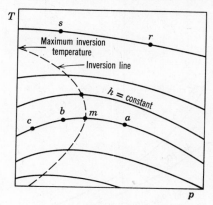

Fig. 10·5   Constant-enthalpy lines and the inversion line for a substance.

The broken line in Fig. 10·5 passes through the maximum temperature points of the constant-enthalpy lines. It is called the *inversion line*. In the region to the left of this line, the Joule–Thomson coefficient is positive; in the region to the right of the inversion line, the Joule–Thomson coefficient is negative. Expansions which occur to the left of the inversion line between states of equal enthalpy (such as from m to b) result in a decrease in temperature, while expansions (such as a to m) occurring to the right of the inversion line result in a temperature rise. Occasionally the Joule–Thomson expansion is used for refrigeration. You can see from Fig. 10·5 that this is possible only when the initial temperature is lower than the maximum inversion temperature or the temperature at which the upper part of the inversion line cuts the axis. For example, starting from point a, a gas will experience an over-all drop in temperature if its pressure is lowered sufficiently—say to point c. A gas initially at point r or s cannot be cooled by a Joule–Thomson expansion (i.e., throttling), no matter how low the downstream pressure is. The maximum inversion temperatures for several gases are given in Table 10·1.

The Joule–Thomson coefficient of a substance can be calculated from the pvT relation and data on c_p. Since entropy is a property and for a pure substance can be a function of p and T, its differential is exact and can be written as

$$ ds = \left(\frac{\partial s}{\partial T}\right)_p dT + \left(\frac{\partial s}{\partial p}\right)_T dp $$

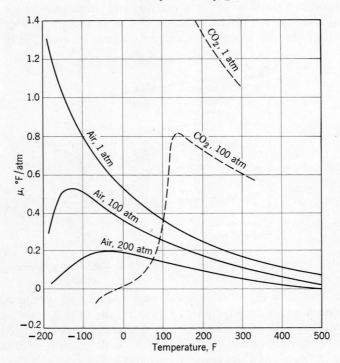

Fig. 10·6 Joule–Thomson coefficients.

TABLE 10·1

Maximum Inversion Temperatures

Gas	Maximum Inversion Temperature, F
Argon	842
Air	628
Helium	Between −415 and −350
Hydrogen	−96
Nitrogen	659

Substituting this value for ds in equation 9·3,

$$dh = T\,ds + v\,dp \qquad (9\cdot3)$$

we have
$$dh = T\left(\frac{\partial s}{\partial T}\right)_p dT + \left[T\left(\frac{\partial s}{\partial p}\right)_T + v\right]dp \qquad (a)$$

We noted in Art. 10·1 that

$$\left(\frac{\partial s}{\partial T}\right)_p = \frac{c_p}{T} \qquad (10\cdot10)$$

and the fourth Maxwell equation is

$$\left(\frac{\partial s}{\partial p}\right)_T = -\left(\frac{\partial v}{\partial T}\right)_p \qquad (10\cdot4)$$

Substituting from equations 10·10 and 10·4 into equation (a),

$$dh = c_p\,dT + \left[v - T\left(\frac{\partial v}{\partial T}\right)_p\right]dp$$

or
$$dT = \frac{dh}{c_p} + \frac{1}{c_p}\left[T\left(\frac{\partial v}{\partial T}\right)_p - v\right]dp \qquad (b)$$

Since $T = f(h, p)$, the differential dT is

$$dT = \left(\frac{\partial T}{\partial h}\right)_p dh + \left(\frac{\partial T}{\partial p}\right)_h dp \qquad (c)$$

Because h and p can be varied independently, the corresponding coefficients in equations (b) and (c) must be equal. Equating the coefficients of dp,

$$\mu = \left(\frac{\partial T}{\partial p}\right)_h = \frac{1}{c_p}\left[T\left(\frac{\partial v}{\partial T}\right)_p - v\right] \qquad (d)$$

By inspection this can be written also as

$$\mu = \frac{T^2}{c_p}\left[\frac{\partial(v/T)}{\partial T}\right]_p \qquad (e)$$

Equations (d) and (e) give μ in terms of the equation of state (pvT relation) and c_p.

For an ideal gas,

$$\mu = \left(\frac{\partial T}{\partial p}\right)_h = \frac{T^2}{c_p}\left[\frac{\partial(v/T)}{\partial T}\right]_p = \frac{T^2}{c_p}\left[\frac{\partial(R/p)}{\partial T}\right]_p = 0$$

The Joule–Thomson coefficient for a substance which follows the equation of state $pv = RT$ is zero, and such a substance experiences no temperature change when it is throttled (i.e., when $\Delta h = 0$).

Another coefficient which is useful and fairly easy to measure is the constant-temperature coefficient c defined by

$$c \equiv \left(\frac{\partial h}{\partial p}\right)_T$$

For its measurement, the fluid is expanded slowly through a porous plug and heat is added or removed (by means of an electric heating coil or a flow of coolant) to maintain the inlet and outlet temperatures equal. The amount of heat required to hold the temperature constant is measured so that enthalpy changes can be computed from the first law.

The general relationship among the partial derivatives of x, y, and z when the three are functionally related is

$$\left(\frac{\partial x}{\partial y}\right)_z\left(\frac{\partial y}{\partial z}\right)_x\left(\frac{\partial z}{\partial x}\right)_y = -1$$

Applying this to h, p, and T, we see the relationship among μ, c, and c_p:

$$\left(\frac{\partial T}{\partial p}\right)_h\left(\frac{\partial p}{\partial h}\right)_T\left(\frac{\partial h}{\partial T}\right)_p = -1$$

$$\frac{\mu c_p}{c} = -1$$

$$\mu = -\frac{c}{c_p} \qquad (f)$$

This is a convenient relationship for checking the consistency of experimental data on these properties.

Equation (f) shows that for an ideal gas, since $\mu = 0$ and c_p is finite,

$$c = \left(\frac{\partial h}{\partial p}\right)_T = 0$$

which shows clearly that the enthalpy of an ideal gas is a function of temperature only.

We shall consider here one other application of the Joule–Thomson effect: its use in relating other temperature scales to the thermodynamic temperature scale. The thermodynamic temperature scale has been defined in terms of the performance of reversible engines, but of course reversible engines cannot be used in practice as thermometers. We have also seen that the ideal-gas temperature scale agrees with the thermodynamic scale; but an ideal gas does not exist and therefore cannot be used in a thermometer, even though the behavior of real gases can be extrapolated to zero pressure at which real gases behave in accordance with the ideal-gas equation of state. The problem is to find a means of relating temperatures on actual, practical thermometers to those on the thermodynamic scale.

The temperature T in equation (d),

$$\left(\frac{\partial T}{\partial p}\right)_h = \frac{1}{c_p}\left[T\left(\frac{\partial v}{\partial T}\right)_p - v\right] \tag{d}$$

is the thermodynamic temperature. Let θ be the temperature indicated by some thermometer such as a real-gas thermometer or a mercury-in-glass thermometer. T and θ are functionally related; that is, for each value of one there is a unique value of the other. In order to make the derivatives in equation (d) involve θ instead of T, we note that

$$\left(\frac{\partial T}{\partial p}\right)_h = \left(\frac{\partial \theta}{\partial p}\right)_h \frac{dT}{d\theta} \qquad \frac{1}{c_p} = \left(\frac{\partial T}{\partial h}\right)_p = \left(\frac{\partial \theta}{\partial h}\right)_p \frac{dT}{d\theta} \qquad \left(\frac{\partial v}{\partial T}\right)_p = \left(\frac{\partial v}{\partial \theta}\right)_p \frac{d\theta}{dT}$$

Making these substitutions in equation (d),

$$\left(\frac{\partial \theta}{\partial p}\right)_h \frac{dT}{d\theta} = \left(\frac{\partial \theta}{\partial h}\right)_p \frac{dT}{d\theta}\left[T\left(\frac{\partial v}{\partial \theta}\right)_p \frac{d\theta}{dT} - v\right]$$

and rearranging gives

$$\frac{dT}{T} = \frac{(\partial v/\partial \theta)_p\, d\theta}{(\partial \theta/\partial p)_h(\partial h/\partial \theta)_p + v}$$

Letting T_0 and θ_0 be corresponding values of T and θ,

$$\int_{T_0}^{T}\frac{dT}{T} = \ln\frac{T}{T_0} = \int_{\theta_0}^{\theta}\frac{(\partial v/\partial \theta)_p\, d\theta}{(\partial \theta/\partial p)_h(\partial h/\partial \theta)_p + v}$$

All terms in the integrand of the right-hand side of this equation can be measured, and the integral is a function of T (and hence θ) only. Therefore, the right-hand side can be integrated numerically or graphically to provide a relationship between θ and T, and this is just what we are looking for. Notice that we placed no restrictions on the substance used for the measurement of the quantities in the integrand. Also notice that the three partial derivatives, $(\partial v/\partial \theta)_p$, $(\partial \theta/\partial p)_h$, and $(\partial h/\partial \theta)_p$, are respectively the coefficient of thermal expansion times v, the Joule–Thomson coefficient, and the specific heat at constant pressure, all defined in terms of θ instead of T. By measuring these three properties of a substance over a range of temperature, we are able to relate our laboratory thermometer readings to thermodynamic temperature scale values.

10·4   General equations for changes in entropy, internal energy, and enthalpy in terms of p, v, T, and specific heats

The entropy of a pure substance may be expressed as a function of T and v so that

$$ds = \left(\frac{\partial s}{\partial T}\right)_v dT + \left(\frac{\partial s}{\partial v}\right)_T dv$$

It has been shown in Art. 10·2 that

$$\left(\frac{\partial s}{\partial T}\right)_v = \frac{c_v}{T} \tag{10·9}$$

and the third Maxwell equation is

$$\left(\frac{\partial s}{\partial v}\right)_T = \left(\frac{\partial p}{\partial T}\right)_v \tag{10·3}$$

Making these two substitutions in the expression for ds gives

$$ds = c_v \frac{dT}{T} + \left(\frac{\partial p}{\partial T}\right)_v dv \tag{10·12}$$

By starting with $s = f(p, T)$, it can be shown in a similar manner that

$$ds = c_p \frac{dT}{T} - \left(\frac{\partial v}{\partial T}\right)_p dp \tag{10·13}$$

Equations 10·12 and 10·13 are general equations for the entropy change of a pure substance. Notice that they can be integrated if specific-heat–temperature and pvT data are available. They are useful in obtaining general expressions for du and dh, as will now be shown.

For any process between equilibrium states of a pure substance,

$$du = T\, ds - p\, dv \tag{9·3}$$

Substituting into this equation the value of ds from equation 10·12,

$$du = c_v\, dT + \left[T\left(\frac{\partial p}{\partial T}\right)_v - p \right] dv \tag{10·14}$$

Substituting into

$$dh = T\, ds + v\, dp \tag{9·3}$$

the value of ds from equation 10·13,

$$dh = c_p\, dT - \left[T\left(\frac{\partial v}{\partial T}\right)_p - v \right] dp \tag{10·15}$$

Equations 10·14 and 10·15 are general equations for du and dh of a pure substance. They too can be integrated if specific-heat–temperature and pvT data are available. Notice that integration of equations 10·12, 10·13, 10·14, and 10·15 can give only *changes* in s, u, and h. Absolute values cannot be obtained from pvT and specific-heat data alone.

EXAMPLE 10·4. Develop an equation for the enthalpy change of a gas which follows the ideal-gas equation of state.

Solution. Differentiating the ideal-gas equation of state,

$$\left(\frac{\partial v}{\partial T}\right)_p = \frac{R}{p}$$

Substituting this value into the general expression for dh,

$$dh = c_p\, dT - \left[T\left(\frac{\partial v}{\partial T}\right)_p - v\right] dp \qquad (10·15)$$

gives

$$dh = c_p\, dT - \left[\frac{RT}{p} - v\right] dp = c_p\, dT - 0$$

Integration gives

$$\Delta h = \int c_p\, dT$$

which can be evaluated if the $c_p T$ relation is known.

EXAMPLE 10·5. Develop an expression for the change in internal energy of a gas which follows van der Waals' equation.

Solution. Differentiating van der Waals' equation,

$$\left(\frac{\partial p}{\partial T}\right)_v = \frac{R_u}{v - b}$$

Substituting this value into the general expression for du,

$$du = c_v\, dT + \left[T\left(\frac{\partial p}{\partial T}\right)_v - p\right] dv \qquad (10·14)$$

gives

$$du = c_v\, dT + \left[\frac{R_u T}{v - b} - p\right] dv$$

Substituting $[R_u T/(v - b) - a/v^2]$ for p gives

$$du = c_v\, dT + \frac{a}{v^2}\, dv$$

Integrating, $\qquad u_2 - u_1 = \int_1^2 c_v \, dT - a\left(\dfrac{1}{v_2} - \dfrac{1}{v_1}\right)$

Knowledge of the $c_v T$ relation is needed for the integration of $\int c_v \, dT$.

EXAMPLE 10·6. It will be assumed that the following p, v, T, and specific-heat data for superheated steam are available from experimental work conducted in the laboratory. From these data, compute the enthalpy and entropy at 600 F and 100 psia.

(1) Specific-volume values for superheated steam in cu ft/lb units.

Pressure, psia	Temperature, F			
	400	500	600	700
1	512.0	571.6	631.2	690.8
2	255.9	285.7	315.5	345.4
4	127.86	142.80	157.73	172.64
5	102.26	114.22	126.16	138.10
6	85.18	95.16	105.12	115.07
8	63.84	71.34	78.82	86.28
10	51.04	57.05	63.03	69.01
20	25.43	28.46	31.47	34.47
40	12.628	14.168	15.688	17.198
60	8.357	9.403	10.427	11.441
80	6.220	7.020	7.797	8.562
100	4.937	5.589	6.218	6.835

(2) The average constant-pressure specific heat for the saturated liquid between 32 and 110 F is approximately 1 B/lb-F.

(3) The latent heat and saturation pressure for a temperature of 110 F are 1031.6 B/lb and 1.275 psia, respectively.

(4) The constant-pressure specific heat values at a pressure of 1.2748 psia for various temperatures follow.

Temperature, F	Specific Heat, B/lb-F
200	0.448
300	0.460
400	0.467
500	0.474
600	0.478

Assume the entropy and enthalpy of the liquid to be zero at 32 F. This will therefore constitute the base condition. At 32 F the saturation pressure is 0.0886 psia. The measured latent heat value h_{fg} at 110 F is 1031.6 B/lb.

Solution. To determine the enthalpy and entropy at 600 F and 100 psia it will be necessary to compute first the changes in these functions between the base state and the final state. Since enthalpy and entropy are both state functions, any path may be chosen between the base and final conditions. The path selected will be such that the data given may be employed in the solution. Hence the path will be divided into four parts:

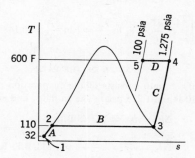

Example 10·6

Part of Path	State Conditions	
	Initial	Final
A	Saturated liquid $t = 32$ F, $p = 0.0886$ psia	Saturated liquid $t = 110$ F, $p = 1.2748$ psia
B	Saturated liquid $t = 110$ F, $p = 1.275$ psia	Saturated vapor $t = 110$ F, $p = 1.275$ psia
C	Saturated vapor $t = 110$ F, $p = 1.275$ psia	Superheated vapor $t = 600$ F, $p = 1.275$ psia
D	Superheated vapor $t = 600$ F, $p = 1.275$ psia	Superheated vapor $t = 600$ F, $p = 100$ psia

The solution will involve first determining the changes in entropy and enthalpy for each part of the path, and then by summation obtaining the total changes.

PART A OF THE PATH

The very first part of the process consists in raising the pressure of the liquid from 0.0886 to 1.2748 psia isentropically. For this part of the path $\Delta s = 0$ and Δh and ΔT are negligibly small. Then the liquid is heated reversibly at constant pressure from 32 to 110 F. For this constant-pressure process the second terms in the general expressions for Δh and Δs,

$$\Delta h = \int c_p \, dT - \int \left[T \left(\frac{\partial v}{\partial T} \right)_p - v \right] dp \tag{10·15}$$

$$\Delta s = \int c_p \frac{dT}{T} - \int \left(\frac{\partial v}{\partial T} \right)_p dp \tag{10·13}$$

become zero, and we have

$$\Delta h_A = \int_{T_1}^{T_2} c_p \, dT = c_p(T_2 - T_1) = 1(570 - 492) = 78.0 \text{ B/lb}$$

$$\Delta s_A = \int_{T_1}^{T_2} c_p \frac{dT}{T} = c_p \ln \frac{T_2}{T_1} = 1 \ln \frac{570}{492} = 0.148 \text{ B/lb-R}$$

PART B OF THE PATH

The second part of the path consists of the evaporation of a saturated liquid to a saturated vapor at 110 F and 1.275 psia. The enthalpy and entropy changes are

$$\Delta h_B = h_{fg} = 1031.6 \text{ B/lb}$$

$$\Delta s_B = \frac{h_{fg}}{T} = \frac{1031.6}{570} = 1.811 \text{ B/lb-R}$$

PART C OF THE PATH

The third step is a constant-pressure heating of a vapor from an initial temperature of 110 F to a final value of 600 F at 1.275 psia. The equations for the enthalpy and entropy changes for this constant-pressure process are

$$\Delta h_C = \int_{570}^{1060} c_p \, dT$$

$$\Delta s_C = \int_{570}^{1060} \frac{c_p \, dT}{T}$$

Usually the values for Δh_C and Δs_C would have to be determined by graphical integration, since the specific heat values may vary considerably with temperature. In this case the values do not vary greatly over the temperature range given; hence an average value of 0.465 will be used. Substituting in the above relation gives

$$\Delta h_C = 0.465(1060 - 570) = 227.6 \text{ B/lb}$$

$$\Delta s_C = 0.465 \ln \tfrac{1060}{570} = 0.289 \text{ B/lb-R}$$

PART D OF THE PATH

During this part of the process the pressure is increased from 1.275 to 100 psia while the temperature remains constant. According to equation 10·13, the entropy change may be expressed by the equation

$$\Delta s_D = -\int_{p_4}^{p_5} \left(\frac{\partial v}{\partial T}\right)_p dp$$

The partial derivative indicates the slope of a curve plotted on a chart of specific volume versus temperature for a given pressure. In general, the value of the integral may be found quickly by means of graphical integration. The first step in the evaluation of the integral is to plot, from the experimental data, a family of specific volume versus temperature curves for various pressure values ranging from 1 to 100 psia. From these curves the slopes for a temperature of 600 F at various pressures may be obtained.

Pressure, psia	Value of $(\partial v/\partial T)_p$ at 600 F, cu ft/lb-R
1	0.59600
2	0.29833
4	0.14926
5	0.11947
6	0.09963
8	0.07480
10	0.05990
20	0.03013
40	0.01523
60	0.01028
80	0.00781
100	0.00633

The value of the integral may be found by plotting the above values for the tangents against the pressure and determining the area under the curve between the pressures of 1.275 and 110 psia. For example, the area was found to be equal to 2.83 cu ft-psia/lb-R. Substituting this value for the integral in the expression for the entropy gives

$$\Delta s_D = -\frac{2.83(144)}{778} = -0.525 \text{ B/lb-R}$$

The enthalpy change for this part of the path may be found by use of equation 10·15, which for a constant-temperature process reduces to

$$\Delta h_D = \int_{p_4}^{p_5} \left[v - T\left(\frac{\partial v}{\partial T}\right)_p \right] dp$$

The value of this integral is determined graphically by plotting values of the term in brackets against the pressure, and measuring the area under the curve between the pressure limits of 1.275 and 100 psia. Values for the term in brackets for several pressures are given in the accompanying table.

Pressure, psia	$T\left(\dfrac{\partial v}{\partial T}\right)_p$, cu ft/lb	$\left[v - T\left(\dfrac{\partial v}{\partial T}\right)_p \right]$, cu ft/lb
1	631.76	−0.56
5	126.64	−0.48
10	63.49	−0.46
20	31.94	−0.47
40	16.14	−0.45
60	10.90	−0.47
80	8.28	−0.48
100	6.71	−0.49

The value of the integral which is equal to the area under the curve is found to be −46.86 cu ft-psia/lb. Hence

$$\Delta h_D = -\frac{46.86(144)}{778} = -8.7 \text{ B/lb}$$

The total changes in enthalpy and entropy for the complete process are

$$\Delta h = h_5 - h_1 = 78.0 + 1031.6 + 227.6 - 8.7 = 1328.5 \text{ B/lb}$$

$$\Delta s = s_5 - s_1 = 0.148 + 1.811 + 0.289 - 0.525 = 1.723 \text{ B/lb-R}$$

Since the initial base values of the enthalpy and entropy were assumed to be zero, the final values are

$$h = 1328.5 \text{ B/lb} \qquad \text{(table value, 1329.1)}$$

and

$$s = 1.723 \text{ B/lb-R} \qquad \text{(table value, 1.758)}$$

The values obtained are in reasonable agreement with the reported table values, in view of the fact that precise calculations were not made.

The values for the enthalpy and entropy being known, other functions such as internal energy and Gibbs function may be calculated directly by use of the general equations.

10·5 Specific heat relations

General equations for the difference between specific heats, $(c_p - c_v)$ and for the ratio of specific heats c_p/c_v will now be derived.

Equating the two general equations for ds (equations 10·12 and 10·13):

$$c_v \frac{dT}{T} + \left(\frac{\partial p}{\partial T}\right)_v dv = c_p \frac{dT}{T} - \left(\frac{\partial v}{\partial T}\right)_p dp$$

Solving for dT,

$$dT = \frac{T(\partial p/\partial T)_v}{c_p - c_v} dv + \frac{T(\partial v/\partial T)_p}{c_p - c_v} dp$$

The temperature may be expressed as a function of v and p. Hence,

$$dT = \left(\frac{\partial T}{\partial v}\right)_p dv + \left(\frac{\partial T}{\partial p}\right)_v dp$$

Equating the coefficients in the last two equations results in the two identical relations

$$\left(\frac{\partial T}{\partial v}\right)_p = \frac{T(\partial p/\partial T)_v}{c_p - c_v} \quad \text{and} \quad \left(\frac{\partial T}{\partial p}\right)_v = \frac{T(\partial v/\partial T)_p}{c_p - c_v}$$

Thus

$$c_p - c_v = T\left(\frac{\partial p}{\partial T}\right)_v \left(\frac{\partial v}{\partial T}\right)_p \tag{10·16}$$

The difference between c_p and c_v can thus be determined for any substance if the equation of state (pvT relation) is known or if the two partial derivatives can be measured. In the case of solids, it is difficult to measure $(\partial p/\partial T)_v$, so a different form of equation 10·16 is desired.

The general relation mentioned earlier,

$$\left(\frac{\partial x}{\partial y}\right)_z \left(\frac{\partial y}{\partial z}\right)_x \left(\frac{\partial z}{\partial x}\right)_y = -1$$

when applied to $f(p, v, T)$ is

$$\left(\frac{\partial p}{\partial T}\right)_v \left(\frac{\partial T}{\partial v}\right)_p \left(\frac{\partial v}{\partial p}\right)_T = -1$$

or

$$\left(\frac{\partial p}{\partial T}\right)_v = -\left(\frac{\partial p}{\partial v}\right)_T \left(\frac{\partial v}{\partial T}\right)_p$$

Making this substitution in equation 10·16,

$$c_p - c_v = -T\left(\frac{\partial p}{\partial v}\right)_T \left(\frac{\partial v}{\partial T}\right)_p^2 \tag{10·17}$$

The coefficient of volume expansion β and the isothermal compressibility κ_T are defined as

$$\beta \equiv \frac{1}{v}\left(\frac{\partial v}{\partial T}\right)_p \quad \text{and} \quad \kappa_T \equiv -\frac{1}{v}\left(\frac{\partial v}{\partial p}\right)_T$$

Making these substitutions in equation 10·17 gives

$$c_p - c_v = \frac{Tv\beta^2}{\kappa_T} \tag{10·17}$$

T, v, and κ_T are always positive, and β^2 is either positive or zero; so c_p can never be less than c_v. When $\beta = 0$ (as for water at 1 atm and about 39 F), $c_p = c_v$. For solids, c_v is difficult to measure, so equation 10·17 is used to calculate c_v from c_p and the other properties.

In order to obtain a general expression for the ratio of the specific heats c_p/c_v, let us combine

$$\frac{c_p}{T} = \left(\frac{\partial s}{\partial T}\right)_p \tag{10·10}$$

and

$$\frac{c_v}{T} = \left(\frac{\partial s}{\partial T}\right)_v \tag{10·9}$$

to give

$$k = \frac{c_p}{c_v} = \frac{(\partial s/\partial T)_p}{(\partial s/\partial T)_v}$$

In order to obtain derivatives which appear in the Maxwell equations, expand both the numerator and the denominator to give

$$k = \frac{c_p}{c_v} = \frac{(\partial s/\partial v)_p (\partial v/\partial T)_p}{(\partial s/\partial p)_v (\partial p/\partial T)_v}$$

Each of the four partial derivatives here appears in one of the Maxwell equations. Substituting for each one from the proper Maxwell equation gives

$$k = \frac{c_p}{c_v} = \frac{-(\partial p/\partial T)_s (\partial s/\partial p)_T}{-(\partial v/\partial T)_s (\partial s/\partial v)_T}$$

$$= \left(\frac{\partial p}{\partial v}\right)_s \left(\frac{\partial v}{\partial p}\right)_T \tag{10·18}$$

If we define isentropic compressibility κ_s by

$$\kappa_s \equiv -\frac{1}{v}\left(\frac{\partial v}{\partial p}\right)_s$$

we have
$$k = \frac{c_p}{c_v} = \frac{\kappa_T}{\kappa_s} \tag{10·18}$$

This relationship holds for gases, liquids, and solids.

Many methods have been developed for obtaining approximate values of the specific heats of substances from other data. A knowledge of some of these is often helpful. In Art. 4·8 it was shown that for monatomic and diatomic gases which can be treated as ideal gases the C_p values are approximately 5 and 7 B/mole-R, respectively, and the C_v values are approximately 3 and 5 B/mole-R, respectively.

Figure 10·7 shows C_v versus temperature for several solid substances. Two things are readily noticed: (1) As temperature increases, C_v approaches a value of about 6 B/mole-R for all the substances, and (2) the curves are approximately the same for all substances except for a temperature scale factor.

The first of these observations was made and reported in 1819 by Dulong and Petit and is sometimes referred to as *the law of Dulong and Petit: For elements in the solid state at high temperatures, the molar specific heat at constant volume is equal to approximately 6 B/mole-R*. There is a question as to what is meant by "high temperature." Figure 10·7 shows that for several solids the Dulong and Petit value is accurate at normal room temperature but that for diamond it is far too high at this temperature. This point was cleared up by Peter Debye who by use of quantum mechanics showed that for all isotropic solids C_v is given very nearly by

$$C_v = 3R_u f\left(\frac{T}{\Theta}\right)$$

where R_u is the universal gas constant (Yes, R_u is used in connection with solids!), Θ is approximately a constant for each substance, and the function

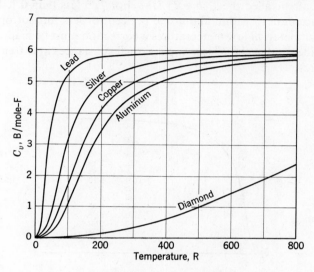

Fig. 10·7 C_v for several solids.

$f(T/\Theta)$ is the same for all substances. A plot of Debye's equation is shown in Fig. 10·8, and values of Θ for several substances are given in Table 10·2.

TABLE 10·2

Debye Constants, Θ

Substance	Θ, R
Lead	158
Mercury	173
Cadmium	302
Sodium	310
Silver	387
Calcium	407
Zinc	423
Copper	567
Aluminum	717
Iron	815
Carbon	3350

Notice that, as T/Θ increases, C_v approaches the Dulong and Petit value of approximately 6 B/mole-R, or more precisely $3R_u$ or 5.96 B/mole-R. As T/Θ approaches zero, Debye's equation becomes

$$C_v \propto T^3$$

and this is often called the *Debye T^3 law*. For T/Θ less than 0.1, Debye's T^3 law is accurate to within about one per cent or less for isotropic non-metals. For metals at low temperatures a correction must be made. There is some evidence that the T^3 law applies to all substances at extremely low temperatures.

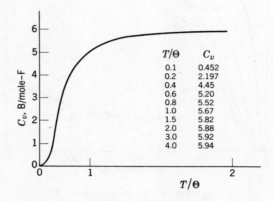

T/Θ	C_v
0.1	0.452
0.2	2.197
0.4	4.45
0.6	5.20
0.8	5.52
1.0	5.67
1.5	5.82
2.0	5.88
3.0	5.92
4.0	5.94

Fig. 10·8 Debye's function.

At very high values of T/Θ, C_v of solids is higher than the 6 B/mole-R given by Debye's equation and by the law of Dulong and Petit. Some isotropic solids have C_v values well over 6 B/mole-R even at fairly low temperatures. Examples are ice with $C_v = 9.0$ B/mole-R at 32 F and the element barium with $C_v = 9.3$ B/mole-R at 70 F. Thus it is apparent that Debye's equation (as well as the law of Dulong and Petit which is the limiting case) must be applied with caution. Nevertheless, it is a convenient means of estimating C_v values, and it is an important step in the development of a complete theory of the solid phase.

Remember that Debye's equation pertains to C_v, not C_p. For solids and liquids, data referred to simply as "specific heat" values are usually C_p (or c_p) values. The difference between C_p and C_v increases as temperature increases, as shown by equation 10·17,

$$C_p - C_v = \frac{T v_N \beta^2}{\kappa_T} \qquad \text{(10·17, molar basis)}$$

Figure 10·9 shows the magnitude of this difference over a wide range of temperature for one solid.

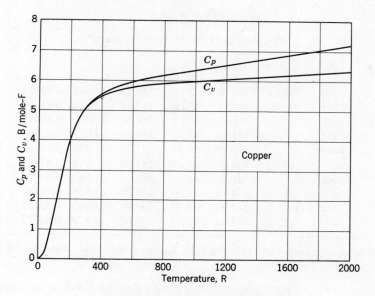

Fig. 10·9 C_p and C_v for copper.

10·6 Ideal-gas property tables

In many engineering applications the behavior of real gases can be adequately represented by the ideal-gas equation of state, $pv = RT$. For any gas which follows this equation of state, changes in internal energy, enthalpy, and entropy for all processes can be calculated from

$$du = c_v \, dT \qquad (4·2)$$

$$dh = c_p \, dT \qquad (4·3)$$

$$ds = \frac{dh}{T} - \frac{v \, dp}{T} = \frac{c_p \, dT}{T} - R \frac{dp}{p} \qquad (9·3, \, 4·3)$$

and c_p and c_v are functions of temperature only. The specific-heat–temperature functions for wide ranges of temperature are generally not simple, however, so in order to avoid laborious computations we use tabulated values of temperature-dependent properties whenever they are available. One valuable collection of ideal-gas properties is the Keenan and Kaye *Gas Tables* for air and certain other gases and gas mixtures.

A greatly abridged version of the air table is given in the appendix as Table A·8, and a sample of the original table is shown below as Table 10·3.

TABLE 10·3

Properties of Air at Low Pressure*

T	t	h	p_r	u	v_r	ϕ
1400	940.3	342.90	42.88	246.93	12.095	0.83604
1401		343.16	43.00	247.12	12.070	0.83623
1402		343.43	43.11	247.32	12.046	0.83641
1403		343.69	43.23	247.51	12.022	0.83660
1404		343.95	43.35	247.70	11.998	0.83679
1405	945.3	344.21	43.47	247.90	11.974	0.83697
1406		344.47	43.58	248.09	11.950	0.83716
1407		344.73	43.70	248.28	11.926	0.83734
1408		345.00	43.82	248.48	11.902	0.83753
1409		345.26	43.94	248.67	11.879	0.83772

* An excerpt from *Gas Tables*, by J. H. Keenan and J. Kaye, John Wiley & Sons, Inc., 1948.

The first two columns give temperatures in degrees Rankine and degrees Fahrenheit. The third and fifth columns are values of h and u, based arbitrarily on $h = 0$ and $u = 0$ at 0 R. Notice that this is a single-argument table, unlike the superheated steam table, for example, in which both pressure and temperature are arguments or independent variables.

Because temperature is the single argument of the air table, only properties which are functions of temperature alone (such as u and h) can be tabulated. Entropy is not a function of temperature alone, so it cannot be tabulated; but for an ideal gas

$$s = f(p, T)$$

can be put in the form

$$s = \phi(T) + \psi(p)$$

Then at least the first term on the right-hand side can be tabulated against temperature. We have seen that for a pure substance in the absence of electricity, magnetism, and surface tension a valuable relationship among properties is

$$T \, ds = dh - v \, dp \tag{9·3}$$

For an ideal gas we can replace dh by $c_p \, dT$ and v by RT/p. Thus

$$s_2 - s_1 = \int_1^2 ds = \int_1^2 \frac{c_p \, dT}{T} - R \int_1^2 \frac{dp}{p}$$

The first term on the right-hand side can be tabulated as a function of temperature only, and the second one can be evaluated from the pressure limits of a process. The symbol ϕ is used for the temperature function which is defined by

$$\phi_2 - \phi_1 \equiv \int_1^2 \frac{c_p \, dT}{T}$$

so that the change in entropy between two states is given by

$$s_2 - s_1 = \phi_2 - \phi_1 - R \ln \frac{p_2}{p_1} \qquad (10\cdot19)$$

Relationships (equations 4·5) between p and v, between v and T, and between p and T were developed in Art. 4·6 for a reversible adiabatic or isentropic process of an ideal gas with constant specific heats. For variable specific heats the relationships are not so simple; so tabulated functions are again used. For an *isentropic process* of an ideal gas we have from equation 10·19

$$s_2 - s_1 = 0 = \phi_2 - \phi_1 - R \ln \frac{p_2}{p_1}$$

Rearranging, we have, for an *isentropic process*,

$$\frac{p_2}{p_1} = \exp\left(\frac{\phi_2 - \phi_1}{R}\right) = \frac{\exp(\phi_2/R)}{\exp(\phi_1/R)} = \frac{f(T_2)}{f(T_1)}$$

This new function of temperature is called *relative pressure** p_r. By definition,

$$p_r \equiv \exp(\phi/R)$$

Then for an *isentropic process* we have

$$\frac{p_2}{p_1} = \frac{p_{r2}}{p_{r1}}$$

Thus a table of p_r versus temperature gives us the pressure–temperature relationship for isentropic processes.

For any two states at the same entropy the ratio of specific volumes can also be expressed as a ratio of temperature functions. For any two states 1 and 2 of an ideal gas,

$$\frac{v_2}{v_1} = \frac{p_1 T_2}{p_2 T_1}$$

---

* Notice that p_r is dimensionless and is not a pressure. The term *relative pressure* is consequently somewhat misleading. Also, be careful not to confuse *relative pressure* p_r with *reduced pressure* p_R.

If the states are at the same entropy,

$$\frac{v_2}{v_1} = \frac{p_1 T_2}{p_2 T_1} = \frac{p_{r1}}{p_{r2}}\frac{T_2}{T_1} = \frac{T_2/p_{r2}}{T_1/p_{r1}} = \frac{\text{function of } T_2}{\text{function of } T_1} \qquad (a)$$

We now define the *relative specific volume*, $v_r \equiv T/p_r$, so that, for an *isentropic process*,

$$\frac{v_2}{v_1} = \frac{v_{r2}}{v_{r1}} \qquad (b)$$

[In the Keenan and Kaye tables, $v_r = RT/144p_r$. This meets the requirement of equations (a) and (b) and is also convenient for certain calculations.]

We have noted that the selection of a temperature at which the enthalpy or internal energy is zero is entirely arbitrary. Also, in the tabulation of ϕ, p_r, and v_r, various additive terms or multipliers may be introduced which have no effect on the use of the table. They must be considered, however, in verifying tabular values by means of defining equations such as $p_r \equiv \exp(\phi/R)$. For example, in the Keenan and Kaye tables for air the p_r value tabulated is the defined p_r times 10^{-10}, and the tabulated ϕ value is the defined ϕ value (with $\phi = 0$ at 0 R) minus 1.0000.

The following examples illustrate the use of the Keenan and Kaye *Gas Tables*.

EXAMPLE 10·7.   Air in a closed rigid tank is initially at 15 psia, 40 F. It is heated until its pressure is 60 psia. The lowest temperature in the surroundings is 40 F. How much of the heat added is available energy?

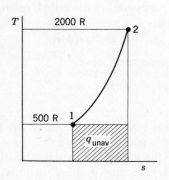

Example 10·7

Solution. The ideal-gas equation of state shows that for a constant-volume process the pressure and absolute temperature are directly proportional to each other. The final temperature is then

$$T_2 = T_1 \frac{p_2}{p_1} = 500\,\frac{60}{15} = 2000 \text{ R}$$

The system under consideration is comprised of the air trapped in the tank. Application of the first law to this closed system and substitution of internal energy values from the Keenan and Kaye table for air gives

$$q = u_2 - u_1 + w = 367.6 - 85.2 + 0 = 282.4 \text{ B/lb}$$

The change in entropy is

$$s_2 - s_1 = \phi_2 - \phi_1 - R \ln \frac{p_2}{p_1} = 0.9320 - 0.5823 - \frac{53.3}{778} \ln \frac{60}{15}$$

$$= 0.255 \text{ B/lb-R}$$

and the amount of heat added which is available energy is

$$q_{av} = q - q_{unav} = q - T_0(s_2 - s_1) = 282.4 - 500(0.255) = 154.9 \text{ B/lb}$$

EXAMPLE 10·8. Air undergoes an isentropic process during which the temperature increases from 500 to 800 R. The initial pressure is 14.7 psia. Compute (a) the final specific volume and (b) the final pressure.

Solution. (a) From the ideal-gas equation of state we can compute the initial specific volume as

$$v_1 = \frac{RT_1}{p_1} = \frac{53.3(500)}{14.7(144)} = 12.6 \text{ cu ft/lb}$$

Then, for this isentropic process we have

$$v_2 = v_1 \frac{v_{r2}}{v_{r1}} = 12.6 \frac{53.63}{174.90} = 3.86 \text{ cu ft/lb}$$

(b) The final pressure for this isentropic process is

$$p_2 = p_1 \frac{p_{r2}}{p_{r1}} = 14.7 \frac{5.526}{1.059} = 76.7 \text{ psia}$$

(Of course, after either p_2 or v_2 is found, the other can be most quickly calculated by means of the ideal-gas equation of state directly. Here we have solved for these quantities in a manner which illustrates the use of both p_r and v_r from the gas tables.)

EXAMPLE 10·9. A turbine expands air isentropically from 5 atm, 1660 R, to a final pressure of 1 atm. The flow rate is 40 lb/sec. Determine the power output.

Solution. We are dealing with a steady-flow system. In order to apply the first law, we must find the enthalpy values at inlet and outlet. The inlet temperature is known; so we can find h_1 immediately from the air table. We find h_2 by first finding p_{r2}.

$$p_{r2} = p_{r1} \frac{p_2}{p_1} = 82.83(\tfrac{1}{5}) = 16.56$$

Corresponding to this value of p_{r2}, we find $h_2 = 262.2$ B/lb. If we neglect changes in kinetic energy, the first law as applied to the steady-flow system for this adiabatic process is

$$\text{Work} = h_1 - h_2 = 411.8 - 262.2 = 149.6 \text{ B/lb}$$

The power output is then

$$P = (\text{work})M = \frac{149.6(40)}{0.707} = 8460 \text{ hp}$$

(The conversion factor in the last step is 0.707 B/sec = 1 hp.)

10.7   Property diagrams

Various property diagrams are used extensively in thermodynamics as aids in analysis and design. Several of these have already been discussed in this book, and you should be familiar with their characteristics. The characteristics of others you should be able to deduce from your knowledge of general physical property relationships. Let us review some of the frequently used property diagrams.

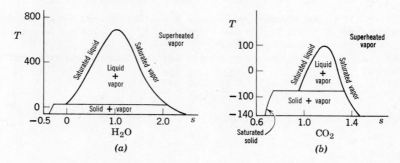

Fig. 10·10 Ts diagrams showing solid, liquid, and vapor states.

The Ts diagram. The outstanding characteristic of the Ts diagram is that for *reversible* processes heat transfer is represented by an area, since $q_{rev} = \int T\,ds$. For *any* process, the unavailable part of the heat transfer can be represented by an area on a Ts diagram, since $q_{unav} = T_0\,\Delta s$. For purposes of analysis, any diagram using entropy as one of its coordinates offers some convenience because for many actual compressions and expansions the corresponding ideal process is an isentropic one. Ts diagrams for water and carbon dioxide are shown in Fig. 10·10 (see also Charts A·1 and A·2 of the appendix). A disadvantage of the Ts diagram is that a convenient scale for showing two- or three-phase regions causes the slopes of constant-pressure and constant-volume lines in the superheat region to be nearly the same.

The hs or Mollier diagram. The hs diagram is used in connection with steam and gas turbines because (1) the ideal process is usually an isentropic one and is therefore easily traced, and (2) Δh values which are used extensively in first-law analyses of turbines are easily scaled or read from this diagram. On an hs diagram for a vapor the constant-pressure lines in the wet region are straight and diverge with increasing quality so that a diagram of moderate size can be read quite accurately in the high quality and superheat regions (see Chart A·3 in the appendix).

The *hs* diagram is convenient for the determination of the quality of a wet vapor from measurements made with a throttling calorimeter as shown in Fig. 10·11. The quality of the wet vapor flowing in the line is to be determined. Measuring the pressure and temperature of the vapor in the line will not suffice because they are dependent on each other and independent of the quality. If a small amount of the vapor is throttled through an orifice to a pressure sufficiently low, it becomes superheated. Then *p* and *T* measurements suffice to determine the state of the vapor in the calorimeter. If the process is adiabatic and the change in kinetic energy is zero,

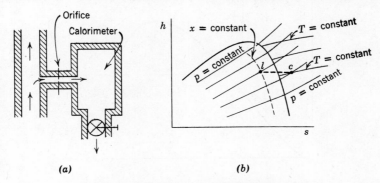

(a)   (b)

Fig. 10·11   Operation of a throttling calorimeter.

the first law applied to the open system formed by the calorimeter and its connecting line gives

$$h_{\text{line}} = h_{\text{calorimeter}}$$

Then from the pressure and enthalpy of the vapor in the line its quality can be determined. The use of the *hs* diagram is shown in Fig. 10·11*b*. From the calorimeter pressure and temperature, point *c* is located. Extending a line horizontally (constant *h*) to its intersection with the line of constant pressure p_l establishes point *l* and the quality x_l which is sought. Notice that this method cannot be used unless the unknown quality is high enough so that the throttling process carries the vapor into the superheat region.

The *ph* diagram. The *ph* diagram is also called a Mollier diagram and is used extensively in refrigeration. Values of Δh can be read or scaled directly from it. Vapor-compression refrigerating machines, such as used in most household refrigerators and air conditioners, operate on a cycle which includes two constant-pressure processes and one throttling process. The simplicity of such a cycle on a *ph* diagram is shown in Fig. 10·12. A *ph* diagram for ammonia is presented in the appendix (Chart A·4).

The *pv* diagram. The *pv* diagram is useful in certain analyses of reversible processes because the quantities $\int p \, dv$ and $\int v \, dp$ are represented by areas on it. It is not a convenient diagram for presenting the properties of both liquid (or solid) and vapor phases of a substance, because the difference between v_f and v_g (except near the critical point) is so much greater than the range of variation of v in the compressed-liquid region. Another disadvantage of the pv diagram is that the slopes of constant-entropy and constant-temperature lines on it in the superheat region are so close together that reading the diagram is difficult.

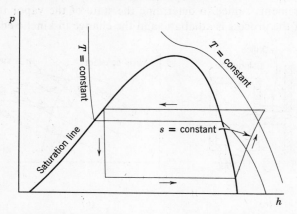

Fig. 10·12 *ph* diagram showing a typical vapor compression refrigeration cycle.

The *hv* diagram. The *hv* diagram is convenient for presenting vapor properties because over a wide range the constant-pressure, constant-temperature, and constant-entropy lines on it make good intersections; that is, their slopes are quite different.* Also, as pointed out in the comments on *hs* and *ph* diagrams, *h* is a convenient coordinate for the purpose of first-law steady-flow analyses. On the *hv* (or *uv*) diagram the triple point is represented by an area.

The stress–strain diagram. The stress–strain diagram used in studying the elastic behavior of solids is generally not thought of as a *thermodynamic* diagram, but one as shown in Fig. 10·13 is the logical one to use in certain thermodynamic analyses. Notice that there are at least two moduli of elasticity: the isothermal modulus and the isentropic modulus.

The above list of diagrams is by no means exhaustive. For one thing, it includes only two-dimensional diagrams, and we have seen in Chapter 3 that three-dimensional ones are occasionally convenient. Also, the

* See, for example, F. O. Ellenwood and C. O. Mackey, *Thermodynamic Charts*, John Wiley & Sons, 2d ed., 1944.

diagrams listed above are for pure substances, but engineers frequently use diagrams (such as the psychrometric chart used in air-conditioning work, for example) which are for mixtures of variable composition. The important thing to remember when selecting diagrams for use in any particular thermodynamic analysis is to use those which are most helpful in that specific instance. If the most helpful ones happen to be unconventional, use them anyway.

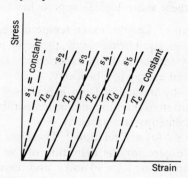

Fig. 10·13 Tensile stress–strain diagram for an elastic substance.

10·8 The rigorous approaches

So far in this book topics have been treated in the following order:

1. Introduction: Undefined terms; definitions, including heat and work (see Chapter 1 for details).

2. The first law: The definition of energy; applications of the first law to various systems (Chapter 2).

3. Physical properties: Phase relationships, tables of properties, the ideal-gas equation of state and specific-heat relationships, real-gas equations of state (Chapters 3, 4, and 5).

4. The second law: Reversibility, the Carnot principle, the thermodynamic temperature scale, the definition of entropy, $T\,ds = du + p\,dv = dh - v\,dp$, the uses of entropy (Chapters 6, 7, 8, and 9).

5. Physical property relationships involving the second law (Chapter 10).

This order was selected for ease of learning. For example, the three chapters on physical properties follow the first-law chapter so that you could practice applying the first law and thereby strengthen your understanding of it before taking up the new material on the second law. Many property relationships depend on the second law, however, so it is necessary to return to the discussion of physical properties after the chapters on the second law.

People who have already studied thermodynamics usually prefer to develop this material in a more direct and perhaps more logical or more rigorous manner, covering all the basic principles which are established by induction (the first and second laws) first before considering the applications which are based on deductions from the basic principles. We have reached a point in this book where you should undertake a thorough review; therefore, because it may help you in making such a review, let us look at an outline of one of these more logical approaches to thermodynamics:

1. The undefined terms: Length, mass, temperature, etc.
2. Definitions: System, equilibrium, state, property, process, heat, work.
3. The first law—by induction from experience: Definition of stored energy, proof that stored energy is a property.
4. The second law—by induction from experience: Reversibility, the Carnot principle, definition of thermodynamic temperature scale, definition of entropy, proof that entropy is a property.
5. Physical properties: (a) pvT relations: These are independent of the first and second laws except for the definition of the temperature scale. (b) Property relations involving u (or e) and s, and therefore depending on the first and second laws. (c) The ideal gas, a hypothetical substance for which it is postulated that $pv = RT$, where T is the thermodynamic temperature.

You must remember that there are many different logical approaches, depending on which terms are selected as undefined, the sequence of definitions, and the manner in which the basic inductions are formulated. It is desirable to organize a science so that it depends on the minimum number of inductive conclusions or basic principles and to state these principles in such a manner that the maximum number of useful deductions can be readily made from them.

10·9 Summary

The Maxwell equations

$$\left(\frac{\partial T}{\partial v}\right)_s = -\left(\frac{\partial p}{\partial s}\right)_v \tag{10·1}$$

$$\left(\frac{\partial T}{\partial p}\right)_s = \left(\frac{\partial v}{\partial s}\right)_p \tag{10·2}$$

$$\left(\frac{\partial p}{\partial T}\right)_v = \left(\frac{\partial s}{\partial v}\right)_T \tag{10·3}$$

$$\left(\frac{\partial v}{\partial T}\right)_p = -\left(\frac{\partial s}{\partial p}\right)_T \tag{10·4}$$

are useful in the correlation of properties of pure substances because they relate entropy to the directly measurable properties pressure, specific volume, and temperature. Many other useful relations can be derived from the four equations

$$du = T\,ds - p\,dv \qquad\qquad (9\cdot3)$$

$$dh = T\,ds + v\,dp \qquad\qquad (9\cdot3)$$

$$da = -p\,dv - s\,dT \qquad\qquad (9\cdot7b)$$

$$dg = v\,dp - s\,dT \qquad\qquad (9\cdot8b)$$

One example of a relation derived from the Maxwell equations is the Clapeyron equation,

$$\frac{dp}{dT} = \frac{h'' - h'}{T(v'' - v')} \qquad\qquad (10\cdot11)$$

which is useful in the study of phase transformations. (The single and double primes denote different phases.)

The importance of the Joule–Thomson coefficient,

$$\mu \equiv \left(\frac{\partial T}{\partial p}\right)_h$$

stems partly from the fact that it can be measured more accurately and more readily than certain other useful properties which are directly related to it.

Another coefficient which is useful and fairly easy to measure is the constant-temperature coefficient which is defined as

$$c \equiv \left(\frac{\partial h}{\partial p}\right)_T$$

The simple relationship among c_p, c, and μ is

$$\mu = -\frac{c}{c_p}$$

General expressions for entropy, internal energy, and enthalpy in terms of pvT and specific-heat data can be derived as

$$ds = c_v\,\frac{dT}{T} + \left(\frac{\partial p}{\partial T}\right)_v dv = c_p\,\frac{dT}{T} - \left(\frac{\partial v}{\partial T}\right)_p dp \qquad (10\cdot12,13)$$

$$du = c_v\,dT + \left[T\left(\frac{\partial p}{\partial T}\right)_v - p\right]dv \qquad (10\cdot14)$$

$$dh = c_p\,dT - \left[T\left(\frac{\partial v}{\partial T}\right)_p - v\right]dp \qquad (10\cdot15)$$

General relations involving c_p and c_v are

$$c_p - c_v = T\left(\frac{\partial p}{\partial T}\right)_v \left(\frac{\partial v}{\partial T}\right)_p \tag{10.16}$$

$$c_p - c_v = -T\left(\frac{\partial p}{\partial v}\right)_T \left(\frac{\partial v}{\partial T}\right)_p^2 = \frac{Tv\beta^2}{\kappa_T} \tag{10.17}$$

$$k = \frac{c_p}{c_v} = \left(\frac{\partial p}{\partial v}\right)_s \left(\frac{\partial v}{\partial p}\right)_T = \frac{\kappa_T}{\kappa_s} \tag{10.18}$$

The laws of Debye and of Dulong and Petit are useful in estimating the specific heats of many solids.

In the tabulation of ideal-gas properties as a function of temperature, three quantities ϕ, p_r (called relative pressure), and v_r (called relative specific volume) are used. ϕ is defined by

$$\phi_2 - \phi_1 \equiv \int_1^2 \frac{c_p \, dT}{T}$$

so that, for any two states 1 and 2 of an ideal gas,

$$s_2 - s_1 = \phi_2 - \phi_1 - R \ln \frac{p_2}{p_1} \tag{10.19}$$

p_r and v_r are so defined that for *isentropic processes only* of an ideal gas

$$\frac{p_{r2}}{p_{r1}} = \frac{p_2}{p_1} \quad \text{and} \quad \frac{v_{r2}}{v_{r1}} = \frac{v_2}{v_1}$$

REFERENCES

10.1 M. W. Zemansky, *Heat and Thermodynamics*, McGraw-Hill Book Co., 4th ed., 1957, chapters 13 and 15.

10.2 V. W. Young, *Basic Thermodynamics*, McGraw-Hill Book Co., 1952, chapter 8.

10.3 J. F. Lee and F. W. Sears, *Thermodynamics*, Addison-Wesley Publishing Co., 1955, chapter 7.

10.4 F. W. Sears, *Thermodynamics, the Kinetic Theory of Gases, and Statistical Mechanics*, Addison-Wesley Publishing Co., 2d ed., 1953, arts. 3-3 and 3-4 and chapter 9.

On the logical approaches to thermodynamics

10.5 J. H. Keenan and A. H. Shapiro, "On the History and Exposition of the Laws of Thermodynamics," *Mechanical Engineering*, vol. 69, 1947, pp. 915–921.

10.6 H. W. Emmons, "Re-examination of Thermodynamic Fundamentals," *Mechanical Engineering*, vol. 72, June 1950, pp. 475–478.

PROBLEMS

10·1 Determine the value of $(\partial s/\partial v)_T$ for air at 10 psia, 40 F.

10·2 Determine $(\partial p/\partial T)_s$ at 11 psia, 480 F, (a) for air, and (b) approximately for steam.

10·3 From the data below on superheated ammonia, determine for ammonia at 90 psia, 70 F, (a) c_p, and (b) the value of Y in the following approximate expression for enthalpy change: $\Delta h = c_p \Delta T + Y \Delta p$.

Pressure,		Temperature, F		
psia		60	70	80
80	h	634.3	640.6	646.7 B/lb
	v	3.812	3.909	4.005 cu ft/lb
90	h	631.8	638.3	644.7
	v	3.353	3.442	3.529
100	h	629.3	636.0	642.6
	v	2.985	3.068	3.149

10·4 Show that the latent heat of vaporization may be expressed as

$$h_{fg} = T \int_{v_f}^{v_g} \left(\frac{\partial p}{\partial T}\right)_v dv$$

10·5 From the data given below, compute the value of h_{fg} for steam at 100 psia, and check the results with the steam-table value.

p Saturation, psia	T Saturation, F	Specific Volume, cu ft/lb	
		v_f	v_g
90	320.27	0.01766	4.896
100	327.81	0.01774	4.432
110	334.77	0.01782	4.049

10·6 From the following data determine the value for the latent heat of Freon 113 at −20 F.

T Saturation, F	p Saturation, psia	Specific Volume, cu ft/lb	
		v_f	v_g
−10	0.6046	0.00959	42.48
−20	0.4288	0.00953	58.61
−30	0.2987	0.00947	82.86

10·7 Compute the amount that the melting-point temperature of ice is lowered for an increase in pressure of 1 atm. The specific volumes of ice and water at 32 F are 0.01747 and 0.01602 cu ft/lb, respectively.

10·8 Ice and water at a pressure and temperature of 0.0886 psia and 32.02 F have the following properties.

Phase	Enthalpy, B/lb	Specific Volume, cu ft/lb
Liquid	0.02	0.01602
Solid	−143.30	0.01747

Assuming that the enthalpy and specific volume are independent of the pressure, compute the melting temperature or equilibrium temperature at 1000 atm.

10·9 Develop the following relation on the basis of the Clapeyron equation, if the vapor in equilibrium with a liquid at a given temperature and pressure behaves as an ideal gas.

$$\frac{d(\ln p)}{dT} = \frac{h_{fg}}{RT^2}$$

10·10 Determine the Joule-Thomson coefficient of a van der Waals gas in terms of a, b, R_u, T, v_N, and C_p.

10·11 Determine the Joule-Thomson coefficient of water at (a) 10 psia, 300 F, and (b) 3000 psia, 750 F.

10·12 Prove that for a van der Waals gas the inversion temperature is given by

$$T = \frac{2a}{bR_u}\left[1 - \frac{b}{v_N}\right]^2$$

10·13 Determine from steam-table data the value of β for water at (a) 10 psia, 300 F, (b) 3000 psia, 750 F, and (c) 3000 psia, 300 F.

10·14 The velocity of sound c in a medium is given by

$$c = \sqrt{g_c\left(\frac{\partial p}{\partial \rho}\right)_s}$$

Determine the velocity of sound in terms of quantities such as g_c, p, v, T, R, k, etc. for (a) an ideal gas, and (b) an incompressible liquid.

10·15 For an ideal gas show that the coefficient of volume expansion is equal to the reciprocal of the absolute temperature.

10·16 For an ideal gas show that the isothermal bulk modulus, $-v(\partial p/\partial v)_T$, is equal to the pressure of the gas.

10·17 Determine the coefficient of volume expansion at 27 C for a gas which obeys the equation of state $p(v_N-b) = R_u T$. Under the conditions stated, v equals 1500 cc/mole and b equals 20 cc/mole.

10·18 Derive an expression for the change in enthalpy for a gas which follows the equation of state $p(v-b) = RT$.

10·19 Establish a relation for the change in enthalpy of a gas which follows the van der Waals equation of state.

10-20 Determine an expression for the change in entropy of a van der Waals gas.

10-21 From equation 10·16 determine the value of $(c_p - c_v)$ for an ideal gas.

10-22 Show that for a reversible adiabatic process of a gas which follows the equation of state $p(v - b) = RT$

$$T(v - b)^{R/c_v} = \text{constant}$$

10-23 Derive the following expression from fundamental relations.

$$\left(\frac{\partial u}{\partial v}\right)_T = T\left(\frac{\partial p}{\partial T}\right)_v - p$$

10-24 Develop the following relation for the Helmholtz function a.

$$a = u + T\left(\frac{\partial a}{\partial T}\right)_v$$

10-25 Derive the following from fundamental relations.

$$\left(\frac{\partial h}{\partial p}\right)_T = v - T\left(\frac{\partial v}{\partial T}\right)_p$$

10-26 Prove the following equality:

$$\left(\frac{\partial c_v}{\partial v}\right)_T = T\left(\frac{\partial^2 p}{\partial T^2}\right)_v$$

10-27 Derive the relation

$$\left(\frac{\partial^2 a}{\partial T^2}\right)_v = -\frac{c_v}{T}$$

10-28 Nitrogen expands reversibly and isothermally in a closed system from 2000 psia, 100 F, to 1000 psia. Determine the heat transfer per pound.

10-29 Starting with the air table values at 600 R and using the specific-heat relation given in Table 4·3, calculate the values of ϕ and h at 2000 R. Compare your results with the tabular values.

10-30 An insulated tank having a volume of 5000 cu ft contains dry air initially at 60 psia, 1000 R. Air flows out through a small nozzle. Determine the state of the air in the tank after one-half the original mass has left. State any assumptions which you make.

10-31 During a constant-pressure heating process, 100 B/lb of heat is added to air initially at 140 F. Determine the final temperature.

10-32 One pound of dry air expands isentropically until the final specific volume is six times the initial value. If the temperature at the start of the process is 3000 R, compute (a) the final temperature, (b) the final enthalpy, and (c) the entropy change.

10-33 Air at 100 psia, 1200 F, enters a nozzle with negligible velocity and expands isentropically to 50 psia. Calculate the exit velocity.

10-34 Air enters a turbine at 50 psia, 1200 F, at a rate of 10 lb/sec and expands isentropically to 14.5 psia. Calculate the work delivered per pound of air. State your assumptions.

10-35 Air enters a gas turbine at 105 psia, 1200 F, and expands adiabatically to 15 psia, 600 F. Neglecting changes in kinetic energy, calculate the work done per pound of air. Is the process reversible?

10·36 In a closed system, air is compressed isentropically from 14.0 psia, 300 F, to 56.5 psia and is then heated reversibly at constant volume until its pressure is 80.6 psia. Sink temperature is 40 F. Using air tables, calculate, per pound of air, (a) the heat added, and (b) the amount of this heat which is unavailable energy.

10·37 It was pointed out in Art. 1·8 that properties may be classified as three types: (1) those which are directly observable, (2) those which can be defined by means of the laws of thermodynamics, and (3) those which are defined as combinations of other properties. Categorize each property in the following list of quantities accordingly: $p, T, u, v, h, s, Q, R, A, U, W, m, g_c, S, c_p, V, G$.

10·38 State the conditions under which each of the following relations is valid:

(a) Work $= \int p \, dV$ (f) Work$_{in} = \int v \, dp + \Delta KE + \Delta PE$

(b) $h_2 - h_1 = c_p(T_2 - T_1)$ (g) $du = c_v \, dT$

(c) $q_{in} + work_{in} = \Delta h + \Delta KE$ (h) $h = u + pv$

(d) $c_p - c_v = R$ (i) $Q = U_2 - U_1 + work$

(e) $\rho_1 A_1 V_1 = \rho_2 A_2 V_2$ (j) $pv^k = constant$

10·39 State the conditions under which each of the following relations is valid:

(a) $du = T \, ds - p \, dv$ (g) $Q_{unav} = T_0 \Delta S$

(b) $\Delta S_{system} = 0$ (h) $\Delta S = \int \dfrac{\delta Q}{T}$

(c) $\Delta S_{isolated\ system} = 0$ (i) $\left(\dfrac{\partial T}{\partial s}\right)_v = \dfrac{T}{c_v}$

(d) $\Delta S_{universe} = 0$ (j) $\oint dx = 0$

(e) $\dfrac{Q_1}{Q_2} = \dfrac{T_1}{T_2}$

(f) $\left(\dfrac{\partial h}{\partial s}\right)_p = T$

10·40 State in not more than two pages which parts of Chapters 1 through 10 you believe you have a sound understanding of and which parts you are weakest in, giving as well as you can the reasons why any parts have caused difficulty.

CHAPTER 11

Availability and Irreversibility

The second law limits the extent to which heat can be converted into work by any continuously operating device. Work can always be converted completely and continuously into heat. These two facts lead to the conclusion that work is a more valuable form of energy than heat. Because work is a valuable form of energy, an engineer is often concerned with either increasing the work output of systems (such as engines, turbines, or entire power plants) or decreasing the work input to other systems (such as pumps, compressors, and refrigerators). An important question is, therefore, "What is the maximum amount of work which can be obtained when a system passes from one state to another?" The first law tells us how much change in stored energy results when a system goes from one state to another, but the second law is needed to tell us how much work can be obtained.

This chapter deals with the calculation of the maximum amount of work obtainable and the evaluation of the effects of irreversibility.

11·1 Maximum work

In this chapter we will frequently refer to the *atmosphere*, so let us establish the meaning of this term. We have defined a system as any region in space within prescribed boundaries. We have defined the surroundings as everything outside the system boundary. For almost all thermodynamic systems one part of the surroundings is an atmosphere of uniform pressure and temperature. This atmosphere is so large in comparison with the system that its pressure and temperature are not changed by any process of the system. The atmosphere does influence the behavior of the system, however. The atmosphere is only part of the surroundings. In Fig. 11·1, for example, the system is the gas in the cylinder, and important parts of the surroundings in addition to the atmosphere are the energy reservoir at T_R and the coil spring. The system exchanges work with the spring and heat with the energy reservoir. Whenever the system changes volume it either does work on the atmosphere (as well as on the spring) or the atmosphere does work on it, so that the total work done by the system is equal to that delivered to systems other than the atmosphere plus that done on the atmosphere.

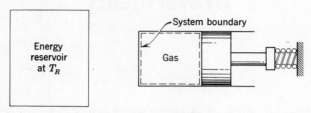

Fig. 11·1   System and surroundings.

Let us determine the maximum amount of work which can be done by a system which goes from one specified state to another while exchanging heat only with the atmosphere. To be general, let us consider an open system as shown in Fig. 11·2 which for some infinitesimal change has a mass δm_1 entering and a mass δm_2 leaving. The special cases of a closed system and of a steady-flow system can be developed later from this general approach. The first law applied to this system for an infinitesimal change is

$$\delta Q - \delta W + (e_1 + p_1 v_1)\,\delta m_1 - (e_2 + p_2 v_2)\,\delta m_2 = dE \qquad (2\cdot 8c)$$

For specified end states and specified flows into and out of the system, the first law can give us *only the difference* $(Q-W)$, and many different values of Q and W are possible. We must use the second law to answer the question: For specified end states, specified flows into and out of the system, and heat exchange only with the atmosphere, what is the maximum amount of work obtainable? We will permit the use of auxiliary devices in producing this maximum work only if they operate cyclically so that they experience no permanent change. The first thing we find as we study this problem is that the maximum work can be done by means of an externally reversible process, as shown by the following reasoning: Consider a system as shown in Fig. 11·2 which exchanges heat only with the atmosphere, has specified amounts of mass in specified states crossing its boundaries, and passes from a state i to a state f. *Suppose* that under these conditions some process A can occur which results in more work output W_A than some externally reversible process R between the same end states. (This is our hypothesis.) Let this process A occur. Then return the system to state i by the reverse of the reversible process R. During this reverse process those parts of the surroundings which exchanged mass with the system during process A are also returned to their initial states. The amount of work done on the system during the reverse process is W_R which (by our hypothesis) is smaller in magnitude than W_A. Thus for the cycle of the system from state i to state f and back to state i there is a net work output of $(W_A - W_R)$, heat has been exchanged only with the atmosphere, and there have been

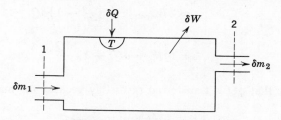

Fig. 11·2   Open system.

no other effects in the surroundings. This is a violation of the second law. Therefore, our hypothesis is false. *Conclusion:* For a specified change in state and specified mass exchange with the surroundings, a system exchanging heat only with the atmosphere produces the maximum work by means of an externally reversible process. We can also conclude that all externally reversible processes conducted under the same conditions result in the same work output.

For the system shown in Fig. 11·2, let T be the temperature of that part of the system where heat enters or leaves. (Remember that for an open system in general T may vary from point to point throughout the system.) T_0 is the temperature of the atmosphere. Heat cannot be transferred reversibly directly between the system and the atmosphere because in general there is a finite difference between T and T_0, but a transfer of heat can be accomplished reversibly by means of an externally reversible engine (such as a Carnot engine) interposed between the system and the atmosphere. This arrangement is shown in Fig. 11·3. Let δQ be the heat added to the system. The heat entering the engine from the atmosphere is δQ_0. For the externally reversible engine,

$$\frac{\delta Q}{T} = \frac{\delta Q_0}{T_0}$$

and
$$\delta W_{\text{eng}} = \delta Q_0 - \delta Q = \left(\frac{T_0}{T} - 1\right)\delta Q$$

(Notice that δW_{eng} is positive whether $T < T_0$ or $T > T_0$. When $T < T_0$, heat enters the system so that δQ is positive. Then both δQ and $(T_0/T - 1)$ are positive, so that their product δW_{eng} is positive. When $T > T_0$, heat leaves the system so that δQ is negative. $(T_0/T-1)$ is also negative so that their product δW_{eng} is positive.) The maximum amount of work that can be obtained then is

$$\delta W_{max} = \delta W_{system} + \delta W_{eng}$$

$$= \delta W_{system} + \left(\frac{T_0}{T} - 1\right)\delta Q$$

$$= (\delta W - \delta Q) + T_0 \frac{\delta Q}{T}$$

Remember that δQ is transferred reversibly because for maximum work

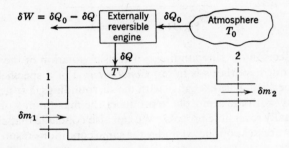

Fig. 11·3   Reversible heat transfer between system and atmosphere.

the system must undergo an externally reversible process. By the first law, for the open system,

$$\delta W - \delta Q = -dE_\sigma + (e_1 + p_1v_1)\,\delta m_1 - (e_2 + p_2v_2)\,\delta m_2 \qquad (2\cdot8c)$$

Also, for an open system we have shown that

$$\left(\frac{\delta Q}{T}\right)_{rev} = dS_\sigma - s_1\,\delta m_1 + s_2\,\delta m_2 \qquad (9\cdot1b)$$

Making these two substitutions from equations $2\cdot8c$ and $9\cdot1b$ in the expression for δW_{max} and collecting terms, we have

$$\delta W_{max} = -d(E - T_0S)_\sigma + (e_1 + p_1v_1 - T_0s_1)\,\delta m_1$$

$$-(e_2 + p_2v_2 - T_0s_2)\,\delta m_2 \qquad (11\cdot1)$$

Now consider the case in which the system exchanges heat with some reservoir at a temperature T_R as well as with the atmosphere. Let the reservoir exchange no mass with the surroundings. Applying equation

11·1 to the combination of the open system and the reservoir, and denoting properties of the reservoir by the subscript R,

$$\delta W_{max} = -d(E - T_0 S)_\sigma - d(E - T_0 S)_R$$
$$+ (e_1 + p_1 v_1 - T_0 s_1)\, \delta m_1 - (e_2 + p_2 v_2 - T_0 s_2)\, \delta m_2 \quad (a)$$

An energy reservoir is usually considered to undergo only internally reversible changes and to do no work. Thus the first law applied to the reservoir, with δQ_R being the heat transferred *to* the system, is

$$\delta Q_R = -dE_R \qquad (b)$$

Then we have for the second term on the right-hand side of equation (a)

$$-dE_R + T_0\, dS_R = \delta Q_R + T_0\, dS_R \qquad (c)$$

But for a reversible process of the reservoir

$$dS_R = -\frac{\delta Q_R}{T_R}$$

(The minus sign is required because δQ_R is heat transferred *to* the system *from* the reservoir.) Then equation (c) becomes

$$-dE_R + T_0\, dS_R = \delta Q_R - T_0 \frac{\delta Q_R}{T_R} = \delta Q_R\left(1 - \frac{T_0}{T_R}\right)$$

and substitution of this into equation (a) and rearrangement gives

$$\delta W_{max} = -d(E - T_0 S)_\sigma + (e_1 + p_1 v_1 - T_0 s_1)\, \delta m_1$$
$$- (e_2 + p_2 v_2 - T_0 s_2)\, \delta m_2 + \delta Q_R\left(1 - \frac{T_0}{T_R}\right) \quad (11·2)$$

This is the expression for the maximum work which can be obtained from an open system which exchanges heat only with the atmosphere at T_0 and an energy reservoir at T_R.

Equation 11·2 can be readily simplified for the case of a closed system or the case of steady flow. For a *closed system*, $\delta m_1 = \delta m_2 = 0$, and

$$\delta W_{max} = -d(E - T_0 S)_\sigma + \delta Q_R\left(1 - \frac{T_0}{T_R}\right) \qquad (11·3a)$$

For a change from state i to state f,

$$W_{max} = (E_i - T_0 S_i) - (E_f - T_0 S_f) + Q_R\left(1 - \frac{T_0}{T_R}\right) \qquad (11·3b)$$

Under *steady-flow* conditions, $dE_\sigma = 0$, $dS_\sigma = 0$, and $\delta m_1 = \delta m_2 = \delta m$.

Then

$$\delta W_{\max} = [(e_1 + p_1v_1 - T_0s_1) - (e_2 + p_2v_2 - T_0s_2)]\, \delta m + \delta Q_R\left(1 - \frac{T_0}{T_R}\right)$$

$$(11\cdot4a)$$

Per unit mass of fluid entering at section 1 and leaving at section 2,

$$w_{\max} = (e_1 + p_1v_1 - T_0s_1) - (e_2 + p_2v_2 - T_0s_2) + q_R\left(1 - \frac{T_0}{T_R}\right)$$

$$(11\cdot4b)$$

Recall that in the absence of electrical, magnetic, and surface tension effects

$$e = u + \frac{V^2}{2g_c} + \frac{g}{g_c}z$$

EXAMPLE 11·1. A tank with a volume of 12 cu ft is evacuated. Atmospheric air outside the tank is at 14.0 psia, 70 F. What is the maximum possible amount of work that can be done by allowing atmospheric air to enter the tank and come to equilibrium with the atmosphere?

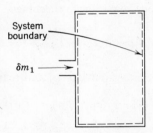

Example 11·1

Solution. For any open system which exchanges heat only with the atmosphere,

$$\delta W_{\max} = -d(E - T_0S)_\sigma + (e_1 + p_1v_1 - T_0s_1)\, \delta m_1 - (e_2 + p_2v_2 - T_0s_2)\, \delta m_2 \quad (11\cdot1)$$

In this case, $\delta m_2 = 0$. All the air which enters the tank crosses the open-system boundary at T_0 and p_0 with negligible kinetic energy, so that the properties of the mass δm_1 are constant and equal to those of the atmosphere. (If the kinetic energy of the mass crossing the system boundary is appreciable, then the pressure and temperature of it are lower than p_0 and T_0. Application of the first law to fluid flowing between some stagnant part of the atmosphere and the system boundary then shows that $h_0 = h_1 + V_1^2/2g_c$, so that any kinetic energy possessed by the fluid at section 1 is balanced by a decrease in h_1 below h_0.) Thus the equation above can be readily integrated to give

$$W_{\max} = (E_i - T_0S_i) - (E_f - T_0S_f) + (e_0 + p_0v_0 - T_0s_0)(m_f - m_i)$$

where the subscripts i and f denote initial and final conditions in the tank. E_i, S_i, and m_i are each zero because there is initially nothing in the tank; so we can simplify the last equation to

$$W_{max} = 0 - (E_f - T_0 S_f) + (e_0 + p_0 v_0 - T_0 s_0) m_f$$
$$= -e_f m_f + T_0 s_f m_f + e_0 m_f + p_0 v_0 m_f - T_0 s_0 m_f$$

The gas finally in the tank comes to equilibrium with the atmosphere and is at rest; so $p_f = p_0$, $T_f = T_0$ and therefore $e_f = e_0$, $s_f = s_0$, and $v_f = v_0$.

$$W_{max} = p_0 v_0 m_f = p_0 V_{tank} = 14.0(144)12 = 24,192 \text{ ft-lb}$$

(Notice that the mechanism for producing this work is entirely unspecified. No matter what devices are used, however, more work than 24,192 ft-lb cannot be obtained from the interaction of this system and the atmosphere.)

EXAMPLE 11·2. Steam enters a steady-flow system at 100 psia, 500 F, with negligible velocity and leaves at 15 psia, 240 F, with a velocity of 500 fps. The flow rate is 8000 lb/hr. Heat is exchanged only with the surrounding atmosphere at 60 F. Determine the maximum possible power output.

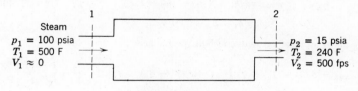

Example 11·2

Solution. For a steady-flow system exchanging heat only with the atmosphere, the maximum work is

$$w_{max} = (e_1 + p_1 v_1 - T_0 s_1) - (e_2 + p_2 v_2 - T_0 s_2) \qquad (11·4, \text{ simplified})$$

In this case, changes in potential energy can be neglected. Initial kinetic energy is negligible; so $e_1 = u_1$ and $e_1 + p_1 v_1 = u_1 + p_1 v_1 = h_1$. At the outlet, $e_2 = u_2 + V_2^2/2g_c$, so that $e_2 + p_2 v_2 = h_2 + V_2^2/2g_c$. The equation above becomes

$$w_{max} = (h_1 - T_0 s_1) - \left(h_2 + \frac{V_2^2}{2g_c} - T_0 s_2 \right) = h_1 - h_2 - T_0(s_1 - s_2) - \frac{V_2^2}{2g_c}$$

Obtaining property values from the steam tables,

$$w_{max} = 1279.1 - 1164.1 - 520(1.7085 - 1.7742) - \frac{(500)^2}{50,000} = 144.2 \text{ B/lb}$$

The maximum possible power output is then

$$P_{max} = M w_{max} = \frac{8000(144.2)}{2545} = 453 \text{ hp}$$

(Notice again that the mechanism for producing this much power is unspecified, but, no matter what devices are used, this power output cannot be exceeded. An actual machine operating with the specified end conditions will produce less power on account of irreversibilities.)

EXAMPLE 11·3.   Air is compressed steadily from 14.0 psia, 60 F (conditions of the atmosphere) to 70.0 psia, 120 F, by a compressor which is cooled only by atmospheric air.   Neglect kinetic energy changes, and determine the minimum work required per pound of air.

Air
$p_1 = 14.0$ psia
$T_1 = 60$ F

Compressor

$p_2 = 70.0$ psia
$T_2 = 120$ F

Example 11·3

Solution.   For this compression process, $w_{max} < 0$ because work must be done *on* the air.   Then $-w_{max}$ = minimum w_{in}.   For example, if we find that $w_{max} = -10$ units, this means that $w = -11$ units is possible but $w = -9$ units is impossible and that the minimum work input is 10 units.   We calculate w_{max} for this steady-flow process (with $\Delta KE = \Delta PE = 0$) by

$$w_{max} = (h_1 - T_0 s_1) - (h_2 - T_0 s_2) \qquad \text{(11·4, simplified)}$$

$$= h_1 - h_2 - T_0(s_1 - s_2)$$

Treating air as an ideal gas with constant specific heats,

$$w_{max} = c_p(T_1 - T_2) - T_0 \int_2^1 ds = c_p(T_1 - T_2) - T_0\left[\int_2^1 \frac{dh}{T} - \int_2^1 \frac{v\,dp}{T} \right]$$

$$= c_p(T_1 - T_2) - T_0\left[\int_2^1 c_p \frac{dT}{T} - R \int_2^1 \frac{dp}{p} \right]$$

$$= c_p(T_1 - T_2) - T_0\left[c_p \ln \frac{T_1}{T_2} - R \ln \frac{p_1}{p_2} \right]$$

$$= 0.24(60 - 120) - 520\left[0.24 \ln \frac{520}{580} - \frac{53.3}{778} \ln \frac{14}{70} \right]$$

$$= -14.4 - 520[-0.0262 + 0.1104] = -58.2 \text{ B/lb}$$

Since $w_{max} = -58.2$ B/lb, $w \leq -58.2$ B/lb or $w_{in} \geq 58.2$ B/lb.   Thus the minimum work input is 58.2 B/lb.

11·2   Availability

In the preceding article we have seen how to calculate the maximum work obtainable from a system which goes from one specified state to another while exchanging heat only with the atmosphere and other constant-temperature energy reservoirs.   As noted earlier, some of the work done by a system may be done on the atmosphere and may consequently serve no useful purpose.   Also, the atmosphere does work on any system which decreases in volume.   For example, consider a gas at a pressure lower than atmospheric trapped in a cylinder which has a weight-less (or very light) piston at the bottom with atmospheric pressure acting upward on it. Several weights also hang from the piston to hold it stationary. If the weights are removed in small increments, the piston rises, and the pressure of the gas increases. Work is thus done on the gas in the cylinder and on the weights which are being lifted. Notice that for the gas in the cylinder $W < 0$, but that for the combination of the gas in the cylinder and the atmosphere $W > 0$.

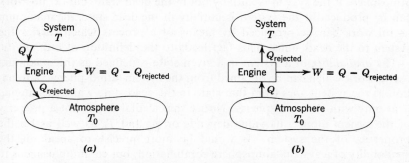

Fig. 11·4 Obtaining work by transfer of heat between system and atmosphere, whether (a) $T > T_0$ or (b) $T < T_0$.

Useful work is defined as the work done by a system exclusive of that done on the atmosphere. If p_0 is the uniform and constant pressure of the atmosphere and V_i and V_f are the initial and final volumes of a system,

$$W_{\text{useful}} = W - p_0(V_f - V_i)$$

In the case described in the preceding paragraph, $V_f < V_i$; so $W_{\text{useful}} > W$, where W is the work done by the system.

An important question is: For a given initial state of a system which exchanges heat only with the atmosphere, what is the final state to which the system must go in order for the maximum useful work to be produced by the combination of the system and the atmosphere? The answer is that the maximum possible amount of useful work can be done if the system goes to a state in which its pressure and temperature equal those of the atmosphere. This answer is supported by the following reasoning: Let the atmosphere be at a pressure p_0 and a temperature T_0. If the system temperature T is different from T_0, work can always be produced by transferring heat from either the system or the atmosphere, whichever is at the higher temperature, to a heat engine which operates cyclically, produces work, and rejects heat to the lower-temperature region, either the atmosphere or the system. The cases of $T > T_0$ and $T < T_0$ are both shown schematically in Fig. 11·4. In both cases, the temperature of the system approaches T_0 as work is done. When $T = T_0$, no work can be obtained in this manner. However, even when $T = T_0$, work can be obtained if $p \neq p_0$ by letting the system change in volume until $p = p_0$. When $T = T_0$ and $p = p_0$, no work can be produced by interaction of the system and the atmosphere. They are in equilibrium with each other, and the system is said to be in the *dead state*. (The stored energy of the system in the dead state is designated as E_0 and is not necessarily zero.) Since (1) work can always be produced by the interaction of a system and the atmosphere if the system is initially not in the dead state, but (2) no work can be produced if the system is initially in the dead state, the maximum useful work can be produced by means of a process which carries the system to the dead state. This fact leads to the definition of *availability*.

The *availability* of a system in a given state is defined as the maximum useful work which can be obtained from the system–atmosphere combination as the system goes from that state to the dead state while exchanging heat only with the atmosphere. Notice that availability is not a property of the system alone; its value depends on p_0 and T_0 as well as on the properties of the system. It would be more precise to speak of the availability of a system–atmosphere combination, but common usage is to refer simply to the availability of the system.

Since we have seen in the preceding article how to calculate maximum work for any two end states and heat exchange only with the atmosphere, we can readily calculate availability by letting the final state be the dead state and subtracting the work done by the system on the atmosphere.

The availability of a *closed system* is given the symbol Φ (and $\phi = \Phi/m$) and is given by

$$
\begin{aligned}
\Phi_1 &= W_{\text{max useful, } 1-0} = W_{\text{max, } 1-0} - p_0(V_0 - V_1) \\
&= (E_1 - T_0 S_1) - (E_0 - T_0 S_0) - p_0(V_0 - V_1) \\
&= (E_1 + p_0 V_1 - T_0 S_1) - (E_0 + p_0 V_0 - T_0 S_0) \qquad (11\cdot5a)
\end{aligned}
$$

where the subscript 0 denotes properties of the system when in the dead state. Since useful work can always be obtained if a closed system is in a state other than the dead state, $\Phi \geq 0$ for all states. Notice that the maximum useful work obtainable from a closed system which exchanges heat only with the atmosphere as it passes from state 1 to state 2 is given by the decrease in Φ:

$$
\begin{aligned}
W_{\text{max useful}} &= -\Delta\Phi = \Phi_1 - \Phi_2 \\
&= [(E_1 + p_0 V_1 - T_0 S_1) - (E_0 + p_0 V_0 - T_0 S_0)] \\
&\quad - [(E_2 + p_0 V_2 - T_0 S_2) - (E_0 + p_0 V_0 - T_0 S_0)] \\
&= (E_1 + p_0 V_1 - T_0 S_1) - (E_2 + p_0 V_2 - T_0 S_2) \qquad (11\cdot5b)
\end{aligned}
$$

Since $W_{\text{max useful}} = -\Delta\Phi$, it follows that the useful work actually produced by a closed system exchanging heat only with the atmosphere is given by

$$W_{\text{useful}} \leq -\Delta\Phi \qquad (11\cdot5c)$$

If the system also receives heat Q_R from an energy reservoir at T_R, we have, from equation 11·3,

$$W_{\text{max useful}} = -\Delta\Phi + Q_R\left(1 - \frac{T_0}{T_R}\right) \qquad (11\cdot5d)$$

It can easily be shown that the availability Φ of a closed system can be increased only by doing work on the system or by transferring heat to it from a body at a temperature other than T_0.

The availability of a *steadily flowing* fluid is the maximum work which can be obtained as the fluid goes reversibly to the dead state while exchanging heat only with the atmosphere. Since the volume of a steady-flow system does not change, there is no concern with work done on or by the atmosphere. In the dead state the fluid is at p_0 and T_0 and is also at rest, $V = 0$. We call the availability of the steadily flowing fluid *stream availability* Y (and $y = Y/m$), to distinguish it from the availability of a closed system Φ (or ϕ). Thus, from equation 11·4,

$$y_1 = w_{\text{max}} = (e_1 + p_1v_1 - T_0s_1) - (e_0 + p_0v_0 - T_0s_0) \qquad (11\cdot6a)$$

In the absence of electrical, magnetic, and surface tension effects,

$$e = u + \frac{V^2}{2g_c} + \frac{g}{g_c}z \quad \text{and} \quad e + pv = h + \frac{V^2}{2g_c} + \frac{g}{g_c}z$$

Thus $\quad y_1 = \left(h_1 + \dfrac{V_1^2}{2g_c} + \dfrac{g}{g_c}z_1 - T_0s_1\right) - \left(h_0 + \dfrac{g}{g_c}z_0 - T_0s_0\right) \qquad (11\cdot6b)$

In availability calculations it is often convenient to use the *Darrieus function* which is defined as $b \equiv h - T_0s$. For any given temperature of the atmosphere, b is a property of a substance. Thus

$$y_1 = \left(b_1 + \frac{V_1^2}{2g_c} + \frac{g}{g_c}z_1\right) - \left(b_0 + \frac{g}{g_c}z_0\right) \qquad (11\cdot6c)$$

and, for a change from state 1 to state 2,

$$w_{\text{max}} = -\Delta y = y_1 - y_2 = \left(b_1 + \frac{V_1^2}{2g_c} + \frac{g}{g_c}z_1\right) - \left(b_2 + \frac{V_2^2}{2g_c} + \frac{g}{g_c}z_2\right)$$

$$(11\cdot6d)$$

Stream availability y is often called simply the availability of a flowing fluid, but it must be remembered that for a fluid which is part of a flowing stream the availability is y and not ϕ.

For a steadily flowing fluid which goes from one state to another while exchanging heat only with the atmosphere, the maximum work obtainable per unit mass is $-\Delta y$. If the fluid also receives heat in the amount q_R per unit mass from an energy reservoir at T_R, the maximum work which can be obtained per unit mass is

$$w_{max} = -\Delta y + \left(1 - \frac{T_0}{T_R}\right)q_R \qquad (11 \cdot 6e)$$

It can easily be shown that the stream availability y of a flowing fluid can be increased only by doing work on the fluid or transferring heat to it from a body at a temperature other than T_0.

EXAMPLE 11·4.   A turbine exhausts 60,000 lb of steam per hour at 1.0 in. of mercury absolute, 94 per cent quality, with a velocity of 450 fps. Atmospheric pressure and temperature are 14.0 psia and 60 F. How much power can be obtained from this steam?

Solution.   The maximum work which can be obtained per pound of this exhaust steam is its stream availability,

$$w_{max} = y = \left(b + \frac{V^2}{2g_c} + \frac{g}{g_c}z\right) - \left(b_0 + \frac{g}{g_c}z_0\right) \qquad (11 \cdot 6c)$$

Noting that gravitational effects are negligible and that $b \equiv h - T_0 s$,

$$w_{max} = y = h - T_0 s + \frac{V^2}{2g_c} - (h_0 - T_0 s_0) \qquad (a)$$

Water in the dead state of 14.0 psia, 60 F, is a compressed liquid. For such a low pressure, the enthalpy and entropy of compressed liquid are very nearly equal to those of saturated liquid at the same temperature. The pertinent properties are obtained from the steam tables as

$$h = h_f + xh_{fg} = 47.05 + 0.94(1049.2) = 1033.3 \text{ B/lb}$$
$$s = s_f + xs_{fg} = 0.0914 + 0.94(1.9473) = 1.9219 \text{ B/lb-R}$$
$$h_0 = h_{f,60F} = 28.06 \text{ B/lb}$$
$$s_0 = s_{f,60F} = 0.0555 \text{ B/lb-R}$$

Making these substitutions in equation (a),

$$w_{max} = y = 1033.3 - 520(1.9219) + \frac{(450)^2}{50,000} - 28.06 + 520(0.0555)$$
$$= 38.1 \text{ B/lb}$$
$$P_{max} = Mw_{max} = \frac{60,000(38.1)}{2545} = 899 \text{ hp}$$

(Notice that this figure is obtained without reference to any specific means for obtaining power from the exhaust steam.)

EXAMPLE 11·5.   Suppose that steam enters the turbine of Example 11·4 at 100 psia, 500 F, with negligible velocity and that the turbine is well insulated. From the specified end conditions, determine the maximum power, and compare it with the actual power output.

Solution. The maximum work per pound is equal to the decrease in stream avail-ability y between inlet (section 1) and outlet (section 2). y_2 has been determined in Example 11·4. Obtaining property values from the steam tables, we calculate y_1:

$$y_1 = h_1 - T_0 s_1 - (h_0 - T_0 s_0)$$
$$= 1279.1 - 520(1.7085) - [28.06 - 520(0.0555)] = 391.4 \text{ B/lb}$$

The maximum work for the specified end conditions and heat exchange only with the atmosphere is

$$w_{max} = y_1 - y_2 = 391.4 - 38.1 = 353.3 \text{ B/lb}$$

and
$$P_{max} = M w_{max} = \frac{60,000(353.3)}{2545} = 8330 \text{ hp}$$

The actual work output can be obtained by application of the first law to the steady-flow system:

$$w = h_1 - h_2 - \frac{V_2^2}{2g_c} + q = 1279.1 - 1033.3 - \frac{(450)^2}{50,000} + 0$$

$$= 241.7 \text{ B/lb}$$

and
$$P = Mw = \frac{60,000(241.7)}{2545} = 5690 \text{ hp}$$

(The following article discusses the significance of the difference between the maximum work or power and the actual work or power.)

11·3 Irreversibility

A reversible process is defined as a process such that, after it has occurred, both the system and all the surroundings can be returned to their initial states. An irreversible process always produces some effects which cannot be undone; so it is impossible to restore both the system and all the surroundings to their initial states after an irreversible process has occurred. The total energy of the system and its surroundings remains constant (in accordance with the first law), but one result of an irreversible process is a decrease in the amount of energy which can be converted into work. A quantitative evaluation of irreversibility can be made in terms of this decrease in the amount of energy which can be converted into work. Consider a system which exchanges heat only with the surrounding atmosphere. For a process in which no work is done, the decrease in the amount of useful work which can be done is simply the decrease in availability. If, however, some work is done during the process, then some of the decrease in availability is compensated for by the work actually done. With this line of reasoning in mind, let us define the irreversibility I of *any* process as

$$I \equiv W_{max} - W \tag{11·7a}$$

W in this equation is the work actually produced. During the process, heat may be exchanged with various energy reservoirs as well as with the atmosphere. W_{max} is the maximum work for a process which (1) is between the same end states as the actual process, (2) involves the same amounts of heat exchange with the various energy reservoirs, and (3) involves heat exchange with the atmosphere also if necessary. Since the

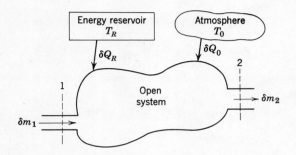

Fig. 11·5 Open system.

work done on the atmosphere, $p_0(V_f - V_i)$, depends only on the end states of a process, it is the same for a maximum work process and for any other process between the same states. If we subtract this quantity from each term on the right-hand side of equation 11·7a, we have

$$I = W_{max\ useful} - W_{useful} \qquad (11\cdot7b)$$

where W_{max} and W of course refer to the maximum work and the work actually done by the system. Notice that the definition of irreversibility I given above is *not* restricted to systems that exchange heat only with the atmosphere. Following the usual convention, the symbol i is used for irreversibility per unit mass, I/m.

Irreversibility I is not a property. It is not a characteristic of a system. For any process, however, it can be evaluated from end states of the system *and the surroundings* as we shall now demonstrate.

Consider an open system as shown in Fig. 11·5. The properties of the system are denoted by the subscript σ; δm_1 is the mass entering the system, δm_2 is the mass leaving the system, and δQ_R is the amount of heat transferred to the system from an energy reservoir at a temperature T_R. δQ_R can be either positive or negative. For such a system, an expression for δW_{max} is

$$\delta W_{max} = -d(E - T_0 S)_\sigma + (e_1 + p_1 v_1 - T_0 s_1)\,\delta m_1$$

$$- (e_2 + p_2 v_2 - T_0 s_2)\,\delta m_2 + \delta Q_R\left(1 - \frac{T_0}{T_R}\right) \quad (11\cdot2)$$

and application of the first law gives the following expression for δW:

$$\delta W = \delta Q - dE + (e_1 + p_1 v_1)\, \delta m_1 - (e_2 + p_2 v_2)\, \delta m_2 \qquad (2 \cdot 8c)$$

Making these two substitutions in the expression above for I (equation 11·7) and collecting terms, we have

$$\delta I = \delta W_{\max} - \delta W = T_0\, dS_\sigma - T_0 s_1\, \delta m_1 + T_0 s_2\, \delta m_2$$
$$+ \delta Q_R - T_0 \frac{\delta Q_R}{T_R} - \delta Q \qquad (a)$$

Since δQ is the total heat transferred to the system and δQ_R is the heat transferred from the energy reservoir to the system,

$$\delta Q - \delta Q_R = \delta Q_0$$

where δQ_0 is the heat transferred from the atmosphere to the system. As long as the atmosphere experiences no internal irreversibilities (mixing, friction, turbulence, etc.), $-\delta Q_0 = T_0\, dS_{\text{atm}}$. (The minus sign is needed because δQ is heat transferred *from* the atmosphere *to* the system.) In the same manner, $-\delta Q_R/T_R = dS_R$. Making these substitutions in equation (a) and collecting terms,

$$\delta I = T_0(dS_\sigma - s_1\, \delta m_1 + s_2\, \delta m_2 + dS_R + dS_{\text{atm}}) \qquad (b)$$

This equation can be readily simplified for the cases of closed systems ($\delta m_1 = \delta m_2 = 0$) and steady-flow systems ($dS_\sigma = 0$; $\delta m_1 = \delta m_2$). The quantity ($s_2\, \delta m_2 - s_1\, \delta m_1$) is the entropy change of those parts of the surroundings which exchange mass with the open system. Therefore, the last four terms in the parentheses of equation (b) comprise dS of the surroundings. (Those parts of the surroundings which exchange work with the system can operate reversibly and adiabatically, and hence for them $dS = 0$. Of course, these systems *may* operate irreversibly, but such irreversibility in no way influences the behavior of the system, atmosphere, or energy reservoir.) Thus equation (b) can be rewritten as

$$\delta I = T_0(dS_\sigma + dS_{\text{surr}}) \qquad (11 \cdot 8a)$$

and, since $T_0 = $ constant,

$$I = T_0(\Delta S_\sigma + \Delta S_{\text{surr}}) \qquad (11 \cdot 8a)$$

$$= T_0\, \Delta S_{\text{isolated system}} \qquad (11 \cdot 8b)$$

This last form is quite general because an isolated system can always be formed by including within a single boundary everything that affects a system during a process.

From equation 11·8b and the increase of entropy principle, we conclude that, for all processes,

$$I \geq 0$$

where the equality holds only for reversible processes. For a *reversible* process, $W = W_{max}$, and both the system and the surroundings can be returned to their initial states. Therefore, there is no decrease in the amount of energy which can be converted into work, and it is reasonable to have $I = 0$.

For any irreversible process, $W < W_{max}$; so even without reference to equation 11·8b and the increase of entropy principle we see that $I > 0$. An irreversible process cannot be completely undone; it always results in some permanent change in the system or the surroundings. Before an irreversible process occurs, a system and its surroundings are in states such that a certain amount of their energy can be converted into work. After the irreversible process occurs, the system and surroundings are in states such that a smaller fraction of their energy can be converted into work; and this decrease in the amount of energy (stored in the system and surroundings) which can be converted into work is equal to I. I is sometimes called "energy made unavailable" because it is the decrease in the amount of energy which is "available" for conversion into work.

Consider a closed system which changes from state 1 to state 2 while exchanging heat with only the atmosphere at T_0. The maximum useful work is given by

$$W_{\text{max useful}} = \Phi_1 - \Phi_2 \qquad (11 \cdot 5c)$$

so that $I = W_{\text{max useful}} - W_{\text{useful}} = \Phi_1 - \Phi_2 - W_{\text{useful}}$

By definition Φ_1 is the maximum amount of useful work that can be obtained by the interaction of the system initially at state 1 and the atmosphere. Φ_2 has the same significance for state 2. If useful work is done during the process, it could lift a body or compress a spring so that energy in the amount W_{useful} is stored and can be reconverted into work. Thus, after the process has occurred, the total amount of useful work obtainable is $(\Phi_2 + W_{\text{useful}})$. Thus,

$$I = \Phi_1 - (\Phi_2 + W_{\text{useful}})$$

$$= \begin{bmatrix} \text{maximum useful work} \\ \text{initially obtainable} \end{bmatrix} - \begin{bmatrix} \text{maximum useful work} \\ \text{finally obtainable} \end{bmatrix}$$

$$= \text{decrease in maximum useful work obtainable}$$

It can readily be shown that this interpretation of I is valid for both open and closed systems and for cases of heat exchange with energy reservoirs other than the atmosphere.

EXAMPLE 11·6.   One-half pound of nitrogen initially at 40 psia, 90 F, is in an insulated tank. An impeller inside the tank is turned by an external motor until the pressure is 48 psia. Determine the irreversibility of this process if the surrounding atmosphere is at 14.0 psia, 90 F.

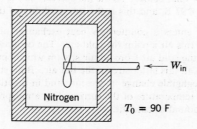

W_{in}

Nitrogen

$T_0 = 90$ F

Example 11·6

Solution.

$$I = T_0 \, \Delta S_{\text{isolated system}} = T_0(\Delta S_{\text{system}} + \Delta S_{\text{surr}})$$

Since there is no change in entropy *of the surroundings* for this adiabatic process of a closed system,

$$I = T_0 \, \Delta S_{\text{system}} = T_0 m \int_1^2 ds = T_0 m \int_1^2 \left(\frac{du}{T} + p \, \frac{dv}{T}\right)$$

$$= T_0 m \int_1^2 \frac{c_v \, dT}{T} + 0 = T_0 m c_v \ln \frac{T_2}{T_1} = T_0 m c_v \ln \frac{p_2}{p_1}$$

$$= 550(0.5)0.178 \ln \tfrac{48}{40} = 8.92 \text{ B}$$

Alternative Solution.

$$I = W_{\max} - W$$

For this adiabatic process of a closed system, $W_{\max} = (E_1 - T_0 S_1) - (E_2 - T_0 S_2)$, and application of the first law gives $W = E_1 - E_2$; so

$$I = (E_1 - T_0 S_1) - (E_2 - T_0 S_2) - (E_1 - E_2) = T_0(S_2 - S_1)$$

From this point the solution is the same as the one presented above.

Discussion.   The problem was solved without calculating $\Delta \Phi$ or W_{useful}. For discussion purposes, let us calculate these.

$$T_2 = T_1 \frac{p_2}{p_1} = 550 \tfrac{48}{40} = 660 \text{ R}$$

$$W_{\text{useful}} = W - p_0(V_2 - V_1) = E_1 - E_2 + Q - p_0(V_2 - V_1)$$
$$= U_1 - U_2 + 0 - 0 = mc_v(T_1 - T_2) = 0.5(0.178)(550 - 660)$$
$$= -9.79 \text{ B}$$

$$\Delta \Phi = \Phi_2 - \Phi_1 = (E_2 + p_0 V_2 - T_0 S_2) - (E_1 + p_0 V_1 - T_0 S_1)$$
$$= E_2 - E_1 - T_0(S_2 - S_1)$$
$$= 9.79 - 8.92 = 0.87 \text{ B}$$

Now we see that by means of the impeller 9.79 B of work was done on the system but the availability of the system (and atmosphere) increased by only 0.87 B. That is, only 0.87 B more useful work can be obtained from a process which starts at state 2 than can be obtained from one which starts at state 1. The surroundings can now (after the process) supply 9.79 B less work than before; so the net *decrease* in the amount of work obtainable is $(9.79-0.87) = 8.92$ B, and this is the irreversibility of the process.

EXAMPLE 11·7.   Air enters a counterflow heat exchanger at 75 psia, 90 F, and is heated to 220 F. Call this air stream the cold air. The cold air flow rate is 0.8 lb/sec. Heat is transferred to the cold air from an air stream which enters at 14.2 psia, 400 F, and leaves at 200 F. Call this latter stream the hot air. Both streams pass through the heat exchanger with negligible change in pressure and in kinetic energy. There are no stray heat losses. The temperature of the surrounding atmosphere is 65 F. Determine the irreversibility per pound of cold air.

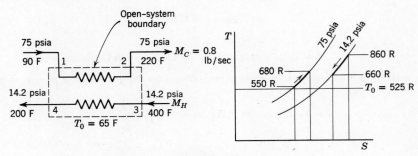

Example 11·7

Solution.   For any process of any system, $I = T_0(\Delta S_\sigma + \Delta S_{\text{surr}})$. Consider the entire heat exchanger as the system. See the sketch. Since it is a steady-flow system, $\Delta S_\sigma = 0$. In order to evaluate ΔS_{surr} per pound of cold air, we must determine the mass ratio of hot air to cold air. The system operates adiabatically (remember that we are taking the entire heat exchanger as the system), there is no work done, and there is no change in kinetic energy; so the first law gives us

$$M_C(h_2 - h_1) = M_H(h_3 - h_4)$$

$$\frac{M_H}{M_C} = \frac{h_2 - h_1}{h_3 - h_4}$$

For the small temperature ranges involved, c_p is nearly constant so that $\Delta h = c_p \, \Delta T$. From Table 4·2, we have mean values of c_p of 0.241^- B/lb-F between 90 and 220 F and 0.243 B/lb-F between 200 and 400 F. As a reasonable approximation, let us use $c_p = 0.241$ B/lb-F for both streams, so that

$$\frac{M_H}{M_C} = \frac{h_2 - h_1}{h_3 - h_4} = \frac{c_p(T_2 - T_1)}{c_p(T_3 - T_4)} = \frac{220 - 90}{400 - 200} = 0.65 \; \frac{\text{lb hot air}}{\text{lb cold air}}$$

Then $$\dot{I} = T_0 \, \Delta \dot{S}_{\text{surr}} = T_0[M_C(s_2 - s_1) + M_H(s_4 - s_3)] \qquad (11·8)$$

Per pound of cold air this is

$$i = \frac{\dot{I}}{M_C} = \frac{T_0 \, \Delta \dot{S}_{\text{surr}}}{M_C} = T_0\left[(s_2 - s_1) + \frac{M_H}{M_c}(s_4 - s_3)\right]$$

For a constant-pressure process, the important relationship among properties $T\,ds = dh - v\,dp$ simplifies to $T\,ds = dh$, so that $ds = dh/T$. For an ideal gas, $dh = c_p\,dT$, so that $ds = c_p\,dT/T$, and we have

$$i = T_0\left(\int_1^2 \frac{c_p\,dT}{T} + \frac{M_H}{M_C}\int_3^4 \frac{c_p\,dT}{T}\right)$$

Again assuming that the c_p values are constant and the same,

$$i = T_0 c_p\left[\ln\frac{T_2}{T_1} + \frac{M_H}{M_C}\ln\frac{T_4}{T_3}\right] = 525(0.241)[\ln\tfrac{680}{550} + 0.65\ln\tfrac{660}{860}]$$

$$= 525(0.241)[0.202 - 0.181] = 2.66 \approx 2.7 \text{ B/lb cold air}$$

(It is well to compare the value of i with the heat transferred per pound of cold air, $h_2 - h_1 = c_p(T_2 - T_1) = 0.241(220 - 90) = 31.3$ B/lb.) (Investigation will show that the maximum work which can be done by the two streams of air passing between the same end states and exchanging heat only with the atmosphere is 2.7 B/lb of cold air. No work was done in the heat exchanger, so that, after the heat exchange process is completed, 2.7 B/lb of cold air less work can be produced by the interaction of the streams with the atmosphere than could have been produced beforehand. This is the meaning of irreversibility.)

EXAMPLE 11·8.   A steam turbine operates adiabatically with a flow rate of 60,000 lb/hr entering at 100 psia, 500 F, with negligible velocity and leaving at 1.0 in. mercury absolute, 94 per cent quality, with a velocity of 450 fps. The surrounding atmosphere is at 14.0 psia, 60 F. Determine the time rate of irreversibility.

Solution.   Per pound of steam,

$$i = T_0[\Delta s_\sigma + \Delta s_{\text{surr}}] \qquad\qquad (11\cdot8)$$

$$= T_0[0 + s_2 - s_1]$$

Taking the entropy values from the steam tables (as in Examples 11·4 and 11·5),

$$i = 520[1.9219 - 1.7085] = 111 \text{ B/lb}$$

$$I = Mi = 60,000(111) = 6,660,000 \text{ B/hr} = 2620 \text{ hp}$$

It is seen that the time rate of irreversibility calculated here is the same (within the accuracy to be expected from slide-rule calculations) as the difference between $P_{\max}$ and P calculated in Example 11·5: $(8330 - 5690) = 2640$ hp.

EXAMPLE 11·9.   Saturated liquid ammonia enters an expansion valve at 150 psia and leaves at 30 psia. The inlet and outlet areas of the valve are such that there is no change in kinetic energy. While passing through the valve, the ammonia receives 10 B/lb of heat from an energy reservoir at 30 F. The atmosphere is at 60 F. Determine the irreversibility of the process.

Solution.   Per pound of ammonia flowing,

$$i = \frac{I}{m} = \frac{T_0}{m}[\Delta S_\sigma + \Delta S_{\text{surr}}]$$

For this steady-flow system, $\Delta S_\sigma = 0$. The entropy of the surroundings changes by an amount $m(s_2 - s_1)$ on account of the mass transfer between the system and the surroundings and also by an amount $-Q_R/T_R$, where Q_R is heat transfer *to* the system *from* the reservoir at T_R. Thus

$$i = \frac{T_0}{m}\left[0 + m(s_2 - s_1) - \frac{Q_R}{T_R}\right] = T_0\left[s_2 - s_1 - \frac{q_R}{T_R}\right]$$

s_1 can be read directly from ammonia tables as s_f at 150 psia. We know the pressure at the outlet, but we must know one other independent property in order to determine the

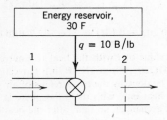

Example 11·9

state and the value of s_2. (Since at the outlet the ammonia is a liquid–vapor mixture, we can find its temperature immediately from the saturated ammonia table, but we must still find another property because p and T are not independent for two-phase mixtures.) By application of the first law we can find h_2 because the first law applied to a steady-flow system,

$$h_2 = h_1 + q - w - \Delta KE - \Delta PE \qquad (2·9)$$

in this case reduces to

$$h_2 = h_1 + q = 130.6 + 10 = 140.6 \text{ B/lb}$$

Now we can find the quality at the outlet,

$$x_2 = \frac{h_2 - h_f}{h_{fg}} = \frac{140.6 - 42.3}{569.3} = 0.173^-$$

and

$$s_2 = s_f + x_2 s_{fg} = 0.0962 + (0.173)(1.2402) = 0.311 \text{ B/lb-R}$$

Now we can calculate i by substituting numerical values in the equation developed above,

$$i = T_0\left[s_2 - s_1 - \frac{q_R}{T_R}\right] = 520\left[0.311 - 0.2724 - \frac{10}{500}\right]$$

$$= 9.36 \text{ B/lb}$$

11·4 Availability accounting

The first law is the basis for energy balances or energy accounting. The second law makes possible availability accounting which gives information which cannot be obtained from the first law. Let us look at an illustration of the fact that comparisons of energy quantities alone may be quite inconclusive if not actually misleading. Consider two streams of water, one (designated A) at 20 psia, 200 F, flowing at a rate of 1000 lb/hr, and the other (designated B) at 20 psia, 88 F, flowing at a rate of 3000 lb/hr. Let the kinetic energy in each case be negligibly small. The lowest temperature in the surroundings is 32 F. These streams flowing into a system would deliver equal amounts of energy because $M_A h_A = 1000(167.99) = 167,990$ B/hr $\approx 168,000$ B/hr, and $M_B h_B = 3000(56.0) = 168,000$ B/hr. The stream availabilities are quite different, however, because

$$M_A b_A = M_A[h_A - T_0 s_A] = 1000[167.99 - 492(0.2938)] = 23,400 \text{ B/hr}$$

and

$$M_B b_B = M_B[h_B - T_0 s_B] = 3000[56.0 - 492(0.1079)] = 8730 \text{ B/hr}$$

Therefore, even though the streams deliver equal energy to a system, much more power can be obtained from stream A than from stream B.

Availability accounting involves the determination of availability changes for each of a series of processes. Comparison of the work done with the availability change gives a measure of the degree to which each process approaches the ideal. It thereby indicates where efforts spent in improving performance are likely to be most fruitful. The following simple example illustrates the general procedure.

EXAMPLE 11·10. A flow diagram and a Ts diagram are shown for a steady-flow power plant using air as a working medium. Both the compressor and the turbine operate adiabatically. Changes in kinetic energy are negligible. Pressures and temperatures are shown on the diagram. The heat-addition process is externally reversible. Atmospheric temperature T_0 is 60 F. For this problem assume that the specific heats are constant, and assign values of $h_0 = 0$ and $s_0 = 0$. Make an energy accounting and an availability accounting for the air flowing through the plant.

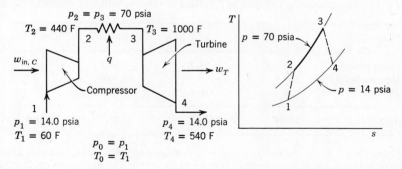

Example 11·10

Solution. Since for an ideal gas with constant specific heats $\Delta h = c_p \, \Delta T$, the enthalpy at any temperature T is given by $h = h_0 + c_p(T - T_0)$. Assigning $h_0 = 0$ when $T_0 = 60$ F and using $c_p = 0.24$ B/lb-F, the enthalpies at points 1, 2, 3, and 4 are determined and tabulated. Also for an ideal gas with constant specific heats $s_x - s_0 = \int_0^x \frac{dh}{T} - \int_0^x \frac{v\,dp}{T} = c_p \ln \frac{T_x}{T_0} - R \ln \frac{p_x}{p_0}$, so that s values are next calculated and tabulated. For use in availability accounting we also tabulate $b = h - T_0 s$.

Point	p, psia	T, F	h, B/lb	s, B/lb-R	b, B/lb
1	14	60	0	0	0
2	70	440	91.2	0.0213	80.1
3	70	1000	225.6	0.1376	154.1
4	14	540	115.2	0.1569	33.7

Application of the first law to each of the three pieces of equipment gives

$$\text{Work}_{in,c} = h_2 - h_1 = 91.2 - 0 = 91.2 \text{ B/lb}$$

$$q = h_3 - h_2 = 225.6 - 91.2 = 134.4 \text{ B/lb}$$

$$\text{Work}_T = h_3 - h_4 = 225.6 - 115.2 = 110.4 \text{ B/lb}$$

The energy balance on the plant is then as follows:

Energy in		Energy out	
With entering fluid,	$h_1 = 0$	With leaving fluid,	$h_4 = 115.2$ B/lb
Compressor work$_{in}$	$w_{in} = 91.2$ B/lb	Turbine work,	$w = 110.4$
Heat	$q = 134.4$		
		Total	225.6 B/lb
Total	$= 225.6$ B/lb		

Since changes in kinetic and potential energy are being neglected, the changes in stream availability equal the changes in the Darrieus function, or $\Delta y = \Delta b = \Delta(h - T_0 s)$. An availability accounting can then be tabulated as follows, with all quantities in B/lb.

Process	q	w	$\Delta y = \Delta b$	$i = T_0 \Delta s$
Compressor	0	−91.2	80.1	11.1
Heat exchanger	134.4	0	74.0	0
Turbine	0	110.4	−120.4	10
Summation	134.4	19.2	33.7	21.1

Conclusions. From the energy balance or first-law analysis we conclude that 134.4 B/lb of heat was added, a net work of $(110.4 - 91.2) = 19.2$ B/lb was produced, and the exhaust gas carried away (as $u + pv$, or h) 115.2 B/lb more energy than the entering stream brought in. The extent of possible improvements in the cycle cannot be determined directly from the energy balance. From the availability accounting or second-law analysis, we see that the 19.2 B/lb net work output was produced from an increase of stream availability in the heat exchanger of 74.0 B/lb. The second-law analysis also shows why more work was not obtained: The air left the plant with a stream availability of 33.7 B/lb more than the incoming fluid, and the irreversibilities in the compressor and turbine cost 11.1 and 10.0 B/lb of stream availability, respectively. Thus the 74.0 B/lb increase in availability in the heat exchanger is disposed of as follows:

Work	19.2 B/lb
Leaving stream availability	33.7
Compressor irreversibility	11.1
Turbine irreversibility	10.0
Total	74.0 B/lb

11·5 Summary

The behavior of most systems is influenced by an *atmosphere* of uniform and constant pressure and temperature which is one part of the surroundings. The pressure and temperature of the atmosphere are designated as p_0 and T_0. T_0, the temperature of the atmosphere, is also called the *sink temperature* or the *lowest temperature in the surroundings* because there is usually no energy reservoir available at a lower temperature for supplying or receiving large quantities of heat.

For a general open system which exchanges heat only with the atmosphere at T_0 and with another energy reservoir at T_R, the maximum work for any infinitesimal change in the system is

$$\delta W_{\max} = -d(E - T_0 S)_\sigma + (e_1 + p_1 v_1 - T_0 s_1)\, \delta m_1$$
$$- (e_2 + p_2 v_2 - T_0 s_2)\, \delta m_2 + \delta Q_R\left(1 - \frac{T_0}{T_R}\right) \quad (11\cdot2)$$

where δm_1 is the mass entering, δm_2 is the mass leaving, δQ_R is the heat transferred to the system from the reservoir at T_R, and the subscript σ designates properties of the system. This equation can be readily simplified for a *closed system* as follows:

$$\delta W_{\max} = -d(E - T_0 S) + \delta Q_R\left(1 - \frac{T_0}{T_R}\right) \quad (11\cdot3a)$$

and for a *steady-flow system* as follows:

$$\delta W_{\max} = [(e_1 + p_1 v_1 - T_0 s_1) - (e_2 + p_2 v_2 - T_0 s_2)]\, \delta m + \delta Q_R\left(1 - \frac{T_0}{T_R}\right)$$
$$(11\cdot4a)$$

Useful work is defined as the work done by a system exclusive of that done on the atmosphere. If p_0 is the pressure of the atmosphere and V_i and V_f are the initial and final volumes of a system,

$$W_{\text{useful}} = W - p_0(V_f - V_i)$$

The greatest possible amount of work can be obtained from a system which exchanges heat only with the atmosphere if the system goes to a final state in which it is in equilibrium with the atmosphere. The pressure and temperature of the system will then be p_0 and T_0, and the system is said to be in the *dead state*.

The *availability* of a system in any state is defined as the maximum useful work which can be obtained as the system goes from that state to the dead state while exchanging heat only with the atmosphere. Availability is not a property of the system alone; its value depends on p_0 and T_0 as well as on the properties of the system.

The availability of a *closed system* is given the symbol Φ (and $\phi = \Phi/m$) and is given by

$$\Phi_1 = W_{\text{max useful, 1-0}} = (E_1 + p_0V_1 - T_0S_1) - (E_0 + p_0V_0 - T_0S_0) \quad (11 \cdot 5a)$$

where the subscript 0 denotes properties of the system when in the dead state. The maximum useful work obtainable from a closed system which exchanges heat only with the atmosphere as it passes from state 1 to state 2 is given by the decrease in Φ:

$$\begin{aligned} W_{\text{max useful}} &= -\Delta\Phi = \Phi_1 - \Phi_2 \\ &= [(E_1 + p_0V_1 - T_0S_1) - (E_0 + p_0V_0 - T_0S_0)] \\ &\quad - [(E_2 + p_0V_2 - T_0S_2) - (E_0 + p_0V_0 - T_0S_0)] \\ &= (E_1 + p_0V_1 - T_0S_1) - (E_2 + p_0V_2 - T_0S_2) \quad (11 \cdot 5b) \end{aligned}$$

Since useful work can always be obtained if a closed system is in a state other than the dead state, $\Phi \geq 0$ for all states. If the system also receives heat Q_R from an energy reservoir at T_R,

$$W_{\text{max useful}} = -\Delta\Phi + Q_R\left(1 - \frac{T_0}{T_R}\right) \quad (11 \cdot 5d)$$

The availability of a *steadily flowing* fluid is called *stream availability* and is denoted by the symbol Y (and $y = Y/m$) to distinguish it from the availability of a closed system Φ (or ϕ). It is defined as the maximum work which can be obtained as the fluid goes to the dead state while exchanging heat only with the atmosphere. In the dead state the fluid is at p_0 and T_0 and is also at rest, $V_0 = 0$. For a steadily flowing fluid in a state 1,

$$y_1 = w_{\text{max, 1-0}} = (e_1 + p_1v_1 - T_0s_1) - (e_0 + p_0v_0 - T_0s_0) \quad (11 \cdot 6a)$$

In the absence of electrical, magnetic, and surface tension effects, this becomes

$$y_1 = \left(h_1 + \frac{V_1^2}{2g_c} + \frac{g}{g_c}z - T_0s_1\right) - \left(h_0 + \frac{g}{g_c}z_0 - T_0s_0\right) \quad (11 \cdot 6b)$$

The *Darrieus function* is defined as $b \equiv h - T_0 s$. For any given temperature of the atmosphere, b is a property of a substance. The use of b shortens the preceding equation to

$$y_1 = \left(b_1 + \frac{V_1^2}{2g_c} + \frac{g}{g_c} z_1 \right) - \left(b_0 + \frac{g}{g_c} z_0 \right) \qquad (11\cdot6c)$$

and, for a change from state 1 to state 2,

$$w_{\max} = -\Delta y = y_1 - y_2 = \left(b_1 + \frac{V_1^2}{2g_c} + \frac{g}{g_c} z_1 \right) - \left(b_2 + \frac{V_2^2}{2g_c} + \frac{g}{g_c} z_2 \right)$$
$$(11\cdot6d)$$

Stream availability y is often called simply the availability of a flowing fluid, but it must be remembered that for a fluid which is part of a flowing stream the availability is y and not ϕ.

For a steadily flowing fluid which goes from one state to another while exchanging heat only with the atmosphere, the maximum work obtainable per unit mass is $-\Delta y$. If the fluid also receives heat q_R per unit mass from an energy reservoir at T_R, the maximum work which can be obtained per unit mass is

$$w_{\max} = -\Delta y + \left(1 - \frac{T_0}{T_R} \right) q_R \qquad (11\cdot6e)$$

The *irreversibility* I of any process is defined as

$$I = W_{\max} - W = W_{\max\,\text{useful}} - W_{\text{useful}} \qquad (11\cdot7)$$

W in this equation is the work actually produced. During the process, heat may be exchanged with various energy reservoirs as well as with the atmosphere. $W_{\max}$ is the maximum work for a process which (1) is between the same end states as the actual process, (2) involves the same amounts of heat exchange with the various energy reservoirs, and (3) involves heat exchange with the atmosphere also if necessary. For any process,

$$I = T_0(\Delta S_\sigma + \Delta S_{\text{surr}}) = T_0 \, \Delta S_{\text{isolated system}} \qquad (11\cdot8)$$

The expression in terms of an isolated system is quite general because an isolated system can always be formed by including within a single boundary everything that affects a system during a process. For all processes, $I \geq 0$, with the equality holding for reversible processes. I can be interpreted as the decrease in the maximum work obtainable as the result of a process.

Availability accounting provides information that cannot be obtained from energy accounting alone. It involves the determination of availability changes for each of a series of processes. Comparison of the work done with the availability change gives a measure of the degree to which each process approaches the ideal. It thereby indicates where efforts spent in improving performance are likely to be most fruitful.

REFERENCES

11·1   G. J. Van Wylen, *Thermodynamics*, John Wiley & Sons, 1959, chapter 10. (In this reference the definition of availability of a *closed* system is different from that in this textbook.)

11·2   J. H. Keenan, *Thermodynamics*, John Wiley & Sons, 1941, chapter XVII.

11·3   J. H. Keenan, "Availability and Irreversibility in Thermodynamics," *British Journal of Applied Physics*, vol. 2, July 1951, pp. 183–192.

11·4   V. W. Young, *Basic Thermodynamics*, McGraw-Hill Book Co., 1952, chapter 16.

11·5   V. M. Faires, *Thermodynamics*, Macmillan Co., 3d ed., 1957, art. 108 to 112.

PROBLEMS

11·1   One-tenth pound of air in a closed system expands from 30 psia, 140 F, to 15 psia, 100 F, while receiving 1.0 B of heat from a reservoir at 250 F. The surrounding atmosphere is at 14.0 psia, 80 F. Determine the maximum work. How much of this work would be done on the atmosphere?

11·2   Steam enters a radiant superheater at 1000 psia, 700 F, with a velocity of 110 fps and leaves at 950 psia, 900 F, with a velocity of 145 fps. Heat is transferred to the steam from a furnace at 2540 F. The atmosphere is at 14.7 psia, 60 F. Determine the maximum work for this process. Devise a means for producing this amount of work without changing the process end states.

11·3   Saturated liquid ammonia at 170 psia is throttled to 30 psia. Determine the maximum work if the sink temperature (see the first paragraph of Art. 11·5) is 65 F.

11·4   Solve Example 11·1 if the tank initially contains air at 5 psia, 70 F.

11·5   Solve Example 11·1 if the tank initially contains air at 5 psia, 0 F.

11·6   Calculate the availability of a 50-lb cake of ice at 32 F if the surrounding atmosphere is at 14.0 psia, 60 F.

11·7   A tank with a volume of 10 cu ft contains air at 100 psia, 70 F. The surrounding atmosphere is at 14.0 psia, 70 F. Determine the availability of the air in the tank. Is this the same as the maximum work which can be obtained from expansion of the air into the surrounding atmosphere?

11·8   A tank with a volume of 10 cu ft contains air at 14.0 psia, 500 F. The surrounding atmosphere is at 14.0 psia, 70 F. Determine the availability of the air in the tank.

11·9   Solve Prob. 11·8 with the air in the tank initially at 2 psia, 70 F.

11·10   Solve Prob. 11·8 with the air in the tank initially at 14.0 psia, −100 F.

11·11   One-tenth pound of air in a closed system expands from 30 psia, 140 F, to 15 psia, 100 F, while receiving heat from a reservoir at 250 F. Determine the maximum amount of heat which can be transferred from the reservoir to the air under these conditions.

11·12 In Art. 11·2 the following statement appears: It can easily be shown that the availability Φ of a closed system can be increased only by doing work on the system or by transferring heat to it from a body at a temperature other than T_0. Prove this.

11·13 Air enters a compressor at the atmospheric conditions of 15 psia, 40 F, and is compressed to 30 psia, 165 F. The flow rate is 13.0 lb/sec. Determine, per pound of air, the stream availability of the entering air, the stream availability of the leaving air, and the minimum work input. What is the physical meaning of the minimum work input? Does it refer to an adiabatic compressor? To a water-cooled compressor?

11·14 Air enters an actual turbine at 45 psia, 400 F, and expands to 15 psia, 300 F. Heat transfer to the atmosphere at 14.7 psia, 80 F, amounts to 3 B/lb of air passing through the turbine. Calculate the entering stream availability, the leaving stream availability, and the maximum work. What is the physical meaning of the maximum work? Does it refer to an adiabatic turbine? To one with a heat loss of 3 B/lb?

11·15 Air expands through a turbine from 60 psia, 940 F, to 15 psia, 640 F, while heat in the amount of 5 B/lb is lost to the atmosphere at 14.7 psia, 70 F. The net change in kinetic energy is negligibly small. Calculate for this process (a) the decrease in stream availability, (b) the maximum work, and (c) the irreversibility.

11·16 One-half pound of air, initially at 60 psia, 140 F, is expanded adiabatically in a closed system until its volume is doubled and its temperature equals that of the surrounding atmosphere, 40 F. Calculate for this process (a) the maximum work, (b) the change in availability, and (c) the irreversibility.

11·17 Steam enters a condenser at 1 psia, 90 per cent quality, (state 1) and is condensed to a saturated liquid (state 2) by cooling water which enters at 60 F (state A) and leaves at 70 F (state B). The steam flow rate is 200 lb/min. The sink temperature is 60 F. Sketch a Ts diagram for each of the fluids. Calculate (a) the maximum work and (b) the irreversibility.

11·18 A closed rigid thermally insulated tank contains 5 lb of air initially at 15 psia, 140 F. A paddle wheel inside the tank is turned by an external motor until the air is at 340 F. The sink temperature is 60 F. Calculate the irreversibility of the process.

11·19 In an air-to-air heat exchanger, the "hot side" air enters at 500 F, 15 psia, and the "cold side" air enters at 140 F, 250 psia, and leaves at 240 F. Frictional pressure losses are negligible. Flow rate of air is 10 lb/sec on each side. Calculate (a) the irreversibility of the process per pound of "hot side" air for a sink temperature of 60 F, and (b) the entropy change of the universe resulting from operation of this process for 1 hr.

11·20 Heat is transferred from an energy reservoir at 1540 F to steam flowing at a rate of 2000 lb/hr. Steam enters the heat exchanger dry and saturated at 750 psia and leaves at 740 psia, 680 F. The lowest temperature in the surroundings is 40 F. Determine the amount of energy made unavailable by this process in B/hr.

11·21 Steam at 100 psia, 520 F, flowing at a rate of 20,000 lb/hr is desuperheated to dry saturated steam at 100 psia by having water at 200 F sprayed into it. The spray chamber in which this occurs is called a desuperheater. The sink temperature is 60 F. Calculate per pound of steam entering the desuperheater (a) the amount of water needed, and (b) the irreversibility of the desuperheating process. Devise a means of carrying out this process reversibly.

11·22 Steam enters a turbine at 100 psia, 400 F, and leaves at 1 psia. The expansion is adiabatic. The flow rate is 20,000 lb/hr. The power output is 1500 hp. Condenser cooling water is available from a large river at 40 F. Per pound of steam, how much energy is made unavailable by the operation of the turbine?

11·23   Steam which is dry and saturated at 300 psia is throttled through a well-insulated valve to 87 psia. There is no change in kinetic energy. The flow rate is 800 lb/hr. The sink temperature is 40 F. Sketch a Ts diagram, and calculate, in B/lb, the irreversibility of the process.

11·24   Air is compressed adiabatically from 15 psia, 40 F, to 45 psia at a rate of 2.78 lb/sec. Kinetic energy changes are negligible. Work input is 60 B/lb. (a) Calculate the irreversibility of the process per pound. (b) Explain the physical significance of the answer to part (a).

11·25   In a steam power plant, the heat rejected to the condenser cooling water may be four times as great as the energy lost up the stack. Why is it that the stack loss is of greater concern; that is, why are greater efforts made to reduce it rather than the condenser loss?

11·26   For a closed system, the first law gives $\oint \delta Q = \oint \delta W$. Comment on the following equation for a closed system which is proposed as an analogous relation given by the second law:

$$\oint \delta Q_{av} = \oint \delta W + T_0 \Delta S_{surr}$$

11·27   Are the following true? (a) All reversible processes between the same two end states produce the same amount of work. (b) All reversible adiabatic processes between the same two end states produce the same amount of work. (c) All reversible processes between the same two end states produce the same amount of work if the system exchanges heat only with a constant-temperature reservoir.

11·28   Make the investigation which is mentioned in the comment at the end of Example 11·7.

CHAPTER 12

Gas and Gas-Vapor Mixtures

A pure substance has been defined as a substance which is homogeneous and unchanging in chemical composition. Homogeneous mixtures of gases which do not react with each other are therefore pure substances, and the properties of such mixtures can be determined, correlated, and tabulated or fitted by equations just like the properties of any other pure substance. This has been done for common mixtures such as air and certain combustion products, but, since an unlimited number of mixtures is possible, properties of all of them cannot be determined experimentally and tabulated. It is therefore important to be able to calculate the properties of any mixture from the properties of its constituents. This chapter pertains to such calculations, first for gas mixtures and then for gas-vapor mixtures.

12·1 Mass fraction; mole fraction

The analysis of a gas mixture based on mass is called a gravimetric analysis. It is based on the fact that the mass of a mixture is equal to the sum of the masses of its constituents:

$$m_m = m_A + m_B + m_C + \cdots \qquad (a)$$

where the subscript m refers to the mixture and the subscripts A, B, and C refer to individual constituents of the mixture. The ratio m_A/m_m is called the mass fraction of constituent A.

The total number of moles* in a mixture is defined as the sum of the

---

* Recall that the mole is a mass unit. One mole of a substance is a mass of that substance equal numerically to its molecular weight. For example, one mole of water is 18 lb of water whether the water is a solid, a liquid, or a gas. This point is mentioned because the fact that one mole of an ideal gas occupies the same volume as one mole of any other ideal gas *at the same pressure and temperature* often misleads people into regarding the mole as a volume unit. It can be treated as a volume unit only for ideal gases at the same pressure and temperature.

391

number of moles of its constituents:

$$N_m \equiv N_A + N_B + N_C + \cdots$$

The mole fraction x is defined as

$$x \equiv \frac{N}{N_m}, \qquad x_A \equiv \frac{N_A}{N_m}, \qquad \text{etc.}$$

The number of moles, the mass, and the molecular weight of a substance are related by

$$m = NM \tag{b}$$

where m is the mass, N is the number of moles, and M is the molecular weight. Substituting from equation (b) into equation (a),

$$m_m = N_m M_m = N_A M_A + N_B M_B + N_C M_C + \cdots$$

and

$$M_m = x_A M_A + x_B M_B + x_C M_C + \cdots$$

where M_m is called the *apparent* (or *average*) *molecular weight* of the mixture.

12·2 Partial pressure; partial volume

The *partial pressure* p_i of a constituent i in a gas mixture is defined as

$$p_i \equiv x_i p_m, \qquad p_A \equiv x_A p_m, \qquad \text{etc.}$$

where x is the mole fraction. From this definition it is clear that the sum of the partial pressures of the constituents of a gas mixture equals the mixture pressure:

$$p_m = p_A + p_B + \cdots$$

This applies to any gas mixture, whether it is an ideal gas or not. (Sometimes partial pressure is defined in a slightly different manner. This is often the case when it is to be used for only ideal-gas mixtures. As we have defined it here, it is also useful in connection with real-gas mixtures.)

The partial volume V_i' of a constituent i in a gas mixture is defined as

$$V_i' \equiv x_i V_m, \qquad V_A' \equiv x_A V_m, \qquad \text{etc.}$$

The sum of the partial volumes of the constituents of a gas mixture equals the volume of the mixture. The partial volume is of course not an actual volume of a constituent as it exists in the mixture because each constituent fills the entire volume of the vessel which holds the mixture. The symbol V_i' instead of V_i is used as a reminder of this fact. We will see that for ideal-gas mixtures partial volume has a physical significance, but for gas mixtures in general no physical picture of partial volume can be given.

12·3   Dalton's law or the law of additive pressures

It is an empirical fact that a mixture of ideal gases is also an ideal gas. The same conclusion can be deduced from the kinetic theory of gases. Thus for a mixture of ideal gases A, B, C, etc.,

$$p_m = \frac{N_m R_u T_m}{V_m} = \frac{(N_A + N_B + \cdots)R_u T_m}{V_m} = \frac{N_A R_u T_m}{V_m} + \frac{N_B R_u T_m}{V_m} + \cdots$$

$$= p_A(T_m, V_m) + p_B(T_m, V_m) + \cdots$$

where $p_A(T_m, V_m)$ is the pressure of constituent A existing at the temperature T_m and the volume V_m. This relationship is known as Dalton's law or the law of additive pressures. Restated, *the pressure of a mixture of ideal gases equals the sum of the pressures of its constituents if each existed alone at the temperature and volume of the mixture.* Dalton's law is strictly true only for ideal-gas mixtures. It holds approximately for real-gas mixtures even in some ranges of pressure and temperature where $pv = RT$ is quite inaccurate.

Another statement of Dalton's law is that *in a mixture of ideal gases each constituent behaves in all respects as though it existed alone at the temperature and volume of the mixture.* The internal energy and entropy of an ideal-gas mixture are equal respectively to the sums of the internal energies and entropies of the constituents if each existed alone at the temperature and volume of the mixture.

In a mixture of *ideal gases* the partial pressure of each constituent equals the pressure which that constituent would exert if it existed alone at the temperature and volume of the mixture. This is shown as follows:

$$p_A = x_A p_m = \frac{N_A}{N_m} p_m = \frac{N_A R_u T_m}{V_m} = p_A(T_m, V_m)$$

This is true only for ideal-gas mixtures. For non-ideal-gas mixtures, in general,

$$p_A \neq p_A(T_m, V_m)$$

12·4   Amagat's law, Leduc's law, or the law of additive volumes

Starting again from the empirical fact that a mixture of ideal gases is itself an ideal gas, we can write

$$V_m = \frac{N_m R_u T_m}{p_m} = \frac{(N_A + N_B + \cdots)R_u T_m}{p_m} = \frac{N_A R_u T_m}{p_m} + \frac{N_B R_u T_m}{p_m} + \cdots$$

$$= V_A(p_m, T_m) + V_B(p_m, T_m) + \cdots$$

where $V_A(T_m, p_m)$ is the volume of constituent A when it exists at the temperature T_m and the pressure p_m. Thus *the volume of a mixture of ideal gases equals the sum of the volumes of its constituents if each existed alone at the temperature and pressure of the mixture.* This is known as Amagat's law, Leduc's law, or the law of additive volumes. Like Dalton's law it is strictly true only for ideal gases but holds approximately for real-gas mixtures even in some ranges of pressure and temperature where $pv = RT$ is inaccurate. When the temperature of a real-gas mixture is well above the critical temperatures of all its constituents, the additive volume law is usually more accurate than the additive pressure law.

For ideal-gas mixtures, volumetric analyses are frequently used. The volume fraction is defined as

$$\text{Volume fraction of } A \equiv \frac{V_A(p_m, T_m)}{V_m} = \frac{\text{volume of } A \text{ existing alone at } p_m, T_m}{\text{volume of the mixture at } p_m, T_m}$$

Notice that in a gas mixture each constituent occupies the total volume, and so volume fraction is *not* defined as the ratio of a constituent volume to the mixture volume because this ratio is always unity. Notice also that we define volume fraction or volumetric analysis only for mixtures of *ideal gases* because only for ideal gases does the law of additive volumes hold strictly. The volume fraction of a constituent in an ideal-gas mixture equals its mole fraction, as can be shown by

$$\frac{V_A(p_m, T_m)}{V_m} = \frac{N_A R_u T_m p_m}{p_m N_m R_u T_m} = \frac{N_A}{N_m} = x_A$$

and the volume of an ideal-gas mixture constituent if it existed alone at p_m and T_m equals the partial volume of the constituent in the mixture,

$$V_A(p_m, T_m) = x_A V_m = V'_A$$

The equality of volume fraction and mole fraction in an ideal-gas mixture enables us to write the units of volume fraction as moles of constituent per mole of mixture, and doing so simplifies the conversion between volumetric and gravimetric analyses. Such conversions must be made because gas mixtures are often analyzed on a volumetric basis, but a gravimetric analysis is generally more useful in relating properties of a mixture to the properties of its constituents. Conversion from one basis to the other is illustrated in the two examples which follow. Notice that the pressure and temperature of the mixture have no bearing on the conversion. An ideal-gas mixture can be heated, cooled, compressed, or expanded, and its volumetric analysis remains constant as long as its gravimetric analysis does. Two suggestions on making the conversions are (1) use a tabular form if there are more than two constituents, and (2) write down the units at the head of each column, and observe them carefully.

EXAMPLE 12·1.   A blast-furnace gas has the following volumetric analysis in percentages: H_2, 9; CO, 24; CH_4, 2; CO_2, 6; O_2, 3; and N_2, 56. Determine the gravimetric analysis.

Solution.   In the table below, the given data are in columns *a* and *b*. The approximate molecular weights are listed in column *c*. The values in column *d* are the products of those in columns *b* and *c*. The summation of column *d* is the mass of 100 moles of mixture or 100 times the apparent molecular weight of the mixture. Column *e* values are obtained by dividing the column *d* values by the column *d* total and multiplying by 100.

a Constituent	*b* Volumetric Analysis, moles/100 moles of Mixture	*c* Mole Weight, lb/mole	*d* lb/100 moles of Mixture	*e* Gravimetric Analysis, lb/100 lb of Mixture
H_2	9	2	18	0.7
CO	24	28	672	25.4
CH_4	2	16	32	1.2
CO_2	6	44	264	10.0
O_2	3	32	96	3.6
N_2	56	28	1568	59.1
	100		2650	100.0

EXAMPLE 12·2.   A gas mixture has the following gravimetric analysis in percentages: H_2, 10; CO, 60; and CO_2, 30. Determine the volumetric analysis.
Solution.

Constituent	Gravimetric Analysis, lb/100 lb of Mixture	Molecular Weight, lb/mole	Moles/100 lb of Mixture	Volumetric Analysis, moles/100 mole of Mixture
H_2	10	2	5.00	64.1
CO	60	28	2.12	27.2
CO_2	30	44	0.68	8.7
	100		7.80	100.0

12·5 Properties of ideal-gas mixtures

For the discussion of the properties of ideal-gas mixtures, let us consider a mixture of three ideal gases, *A*, *B*, and *C*. The properties of such a mixture in terms of the properties of its constituents are listed below.

Temperature. For any uniform mixture the temperature is the same for each constituent and for the mixture.

$$T_m = T_A = T_B = T_C$$

Mass, number of moles, and apparent molecular weight. The mass of a mixture, the number of moles of mixture, and its apparent molecular weight are shown in Art. 12·1 to be given by

$$m_m = m_A + m_B + m_C$$
$$N_m = N_A + N_B + N_C$$
$$M_m = x_A M_A + x_B M_B + x_C M_C$$

(These relationships hold for all mixtures, not just for ideal gases.)

Pressure. According to Dalton's law, the pressure of an ideal-gas mixture equals the sum of the pressures of the constituents if each existed alone at the temperature and volume of the mixture.

$$p_m = p_A(T_m, V_m) + p_B(T_m, V_m) + p_C(T_m, V_m)$$

For ideal-gas mixtures the pressure of any constituent if it existed alone at the temperature and volume of the mixture equals its partial pressure,

$$p_A(T_m, V_m) = p_A = x_A p_m$$

For ideal-gas mixtures the partial pressure of a constituent or its pressure if it existed alone at the temperature and volume of the mixture (these two pressures are equal only for ideal gases) can be thought of as the pressure exerted by that constituent *as it exists in the mixture.* This concept is in keeping with the molecular picture which shows the pressure of an ideal gas to be caused by the bombardment of the vessel walls by the gas molecules. From this point of view it is easy to separate the pressure of a mixture into parts, each attributable to the bombardment of the vessel walls by the molecules of one constituent. It is impossible to measure directly the pressure of just one constituent of a mixture, but nevertheless it is often convenient to treat the partial pressure of a constituent in an ideal-gas mixture as the pressure exerted by that constituent *as it exists in the mixture.*

Volume. The volume of each constituent of a gas mixture is the same as the volume of the mixture because the molecules of each constituent are free to move throughout the entire space occupied by the mixture.

$$V_m = V_A = V_B = V_C$$

The law of additive volumes equates the volume of an ideal-gas mixture to the sum of the volumes of its constituents if each existed alone at the pressure and temperature of the mixture,

$$V_m = V_A(p_m, T_m) + V_B(p_m, T_m) + V_C(p_m, T_m)$$

For ideal gases, the volume of a constituent existing alone at the pressure and temperature of the mixture is equal to its partial volume,

$$V_A(p_m, T_m) = V'_A = x_A V_m = x_A V_A(p_A, T_m)$$

Internal energy. The Dalton's law statement that in a mixture of ideal gases each constituent behaves in all respects as though it existed alone at the temperature and volume of the mixture leads to the fact that the internal energy of an ideal-gas mixture equals the sum of the internal energies of the constituents if each existed alone at the temperature and volume of the mixture. The internal energy of an ideal gas is a function of temperature only and the only temperature we use in evaluating properties of a mixture or its constituents is the mixture temperature T_m; so $U_A(T_m, V_m) = U_A(T_m) = U_A$, and

$$U_m = U_A + U_B + U_C$$

$$u_m \equiv \frac{U_m}{m_m} = \frac{U_A + U_B + U_C}{m_m} = \frac{m_A u_A + m_B u_B + m_C u_C}{m_m}$$

The specific internal energy of a mixture thus equals the weighted average (weighted by mass) of the specific internal energies of the constituents.

Enthalpy. For ideal-gas mixtures, it can easily be shown that

$$H_m = H_A + H_B + H_C$$

$$h_m \equiv \frac{H_m}{m_m} = \frac{m_A h_A + m_B h_B + m_C h_C}{m_m}$$

Specific heats, gas constant. Since

$$u_m = \frac{m_A}{m_m} u_A + \frac{m_B}{m_m} u_B + \frac{m_C}{m_m} u_C$$

the c_v of a mixture is given by

$$c_{vm} \equiv \left(\frac{\partial u_m}{\partial T}\right)_v = \frac{m_A}{m_m}\left(\frac{\partial u_A}{\partial T}\right)_v + \frac{m_B}{m_m}\left(\frac{\partial u_B}{\partial T}\right)_v + \frac{m_C}{m_m}\left(\frac{\partial u_C}{\partial T}\right)_v$$

$$= \frac{m_A c_{vA} + m_B c_{vB} + m_C c_{vC}}{m_m}$$

In a similar manner,

$$c_{pm} = \frac{m_A c_{pA} + m_B c_{pB} + m_C c_{pC}}{m_m}$$

and

$$R_m = \frac{m_A R_A + m_B R_B + m_C R_C}{m_m}$$

The gas constant of the mixture can also be obtained by

$$R_m = \frac{R_u}{M_m}$$

Entropy. From Dalton's law we can conclude that

$$S_m = S_A(T_m, V_m) + S_B(T_m, V_m) + S_C(T_m, V_m^*)$$

$$s_m = \frac{S_m}{m_m} = \frac{m_A s_A + m_B s_B + m_C s_C}{m_m}$$

Remember that the constituent entropies here must be evaluated at the temperature and volume of the mixture or at the mixture temperature and the constituent partial pressures. The entropy of any constituent at the volume and temperature of the mixture (and hence at its partial pressure) is greater than its entropy when existing at the pressure and temperature of the mixture (and hence at its partial volume). One simple way to prove this is by means of the increase of entropy principle.

EXAMPLE 12·3. The gravimetric analysis of a gas mixture is 10 per cent hydrogen, 30 per cent nitrogen, 40 per cent carbon monoxide, and 20 per cent carbon dioxide. For the mixture at 10 psia, 70 F, compute (a) the partial pressures of the constituents, (b) the constant-volume specific heat, (c) the internal energy, and (d) the enthalpy. Assume that $u_m = 0$ and $h_m = 0$ at $T = 0$ R. Approximate specific heats of the constituents are given in the following table.

Gas	c_p, B/lb-F	c_v, B/lb-F
Hydrogen	3.41	2.42
Nitrogen	0.248	0.177
Carbon monoxide	0.248	0.177
Carbon dioxide	0.195	0.150

Solution. (a) In order to determine the partial pressures we first convert the gravimetric analysis to a volumetric analysis.

Constituent	Gravimetric Analysis, lb/100 lb of Mixture	Molecular Weight, lb/mole	Moles/100 lb of Mixture	Volumetric Analysis, moles/100 moles of Mixture
H_2	10	2	5.00	62.8
N_2	30	28	1.07	13.5
CO	40	28	1.43	17.9
CO_2	20	44	0.46	5.8
			7.96	100.0

The partial pressures could conveniently be tabulated in an additional column, but to make clear the calculation we list them separately as

$$p_{H_2} = x_{H_2}p_m = 0.628(10) = 6.28 \text{ psia}$$

$$p_{N_2} = x_{N_2}p_m = 0.135(10) = 1.35 \text{ psia}$$

$$p_{CO} = x_{CO}p_m = 0.179(10) = 1.79 \text{ psia}$$

$$p_{CO_2} = x_{CO_2}p_m = 0.058(10) = 0.58 \text{ psia}$$

$$p_m = 10.00 \text{ psia}$$

(b) The constant-volume specific heat of the mixture is the weighted average of the constituent c_v's.

$$c_{vm} = \Sigma \frac{m}{m_m} c_v = 0.10(2.42) + 0.30(0.177) + 0.40(0.177) + 0.20(0.150)$$

$$= 0.396 \text{ B/lb-F}$$

(c) For an ideal-gas mixture,

$$u_m - u_{m0} = c_{vm}(T - T_0)$$

where u_{m0} is the internal energy of the mixture at some reference temperature T_0. Here we are told that $u_{m0} = 0$ when $T_0 = 0$ R, so we have

$$u_m = c_{vm}T = 0.396(530) = 210 \text{ B/lb}$$

(d) The enthalpy could be determined by first determining c_{pm} and following the procedure used for finding u_m. After noting from part a that the mixture molecular weight is $100/7.96$, it is quicker to write

$$h_m = u_m + p_m v_m = u_m + R_m T = u_m + \frac{R_u}{M_m} T$$

$$= 210 + \frac{1544(7.96)}{778(100)} 530 = 294 \text{ B/lb}$$

EXAMPLE 12·4. A mixture which has a volumetric analysis of 30 per cent argon and 70 per cent nitrogen is compressed reversibly and adiabatically in a closed system from 14 psia, 60 F, to 50 psia. Assume that the specific heats are constant at the following values: Argon, $c_p = 0.124$ B/lb-F and $c_v = 0.0743$ B/lb-F; nitrogen, $c_p = 0.249$ B/lb-F and $c_v = 0.178$ B/lb-F. Determine (a) the final temperature, (b) the work done per pound of mixture, and (c) the entropy change of each constituent per pound of mixture.

Solution. (a) In order to determine the specific heats of the mixture, we first determine the gravimetric analysis or the mass fractions.

Constituent	Volumetric Analysis, moles/100 moles of Mixture	Molecular Weight, lb/mole	lb/100 moles of Mixture	Gravimetric Analysis, lb/100 lb of Mixture
A	30	40	1200	38.0
N₂	70	28	1960	62.0
			3160	

Then the mixture specific heats are given by

$$c_{pm} = \frac{m_A}{m_m} c_{v,A} + \frac{m_{N_2}}{m_m} c_{p,N_2} = 0.38(0.124) + 0.62(0.249) = 0.2015 \text{ B/lb-R}$$

$$c_{vm} = \frac{m_A}{m_m} c_{v,A} + \frac{m_{N_2}}{m_m} c_{v,N_2} = 0.38(0.0743) + 0.62(0.178) = 0.1386 \text{ B/lb-R}$$

and $\quad k_m = \dfrac{c_{pm}}{c_{vm}} = \dfrac{0.2015}{0.1386} = 1.454$

Since we are assuming that the specific heats are constant, the final temperature for the reversible adiabatic process is

$$T_2 = T_1 \left(\frac{p_2}{p_1}\right)^{(k_m-1)/k_m} = 520 \left(\frac{50}{14}\right)^{0.454/1.45} = 774 \text{ R}$$

(b) Applying the first law to the closed system for this adiabatic process, we have
$$w'_{in} = u_{m2} - u_{m1} - q = c_{vm}(T_2 - T_1) - 0$$
$$= 0.1386(774 - 520) = 35.2 \text{ B/lb}$$

(c) For this reversible adiabatic process the entropy of the mixture must remain constant. The entropy of each constituent may change, but the sum of the entropy changes of the two constituents must be zero. For any process of an ideal gas,

$$\Delta s = \int_1^2 ds = \int_1^2 \frac{dh}{T} - \int_1^2 \frac{v\,dp}{T} = \int_1^2 \frac{c_p\,dT}{T} - R \int_1^2 \frac{dp}{p}$$

and, if c_p is constant,

$$\Delta s = c_p \ln \frac{T_2}{T_1} - R \ln \frac{p_2}{p_1}$$

In applying this equation to each constituent in the mixture, the pressures to be used are the partial pressures, but note that for each gas

$$\frac{p_2}{p_1} = \frac{x_2 p_{m2}}{x_1 p_{m1}} = \frac{p_{m2}}{p_{m1}}$$

Thus, applying the equation for Δs to the argon, we have

$$\Delta s_A = 0.124 \ln \frac{774}{520} - \frac{38.7}{778} \ln \frac{50}{14} = -0.0140 \text{ B/lb-R}$$

Per pound of mixture,

$$\frac{\Delta S_A}{m_m} = \frac{m_A \Delta s_A}{m_m} = 0.38(-0.0140) = -0.00532 \text{ B/lb mixture-R}$$

For the nitrogen,

$$\Delta s_{N_2} = 0.249 \ln \frac{774}{520} - \frac{55.1}{778} \ln \frac{50}{14} = 0.0087 \text{ B/lb-R}$$

$$\frac{\Delta S_{N_2}}{m_m} = \frac{m_{N_2} \Delta s_{N_2}}{m_m} = 0.62(0.0087) = 0.00539 \text{ B/lb mixture-R}$$

Within the limits of accuracy of the data and of slide-rule calculations, these two Δs values are equal in magnitude (although opposite in sign). It is actually unnecessary to calculate both Δs values in this manner, except as a check on the computations, because we know that their sum is zero.

12·6 Mixing of ideal gases initially at different pressures and temperatures

Thus far in this chapter we have dealt with mixtures which have already been formed. Now let us look at the *formation* of an ideal-gas mixture or the *mixing* of ideal gases initially at different pressures and temperatures. The general problem is to determine the properties of a mixture which results from mixing constituents of known properties. No new principles

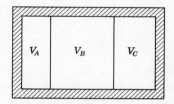

Fig. 12·1 Three gases in adiabatic system before mixing.

are involved. We simply apply the first law and the conservation of mass principle to a conveniently selected system to relate the mixture properties to the properties of the constituents before mixing. For example, consider the adiabatic mixing of three gases, A, B, and C, in a closed system of fixed volume. The gases might be initially in three tanks connected by piping, or they might be in three parts of a tank separated by partitions as in Fig. 12·1. If the partitions are ruptured or removed, the three gases will form a mixture which has a mass and a volume given by

$$m_m = m_A + m_B + m_C$$
$$V_m = V_A + V_B + V_C$$

where V_A, V_B, and V_C are the volumes of the constituents *before mixing*. The mixing process was specified as adiabatic and there is no work done; so the internal energy of the system remains constant and

$$U_m = U_A + U_B + U_C$$

where U_A, U_B, and U_C are the internal energies of the constituents before mixing. The internal energy of the mixture is also equal to the sum of the internal energies of the constituents after mixing, in accordance with

Dalton's law, but the internal energy of each constituent is generally not the same before and after mixing. Since the internal energy of the entire system remains constant, the sum of the internal energy changes of the constituents is zero.

$$\Delta U = \Delta U_A + \Delta U_B + \Delta U_C = 0$$

If c_v for each constituent is constant in the temperature range between the constituent's initial temperature and the mixture temperature, an equation such as

$$\Delta U_A = m_A c_{vA}(T_m - T_A)$$

can be written for each constituent. Then

$$\Delta U = m_A c_{vA}(T_m - T_A) + m_B c_{vB}(T_m - T_B) + m_C c_{vC}(T_m - T_C) = 0$$

Solving for the mixture temperature,

$$T_m = \frac{m_A c_{vA} T_A + m_B c_{vB} T_B + m_C c_{vC} T_C}{m_A c_{vA} + m_B c_{vB} + m_C c_{vC}}$$

The denominator is equal to $m_m c_{vm}$. Notice that in deriving this expression for the mixture temperature no assumption was made regarding a temperature at which $U = 0$, nor was it stipulated that $U = 0$ at the same temperature for all constituents.

After the temperature of the mixture has been determined, the pressure can be calculated from

$$p_m = \frac{m_m R_m T_m}{V_m}$$

R_m can be determined from the gravimetric analysis of the mixture.

Since the mixing process we are considering is irreversible and adiabatic, the entropy of the system must increase. The entropy of the mixture, while equal to the sum of the entropies of the constituents as they exist in the mixture, is greater than the sum of the entropies of the constituents before mixing. The entropy change of the entire system is

$$\Delta S = \Delta S_A + \Delta S_B + \Delta S_C > 0$$

and the entropy change for each constituent can be calculated as though each constituent existed alone and expanded from its initial conditions to the mixture temperature and volume, its final pressure being therefore its partial pressure in the mixture.

We have illustrated here that no new principles or techniques are involved in the determination of the properties of an ideal-gas mixture formed from constituents of known properties in a closed rigid adiabatic system. Nonadiabatic mixing and mixing in open systems, both steady flow and transient flow, can also be analyzed by means of the principles which have already been introduced.

EXAMPLE 12·5. In a steady-flow system, hydrogen initially at 70 F and methane initially at 150 F are to be mixed adiabatically to form a mixture which is 50 per cent hydrogen by volume. Each gas enters the mixing chamber at a pressure of 1 atm, and the mixing occurs under a constant total pressure of 1 atm. The hydrogen mass flow rate is 0.01 lb/sec. The lowest temperature in the surroundings is 70 F. Assuming that kinetic-energy changes are negligible, determine (a) the temperature of the mixture, and (b) the irreversibility in B/sec.

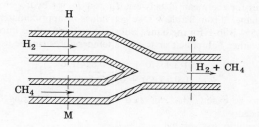

Example 12·5

Solution.   (a) The mass analysis (or gravimetric analysis) of the mixture is first found.

Constituent	Volumetric Analysis, moles/100 moles of Mixture	Molecular Weight, lb/mole	lb/100 moles of Mixture	Gravimetric Analysis, lb/100 lb of Mixture
H_2	50	2	100	11.11
CH_4	50	16	800	88.89
			900	

The methane mass flow rate is thus 0.08 lb/sec.

The mixing is adiabatic, the kinetic-energy change is negligible, and there is no work done; so application of the first law to the steady-flow system in which the mixing occurs gives (with the subscripts H and M referring to hydrogen and methane, respectively, and the subscript m referring to the mixture)

$$(M_H h_H + M_M h_M)_{\text{before mixing}} = (M_H + M_M)h_m = (M_H h_H + M_M h_M)_{\text{after mixing}}$$

where each M stands for a mass rate of flow. If we now let h_H and h_M represent the enthalpies of hydrogen and methane at their initial temperatures T_H and T_M, and let the enthalpies of the constituents in the mixture be represented by h_{H,T_m} and h_{M,T_m}, the energy balance above can be written as

$$M_H h_H + M_M h_M = M_H h_{H,T_m} + M_M h_{M,T_m}$$

Assuming that the c_p values are constant,

$$M_H c_{p,H}(T_H - T_m) + M_M c_{p,M}(T_M - T_m) = 0$$

$$T_m = \frac{M_H c_{p,H} T_H + M_M c_{p,M} T_M}{M_H c_{p,H} + M_M c_{p,M}}$$

Inspection of Table 4·3 shows that the c_p of hydrogen is about seven times that of methane. The mass of methane in this mixture is eight times the mass of hydrogen. Therefore the product mc_p (or Mc_p) is approximately the same for the two constituents so that the mixture temperature will be approximately midway between T_H and T_M and a little closer to T_M. Let us estimate it as 115 F. This estimate of T_m enables us to select reasonable values for the mean c_p between T_H and T_m for hydrogen and between T_M and T_m for methane. From Table 4·3 we get values of approximately 3.45 B/lb-F for hydrogen and 0.554 B/lb-F for methane. Substituting these values into the last equation and noting that either Fahrenheit or Rankine temperatures can be used,

$$T_m = \frac{0.01(3.45)70 + 0.08(0.554)150}{0.01(3.45) + 0.08(0.554)} = 115 \text{ F}$$

(This happens to be exactly the estimated value used in selecting c_p values; so no correction is needed.)

(b) The irreversibility is given by

$$I = T_0 \Delta S = T_0[m_H \Delta s_H + m_M \Delta s_M]$$

Per unit time, this is

$$\frac{I}{\tau} = \dot{I} = T_0[M_H \Delta s_H + M_M \Delta s_M]$$

For each constituent, assuming that c_p values are constant,

$$\Delta s = \int ds = \int \frac{dh}{T} - \int \frac{v\,dp}{T} = \int \frac{c_p\,dT}{T} - R \int \frac{dp}{p} = c_p \ln \frac{T_m}{T_{\text{initial}}} - R \ln \frac{p}{p_{\text{initial}}}$$

The volume fraction of each constituent is 0.5; so the partial pressure of each constituent is one half of the mixture pressure. The mixture pressure equals the initial pressure of each constituent; so $p/p_{\text{initial}} = 0.5$.

$$\dot{I} = T_0 \left\{ M_H \left[c_{p,H} \ln \frac{T_m}{T_H} - R_H \ln \frac{p_{H,m}}{p_H} \right] + M_M \left[c_{p,M} \ln \frac{T_m}{T_M} - R_M \ln \frac{p_{M,m}}{p_M} \right] \right\}$$

$$= 530 \left\{ 0.01 \left[3.45 \ln \frac{575}{530} - \frac{767}{778} \ln 0.5 \right] + 0.08 \left[0.554 \ln \frac{575}{610} - \frac{96.5}{778} \ln 0.5 \right] \right\}$$

$$= 7.35 \text{ B/sec}$$

12·7 Mixtures of real gases

We have observed that the behavior of real gases can often be adequately represented by the ideal-gas equation of state. In such cases, mixtures of these gases can in turn be treated as ideal gases. When the constituents of a gas mixture deviate considerably from ideal-gas behavior, however, the simple relations which apply to ideal-gas mixtures do not hold, and we must resort to certain approximations in determining the properties of a mixture from the properties of its constituents. Three approximation procedures will be considered here: the use of the additive pressure law in conjunction with equations of state of the constituents, the use of the additive volume law in a similar manner, and the use of constituent compressibility factors.

Law of additive pressures. As pointed out in Art. 12·3, the law of additive pressures holds approximately for real-gas mixtures even in some ranges of pressure and temperature where $pv = RT$ is quite inaccurate. If we assume that it does hold for a real-gas mixture, then we write

$$p_m = p_A(T_m, V_m) + p_B(T_m, V_m) + \cdots$$

In this equation $p_A(T_m, V_m)$, $p_B(T_m, V_m)$, etc. denote the pressures that would be exerted by individual constituents if they existed alone at the temperature and volume of the mixture. These are not partial pressures, because partial pressure is defined by $p_i \equiv x_i p_m$, and $p_i = p_i(T_m, V_m)$ only for ideal-gas mixtures. By selecting a suitable equation of state it is possible to determine the pressure of each constituent in a mixture if it existed alone at T_m and V_m. For example, if it is assumed that each gas follows the van der Waals equation of state, the pressure of each gas in the mixture will be represented by an equation such as

$$p_A(T_m, V_m) = \frac{R_u T}{v_{NA} - b_A} - \frac{a_A}{(v_{NA})^2}$$

Other equations of state may also be used. Following through with the use of the van der Waals equation, we relate the molar specific volume of each constituent at T_m and V_m to that of the mixture by

$$v_{NA} \equiv \frac{V_A}{N_A} = \frac{V_m}{N_A} = \frac{V_m}{x_A N_m} = \frac{v_{Nm}}{x_A}$$

and make this substitution in the van der Waals equation to get

$$p_A(T_m, V_m) = \frac{x_A R_u T}{v_{Nm} - x_A b_A} - \frac{x_A^2 a_A}{v_{Nm}^2}$$

Substituting this type of relation for the pressure of each constituent in the additive pressure law equation and collecting terms gives

$$p_m = R_u T \left[\frac{x_A}{v_{Nm} - x_A b_A} + \frac{x_B}{v_{Nm} - x_B b_B} + \cdots \right]$$

$$- \frac{1}{v_{Nm}^2} [a_A x_A^2 + a_B x_B^2 + \cdots]$$

EXAMPLE 12·6.   A gas mixture which is 55 and 45 per cent by mass of nitrogen and carbon dioxide, respectively, occupies 150 cu ft at 14.7 psia, 70 F.   It is compressed to a final volume of 0.5 cu ft.   If the final temperature of the mixture is 100 F, compute the approximate pressure if the gases are assumed to follow the van der Waals equation of state.   Values for the constants in the equation of state follow.

Gas	a, atm-ft^6/(lb mole)^2	b, cu ft/lb mole
Nitrogen	346	0.618
Carbon dioxide	926	0.686

The universal gas constant 0.729 atm-cu ft/lb mole-R is used in connection with these constants.

Solution.   The mole fractions are first determined.

Constituent	Mass Fraction, lb/100 lb of Mixture	Molecular Weight, lb/mole	Moles/100 lb of Mixture	Mole Fraction, moles/100 moles of Mixture
N_2	55	28	1.965	65.8
CO_2	45	44	1.023	34.2
			2.988	

The next step is to determine the number of moles in the mixture.   If it is assumed that the mixture behaves as an ideal gas under the initial low-pressure condition, the number of moles equals

$$N = \frac{pV_m}{R_u T} = \frac{1(150)}{0.729(530)} = 0.388 \text{ mole}$$

After compression the molar specific volume for the mixture is

$$v_{Nm} = \frac{0.5}{0.388} = 1.288 \text{ cu ft/mole}$$

When the mole fractions, molar specific volume for the mixture, and the various constants are known, it is possible to obtain the pressure by substitution into the last equation derived before the statement of this problem:

$$p_m = 0.729(560)\left[\frac{0.658}{1.288 - 0.658(0.618)} + \frac{0.342}{1.288 - 0.342(0.686)}\right]$$
$$- \frac{1}{(1.288)^2}[346(0.658)^2 + 926(0.342)^2] = 438 - 156 = 282 \text{ atm}$$

Law of additive volumes.   As pointed out in Art. 12·4, the law of additive volumes also holds approximately for real-gas mixtures even in some ranges of pressure and temperature where $pv = RT$ is quite inaccurate. If we assume that it does hold for a real-gas mixture, then we write

$$V_m = V_A(p_m, T_m) + V_B(p_m, T_m) + \cdots$$

In this equation $V_A(p_m, T_m)$, $V_B(p_m, T_m)$, etc. denote the volumes of the individual constituents if they existed alone at the pressure and temperature of the mixture. These are not partial volumes, because partial volume is defined by $V' \equiv xV_m$, and $V' = V(p_m, T_m)$ only for ideal-gas mixtures. To get the additive volume formulation in terms of molar specific volumes, divide the form given above by the number of moles in the mixture and use the definition of mole fraction, $x \equiv N/N_m$, to give

$$v_{Nm} = \frac{V_m}{N_m} = \frac{V_A(p_m, T_m)}{N_m} + \frac{V_B(p_m, T_m)}{N_m} + \cdots$$

$$= \frac{x_A V_A(p_m, T_m)}{N_A} + \frac{x_B V_B(p_m, T_m)}{N_B} + \cdots$$

$$= x_A v_{NA}(p_m, T_m) + x_B v_{NB}(p_m, T_m) + \cdots$$

By selecting a suitable equation of state it is possible to determine the molar specific volume of each constituent if it existed alone at p_m and T_m, but a trial-and-error method may be required if the equations of state used are not in an explicit volume form. (For ideal gases, the molar specific volume is the same for all constituents if they existed alone at the same pressure and temperature, but remember that this is not true for real gases.)

EXAMPLE 12·7. Solve Example 12·6 by using the law of additive volumes and the van der Waals equation of state.

Solution. Substituting the mixture molar specific volume and the mole fractions determined in the solution of Example 12·6 into the additive volume formulation

$$v_{Nm} = x_A v_{NA}(p_m, T_m) + x_B v_{NB}(p_m, T_m)$$

gives $$v_{Nm} = 1.288 = 0.658 v_{NA}(p_m, T_m) + 0.342 v_{NB}(p_m, T_m)$$

where the subscript A refers to nitrogen and the subscript B refers to carbon dioxide. Solving for v_{NA} and dropping the notation which reminds us that the molar specific volumes are to be evaluated at the pressure and temperature of the mixture gives

$$v_{NA} = 1.958 - 0.520 v_{NB}$$

The remainder of the solution consists of assuming a value of v_{NB}, solving for v_{NA}, and then using these values in the van der Waals equation to solve for the pressures. Several trials may be needed until the two pressure values are equal as required by the law of additive volumes.

Assuming a value of 1.02 cu ft/mole for v_{NB} gives

$$v_{NA} = 1.958 - 0.520(1.02) = 1.427 \text{ cu ft/mole}$$

Substituting these values into the van der Waals equation and solving for the pressure of each constituent, which is equal to the mixture pressure when the additive volume law is being applied,

$$p_A = \frac{R_u T}{v_{NA} - b} - \frac{a}{v_{NA}^2} = \frac{0.729(560)}{(1.427 - 0.618)} - \frac{346}{(1.427)^2} = 505 - 170 = 335 \text{ atm}$$

$$p_B = \frac{0.729(560)}{(1.02 - 0.686)} - \frac{926}{(1.02)^2} = 1222 - 890 = 332 \text{ atm}$$

This constitutes a satisfactory solution. If the pressures were not equal, other trial values for v_{NA} and v_{NB} would have to be used.

Compressibility factors. If compressibility factors for various gas mixtures were available, it would be possible to employ the relation

$$p_m V_m = Z_m N_m R_u T_m$$

Values of the compressibility factor Z_m for real-gas mixtures are difficult to obtain; hence it is convenient to employ an approximate relation of the type

$$Z_m = x_A Z_A + x_B Z_B + \cdots$$

x_A, x_B, etc. are the mole fractions of the constituents, and Z_A, Z_B, etc. are their compressibility factors. If these compressibility factors are evaluated at the pressure and temperature of the mixture, this equation reduces to the law of additive volumes. This is a convenient procedure because charts of Z as a function of P_R and T_R are available. If the compressibility factors are evaluated at the volume and temperature of the mixture, the equation above reduces to the law of additive pressures. The use of the additive pressure law with compressibility factors is complicated by the fact that charts of Z as a function of v_R and T_R are required, and these are not readily available.

EXAMPLE 12·8. Solve Example 12·6 by using a compressibility factor for the mixture.
Solution. We will use the constituent compressibility factors at the pressure and temperature of the mixture. Thus we will be using the additive volume law. The first step is to determine the reduced pressure and temperature values for the nitrogen and carbon dioxide. From Table 5·2, the following values are obtained for the critical temperatures and pressures of the gases.

Gas	Critical Temperature, R	Critical Pressure, atm
Nitrogen	227.2	33.5
Carbon dioxide	547.8	72.9

The reduced values are

Nitrogen:
$$T_R = \frac{T}{T_c} = \frac{560}{227.2} = 2.47$$

$$P_R = \frac{P}{P_c} = \frac{P}{33.5}$$

Carbon dioxide
$$T_R = \frac{T}{T_c} = \frac{560}{547.8} = 1.02$$

$$P_R = \frac{P}{P_c} = \frac{P}{72.9}$$

Since the pressure is unknown, a trial value of 300 atm will be assumed, for which the reduced pressures are

Nitrogen:
$$P_R = 8.96$$

Carbon dioxide:
$$P_R = 4.12$$

By using the reduced values and Fig. 5·4, the following compressibility factor values are found:

Nitrogen:
$$Z_A = 1.15$$

Carbon dioxide:
$$Z_B = 0.57$$

The composite compressibility factor for the mixture may be found from
$$Z_m = x_A Z_A + x_B Z_B = 0.658(1.15) + 0.342(0.57) = 0.952$$
Then
$$p = \frac{Z_m R_u T}{v_{Nm}} = \frac{0.952(0.729)560}{1.288} = 301 \text{ atm}$$

If this calculated pressure value were not equal to the assumed pressure, it would be necessary to make other trial solutions.

Few experimental data for real-gas mixtures are available from which it would be possible to draw conclusions relative to the accuracy of the three methods used to solve the same problem in Examples 12·6, 7, and 8. This is one illustration of the fact that the general problem of determining the properties of real-gas mixtures has not been fully solved.

12·8   Mixtures of ideal gases and vapors

For the purpose of the following discussion, let us call a gas which exists at a temperature lower than its critical temperature a vapor. Thus a vapor can be liquefied by an increase in pressure at constant temperature. The analysis of problems dealing with gas-vapor mixtures is, in general, similar to that for a gas mixture. However, an important additional fact must be considered; that is, the maximum pressure of a vapor in a mixture depends on the temperature of the mixture. To illustrate this, consider a mixture of nitrogen and oxygen at a mixture pressure of 15 psia and a temperature of 100 F. The mole fraction of either constituent can have any value from 0 to 1.0, and the partial pressure can have a corresponding value from 0 to 15 psia. Under the stated conditions these gases follow very closely the ideal-gas equation of state; so a partial pressure equals the pressure of the constituent existing alone at the temperature and volume of the mixture. Now, in contrast, consider a mixture of nitrogen and water vapor at 100 F and a mixture pressure of 15 psia. The steam tables show that at 100 F the maximum pressure under which water vapor can exist is 0.9492 psia; so the mole fraction and partial pressure of water vapor in this mixture are strictly limited. Furthermore, the pressure and temperature of the nitrogen–oxygen mixture can be varied over wide ranges without affecting the composition of the mixture; but increasing the pressure or decreasing the temperature of the nitrogen–water-vapor mixture even slightly may cause some of the water vapor to condense, thereby changing the composition of the gas-vapor mixture. Several examples will show the application of the principles involved.

EXAMPLE 12·9. A mixture of 0.1 lb of saturated water vapor and $\frac{1}{2}$ lb of air is contained in a tank at a temperature of 240 F. Compute the total pressure of the mixture and the volume of the tank.

Solution. From the tables of the properties of steam, the saturation pressure and saturation specific volume for water vapor at 240 F are

$$p_v = 24.969 \text{ psia}$$
$$v_g = 16.323 \text{ cu ft/lb}$$

The actual volume occupied by the water vapor or the volume of the tank is

$$V = m_v v_g = 0.1(16.323) = 1.63 \text{ cu ft}$$

This is also the volume occupied by the air. If we assume in accordance with Dalton's law that the air behaves as though it existed alone at the temperature and volume of the mixture, the pressure of the air may be determined from the ideal-gas equation of state.

$$p_a = \frac{m_a R_a T}{V} = \frac{0.5(53.3)700}{1.63(144)} = 79.3 \text{ psia}$$

Again assuming that Dalton's law holds, the total pressure of the mixture is equal to the sum of the pressures exerted by the water vapor and the air.

$$p_m = p_v + p_a = 24.97 + 79.3 = 104.3 \text{ psia}$$

EXAMPLE 12·10. A vessel contains 0.1 lb of wet steam having a quality of 4 per cent and 0.2 lb of nitrogen at a temperature of 100 F. Compute the total pressure of the mixture and the mass of nitrogen per pound of liquid water.

Solution. The data taken from the steam tables for water at 100 F follow.

$$p_v = 0.949 \text{ psia}$$
$$v_f = 0.0161 \text{ cu ft/lb}$$
$$v_g = 350.4 \text{ cu ft/lb} = v_{fg} \quad \text{approximately}$$

The specific volume of the wet vapor (liquid–vapor mixture) equals

$$v_x = v_f + x v_{fg} = 0.0161 + 0.04(350.3) = 14.028 \text{ cu ft/lb}$$

or, using the approximate relation for v_x which actually gives the specific volume of the vapor only

$$v_x = xv_g = 0.04(350.3) = 14.012 \text{ cu ft/lb}$$

The volume of the vapor is, therefore,

$$V = mv_x = 0.1(14.0) = 1.40 \text{ cu ft}$$

This is the volume occupied by the 0.2 lb of nitrogen as well as by the water vapor. The pressure exerted by the nitrogen can be computed by use of the ideal-gas equation of state.

$$p_{N_2} = \frac{mR_uT}{VM} = \frac{0.2(1544)560}{1.4(28)144} = 30.6 \text{ psia}$$

The total pressure of the mixture is

$$p_m = p_v + p_{N_2} = 0.949 + 30.6 = 31.55 \text{ psia}$$

Since the quality is 4 per cent, 96 per cent of the water is liquid; therefore the mass of liquid present is

$$m_f = 0.96(0.1) = 0.096 \text{ lb}$$

The mass of nitrogen per pound of liquid water is

$$\frac{m_{N_2}}{m_f} = \frac{0.2}{0.096} = 2.08 \text{ lb N}_2/\text{lb liquid water}$$

EXAMPLE 12·11.   One pound of water vapor and 0.1 lb of air are contained in a tank having a volume of 13.04 cu ft. If the temperature of the mixture is 300 F, compute the pressure of the mixture.

Solution.   From the superheated steam table, the pressure of steam at a temperature of 300 F and a volume of 13.04 cu ft/lb is 34 psia. The air pressure may be determined from the ideal-gas equation of state.

$$p_a = \frac{m_aR_aT}{V} = \frac{0.1(53.3)760}{13.04(144)} = 2.15 \text{ psia}$$

The total pressure of the mixture is, therefore, equal to

$$p_m = p_a + p_v = 2.15 + 34 = 36.15 \text{ psia}$$

12·9 Atmospheric air

Many different gas-vapor mixtures are encountered in engineering, but the one which receives the most attention by far is the mixture of air and water vapor commonly referred to as *atmospheric air*. In most applications dealing with atmospheric air the temperatures—and consequently the maximum vapor partial pressures—are low enough so that the water vapor behaves as an ideal gas. That is, the water vapor follows $pv = RT$, its enthalpy is a function of temperature only, and its partial pressure in the mixture equals the pressure it would exert if it existed alone at the temperature and volume of the mixture.

For support of the statement that water vapor in atmospheric air follows $pv = RT$, you can calculate from steam-table data some compressibility factor values for steam at low pressures. For example, even at a partial pressure as high as 4 psia, which cannot be reached unless the mixture is at a temperature of nearly 153 F, the compressibility factor is 0.994⁻. For vapor pressures and temperatures usually encountered in atmospheric air, the compressibility factor is even closer to unity.

The fact that the enthalpy of water at low pressure depends only on temperature can be verified by means of a Ts diagram for steam such as Chart A·2 in the appendix. For superheated steam at low pressures the constant-enthalpy lines coincide with constant-temperature lines. Thus no matter what the pressure of water vapor in atmospheric air is, its enthalpy can be read from the superheated vapor tables at 1 psia (the lowest pressure entry in the table) and the atmospheric air temperature. For temperatures lower than 120 F (the lowest temperature entry in the superheated steam table), the enthalpy of water vapor at any pressure equals very nearly the enthalpy of saturated vapor at the same temperature. Repeating this important fact for emphasis, *in atmospheric air the enthalpy of the water vapor equals (very nearly) the enthalpy of saturated vapor at the same temperature.*

For an ideal-gas mixture the partial pressure of each constituent equals the pressure which that constituent would exert if it existed alone at the temperature and volume of the mixture. For this reason we will henceforth often refer to the partial pressure of water vapor in atmospheric air simply as *the pressure of the vapor* in the air, since the vapor behaves in all respects as though it were alone at this pressure and the mixture temperature. (The presence of air actually has a slight effect on the equilibrium temperature of liquid and vapor water at a given pressure, making it different from that given in the steam tables for water as a pure substance, but this effect is negligible with atmospheric air.)

The air constituent of atmospheric air is often referred to as the *dry air* to distinguish it from the mixture. Thus atmospheric air is composed of dry air plus water vapor. In situations involving atmospheric air the temperature range is nearly always so limited that the c_p of dry air can be considered constant at 0.24 B/lb-F.

12·10   Relative humidity and humidity ratio

Two terms frequently used in dealing with mixtures of air and water vapor are *relative humidity* and *humidity ratio*. It is important to learn the definitions of these terms and the relationship between them.

Relative humidity ϕ is defined as the ratio of the pressure (i.e. partial pressure) of the vapor in the mixture to the saturation pressure of the vapor at the temperature of the mixture. Let the pressure of the vapor in the mixture be designated by p_v, and let the vapor saturation pressure at the mixture temperature be designated by p_g. (The subscript g has been adopted because it is used in the steam tables to refer to saturated vapor.) Then the relative humidity is defined as

$$\phi \equiv \frac{p_v}{p_g} \qquad (12\cdot1)$$

If the water vapor in the mixture and saturated water vapor at the same temperature follow the ideal-gas equation of state, as they do to a high degree of accuracy at the temperatures normally encountered with atmospheric air, relative humidity can be expressed in other forms by substituting for each pressure its equivalent RT/v. Thus

$$\phi \equiv \frac{p_v}{p_g} = \frac{RTv_g}{v_vRT} = \frac{v_g}{v_v} = \frac{\rho_v}{\rho_g} \qquad (12\cdot2)$$

The specific volume of the vapor in atmospheric air can thus be determined from the mixture temperature and the relative humidity,

$$v_v = \frac{v_g}{\phi} \qquad (12\cdot2)$$

Notice that relative humidity pertains only to the *vapor* in atmospheric air. It is independent of the pressure and density of the dry air in the mixture. It is independent of the barometric pressure.

Atmospheric air which contains saturated water vapor has a relative humidity of 1.0 or 100 per cent and is called *saturated air*, although it is only the water vapor in the air which is in a saturation state.

A *Ts* diagram for water vapor in atmospheric air is shown in Fig. 12·2. If point 1 represents the state of the water vapor as it exists in the mixture, relative humidity is the ratio of p_1 to p_2, where state 2 is a saturation state at the mixture temperature.

Humidity ratio ω is defined as the ratio of the mass of vapor in atmospheric air to the mass of dry air. Notice that it is not the same as the mass fraction of water vapor in the mixture. Using the subscript v for vapor and a for dry air,

$$\omega \equiv \frac{m_v}{m_a} \qquad (12\cdot3)$$

and, since the volume is the same for both constituents of the mixture,

$$\omega \equiv \frac{m_v}{m_a} = \frac{\rho_v}{\rho_a} = \frac{v_a}{v_v} \qquad (12\cdot3)$$

Assuming that both the air and the water vapor behave as ideal gases, we can express the humidity ratio as

$$\omega \equiv \frac{m_v}{m_a} = \frac{p_v V R_a T}{R_v T p_a V} = \frac{p_v R_a}{p_a R_v} = \frac{p_v R_a}{(p_m - p_v)R_v}$$

Solving for p_v gives

$$p_v = \frac{\omega R_v p_m}{\omega R_v + R_a}$$

This relation is quite useful in dealing with combustion products at low pressures, R_a being taken as the gas constant of the dry products of combustion.

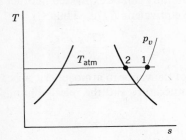

Fig. 12·2   *Ts* diagram of water vapor in atmospheric air.

Humidity ratio is also called specific humidity and absolute humidity. The relationship between humidity ratio and relative humidity is obtained by combining equations 12·2 and 12·3:

$$\omega = \frac{v_a}{v_g} \phi \qquad (12\cdot4)$$

EXAMPLE 12·12.   Atmospheric air at 14.696 psia, 90 F, has a relative humidity of 70 per cent. Compute the humidity ratio.

Solution.   From the steam tables, the saturation pressure for water vapor at 90 F is 0.6982 psia. The partial pressure of the water vapor in the mixture is then

$$p_v = \phi(p_g) = 0.7(0.6982) = 0.489 \text{ psia}$$

Since the total atmospheric pressure is equal to the sum of the partial pressures, the air pressure equals

$$p_a = p_m - p_v = 14.696 - 0.489 = 14.207 \text{ psia}$$

The specific volume of the air may now be found from the ideal-gas equation.

$$v_a = \frac{RT}{p} = \frac{53.3(90 + 460)}{(14.207)144} = 14.4 \text{ cu ft/lb}$$

The value for v_g, taken from the steam tables, is 468 cu ft/lb. The humidity ratio is then

$$\omega = \frac{v_a \phi}{v_g} = \frac{14.4(0.7)}{468} = 0.0215 \frac{\text{lb water vapor}}{\text{lb dry air}}$$

$$= 150.5 \frac{\text{grains of water vapor}}{\text{lb dry air}}$$

The result is often expressed as grains of water vapor per pound of air, where

$$1 \text{ lb} = 7000 \text{ grains}$$

12·11 Temperatures used in the determination of the properties of atmospheric air

Four temperatures referred to in the determination of the properties of atmospheric air are dry-bulb temperature, dew-point temperature, adiabatic saturation temperature or thermodynamic wet-bulb temperature, and wet-bulb temperature.

Dry-bulb temperature. By dry-bulb temperature is meant simply the temperature of the mixture as it would be measured by any of several types of ordinary thermometers placed in the mixture. Care must be exercised in measuring the temperature of atmospheric air to avoid errors caused by radiant heat transfer between the thermometer and the walls of the containing vessel. Where temperature differences exist, shielded thermometer elements should be used. The term *dry-bulb* temperature is used to distinguish the temperature of the mixture from the temperature reading obtained from a thermometer which has its temperature-sensitive element wrapped in gauze which is soaked in water.

Dew-point temperature. The dew-point temperature of an air–vapor mixture is defined as the saturation temperature of the vapor corresponding to its partial pressure in the mixture. It is thus the temperature at which condensation begins if the mixture is cooled at constant pressure.

A simple laboratory determination of dew-point temperature consists of partially filling a metal cup with water, adding ice, and then stirring while observing the water temperature as it is lowered. The temperature at which moisture begins to collect on the outside of the cup is approximately the dew-point temperature of the room air. One of the errors in this method results from the fact that the water temperature and the temperature of the air in contact with the cup are not exactly the same.

If point 1 in Fig. 12·3 represents the water vapor in atmospheric air, the dew point is the temperature at point 2 or the saturation temperature corresponding to the vapor pressure. States 1, 2, and x as well as any other states with the same vapor pressure have the same dew point. For air at 100 per cent relative humidity (saturated air) the dew-point temperature equals the dry-bulb temperature.

EXAMPLE 12·13. Determine the dew point of atmospheric air at 14.696 psia, 90 F, 70 per cent relative humidity.

Solution. From the steam tables, the saturation pressure for water vapor at 90 F is 0.6982 psia. The partial pressure of the water vapor in the mixture is then

$$p_v = \phi(p_g) = 0.70(0.6982) = 0.489 \text{ psia}$$

The dew point is the saturation temperature corresponding to this pressure. This is found from the steam tables to be approximately 79 F.

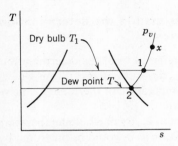

Fig. 12·3 T_2 is dew point of states 1, 2, and x.

Adiabatic saturation temperature. In atmospheric air with a relative humidity of less than 100 per cent, the water vapor is at a pressure lower than its saturation pressure. Therefore, if this air is placed in contact with liquid water, some of the water will evaporate into the air. The humidity ratio of the air will increase. If the evaporation occurs in a thermally insulated container, the temperature of the air will decrease because at least part of the latent heat of vaporization of the water that evaporates will come from the air. The lower the initial humidity ratio is, the greater the amount of evaporation, and the greater the temperature decrease will be; so we have here the basis of an indirect measurement of humidity ratio.

Adiabatic saturation temperature of atmospheric air is defined as the temperature which results from adiabatically adding water to the atmospheric air in steady flow until it becomes saturated, the water being supplied at the final temperature of the mixture. At first it appears that this definition is circular, because to determine the adiabatic saturation temperature we must supply water which is at that temperature. Actually the definition is operational and sufficient, and the adiabatic saturation temperature can be found by the following operations: (1) Add water at any temperature adiabatically to steadily flowing atmospheric air until it becomes saturated. (2) Measure the temperature of the saturated air. (3) Change the temperature of the water being added to equal that of the saturated air as measured in step 2. (4) Repeat steps 2 and 3 until the temperature of the saturated air equals that of the water being added. This is the adiabatic saturation temperature of the atmospheric air.

To see how a measurement of the adiabatic saturation temperature can be used to determine the humidity ratio of atmospheric air, consider the steady-flow system shown in Fig. 12·4. Air of unknown humidity ratio ω_1 enters at section 1. The air leaving at section 2 is saturated, and, since the water added is at the same temperature, this is the adiabatic saturation

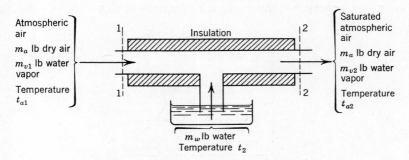

Fig. 12·4   Steady-flow system for determining adiabatic saturation temperature.

temperature. The total or mixture pressure is constant throughout the system. The mixture pressure and the temperatures at sections 1 and 2 can be measured.

Noting that there is no work done, the process is adiabatic, and changes in kinetic and potential energy are negligible, we can apply the first law to this steady-flow system to get

$$m_a h_{a1} + m_{v1} h_{v1} + (m_{v2} - m_{v1})h_{f2} = m_a h_{a2} + m_{v2} h_{v2}$$

In this equation, $(m_{v2} - m_{v1})$ is the amount of water added, and the enthalpy of the water is written as h_{f2} because the water is introduced at the temperature t_2. Dividing by the mass of air m_a, and noting that $h_{v1} = h_{g1}$ very nearly, as explained in Art. 12·9, and $h_{v2} = h_{g2}$ exactly because the vapor at section 2 is saturated, we have

$$h_{a1} + \omega_1 h_{g1} + (\omega_2 - \omega_1)h_{f2} = h_{a2} + \omega_2 h_{g2}$$

$$\omega_1 = \frac{h_{a2} - h_{a1} + \omega_2(h_{g2} - h_{f2})}{h_{g1} - h_{f2}}$$

$$= \frac{c_{pa}(t_2 - t_1) + \omega_2 h_{fg2}}{h_{g1} - h_{f2}}$$

This expression can be evaluated if t_1, t_2, and p_m are measured. Since $\phi_2 = 1.0$,

$$\omega_2 = \frac{v_{a2}}{v_{g2}} = \frac{R_a T_2}{(p_m - p_{g2})v_{g2}}$$

so that ω_2 is a function of only p_m and T_2 (or t_2, the difference between T_2 and t_2 depending only on the scales on which they are measured).

The states of the water vapor in the mixture during the adiabatic saturation process are shown on a Ts diagram in Fig. 12·5. During the

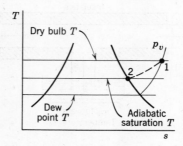

Fig. 12·5 Adiabatic saturation.

process the vapor pressure increases and the temperature decreases; so the adiabatic saturation temperature is higher than the dew-point and lower than the dry-bulb temperature. For the limiting case of a saturated mixture, the dry-bulb, dew-point, and adiabatic saturation temperatures are the same.

The procedure and analysis just outlined provide a method of determining the humidity ratio of atmospheric air from temperature and barometric-pressure measurements. Actually it is inconvenient to saturate atmospheric air by the procedure described, so other methods are used.

Wet-bulb temperature. To avoid the difficulty of adiabatically saturating a sample of atmospheric air, the wet-bulb temperature analysis has been devised. This procedure involves the passage of an unsaturated air-vapor mixture over a wetted surface until a condition of dynamic equilibrium has been attained. When this condition has been reached, the heat transferred from the air-vapor stream to the liquid film to evaporate part of it is equal to the energy carried from the liquid film to the air-vapor stream by the diffusing vapor.

The equilibrium condition is obtained and the temperature of the resulting air-vapor mixture is measured by means of a thermometer, the bulb of which is covered with gauze soaked in clean water. A schematic diagram is shown as Fig. 12·6. The flow of atmospheric air is provided either by a fan or by mounting the thermometer in a holder with a swivel handle so that it can be rotated or whirled through the air. The thermometer reading is called the wet-bulb temperature.

The relationship between the wet-bulb temperature and the adiabatic saturation temperature for any gas-vapor mixture depends on the heat-transfer and diffusion characteristics of the mixture. It happens that for air–water-vapor mixtures in the normal pressure and temperature range of atmospheric air the wet-bulb temperature measured by the usual type of

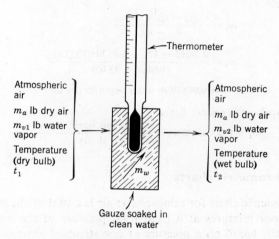

Fig. 12·6 Wet-bulb thermometer.

instrument is very nearly equal to the adiabatic saturation temperature. This is simply fortuitous, and the equality does not hold for most gas-vapor mixtures. For example, in the air-vapor mixtures in oil-storage tanks and in alcohol–air mixtures, the difference between the wet-bulb temperature and the adiabatic saturation temperature is quite large, and serious errors would follow from the assumption that they are equal.

EXAMPLE 12·14. Determine the humidity ratio of air that has a dry-bulb temperature of 85 F, a wet-bulb temperature of 65 F, and a barometric pressure of 14.696 psia.

Solution. The solution involves first assuming that the wet-bulb temperature is equal to the adiabatic saturation temperature and then applying the first law to an adiabatic saturation process which proceeds from the specified state to the saturated state at 65 F. Call these two states 1 and 2, respectively.

The relative humidity at state 2 is 100 per cent, since complete saturation is assumed. For this condition the vapor pressure equals the saturation pressure at 65 F, which is found from the steam tables to be 0.3056 psia. The pressure of the dry air is then

$$p_{a2} = p_m - p_{v2} = 14.696 - 0.3056 = 14.39 \text{ psia}$$

The specific volume of dry air is

$$v_{a2} = \frac{R_a T_2}{p_{a2}} = \frac{53.3(525)}{14.39(144)} = 13.52 \text{ cu ft/lb}$$

and the humidity ratio at state 2 is

$$\omega_2 = \frac{v_{a2}}{v_{g2}} \phi = \frac{13.52(1.0)}{1021.4} = 0.01321 \text{ lb/lb dry air}$$

Application of the first law to the adiabatic saturation process leads (as is shown earlier in this article) to

$$\omega_1 = \frac{c_{pa}(t_2 - t_1) + \omega_2 h_{fg2}}{h_{g1} - h_{f2}}$$

$$\omega_1 = \frac{0.24(65 - 85) + 0.01321(1057.1)}{(1098.8 - 33.05)}$$

$$= 0.00859 \text{ lb water vapor/lb dry air}$$

This is often expressed in grains; hence

$$\omega_1 = 0.00859(7000) = 60.1 \frac{\text{grains water vapor}}{\text{lb dry air}}$$

12·12 Psychrometric charts

A psychrometric chart for atmospheric air is a plot of the properties of air–water-vapor mixtures at a fixed total pressure of the mixture. The chart is usually based on a pressure of one standard atmosphere (14.696 psia), but charts for other barometric pressures are available. The specific properties are expressed not per pound of mixture but per pound of dry air in the mixture.

A skeleton outline of a psychrometric chart is shown in Fig. 12·7. (A complete chart is included in the appendix.) The horizontal and vertical axes are selected to represent dry-bulb temperature and humidity ratio, respectively.

The line *A-B* is the saturation line and represents states for which the relative humidity is 100 per cent. This line and other constant ϕ lines can be readily plotted because for states of constant relative humidity the humidity ratio is a function of only the mixture pressure and the dry-bulb temperature. This fact is shown by

$$\omega = \frac{v_a}{v_g} \phi = \frac{R_a T}{p_a v_g} \phi = \frac{R_a T}{(p_m - p_v) v_g} \phi = \frac{R_a T}{(p_m - \phi p_g) v_g} \phi$$

As long as the air and water vapor both behave as ideal gases and the mixture pressure is constant, there is a unique relationship between the vapor pressure and the humidity ratio as can be seen from

$$\omega \equiv \frac{m_v}{m_a} = \frac{p_v V R_a T}{p_a V R_v T} = \frac{p_v R_a}{p_a R_v} = \frac{p_v R_a}{(p_m - p_v) R_v}$$

Thus a vapor-pressure scale can be constructed along with the humidity ratio scale on the vertical axis. The humidity ratio scale was selected as a linear scale so the vapor-pressure scale is not linear.

The dew point of atmospheric air is a function of the vapor pressure only; so a dew-point temperature scale can also be constructed along the

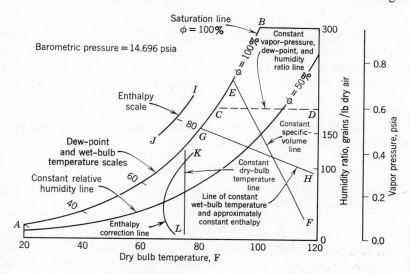

Fig. 12·7 Skeleton outline of psychrometric chart.

vertical axis. To facilitate the reading of the chart, the dew-point temperature scale is laid out along the saturation line *A-B* instead of as another scale at one side of the chart. For each state on line *A-B* ($\phi = 100$ per cent) the dew-point equals the dry-bulb temperature; so the dew-point scale values can be plotted by simply following vertical lines up from the various dry-bulb temperature scale values.

Horizontal lines such as *C-D* therefore are lines of constant humidity ratio, vapor pressure, and dew point.

The chart also has lines of constant specific volume, given as volume of mixture (or, identically, of dry air or of vapor) per pound of dry air. One of these lines is shown as line *E-F*.

Consider again the adiabatic saturation process which was discussed in the preceding article. By definition, every state that air passes through during the adiabatic saturation process has the same adiabatic saturation temperature. Thus the path of an adiabatic saturation process, along which the vapor pressure increases and the dry-bulb temperature decreases, is a line of constant adiabatic saturation temperature and for the special case of air–water-vapor mixtures it is a constant wet-bulb temperature line. Such a line is shown as *G-H*.

Lines of constant wet-bulb temperature are approximately lines of constant mixture enthalpy. In order to demonstrate this, we first write an energy balance for an adiabatic saturation process,

$$h_{a1} + \omega_1 h_{v1} + (\omega_2 - \omega_1) h_{f2} = h_{a2} + \omega_2 h_{v2}$$

where the subscript 1 refers to any section in the adiabatic saturation flow path and the subscript 2 refers to the fully saturated state. If we now define the mixture enthalpy as $h_m \equiv h_a + \omega h_v$, noting that this is the enthalpy *of the mixture* expressed *per pound of dry air*, the energy balance becomes

$$h_{m1} - \omega_1 h_{f2} = h_{m2} - \omega_2 h_{f2}$$

Since subscript 1 refers to *any* section in the adiabatic saturation flow path, this last equation can be written as

$$h_m - \omega h_{f2} = \text{constant}$$

Since ωh_f evaluated at the adiabatic saturation temperature is always very small in comparison with h_m, we have

$$h_m \approx \text{constant}$$

for the adiabatic saturation process. Thus a constant wet-bulb temperature line (which for atmospheric air is very nearly a constant adiabatic saturation temperature line) such as *G-H* is approximately a constant-enthalpy line, so the psychrometric chart carries an enthalpy scale which is read against the constant wet-bulb temperature lines. For accurate determination of the enthalpy of an unsaturated air–vapor mixture, a correction must be applied to the scale value. If we do not neglect the ωh_{f2} term, the enthalpy of the mixture at any state is

$$h_m = h_{m2} - (\omega_2 - \omega) h_{f2} = h_{m2} + \text{correction}$$

where the subscript 2 refers to the adiabatic saturation end state. The correction term, $-(\omega_2 - \omega) h_{f2}$, which literally corrects for the assumption that the mixture enthalpy is constant along a constant wet-bulb temperature line, is a function of specific humidity and wet-bulb temperature only, and so it can be plotted on the chart. *K-L* is such a line of constant enthalpy correction. The enthalpy of any mixture then is the enthalpy at the corresponding adiabatic saturation state plus the correction which is read from a curve such as *K-L* passing through the mixture state on the chart. (Several other methods are used to show the correction on psychrometric charts, and the correction is usually so small that many charts do not show it at all.)

EXAMPLE 12·15. If the dry-bulb and wet-bulb temperatures of atmospheric air are 90 and 70 F, respectively, determine by use of the psychrometric chart (*a*) the humidity ratio, (*b*) the relative humidity, (*c*) the dew-point temperature, (*d*) the pressure of the water vapor, (*e*) the volume per pound of dry air, and (*f*) the enthalpy per pound of dry air.

Solution. The particular point on the chart which designates the condition of the atmospheric air is located by finding the intersection of the vertical 90 F dry-bulb temperature line and the sloping 70 F wet-bulb temperature line.

(*a*) The humidity ratio is found by moving along a horizontal line to the proper scale on the diagram. The approximate value is 78 grains of water vapor per pound of dry air.

(*b*) The relative humidity is estimated by observing the location of the point between two of the curved relative humidity lines. The approximate value is 37 per cent.

(*c*) The dew-point temperature is found by moving along a horizontal line through the point until the dew-point temperature scale is reached. The approximate value is 60.2 F.

(*d*) The partial pressure of the water vapor is found by following a horizontal line until the vapor-pressure scale is reached. The value is 0.26 psia.

(*e*) The volume per pound of dry air is estimated by observing the location of the point between two of the constant-volume lines. The approximate value is 14.1 cu ft/lb dry air.

(*f*) The enthalpy may be found by first following the sloping 70 F wet-bulb temperature line until it intersects the enthalpy scale. The enthalpy value is 34.1 B/lb for saturated air at 70 F wet-bulb temperature. For 90 F dry-bulb and 70 F wet-bulb temperatures, the enthalpy correction is approximately −0.2 B/lb, so the mixture enthalpy is 34.1 − 0.2 = 33.9 B/lb.

12·13 Processes of air–vapor mixtures under constant total pressure

Many processes of air–vapor mixtures occur under conditions of constant total pressure. Among these are the heating, cooling, humidification, and dehumidification which occur in air-conditioning systems, evaporative cooling, and drying. The application of the principles discussed in this chapter to some of these processes is illustrated in the following three examples. Many more applications are treated in the problems at the end of this chapter.

EXAMPLE 12·16. Atmospheric air has a relative humidity of 68 per cent at a dry-bulb temperature of 50 F. If the air is heated to 70 F, determine the amount of heat that must be transferred per pound of dry air under steady-flow conditions. Atmospheric pressure equals 14.696 psia.

Solution. Under the specified condition there will be no change in the quantity of vapor present for each pound of dry air, since moisture is neither added nor removed during the process.

The first step is to determine the value of the initial humidity ratio. The saturation pressure and specific volume values for the water vapor corresponding to 50 F, taken from the steam tables, are 0.17811 psia and 1703.2 cu ft/lb, respectively. From the relation for relative humidity, the vapor pressure is

$$p_v = \phi(p_g) = 0.68(0.17811) = 0.121 \text{ psia}$$

The air pressure equals

$$p_a = p_m - p_v = 14.696 - 0.121 = 14.575 \text{ psia}$$

From the ideal-gas equation of state the specific volume of the air is

$$v_a = \frac{R_a T}{p_a} = \frac{53.3(510)}{14.575(144)} = 12.95 \text{ cu ft/lb dry air}$$

The humidity ratio is then

$$\omega = \frac{v_a}{v_g} \phi = \frac{12.95(0.68)}{1703.2} = 0.00516 \text{ lb/lb dry air}$$

Application of the first law to this steady-flow process in which work = 0 and $\Delta KE = 0$ gives

$$q = h_{a2} + \omega h_{v2} - (h_{a1} + \omega h_{v1})$$

$$= h_{a2} - h_{a1} + \omega(h_{v2} - h_{v1}) = c_p(t_2 - t_1) + \omega(h_{g2} - h_{g1})$$

$$= 0.24(70 - 50) + 0.00516(1092.3 - 1083.7) = 4.85 \text{ B/lb}$$

(The energy balance can also be written as

$$q = h_{m2} - h_{m1}$$

and the mixture enthalpy values can be obtained from a psychrometric chart.)

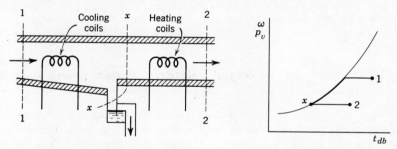

Fig. 12·8 Dehumidification and reheating.

The next example deals with the dehumidification of air in an air-conditioning system. The air is first cooled to a temperature lower than its initial dew point to cause some of the water vapor to condense. The air leaving the cooler is saturated at a low temperature and is unsuitable for use in rooms occupied by people because it is clammy. It must be heated or mixed with warmer air to produce a condition which is normally regarded as comfortable. The dehumidification and reheating processes are shown on a psychrometric chart in Fig. 12·8. Notice that the temperature to which the mixture must be cooled is the dew point corresponding to the desired final condition.

EXAMPLE 12·17. Atmospheric air at 80 F and 60 per cent relative humidity is to be brought to 75 F and 40 per cent relative humidity by means of a system comprised of a cooler, with provision for removing condensate, followed by a heater. Barometric pressure is 14.696 psia. The mass rate of flow of atmospheric air entering the system is 202.6 lb/hr. Determine (a) the mass of water removed per hour, (b) the heat removed in the cooler per hour, and (c) the heat added in the heater per hour.

Solution. Refer to Fig. 12·8 for a sketch of the system. The first step in the solution is to determine the humidity ratios for the initial and final conditions.

$$\text{Initial Condition} \qquad\qquad \text{Final Condition}$$

$$p_v = \phi p_g = 0.60(0.5069) = 0.304 \text{ psia} \qquad p_v = 0.40(0.4298) = 0.172 \text{ psia}$$

$$p_a = p_m - p_v = 14.696 - 0.304 = 14.392 \text{ psia} \qquad p_a = 14.696 - 0.172 = 14.524 \text{ psia}$$

$$v_a = \frac{R_a T}{p_a} = \frac{53.3(540)}{14.392(144)} = 13.89 \text{ cu ft/lb} \qquad v_a = \frac{53.3(535)}{14.524(144)} = 13.64 \text{ cu ft/lb}$$

$$\omega = \frac{v_a}{v_g}\phi = \frac{13.89(0.60)}{633.1} = 0.01316 \text{ lb/lb} \qquad \omega = \frac{13.64(0.40)}{740.0} = 0.00738 \text{ lb/lb}$$

We now find the mass flow rate of dry air from

$$M_{\text{atm air,1}} = M_{da} + M_{v1} = M_{da} + \omega_1 M_{da} = M_{da}(1 + \omega_1)$$

$$M_{da} = \frac{M_{\text{atm air,1}}}{1 + \omega_1} = \frac{202.6}{1.01316} = 200 \text{ lb/hr}$$

(a) The mass flow rate of water removed is

$$M_w = M_{da}(\omega_1 - \omega_2) = 200(0.01316 - 0.00738) = 1.156 \text{ lb/hr}$$

(b) The mixture leaving the cooler will be saturated and must have the same humidity ratio as the mixture in the desired final condition. Thus the temperature at the cooler outlet must be the dew point corresponding to the final condition. This is the saturation temperature corresponding to the final vapor pressure of 0.172 psia and is approximately 49 F. The cooler must, therefore, cool the air from 80 to 49 F. During the latter part of this cooling process (while the mixture is at temperatures lower than the dew point of the initial state) water is removed. Per pound of dry air the amount of water removed is $(\omega_1 - \omega_2) = 0.01316 - 0.00738 = 0.00578$ lb/lb dry air. Application of the first law to the cooler in which work $= 0$, $\Delta KE = 0$, and the flow is steady gives

$$q_{\text{out}} = h_{a1} + \omega_1 h_{v1} - h_{ax} - \omega_x h_{vx} - (\omega_1 - \omega_2)h_{fx}$$

We assume that all the condensate leaves at the temperature t_x. Noting that $\omega_x = \omega_2$, $h_v = h_g$ at the same temperature, and $\Delta h_a = c_{pa}\,\Delta t$, we have then

$$q_{\text{out}} = c_{pa}(t_1 - t_x) + \omega_1 h_{g1} - \omega_2 h_{gx} - (\omega_1 - \omega_2)h_{fx}$$

$$= 0.24(80 - 49) + 0.01316(1096.6) - 0.00738(1083.2) - 0.00578(17.1)$$

$$= 13.8 \text{ B/lb dry air}$$

The rate of heat removal is

$$\dot{Q} = M_{da}q_{\text{out}} = 200(13.8) = 2760 \text{ B/hr}$$

(c) Application of the first law in similar fashion to the heater gives

$$q = h_{a2} + \omega_2 h_{v2} - h_{ax} - \omega_x h_{vx}$$

$$= c_p(t_2 - t_x) + \omega_2(h_{g2} - h_{gx})$$

$$= 0.24(75 - 49) + 0.00738(1094.5 - 1083.2)$$

$$= 6.3 \text{ B/lb dry air}$$

The rate of heat addition is

$$\dot{Q} = M_{da}q = 200(6.3) = 1260 \text{ B/hr}$$

(This problem can also be solved quickly and with only a slight loss in accuracy by means of the psychrometric chart.)

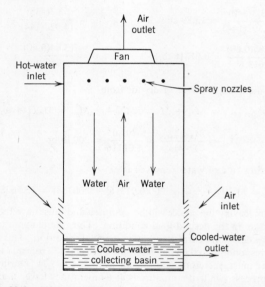

Fig. 12·9 Schematic diagram of induced-draft cooling tower.

In locations where sufficient cooling water cannot be obtained from a river, lake, or ocean, it is necessary to cool water by means of a cooling tower or spray pond so that it can be used over and over again to remove heat from buildings, power plants, refrigerators, and other equipment. A schematic sketch of an induced draft cooling tower is shown in Fig. 12·9. The warm water which is to be cooled is introduced at the top of the tower through distributing troughs or spray nozzles and falls through a series of trays which are arranged to keep the falling water broken up in fine drops which have a large surface area from which evaporation can occur. In the induced draft tower, fans located at the top of the tower draw in atmospheric air at the bottom of the tower and cause it to flow upward through the falling water. The water falling through the tower may be cooled somewhat by a transfer of heat from it to the air, but the cooling results chiefly from the evaporation of some of the water, because the water which evaporates must be supplied with its latent heat of vaporization, and this is obtained chiefly from the water which does not evaporate.

In making an energy balance on a cooling tower, we can usually neglect the heat transfer to the fluids within the tower from the surrounding atmosphere. Also, the work of the fans is negligible in comparison with the other energy quantities involved. The following example illustrates the application of the first law (energy balance) and the law of conservation of mass (mass balance) to a cooling tower.

EXAMPLE 12·18.   A cooling tower is used to cool water from 110 to 80 F. Water enters the tower at a rate of 250,000 lb/hr. The air entering the tower is at 70 F with a relative humidity of 55 per cent; the air leaving is at 105 F with a relative humidity of 95 per cent. The air enters at the bottom of the tower and flows upward. Barometric pressure is 14.7 psia. Compute (a) the required flow rate of atmospheric air in lb/hr and (b) the amount of water lost by evaporation per hour.

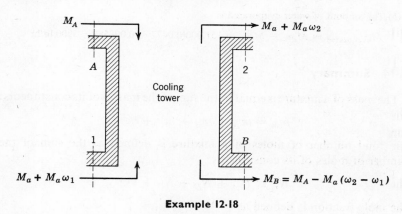

Example 12·18

Solution.   First a sketch of the steady-flow system comprised of the cooling tower is made. Designate the air inlet as section 1, the air outlet as section 2, the water inlet as section A, and the water outlet as section B. The properties of the entering and leaving air streams are calculated as in Example 12·17 with the following results:

Entering Air	Leaving Air
$p_{v1} = 0.1997$ psia	$p_{v2} = 1.047$ psia
$p_{a1} = 14.50$ psia	$p_{a2} = 13.65$ psia
$\omega_1 = 0.00855$ lb/lb dry air	$\omega_2 = 0.0477$ lb/lb dry air

(a) Let M_a be the mass flow rate of dry air required. $M_{a1} = M_{a2} = M_a$. Applying the first law to the cooling tower, assuming that $Q = 0$, $W = 0$, and $\Delta KE = 0$,

$$M_a h_{a1} + M_{v1} h_{v1} + M_A h_A = M_a h_{a2} + M_{v2} h_{v2} + M_B h_B$$

However,
$$M_{v1} = \omega_1 M_a$$
$$M_{v2} = \omega_2 M_a$$
$$M_B = M_A - M_a(\omega_2 - \omega_1)$$

so that the energy balance becomes

$$M_a h_{a1} + M_a \omega_1 h_{v1} + M_A h_A = M_a h_{a2} + M_a \omega_2 h_{v2} + [M_A - M_a(\omega_2 - \omega_1)]h_B$$

$$
\begin{aligned}
M_a &= \frac{M_A(h_A - h_B)}{h_{a2} - h_{a1} + \omega_2 h_{v2} - \omega_1 h_{v1} - (\omega_2 - \omega_1)h_B} \\[2mm]
&= \frac{M_A(h_A - h_B)}{c_{pa}(t_2 - t_1) + \omega_2 h_{g2} - \omega_1 h_{g1} - (\omega_2 - \omega_1)h_B} \\[2mm]
&= \frac{250{,}000(77.94 - 48.02)}{0.24(105 - 70) + 0.0477(1107.3) - 0.00855(1092.3) - (0.0477 - 0.00855)48.02}
\end{aligned}
$$

$$= 151{,}000 \text{ lb dry air/hr}$$

(b) The amount of water evaporated is

$$M_{\text{evaporated}} = M_a \omega_2 - M_a \omega_1 = 151{,}000(0.0477 - 0.00855) = 5900 \text{ lb/hr}$$

12·14 Summary

The mass of a mixture is equal to the sum of the masses of its constituents:

$$m_m = m_A + m_B + m_C + \cdots$$

The total number of moles of a mixture is defined as the sum of the number of moles of its constituents:

$$N_m \equiv N_A + N_B + N_C + \cdots$$

The mole fraction is defined as

$$x \equiv \frac{N}{N_m}, \qquad x_A \equiv \frac{N_A}{N_m}, \qquad \text{etc.}$$

The partial pressure p_i of a constituent i in a gas mixture is defined as

$$p_i \equiv x_i p_m, \qquad p_A \equiv x_A p_m, \qquad \text{etc.}$$

The partial volume V_i' of a constituent i in a gas mixture is defined as

$$V_i' \equiv x_i V_m, \qquad V_A' \equiv x_A V_m, \qquad \text{etc.}$$

A mixture of ideal gases is also an ideal gas.

Dalton's law or the law of additive pressures states that the pressure of a mixture of ideal gases equals the sum of the pressures of its constituents if each existed alone at the temperature and volume of the mixture. Another statement of this law is that, in a mixture of ideal gases, each constituent behaves in all respects as though it existed alone at the temperature and volume of the mixture. It follows that in a mixture of ideal gases the partial pressure of each constituent is equal to the pressure which that constituent would exert if it existed alone at the temperature and volume of the mixture.

Amagat's law, Leduc's law, or the law of additive volumes states that the volume of a mixture of ideal gases equals the sum of the volumes of its constituents if each existed alone at the temperature and pressure of the mixture. It follows that in a mixture of ideal gases the partial volume of each constituent is equal to the volume which that constituent would occupy if it existed alone at the pressure and temperature of the mixture.

The law of additive pressures and the law of additive volumes hold strictly only for ideal-gas mixtures, but they hold approximately for real-gas mixtures even in some ranges of pressure and temperature where $pv = RT$ is inaccurate.

Properties of ideal-gas mixtures can be obtained accurately and properties of real-gas mixtures can be obtained approximately in terms of constituent properties by application of the principles stated above.

In many gas-vapor mixtures all constituents can be treated as ideal gases, but an additional fact must be considered: The maximum pressure of a vapor in a mixture depends on the temperature, since it cannot be higher than the saturation pressure corresponding to the mixture temperature.

In *atmospheric air* the water vapor can be treated as an ideal gas; so it follows the equation of state $pv = RT$, and its enthalpy is a function of temperature only. Thus the enthalpy of water vapor in atmospheric air can be read from the steam tables by reading the enthalpy of saturated vapor at the same temperature.

Relative humidity ϕ is defined as the ratio of the pressure (i.e., partial pressure) of the vapor in atmospheric air to the saturation pressure of the vapor at the temperature of the mixture.

$$\phi \equiv \frac{p_v}{p_g} \tag{12·1}$$

Humidity ratio ω is defined as the ratio of the mass of vapor in atmospheric air to the mass of dry air.

$$\omega \equiv \frac{m_v}{m_a} \tag{12·3}$$

The relationship between relative humidity and humidity ratio for gas-vapor mixtures in which each constituent behaves as an ideal gas is

$$\omega = \frac{v_a}{v_g} \phi \qquad (12\cdot4)$$

The *dew-point temperature* of an air-vapor mixture is defined as the saturation temperature corresponding to the partial pressure of the vapor in the mixture.

The *adiabatic saturation temperature* of an air-vapor mixture is defined as the temperature which results from adiabatically adding water to the mixture in steady flow until it becomes saturated, the water being supplied at the final temperature of the mixture.

The *wet-bulb temperature* is the temperature measured by a thermometer wrapped in gauze soaked in clean water and placed in a stream of atmospheric air. For atmospheric air it happens that the wet-bulb temperature is very close to the adiabatic saturation temperature. This approximation does not hold for other air-vapor mixtures.

Charts of atmospheric air properties called *psychrometric charts* are useful in reducing the time required for various calculations.

REFERENCES

12·1 B. F. Dodge, *Chemical Engineering Thermodynamics*, McGraw-Hill Book Co., 1944, pp. 187–201.

12·2 E. F. Obert, *Thermodynamics*, McGraw-Hill Book Co., 1948, chapter X.

12·3 J. S. Doolittle and A. H. Zerban, *Engineering Thermodynamics*, International Textbook Co., 1948, chapter 15.

12·4 F. W. Hutchinson, *Thermodynamics of Heat-Power Systems*, Addison-Wesley Publishing Co., 1957, chapter 17.

PROBLEMS

12·1 A mixture at 70 F consists of 0.2 lb of carbon dioxide, 0.4 lb of hydrogen, and 0.6 lb of nitrogen. Compute the apparent molecular weight and the gas constant for the mixture.

12·2 A mixture having a volumetric analysis as follows is cooled under constant-volume conditions from 200 F and 20 psia to a final temperature of 50 F: oxygen 40 per cent, nitrogen 60 per cent. Compute the partial pressures of the constituents at 50 F and the volumetric analysis at 50 F.

12·3 The mass analysis of a gas mixture shows that it consists of 60 per cent nitrogen, 30 per cent carbon dioxide, and 10 per cent carbon monoxide. If the temperature and pressure for the mixture are 100 F and 50 psia, compute (*a*) the partial pressures of the components, (*b*) the apparent molecular weight, and (*c*) the apparent gas constant.

12·4 The volumetric analysis for a gas mixture shows that it consists of 50 per cent nitrogen, 30 per cent carbon dioxide, and 20 per cent carbon monoxide. If the temperature and pressure of the mixture are 70 F and 100 psia, respectively, compute (a) the partial pressures, (b) the apparent molecular weight, and (c) the apparent gas constant.

12·5 A mixture having the following volumetric analysis is contained in a closed tank: water vapor 11 per cent, oxygen 12 per cent, nitrogen 77 per cent. Compute the gravimetric analysis and the apparent molecular weight of the mixture.

12·6 A sample of blast-furnace gas had the following volumetric analysis: hydrogen 3 per cent, carbon monoxide 27 per cent, carbon dioxide 10 per cent, nitrogen 60 per cent. Compute (a) the mass analysis, (b) the partial pressures, and (c) the specific heats for the mixture at 70 F. The total pressure equals 14.69 psia.

12·7 A mixture comprised of the following gases is at a pressure of 15 psia and at a temperature of 32 F: 3 lb of oxygen, 2 lb of carbon monoxide, 0.5 lb of hydrogen, 1 lb of helium, 3 lb of nitrogen, and 0.5 lb of argon. Compute the specific heat values and the partial pressures.

12·8 Prove that the density of an ideal-gas mixture equals the sum of the densities of its constituents.

12·9 A tank containing 15 cu ft of helium at 100 psia and 50 F is connected by means of a pipe and valve system to a 10-cu-ft tank containing nitrogen at 50 psia and 150 F. If no heat losses occur, compute the resulting pressure and temperature after the valve has been opened and mixing occurs.

12·10 Three cubic feet of methane at 300 psia, 100 F, is mixed with 7 cu ft of oxygen at 100 psia, 40 F, by opening a valve between the two tanks. Calculate the heat transfer if the final temperature is 100 F.

12·11 Six pounds of nitrogen at 200 psia, 100 F, and 4 lb of oxygen at 30 psia, 200 F, are mixed adiabatically with no change in the total volume. Determine the mixture pressure and temperature.

12·12 A tank containing 2 lb of methane at 20 psia, 50 F, and a tank holding 4 lb of oxygen at 100 psia, 20 F, are connected through a valve. The valve is opened and the gases mix adiabatically. Atmospheric temperature is 50 F. Determine (a) the mixture pressure, (b) the mixture temperature, (c) the volumetric analysis of the mixture, and (d) the irreversibility of the process.

12·13 A system consisting of three tanks, all interconnected by pipes and valves, contains nitrogen, oxygen, and argon. One tank contains 10 lb of nitrogen at 100 psia, 90 F; another 5 lb of argon at 75 psia, 120 F; and the third 15 lb of oxygen at 50 psia, 180 F. After the valves are open, compute (a) the temperature of the mixture, (b) the apparent molecular weight, (c) the constant-pressure specific heat of the mixture, (d) the gas constant, (e) the pressure of the mixture, and (f) the partial pressure of each constituent.

12·14 Prove that for the adiabatic mixing of ideal gases initially at the same pressure and temperature in a rigid tank the entropy change depends only on the number of moles of constituents and not on what the constituents are.

12·15 Is it true that adiabatic mixing in a constant-volume system of two ideal gases with different k values results in a change in enthalpy but no change in internal energy? Prove your answer.

12·16 Determine the minimum work input required per pound of air to separate air at 1 atm, 60 F, into nitrogen and oxygen, each at 1 atm, 60 F.

12·17 A tank having a volume of 6.0 cu ft contains oxygen at 10.5 psia, 100 F. Carbon monoxide is forced into the tank until the mixture is at 30 psia, 100 F. Determine for the mixture (a) the volumetric analysis, and (b) the gravimetric analysis.

12·18 Calculate the specific volume of a mixture of 30 per cent CO_2, 20 per cent CO, and 50 per cent N_2 by mass at 14.0 psia, 100 F.

12·19 The mass fraction of each constituent in a mixture of N_2 and CO_2 is 50 per cent. The mixture is compressed from 15 psia, 40 F, to 75 psia, 340 F. Calculate the entropy change of the CO_2.

12·20 One tank contains 3.77 moles of nitrogen at 20 psia, 100 F, and another tank contains 1 mole of oxygen at 20 psia, 100 F. A valve connecting the tanks is opened, and the gases mix adiabatically. The lowest temperature in the surroundings is 40 F. Determine the irreversibility of the process. Explain the physical significance of this value.

12·21 Argon at 100 psia, 100 F, flows steadily through a pipe line. A tank of 2 cu ft volume which contains air at 14.7 psia, 60 F, is connected to the pipe line, and argon is allowed to flow into the tank until the total pressure in the tank is 50 psia. Assuming that no air leaves the tank and that the filling is adiabatic, determine the mass of argon which flows into the tank.

12·22 Argon at 100 psia, 100 F, flows steadily through a pipe line. A tank of 2 cu ft volume which contains air at 14.7 psia, 60 F, is connected to the pipe line, and argon is allowed to flow into the tank until the total pressure in the tank is 50 psia. Assuming that no air leaves the tank, determine the heat transfer which is required to maintain the contents of the tank at 60 F.

12·23 Helium at 50 psia, 120 F, flows through an insulated pipe line. A well-insulated tank 2 cu ft in volume containing air at 14.7 psia, 70 F, is connected to the helium line through a small valve which is opened until the pressure in the tank becomes 30 psia. The valve is then closed. Assuming that no air flows from the tank and that the process is adiabatic, determine the final temperature of the mixture in the tank.

12·24 A mixture consisting of 0.2 lb of dry saturated steam and 0.01 lb of air is contained in a tank at a temperature of 200 F. Compute the total pressure in the tank and the total volume occupied by the mixture.

12·25 A mixture consists of 0.2 lb of dry saturated water vapor, 0.3 lb of nitrogen, and 0.05 lb of oxygen. If the temperature of the mixture is 200 F, compute the total and partial pressures for the mixture.

12·26 One pound of nitrogen and 0.2 lb of water vapor occupy a volume of 4.12 cu ft. Compute the total pressure for the mixture if the temperature is 480 F.

12·27 If the wet-bulb and dry-bulb temperatures for atmospheric air are 70 and 80 F, respectively, determine (a) the partial pressure of the water vapor, (b) the relative humidity, (c) the mass of water vapor per pound of dry air, (d) the cubic feet per pound of dry air, and (e) the enthalpy per pound of dry air. Use the psychrometric chart. Assume that the atmospheric pressure is 14.696 psia.

12·28 If the relative humidity is 30 per cent and the dry-bulb temperature is 100 F, determine by means of the psychrometric chart the humidity ratio and the pressure of the water vapor. Atmospheric pressure equals 14.696 psia.

12·29 If the mass of water vapor per pound of dry air is 90 grains and the relative humidity is 60 per cent, determine from the psychrometric chart the dry-bulb temperature and the pressure of the water vapor.

12·30 Atmospheric air at 80 F and a total pressure of 14.7 psia has a relative humidity of 50 per cent. What are the partial pressures of the constituents? What is the dew-point temperature?

12·31 The partial pressure of water vapor in moist air at a total pressure of 14.7 psia and temperature of 90 F is 0.4 psia. Determine the relative humidity and dew-point temperature.

12·32 Determine the humidity ratio of moist air at a pressure and temperature of 14.5 psia and 90 F for a relative humidity of 60 per cent.

12·33 Determine the humidity ratio for moist air at a total pressure of 12.5 psia and a temperature of 90 F. The relative humidity is 60 per cent.

12·34 Determine the mass of water vapor per pound of dry air for moist air at 100 F and 50 per cent relative humidity. The total pressure is 14.7 psia. What is the dew-point temperature?

12·35 How many pounds of moisture are removed from moist air at 80 F and 14 psia when cooled to 40 F? The initial relative humidity is 60 per cent. Consider this as a constant total pressure cooling process.

12·36 Air at 50 F and relative humidity of 10 per cent is heated under constant pressure of 14.7 psia to a final temperature of 90 F. Determine the humidity ratio at 90 F.

12·37 Air at 90 F has a relative humidity of 100 per cent. What is the dew-point temperature? What mass of water per pound of dry air will be removed if the mixture is cooled to 40 F at a constant pressure of 12.5 psia?

12·38 Six hundred pounds per hour of moist air at 90 F and relative humidity of 40 per cent is to be cooled to 50 F at constant atmospheric pressure. Compute the heat removed per hour. The barometric pressure is 14.696 psia.

12·39 Atmospheric air at 25 in. mercury pressure, 80 F, and relative humidity of 50 per cent is heated at constant pressure to a temperature of 100 F. Compute the final relative humidity.

12·40 The percentage composition by weight for a gas-vapor mixture is nitrogen 70, carbon monoxide 4, carbon dioxide 22, water 4. Compute the dew point of the mixture, assuming that the total pressure is 14.696 psia.

12·41 Air at 50 F, 90 per cent relative humidity, and air at 90 F, 90 per cent relative humidity, are mixed steadily and adiabatically. The mass flow rate of the colder stream is twice that of the other stream. What is the resulting state?

12·42 Which has the greater density, dry air or air with a high humidity ratio? Does this explain why fog collects in valleys and low places?

12·43 A glass tank with a volume of 12 cu ft contains an air–water-vapor mixture. When the temperature of the mixture is 100 F, its pressure is 20 psia. If the mixture cools to 60 F, condensation on the glass begins. Determine the mass of water in the tank.

12·44 An air–water-vapor mixture initially at 20 psia, 140 F, 100 per cent relative humidity undergoes a reversible adiabatic expansion to 15 psia. Give all the information you can about the entropy change of (a) the air, (b) the water, (c) the mixture, and (d) the surroundings.

12·45 Under what conditions does a water pipe or a glass of water "sweat"? Under what conditions may water from the atmosphere contaminate the gasoline in an automobile tank?

12·46 Why do building and automobile windows "fog" or "frost"? If a double layer of glass is used, should the air space between them be vented to the inside or the outside?

12-47 What is dew? Under what conditions does it form? Under what conditions does frost form?

12-48 Under what conditions can a person see his "breath"?

12-49 A piece of toast is taken from the toaster and placed on a dry plate. A minute later the toast is removed from the plate, and the plate is seen to be wet where the toast was lying. Explain this.

12-50 An insulated tank contains dry air. Also in the tank is a covered dish of water at the same pressure and temperature as the air. If the cover is removed from the dish of water, will the entropy of the system (air and water) change? Will the temperature of the system change? Explain your reasoning.

12-51 Air at 100 F, 40 per cent relative humidity, is cooled to 80 F by spraying water at 60 F into it. Mixture pressure remains constant at 14.7 psia. Assuming that all of the water evaporates and that the mixing occurs in an insulated pipe, calculate the mass of water added per pound of air.

12-52 Atmospheric air at 29.6 in. mercury, 50 per cent relative humidity, is compressed isothermally to 3 psig. State whether each of the following quantities increases, decreases, remains constant, or varies indeterminately: (a) humidity ratio, (b) relative humidity, and (c) dew point.

12-53 An engineer speaks of the "moisture in the atmosphere" and the "moisture in a steam-turbine exhaust." Compare the two meanings of the term *moisture*.

12-54 Explain how it is possible to dehumidify air by passing it through water sprays.

12-55 A gas-vapor mixture having a composition by mass of nitrogen 70 per cent, carbon monoxide 4 per cent, carbon dioxide 22 per cent, water 4 per cent, is heated under a constant total pressure of 14.7 psia from an initial temperature of 50 F to a final temperature of 100 F. Compute the heat required per pound of mixture.

12-56 Atmospheric air at 14.7 psia, 70 F, 60 per cent relative humidity, is to be used to cool a transformer at a rate of 200,000 B/hr. To increase the cooling effect per pound of air and thereby decrease the amount of air needed, the air is first adiabatically saturated with water and then passed over the transformer. If the temperature of the air leaving the transformer should not exceed 90 F, determine the required flow rate in pounds of dry air per hour.

12-57 Air at 80 F and relative humidity of 100 per cent is heated at constant pressure to a final temperature of 100 F. Determine (a) the dew-point temperature at 80 F, (b) the initial partial pressure of the water vapor, (c) the initial humidity ratio, and (d) the final humidity ratio.

12-58 Outside air having a temperature and relative humidity of 90 F and 45 per cent, respectively, is to be conditioned so that the final temperature and relative humidity are 70 F and 30 per cent. If the flow process occurs under constant-pressure conditions, compute (a) the quantity of water removed per pound of dry air, (b) the heat removed in the initial cooling process per pound of dry air, and (c) the heat added per pound of dry air. Assume that the atmospheric pressure equals 14.696 psia.

12-59 An air-conditioning unit consists of a cooler (with provision for removing condensate) followed by a heater. Air at 14.696 psia enters at 90 F, 80 per cent relative humidity, and leaves at 70 F, 49 per cent relative humidity. The flow rate is 1000 lb of dry air per hour. Calculate (a) the amount of water removed per hour, and (b) the heat removed (in B/lb dry air) in the cooler.

12·60 Air at 60 F, 100 per cent relative humidity, enters a dehumidifier and passes over the cold coils of a refrigerating unit. The moisture condensed is drained away and then the air passes over the motor and warm coils of the refrigerating unit. All heat rejected by the refrigerating unit thus goes into reheating the air which emerges at 85 F, 30 per cent relative humidity. The flow rate is 10 lb of dry air per minute. Barometric pressure is 14.0 psia. Determine the power input to the refrigerating unit.

12·61 A cooling tower is used to cool 2000 gal of water per minute from an initial temperature of 110 F to a final temperature of 88 F. Air enters the cooling tower at 80 F and 40 per cent relative humidity and leaves at a temperature and relative humidity of 105 F and 100 per cent. Compute the mass of air required per minute, and the mass of water lost per minute. Assume that 2000 gal enter the tower per minute. Atmospheric pressure equals 14.69 psia.

12·62 Water enters a cooling tower at 120 F and leaves at 90 F. The dry-bulb and wet-bulb temperatures of the entering air are 85 and 70 F, respectively. The air on discharging from the tower is completely saturated and has a temperature of 105 F. If 100,000 lb of water enter the tower each hour, compute the mass of air required and the water lost by evaporation. Atmospheric pressure equals 14.696 psia.

12·63 Determine the dew point of the products of the following reaction if the products are at 15.0 psia, 500 F:

$$H_2 + O_2 + 3.77N_2 \rightarrow H_2O + \tfrac{1}{2}O_2 + 3.77N_2$$

12·64 Dry air at 40 F enters a heating and humidifying unit, and air at 80 F, 80 per cent relative humidity, leaves the unit. Spray water for humidification is supplied to the unit at 60 F. Barometric pressure is 14.2 psia. Determine the heat transfer per pound of dry air.

12·65 Consider the design of a cooling tower. What are the relative advantages and disadvantages of a high air velocity? Is it desirable to have the air leaving the tower carry liquid drops?

12·66 Sketch a *Ts* diagram for the water vapor in atmospheric air, showing a few lines of constant relative humidity (i.e., loci of vapor states for which the relative humidity is the same).

12·67 Explain why some of the enthalpy correction curves on the psychrometric chart are positive and some are negative.

CHAPTER **13**

Chemical Reactions: Combustion

The preceding chapters have been concerned chiefly with pure substances and other nonreacting systems. In this chapter we consider the application of thermodynamic principles to chemical reactions. For simplicity, we deal with a particular type of chemical reaction: combustion. Combustion reactions are chosen for attention because of their importance in engineering, but you should keep in mind that the analysis presented here of combustion reactions may be applied to other chemical reactions.

Three aspects of chemical reactions are considered in this book: (1) the mass balance by which we determine the products formed by known reactants or the reactants required to form known products, (2) the energy balance or application of the first law by means of which we determine the energy transfers and conversions accompanying a reaction, and (3) the application of the second law to determine the extent to which a reaction will proceed and to determine the irreversibility of a reaction. Mass and energy balances are treated in this chapter. Second-law considerations, except for a brief mention in this chapter, are taken up in Chapter 14. (A fourth important aspect of chemical reactions—the rate at which reactions occur—is not treated in this book.)

13·1 The basic combustion reactions

The combustible constituents of fuels are carbon, hydrogen, and sulfur and their compounds. The basic reactions for complete combustion of these three elements are

$$C + O_2 \rightarrow CO_2$$

$$H_2 + \tfrac{1}{2}O_2 \rightarrow H_2O$$

$$S + O_2 \rightarrow SO_2$$

The substances present before a reaction occurs are called the reactants, and those present after the reaction has occurred are called the products.

In a reaction such as

$$C + \tfrac{1}{2}O_2 \rightarrow CO$$

combustion is said to be incomplete because the products are not completely oxidized.

The complete combustion of hydrocarbon compounds results in the formation of carbon dioxide and water. Thus

$$C_8H_{18} + 12\tfrac{1}{2}O_2 \rightarrow 8CO_2 + 9H_2O$$

This equation may be interpreted as follows:

1 mole C_8H_{18} + 12½ moles O_2 = 8 moles CO_2 + 9 moles H_2O

or   114 lb C_8H_{18} + 400 lb O_2 = 352 lb CO_2 + 162 lb H_2O

Notice that the total mass of matter is the same on both sides of the equality sign. Also the total mass of each chemical element is the same on each side of the equality sign. The total number of moles on each side of the equality sign may not be the same.

The masses in the last equation are based on approximate molecular weights of 12 for carbon and 2 for hydrogen. The more accurate values of 12.011 for carbon and 2.016 for hydrogen should be used where greater precision is required. As an illustration of this point, the use of the approximate molecular weights indicates that the complete burning of 1 lb of hydrogen produces 9 lb of water, but more precise molecular weights give a value of 8.94 lb of water per pound of hydrogen.

13·2   The composition of dry air

The oxygen for most combustion reactions comes from air. The composition of dry air is given by the following mole fractions: $0.7809N_2$, $0.2095O_2$, $0.0093A$ (argon), and $0.0003CO_2$. The molecular weight of this mixture is 28.966 lb/mole. For nearly all combustion calculations we can treat the argon and carbon dioxide as nitrogen and use the approximate composition of 0.79 mole N_2 per mole of air and 0.21 mole O_2 per mole of air, corresponding to mass fractions of $0.768N_2$ and $0.232O_2$. Convenient forms in which to remember the approximate composition of air are

1 mole O_2 + 3.77 moles N_2 = 4.77 moles air

1 lb O_2 + 3.31 lb N_2 = 4.31 lb air

The nitrogen, being inert, does not enter into the combustion reaction and merely appears in the products of combustion as a diluent. It is therefore often omitted in writing the combustion reactions.

Stoichiometric air is the quantity of air required to burn one pound, one mole, or one cubic foot of fuel completely without any oxygen appearing in the products of combustion. The products of combustion would then consist of carbon dioxide, water, sulfur dioxide, and the nitrogen which accompanied the oxygen in the air as well as any nitrogen from the fuel.

Excess air is air supplied in excess of that necessary to burn the fuel completely and appears in the products of combustion unchanged, that is, as oxygen and nitrogen. The amount of excess air is normally expressed as a percentage of the stoichiometric amount required for complete combustion of the fuel.

13·3 Ideal combustion

It is often necessary to determine for a fuel of known composition the amount of air (or other oxidizer) required to burn the fuel and to determine the analysis of the resulting products, assuming that combustion is complete. This calculation is an application of elementary chemistry and is illustrated in the following two examples. The first example pertains to a gaseous fuel for which the analysis is given on a molar or (for ideal gases) volumetric basis. The second example pertains to solid fuel which, like a liquid fuel, is analyzed on a mass basis. Two forms of analysis of a solid fuel such as coal are used by engineers. The *proximate analysis* comprises an analysis of the coal into arbitrary constituents which are designated as moisture, volatile matter, fixed carbon, and ash. The *ultimate analysis* shows the composition of coal in terms of chemical elements, except for ash which is reported as such and consists of various oxides.

No matter what type of fuel or which type of analysis—mass or molar—we have to start with, it is always possible to convert from the mass basis to the molar basis or vice versa in order to handle all combustion calculations in the same way. This is unnecessary, however, and in each of the following examples the calculations are made directly from the fuel analysis as given.

EXAMPLE 13·1.   A blast-furnace gas has the following volumetric analysis: H_2 9 per cent, CO 24, CH_4 2, CO_2 6, O_2 3, and N_2 56. For the burning of this gas at 14.7 psia with 50 per cent excess air, determine the following:

(a) The volume of air in cubic feet required per cubic foot of fuel (both measured at the same pressure and temperature).

(b) The volumetric analysis of the dry products of combustion.

(c) The mass of the total products of combustion per pound of fuel.

(d) The mass of the dry products of combustion per pound of fuel.

(e) The mass of air supplied per pound of fuel.

(f) The dew point of the products.

Solution.   This problem will be solved by dealing with 100 moles of fuel gas. Necessary preliminary computations are presented in the table below. In this table the combustion reaction for CH_4 indicates that 1 mole of CH_4 requires 2 moles of O_2 and produces 1 mole of CO_2 and 2 moles of water vapor. Therefore 2 moles of CH_4 requires 4 moles of oxygen and produces 2 moles of CO_2 and 4 moles of water vapor. The products of combustion of H_2 and CO are determined similarly from the reactions and tabulated. CO_2 and N_2 in the fuel are inert. The oxygen in the fuel reduces the oxygen required from the air to 17.5 moles per 100 moles of fuel. The 17.5 moles of O_2 is accompanied by 66.0 moles of N_2. For 50 per cent excess air 8.75 moles of additional O_2 is supplied, which appears unchanged in the products of combustion. The oxygen is accompanied by 33.0 moles of inert nitrogen. The total products of combustion without and with 50 per cent excess air are obtained by addition.

Con-stituents	Number of Moles based on 100 moles	Combustion Reaction	Number of Moles of oxygen supplied by air	Number of Moles in products of combustion			
				CO_2	H_2O	N_2	O_2
H_2	9	$H_2 + \frac{1}{2}O_2 = H_2O$	4.5	..	9	....	....
CO	24	$CO + \frac{1}{2}O_2 = CO_2$	12.0	24	..	....	....
CH_4	2	$CH_4 + 2O_2 = CO_2 + 2H_2O$	4.0	2	4	....	....
						→ 66.0	
CO_2	6	....	......	6	..	....	....
O_2	3	....	(−3.0)	..	..	....	....
N_2	56	....	......	..	..	56	....
Total	100	No excess air	17.5 —	32	13	122.0	....
		Excess O_2 and N_2	8.75	..	..	33.0	8.75
		Total for 50% excess air	26.25	32	13	155.0	8.75

(a) The volume of air required per cubic foot of fuel burned without excess air may be found as follows.

$$V_a = \frac{17.5 \text{ moles } O_2}{100 \text{ moles fuel}} \times \frac{4.77 \text{ moles air}}{\text{mole } O_2} = \frac{0.835 \text{ mole air}}{\text{mole fuel}}$$

Since a mole of air and a mole of fuel at the same pressure and temperature occupy the same volume, the result, 0.835 mole of air per mole of fuel, also represents 0.835 cu ft of air per cubic foot of fuel.

For 50 per cent excess air, the air supplied equals 1.50(0.835) or 1.255 cu ft/cu ft of fuel.

(b) The volumetric analysis of the dry products of combustion may be obtained from the tabular data as follows. In the determination of a dry analysis, the water vapor formed is not included.

Products Constituent	Moles of Constituent per 100 moles of Fuel	Volumetric Analysis
CO_2	32.0	16.3
O_2	8.75	4.5
N_2	155.0	79.2
	195.8	100.0

(c) The following table shows the computation of the total mass of products per 100 moles of fuel.

Products Constituent	Moles of Constituent per 100 moles of fuel	Mass of Constituent per 100 moles of fuel
CO_2	32.0	32(44) = 1408
H_2O	13.0	13(18) = 234
O_2	8.75	8.75(32) = 280
N_2	155.0	155.0(28) = 4340
	208.8	6262

We now determine the mass of the fuel per 100 moles of fuel (or 100 times the molecular weight of the fuel) by

$$100 M_{fuel} = \Sigma\, 100xM = 9(2) + 24(28) + 2(16) + 6(44) + 3(32) + 56(28)$$

$$= 2650 \text{ lb/100 moles}$$

Then the mass of products per pound of fuel is given by

$$\frac{m_p}{m_f} = \frac{6262}{2650} = 2.36 \text{ lb products/lb fuel}$$

(d) The mass of dry products equals the mass of total products minus the mass of water vapor formed.

$$\frac{m_{dp}}{m_f} = \frac{m_p}{m_f} - \frac{m_v}{m_f} = 2.36 - \frac{234}{2650} = 2.27 \text{ lb/lb fuel}$$

(e) The mass of air supplied per pound of fuel equals the mass of products per pound of fuel minus the mass of fuel per pound of fuel (which is identically 1.0):

$$\frac{m_a}{m_f} = \frac{m_p}{m_f} - \frac{m_f}{m_f} = 2.36 - 1.00 = 1.36 \text{ lb air/lb fuel}$$

(f) The dew point of the products is the saturation temperature corresponding to the partial pressure of the water vapor in the products. (We are assuming that the products behave like an ideal gas.) The water-vapor partial pressure is

$$p_v = x_v p_m = \frac{N_v}{N_m} p_m = \frac{13}{208.8} (14.7) = 0.915 \text{ psia}$$

The corresponding saturation temperature, and thus the dew point of the products, is approximately 99 F.

EXAMPLE 13·2.   A coal has the following ultimate analysis in percentages: carbon 70, hydrogen 5, sulfur 1, oxygen 12, nitrogen 2, and ash 10. For complete combustion with 20 per cent excess air at 14.7 psia, determine

(a) The mass of air required per pound of fuel.
(b) The volumetric analysis of the dry products of combustion.
(c) The dew point of the products.

Solution. The solution for the mass of air required and for the mass of the various products is shown in the following table.

Ultimate Analysis	Reactions	Mass of O_2 Required per lb of Coal	Mass of Products per lb of Coal
C = 0.70	$C + O_2 = CO_2$ $12 + 32 = 44$ lb	$\dfrac{32\ \text{lb}\ O_2}{12\ \text{lb}\ C}(0.70)\dfrac{\text{lb}\ C}{\text{lb coal}} = 1.87\ \text{lb}$	$\dfrac{44}{12}(0.70) = 2.57\ \text{lb}\ CO_2$
H = 0.05	$2H_2 + O_2 = 2H_2O$ $4 + 32 = 36$	$\dfrac{32\ \text{lb}\ O_2}{4\ \text{lb}\ H}(0.05)\dfrac{\text{lb}\ H}{\text{lb coal}} = 0.40$	$\dfrac{36}{4}(0.05) = 0.45\ \text{lb}\ H_2O$
S = 0.01	$S + O_2 = SO_2$ $32 + 32 = 64$ lb	$\dfrac{32\ \text{lb}\ O_2}{32\ \text{lb}\ S}(0.01)\dfrac{\text{lb}\ S}{\text{lb coal}} = 0.01$	$\dfrac{64}{32}(0.01) = 0.02\ \text{lb}\ SO_2$
O = 0.12 N = 0.02 Ash = 0.10	Less O_2 supplied by coal	−0.12	....
		....	0.02 lb N_2
		....	0.10 lb ash
	Total O_2 required, no excess	2.16	....
	Additional O_2 for 20% excess	0.43	0.43 lb O_2
	Total O_2 required, 20% excess	2.59	....
	N_2 supplied with air = 2.59(3.31) =	8.57	8.57 lb N_2
	Total air required, 20% excess	11.16	....
	Plus 1 lb of fuel	1.00	....
Total mass per lb of coal		In: 12.16 lb	Out: 12.16 lb

(*b*) The dry products of combustion consist of all of the gaseous products except water vapor. From the masses of these products determined in the table above we can obtain the volumetric analysis as follows:

Constituent	Mass of Constituent per lb of Coal	Molecular Weight	Moles of Constituent per lb of Coal	Volumetric Analysis
CO_2	2.57	44	0.0584	0.154
SO_2	0.02	64	0.0003	0.001
O_2	0.43	32	0.0134	0.035
N_2	8.59	28	0.307	0.810
Total	11.61		0.379	1.000

(*c*) Assuming that all the water formed is in the vapor phase, the number of moles of water vapor per pound of coal is $0.45/18 = 0.025$, so the total number of moles of gaseous products is $0.379 + 0.025 = 0.404$ mole/lb of coal. The mole fraction of water vapor in the gaseous products is then $0.025/0.404 = 0.0619$. The partial pressure of the water vapor is then

$$p_v = x_v p_m = 0.0619(14.7) = 0.91\ \text{psia}$$

and the dew point is the saturation temperature corresponding to this pressure, approximately 99 F.

13·4 Actual combustion mass balance

In the preceding article we calculated the amount of air which should be supplied to burn a fuel and calculated the products analysis which results from the complete burning of a fuel with a specified amount of air. This is a calculation which can be made from the fuel analysis alone; no measured data on an actual combustion process are involved. Another problem engineers encounter is determining how much air was actually supplied in a combustion process. Often it is difficult to measure the air flow into a combustion chamber—whether it is a jet engine, a boiler furnace, or an internal-combustion engine—so an inferential method is used which is based on the analyses of the fuel, the solid refuse, and the dry gaseous products.

The most commonly used apparatus for analyzing the gaseous products of combustion is the Orsat gas analyzer. In this apparatus a sample of gas of known volume is first trapped at atmospheric pressure in a water-jacketed measuring burette. The purpose of the water jacket is to maintain the sample at constant temperature. The sample is then passed sequentially into vessels containing reagents which absorb CO_2, O_2, and CO. After the gas sample is passed through each vessel, it is returned to the burette where its volume is measured at the original pressure and temperature. The reduction in volume during each absorption divided by the original sample volume is the fraction by volume of the constituent which was absorbed. After CO_2, O_2, and CO are measured, the remainder of the sample is usually assumed to be nitrogen. Sulfur dioxide is absorbed as carbon dioxide, introducing a small error which can be corrected for by adding three eighths (12/32) of the mass of sulfur in the fuel to the mass of carbon, thus treating it as additional carbon. In applications where appreciable amounts of hydrogen and hydrocarbon gases are expected in the products, several refinements are made in the usual Orsat apparatus to measure these constituents. The Orsat analysis is on a dry basis; that is, no water vapor is considered. The gas sample in the Orsat apparatus does contain saturated water vapor, but since the sample temperature is constant the partial pressure of the saturated water vapor remains constant. From this fact it can easily be shown that the analysis obtained is the same that would be obtained if no water vapor were present.

In analyzing products of combustion, care must be taken to insure that the sample drawn into the gas analyzer is a representative sample of the total flow of gaseous products.

A mass balance for a steady-flow combustion process is

$$\text{Mass entering} = \text{mass leaving}$$

If the fuel is burned in air and the total products of combustion contain some solid material, the mass balance can be written as

$$m_f + m_a = m_{dg} + m_v + m_{\text{solid}}$$

where the subscripts f, a, dg, and v stand for fuel, air, dry gaseous products, and water vapor, respectively. m_f and m_{solid} can usually be measured accurately. If we assume that all the hydrogen in the fuel combines with oxygen, then m_v is nine (or, more accurately, 8.94) times the amount of hydrogen in the fuel. We still cannot solve for m_a because there is another unknown, m_{dg}, in the equation. Therefore, something more than a total mass balance is needed.

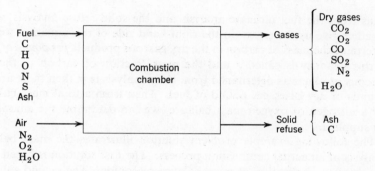

Fig. 13·1 Combustion mass balance.

A mass balance can also be written for each element as well as for all the matter passing through the system. The distribution of the various elements is shown in Fig. 13·1. Remembering that we are trying to determine the amount of air supplied per pound of fuel and that this can be determined if we find the amount of dry gaseous products per pound of fuel, we first look for an element which appears in both the fuel and the dry gaseous products and only in those two places. This would solve the problem because, if the same mass of such an element amounts to x per cent (by mass) of the fuel and y per cent (by mass) of the dry gaseous products, then the mass ratio of dry gaseous products to fuel is x/y. Sulfur is distributed in the manner desired, but a sulfur balance is unsatisfactory, because (1) the fraction of sulfur in the fuel is usually so low that a sulfur balance would be inaccurate and (2) SO_2 (and therefore S) is usually not measured in exhaust gases. An Orsat gas analyzer measures SO_2 as part of the CO_2 content.

The next choice of an element on which to base a mass balance is carbon, which appears in the fuel, in the dry gaseous products, and in the solid refuse. In each of these three places the mass fraction of carbon can be readily determined. The amount of solid refuse per pound of fuel can be measured, or it can be determined by assuming that all the ash in the fuel becomes part of the solid refuse; so a carbon balance

$$\begin{bmatrix} \text{Mass of carbon} \\ \text{in dry gases} \end{bmatrix} = \begin{bmatrix} \text{mass of carbon} \\ \text{in fuel} \end{bmatrix} - \begin{bmatrix} \text{mass of carbon} \\ \text{in solid refuse} \end{bmatrix}$$

can be used in the form

$$\begin{bmatrix} \text{Mass of carbon} \\ \text{in dry gases} \\ \text{per lb of fuel} \end{bmatrix} = \begin{bmatrix} \text{mass of carbon} \\ \text{in fuel per} \\ \text{lb of fuel} \end{bmatrix} - \begin{bmatrix} \text{mass of carbon} \\ \text{in solid refuse} \\ \text{per lb of fuel} \end{bmatrix}$$

Thus from the fuel ultimate analysis and the solid refuse analysis which together give us the terms on the right-hand side of this equation we can determine the mass of carbon in the dry gaseous products *per pound of fuel.* If this quantity is called x and the mass fraction of carbon in the dry gaseous products as determined from their analysis is y, then there are x/y pounds of dry gases per pound of fuel. Then from a total mass balance (or a nitrogen or oxygen mass balance) we can determine the amount of air supplied.

The following example problem solution illustrates the mass balance analysis of an actual combustion process. The first solution is based on a step-by-step application of mass balance reasoning. The second solution is shorter because it is based on a single equation which expresses the mass balances for all elements.

EXAMPLE 13·3. A coal (the same one referred to in Example 13·2) has an ultimate analysis as follows in percentages: carbon 70, hydrogen 5, sulfur 1, oxygen 12, nitrogen 2, and ash 10. It is burned in a furnace, and the solid refuse is found to contain 33 per cent carbon. The Orsat analysis of the dry products of combustion is as follows: CO_2 14.3 per cent, O_2 4.0, CO 1.2. Barometric pressure is 14.7 psia. Determine (a) the amount of dry air supplied per pound of fuel, (b) the per cent excess air, and (c) the dew point of the products.

Solution. (a) The first solution will be obtained by determining the mass of dry gaseous products per pound of fuel and then using a total mass balance to find the amount of air supplied. The mass of dry gas will be found by means of a carbon balance, so the first step is to calculate the mass of carbon in the dry gas (abbreviated dg) per pound of fuel.

$$\frac{\text{lb C in } dg}{\text{lb fuel}} = \frac{\text{lb C in fuel}}{\text{lb fuel}} - \frac{\text{lb C in refuse}}{\text{lb fuel}}$$

$$= \frac{\text{lb C in fuel}}{\text{lb fuel}} - \left(\frac{\text{lb C in refuse}}{\text{lb ash}}\right) \frac{\text{lb ash}}{\text{lb fuel}}$$

$$= 0.70 - \left(\frac{0.33}{0.67}\right) 0.10 = 0.65 \frac{\text{lb C in } dg}{\text{lb fuel}}$$

Now from the Orsat analysis we obtain the mass of carbon in the dry gas per pound of dry gas.

Con-stituent	Mole Fraction, moles/100 mole dg	Molecular Weight, lb/mole	lb/100 mole dg	lb C/100 mole dg
CO_2	14.3	44	629	171.6
O_2	4.0	32	128	
CO	1.2	28	33.6	14.4
N_2	80.5	28	2254	
			3045	186.0

Thus we have (186/3045) lb C in dg/lb dg and

$$\frac{m_{dg}}{m_f} = 0.65 \frac{\text{lb C in } dg}{\text{lb fuel}} \frac{3045}{186} \frac{\text{lb } dg}{\text{lb C in } dg} = 10.63 \frac{\text{lb } dg}{\text{lb fuel}}$$

A total mass balance then gives the air–fuel ratio:

$$\frac{m_a}{m_f} = \frac{m_{dg}}{m_f} + \frac{m_v}{m_f} + \frac{m_{\text{ref}}}{m_f} - \frac{m_f}{m_f}$$

$$= 10.63 + 9(0.05) + 0.10/0.67 - 1.0 = 10.23 \text{ lb air/lb fuel}$$

(In this equation the mass of vapor is nine times the mass of hydrogen in the fuel, and the mass of refuse is 0.10 lb of ash per pound of fuel divided by 0.67 lb of ash per pound of refuse.)

(b) In Example 13·2 it was found that the stoichiometric amount of oxygen to burn this coal is 2.16 lb of O_2 per pound of coal. Thus the stoichiometric amount of air is 2.16(4.31) = 9.30 lb of air per pound of coal and the per cent excess air is

$$\text{Excess air} = \frac{m_a - m_{a,\,\text{stoichiometric}}}{m_{a,\,\text{stoichiometric}}} = \frac{10.23 - 9.30}{9.30} = 10.0 \text{ per cent}$$

(c) In order to find the dew point of the gaseous products, we must determine the partial pressure of the water vapor, and this depends on the mole fraction of the vapor in the gases. We have already determined in part (a) the mass of dry gas and the mass of water vapor per pound of coal. From the Orsat analysis we also have the molecular weight of the dry gases, 30.45 lb/mole. Thus

$$x_v = \frac{N_v}{N_{dg} + N_v} = \frac{m_v/M_v}{m_{dg}/M_{dg} + m_v/M_v} = \frac{9(0.05)/18}{10.63/30.45 + 9(0.05)/18} = 0.0669$$

$$p_v = x_v p_m = 0.0669(14.7) = 0.983 \text{ psia}$$

$$T_{dp} = T_{\text{sat.,}} 0.983 \text{ psia} = 101^+ \text{ F}$$

Alternative solution. (a) The amount of dry air supplied can be determined more directly by writing the chemical equation for the actual combustion process with unknown coefficients where necessary and then solving for these coefficients by means of mass balances for the various elements. Let there be a moles of O_2 supplied per pound of coal and x moles of dry gas formed per pound of coal. As in the initial step of the first solution we find that per pound of fuel only 0.65 lb of carbon is burned. The remainder of the carbon and the ash undergo no change during the combustion process, and so they can be omitted from the chemical equation. Then we have, per pound of fuel,

$$\frac{0.65}{12} C + \frac{0.05}{2} H_2 + \frac{0.01}{32} S + \frac{0.12}{32} O_2 + \frac{0.02}{28} N_2 + aO_2 + 3.77aN_2$$

$$\rightarrow 0.143xCO_2 + 0.04xO_2 + 0.012xCO + 0.805xN_2 + 0.025H_2O$$

The coefficient of H_2O on the right-hand side of this equation was established from the fact that hydrogen appears in only one term on each side of the equation; that is, a hydrogen balance was used to establish 0.025 as the number of moles of hydrogen (in H_2O) in the products. x and a can be determined by means of carbon and oxygen balances as follows:

$$\text{C balance:} \qquad \frac{0.65}{12} = 0.143x + 0.012x$$

$$x = 0.349 \text{ mole dry gas/lb coal}$$

$$\text{O}_2 \text{ balance:} \qquad \frac{0.12}{32} + a = x\left(0.143 + 0.04 + \frac{0.012}{2}\right) + \frac{0.025}{2}$$

$$a = 0.0748 \text{ mole } O_2/\text{lb coal}$$

As a check on the oxygen balance, a nitrogen balance can be used:

$$\frac{0.02}{28} + 3.77a = 0.805x$$

$$a = 0.0743 \text{ mole } O_2/\text{lb coal}$$

This is as close a check as can be expected. The mass of air supplied is then

$$\frac{m_a}{m_f} = 0.0748(32)4.31 = 10.3 \text{ lb air/lb fuel}$$

using the a value from the O_2 balance, and

$$\frac{m_a}{m_f} = 0.0743(32)4.31 = 10.2 \text{ lb air/lb fuel}$$

using the a value from the N_2 balance.

(c) From the values found in part (a) we can determine the mole fraction of water vapor in the products as

$$x_v = \frac{N_v}{N_{dg} + N_v} = \frac{0.025}{x + 0.025} = \frac{0.025}{0.349 + 0.025} = 0.0669$$

and the dew point can then be found as in the first solution.

EXAMPLE 13·4. A fuel gas has the following volumetric analysis: H_2 40 per cent, CH_4 30, C_2H_6 20, N_2 10. It is burned with air supplied at 14.0 psia, 100 F, 90 per cent relative humidity, and the Orsat analysis of the products is as follows: CO_2 8.2 per cent, O_2 4.1, CO 0.6. Determine (a) the air–fuel (mass) ratio, and (b) the dew point of the products.

Analysis. To determine the air–fuel ratio, the chemical equation for this actual combustion reaction can be written without regard to the atmospheric moisture because the moisture undergoes no chemical change during the combustion process. Then, for the determination of the products dew point, the atmospheric moisture, calculated separately, can be added to the water vapor formed by the combustion of hydrogen. An alternative method is to include the atmospheric moisture in the chemical equation so that the coefficient of H_2O on the products side can be used directly to determine the mole fraction of H_2O in the products. We shall use the former method and write the chemical equation without regard to the atmospheric moisture.

Solution. Letting a be the number of moles of oxygen supplied per mole of fuel and b be the number of moles of dry gaseous products per mole of fuel, we have per mole of fuel

$$0.4H_2 + 0.3CH_4 + 0.2C_2H_6 + 0.1N_2 + aO_2 + 3.77aN_2$$
$$= 0.082bCO_2 + 0.006bCO + 0.041bO_2 + 0.871bN_2 + (0.4 + 0.6 + 0.6)H_2O$$

The coefficient of H_2O was obtained by means of a hydrogen balance. b and a are determined by means of carbon and oxygen balances:

C balance: $0.3 + 0.2(2) = 0.082b + 0.006b$

$$b = 7.96 \text{ moles dry gas/mole fuel}$$

O_2 balance: $a = 0.082b + \dfrac{0.006}{2}b + 0.041b + \dfrac{1.6}{2}$

$$= (0.082 + 0.003 + 0.041)7.96 + 0.8$$
$$= 1.80 \text{ moles } O_2/\text{mole fuel}$$

As a check, a nitrogen balance gives

$$0.1 + 3.77a = 0.871b$$
$$a = 1.81 \text{ moles } O_2/\text{mole fuel}$$

In order to convert from a molar to a mass basis, we determine the apparent molecular weight of the fuel:

$$M_f = \Sigma xM = 0.4(2) + 0.3(16) + 0.2(30) + 0.10(28) = 14.4 \text{ lb/mole}$$

Then the air–fuel (mass) ratio is

$$\frac{m_a}{m_f} = \frac{N_aM_a}{N_fM_f} = \frac{1.80(4.77)28.966}{14.4} = 17.3 \frac{\text{lb air}}{\text{lb fuel}}$$

(*b*) To find the dew point of the products, we must know the mole fraction of water vapor in the products. The amount of water formed by the combustion of hydrogen was determined for balancing the chemical equation in part (*a*). The amount of water introduced as atmospheric moisture can be determined if we first calculate the humidity ratio of the air.

$$p_a = p_m - p_v = p_m - \phi p_g = 14.0 - 0.9(0.9492) = 13.15 \text{ psia}$$
$$v_a = \frac{RT}{p_a} = \frac{53.3(560)}{13.15(144)} = 15.8 \text{ cu ft/lb}$$
$$\omega = \frac{v_a}{v_g}\phi = \frac{15.8(0.90)}{350.4} = 0.0405 \text{ lb } v/\text{lb dry air}$$

The number of moles of water vapor carried in with the air per mole of fuel is

$$\frac{N_{v,\text{with air}}}{N_f} = 4.77a \left[\frac{\text{moles air}}{\text{mole fuel}}\right] \omega \frac{M_a}{M_v} \left[\frac{\text{moles vapor}}{\text{mole air}}\right]$$

$$= 4.77(1.80)0.0405 \frac{28.966}{18} = 0.56 \frac{\text{mole vapor}}{\text{mole fuel}}$$

The mole fraction of water vapor in the products is

$$x_v = \frac{N_v}{N_{dg} + N_v} = \frac{N_v/N_f}{b + N_v/N_f} = \frac{1.60 + 0.56}{7.96 + 1.60 + 0.56} = 0.214$$

Then $p_v = x_v p_m = 0.214(14.0) = 3.0$ psia

$T_{dp} = T_{\text{sat.,3.0 psia}} = 141.5$ F

13·5 Energy balance for a chemical reaction

The first law of thermodynamics as applied to any system has the same form whether a chemical reaction occurs within the system or not. For example, for any (stationary) closed system we have

$$Q = U_2 - U_1 + W \tag{2·7}$$

where the subscripts 1 and 2 refer to the initial and final states of the system. The chemical composition of the system may be different in states 1 and 2. This fact does not alter equation 2·7 at all, but it may complicate the calculation of ΔU of the system from other properties. We have discussed already some means of evaluating ΔU as a function of p, v, T, c_v, etc. for pure substances; now we must investigate the determination of ΔU (and ΔH and ΔpV) for systems which vary in chemical composition. (Remember that a pure substance is defined as one which is chemically homogeneous and also chemically *invariant* with respect to time. If a chemical reaction occurs, we are not dealing with a pure substance.)

Consider the application of the first law to a closed system comprised initially of 1 mole of CO and $\frac{1}{2}$ mole of O_2 which undergo the reaction

$$CO + \tfrac{1}{2}O_2 \rightarrow CO_2$$

so that the system is comprised finally of 1 mole of CO_2. Suppose that this process occurs in a rigid thermally insulated tank so that $Q = 0$ and $W = 0$. Then the first law,

$$Q = U_2 - U_1 + W$$

shows that

$$U_2 = U_1$$

We know from experience that the final temperature of this system would be appreciably greater than the initial temperature. Both the reactants (CO and O_2) and the product (CO_2) at low pressures can be treated as ideal gases so that their internal energies are functions of temperature only, but notice that 1 mole of CO_2 at a temperature T_2 has the same internal energy as 1 mole of CO plus $\frac{1}{2}$ mole of O_2 at T_1 when $T_2 > T_1$. To examine this point from another angle, suppose that the reaction occurs in a rigid tank but a sufficient amount of heat is removed to bring the product to the initial temperature of the reactants, $T_2 = T_1$. Then application of the first law shows that

$$Q_{\text{out}} = U_1 - U_2$$

From experience we know that in order to bring the CO_2 to the same temperature that the CO and O_2 started at we must remove heat. Thus $Q_{\text{out}} > 0$ and $U_1 > U_2$ if $T_2 = T_1$. Thus a mixture of 1 mole of CO plus $\frac{1}{2}$ mole of O_2 has a higher internal energy than 1 mole of CO_2 at the same temperature. Of course we can calculate ΔU of an ideal gas by $\Delta U = \int mc_v \, dT$ (as discussed in Art. 4·4), but how do we determine the difference between the internal energies of two different substances such as the products and reactants of a chemical reaction? This is the question to which we now turn our attention.

If we know the specific heats, we can plot curves of U vs. T for the reactants $CO + \frac{1}{2}O_2$ and for the product CO_2 as shown in Fig. 13·2a and b, respectively. In each of these plots the temperature at which $U = 0$ is chosen arbitrarily. In part (c) of Fig. 13·2, the U vs. T curves for the reactants and for the product are superposed with $U = 0$ at the same temperature for both. By the use of such a plot or the plots of Figs. 13·2a and b we can determine ΔU of $CO + \frac{1}{2}O_2$ and ΔU of CO_2 for any ΔT, but we cannot determine the difference between $U_{CO + \frac{1}{2}O_2}$ and U_{CO_2} at any temperature. Suppose now that we determine experimentally $U_{CO_2} - U_{CO + \frac{1}{2}O_2}$ at any one temperature by allowing the reaction to occur in a closed rigid vessel and measuring the amount of heat transfer required to bring the product to the initial temperature of the reactants. Let us call the ΔU between reactants and products *at the same temperature* ΔU_R, the subscript R denoting that the internal energy change is associated with a chemical reaction and not with a temperature change. Then we can shift one of the lines of Fig. 13·2c so that the vertical distance between the two lines at this one temperature equals the measured value of ΔU_R. Thus we have Fig. 13·2d which enables us to calculate ΔU for any process involving the reaction $CO + \frac{1}{2}O_2 \rightarrow CO_2$, regardless of the temperatures of the reactants and the product. For example, referring to Fig. 13·2d, ΔU for a process which begins with the reactants at state A and ends with the product at state B is

$$\Delta U = U_B - U_A = (U_B - U_x) + (U_x - U_y) + (U_y - U_A)$$
$$= U_B - U_x + \Delta U_R + U_y - U_A$$

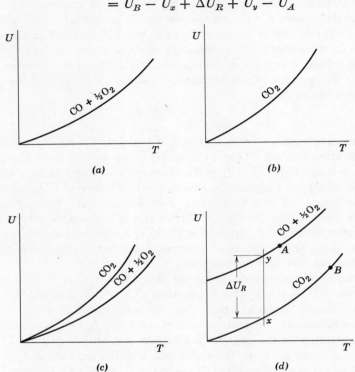

Fig. 13·2 U vs. T for reactants and products.

Treating both the reactants and the products as ideal gases,

$$\Delta U = U_B - U_A = \int_{T_x}^{T_B} (mc_v)_{CO_2}\, dT + \Delta U_R + \int_{T_A}^{T_x} (mc_v)_{CO + \frac{1}{2}O_2}\, dT$$

where T_x is the temperature at which ΔU_R is measured. The two integrals on the right-hand side of this equation can be evaluated from data on the individual gases; but ΔU_R must be evaluated from data on the chemical reaction.

In a similar manner for a steady-flow process between states A and B in which $\Delta KE = \Delta PE = 0$, the first law states that

$$Q = H_B - H_A + W \qquad\qquad (a)$$

and this equation is the same whether a chemical reaction occurs or not. If a chemical reaction does occur, though, we must have in addition to enthalpy data on the reactants and products separately a ΔH_R value—the enthalpy change for the reaction without a change in temperature. If the reactants and products are ideal gases, the HT data for the reactants and

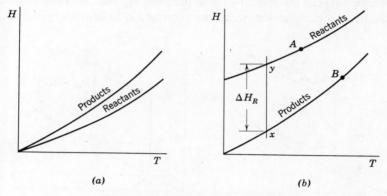

Fig. 13·3 H vs. T for reactants and products.

products separately can be shown as in Fig. 13·3a, but for the proper relationship between these data a plot like Fig. 13·3b must be used. Thus

$$H_B - H_A = (H_B - H_x) + \Delta H_R + (H_y - H_A)$$

and the first-law formulation becomes

$$Q = (H_B - H_x) + \Delta H_R + (H_y - H_A) + W \qquad (b)$$

Notice that equation (b) is the same as equation (a) except that the term $H_B - H_A$ has been expanded in order to use ΔH_R data for relating the enthalpy of the products to that of the reactants.

The purpose of this article is to show that the first law is applied in the same form to chemically reacting systems as to chemically inert systems, and the only complication with a chemical reaction is to evaluate ΔU or ΔH for use in the first law. In the following two articles we take up some useful definitions and discuss in more general terms the evaluation of ΔU and ΔH for processes which involve chemical reactions.

13·6 Enthalpy of reaction

Consider a process in which some substances called the reactants react chemically to form other substances called the products. Let us consider only cases in which the enthalpy of the reactants and of the products depends only on temperature. At a given temperature, the enthalpy of the reactants is fixed, and so is the enthalpy of the products, but measurements of Q and W for a steady-flow reaction with $\Delta KE = \Delta PE = 0$ and with the same initial and final temperature shows that *the enthalpy of the reactants and of the products at the same temperature is not the same.* The difference between the enthalpy of the products H_p and the enthalpy of the reactants H_r, both at the same temperature, is called the *enthalpy of*

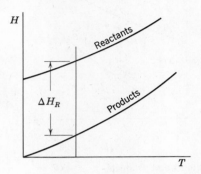

Fig. 13·4   Definition of ΔH_R.

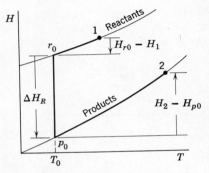

Fig. 13·5   Evaluation of $H_2 - H_1$.

reaction ΔH_R. (Enthalpy *change* of reaction would be a more accurate description, but this terminology is not widely used.) Thus

$$\Delta H_R \equiv (H_p - H_r)_{T_p = T_r}$$

ΔH_R can be determined by measuring Q and W (with $\Delta KE = \Delta PE = 0$) for a steady-flow reaction which is carried out so that the products leave at the temperature of the entering reactants. Then, if the variation of enthalpy with temperature both for the products and for the reactants is known, a plot like Fig. 13·4 can be made. Then the enthalpy change between reactants at state 1 and products at state 2 is, referring to Fig. 13·5,

$$H_2 - H_1 = (H_2 - H_{p0}) + (H_{p0} - H_{r0}) + (H_{r0} - H_1) \qquad (a)$$

$$= (H_2 - H_{p0}) + \Delta H_R - (H_1 - H_{r0}) \qquad (b)$$

where the subscript 0 refers to the temperature T_0 at which ΔH_R is measured. If the reactants mixture is comprised of substances j and k, the enthalpy of the reactants H_1 is given by

$$H_1 = N_j h_j + N_k h_k \qquad (c)$$

where the h's are on a molar basis. A similar expression can be written for the enthalpy of the products in terms of the numbers of moles and specific molar enthalpies of the various constituents of the products mixture.

Substituting such expressions for the H values on the right-hand side of equation (b) gives the following relation for the enthalpy change for a process involving a chemical reaction:

$$H_2 - H_1 = \sum_{\text{prod}} N(h_2 - h_0) + \Delta H_R - \sum_{\text{reac}} N(h_1 - h_0) \qquad (13\cdot1)$$

where h_0 is in each case the enthalpy of a constituent at the temperature at which ΔH_R is measured. Notice that in equation 13·1 the specific enthalpies of the various constituents in the mixtures do not have to be on the same scale because for each constituent only an enthalpy *difference* is required. For example, the enthalpies of some constituents might be taken from Tables 13·1 and 13·2 which are based on $h = 0$ at $T = 0$, the enthalpies of other constituents might be taken from other tables with $h = 0$ at 32 F or at 400 R, and the enthalpy differences of still other constituents might be calculated by $\int_{T_0}^{T} c_p \, dT$ or $\overline{c_p}(T - T_0)$ as long as they are ideal gases. This is fortunate because often data on all constituents involved in a reaction cannot be found in the same form or in the same source. Several sources of enthalpy data on ideal gases are listed among the references at the end of this chapter.

For each chemical reaction, ΔH_R can be determined by calorimetric measurements, either by having the reactants and products at the reference temperature or by having them at other temperatures and applying corrections to the measurements. ΔH_R is generally expressed in B/mole (or per pound) of one of the reactants, but the symbol ΔH_R instead of Δh_R is conventionally used. This serves as a reminder that in equations such as 13·1 each specific enthalpy must be multiplied by the proper mass or number of moles. The reference state usually used is 1 atm, 77 F (25 C), although temperatures of 65 and 68 F are also used. The difference between enthalpies of reaction measured at 77 and 65 F can usually be neglected. Pressure increases of a few atmospheres also have a negligible effect on enthalpies of reaction.

The enthalpy of reaction for any chemical reaction depends on the phases in which the reactants and products appear. Therefore, in Table 13·3 the phase of each constituent is indicated by an s, l, or g (for solid, liquid, and gas). Such notation should always be used where there would be reasonable doubt as to the phase.

For a steady-flow process with no change in kinetic or potential energy, the first law gives

$$Q - W = H_2 - H_1$$

Expanding the right-hand side in accordance with equation 13·1, we obtain

$$Q - W = \sum_{\text{prod}} N(h_2 - h_0) + \Delta H_R - \sum_{\text{reac}} N(h_1 - h_0)$$

TABLE 13·1

Properties of Ideal Gases*

h in B/mole; ϕ in B/mole-R

T, R	CO h	CO ϕ	CO$_2$ h	CO$_2$ ϕ	H$_2$ h	H$_2$ ϕ	H$_2$O h	H$_2$O ϕ	N$_2$ h	N$_2$ ϕ	O$_2$ h	O$_2$ ϕ	T, R
0	0		0		0		0		0		0		0
300	2082	43.223	2108	46.353	2064	27.337	2368	40.439	2082	41.695	2074	44.927	300
400	2777	45.223	2875	48.555	2710	29.195	3164	42.728	2777	43.694	2769	46.927	400
500	3472	46.775	3706	50.408	3386	30.703	3962	44.508	3472	45.246	3466	48.483	500
537	3730	47.272	4030	51.032	3640	31.194	4258	45.079	3730	45.743	3725	48.982	537
600	4168	48.044	4601	52.038	4076	31.959	4765	45.970	4168	46.514	4168	49.762	600
700	4866	49.120	5552	53.503	4770	33.031	5575	47.219	4865	47.588	4879	50.858	700
800	5568	50.058	6553	54.839	5467	33.961	6397	48.316	5564	48.522	5602	51.821	800
900	6276	50.892	7598	56.070	6165	34.784	7231	49.298	6268	49.352	6338	52.688	900
1000	6992	51.646	8682	57.212	6865	35.520	8079	50.191	6978	50.099	7088	53.477	1000
1100	7717	52.337	9803	58.281	7565	36.188	8942	51.013	7695	50.783	7850	54.204	1100
1200	8451	52.976	10955	59.283	8266	3o.798	9820	51.777	8420	51.413	8626	54.879	1200
1300	9195	53.571	12137	60.229	8969	37.360	10715	52.494	9154	52.001	9413	55.508	1300
1400	9948	54.129	13345	61.124	9674	37.883	11625	53.168	9897	52.551	10210	56.099	1400
1500	10711	54.655	14576	61.974	10382	38.372	12551	53.808	10649	53.071	11017	56.656	1500
1600	11483	55.154	15829	62.783	11093	38.830	13495	54.418	11410	53.561	11833	57.182	1600
1700	12264	55.628	17101	63.555	11807	39.264	14455	54.999	12179	54.028	12656	57.680	1700
1800	13053	56.078	18392	64.292	12527	39.675	15433	55.559	12956	54.472	13486	58.155	1800
1900	13850	56.509	19698	64.999	13251	40.067	16428	56.097	13742	54.896	14322	58.607	1900
2000	14653	56.922	21019	65.676	13980	40.441	17439	56.617	14534	55.303	15164	59.039	2000

TABLE 13·1 Continued

T, R	CO		CO$_2$		H$_2$		H$_2$O		N$_2$		O$_2$		T, R
	h	ϕ	h	ϕ	h	ϕ	h	ϕ	h	ϕ	h	ϕ	
2200	16279	57.696	23699	66.953	15454	41.143	19511	57.605	16140	56.068	16863	59.848	2200
2400	17927	58.414	26424	68.139	16951	41.794	21646	58.535	17768	56.777	18579	60.594	2400
2600	19594	59.081	29187	69.245	18470	42.403	23840	59.414	19416	57.436	20311	61.287	2600
2800	21277	59.705	31983	70.282	20012	42.973	26088	60.248	21081	58.053	22058	61.934	2800
3000	22973	60.290	34807	71.255	21577	43.514	28386	61.043	22762	58.632	23818	62.540	3000
3200	24681	60.841	37655	72.175	23164	44.026	30730	61.801	24455	59.179	25591	63.113	3200
3400	26399	61.362	40524	73.045	24772	44.513	33116	62.526	26160	59.697	27376	63.654	3400
3600	28127	61.855	43411	73.870	26399	44.978	35540	63.221	27874	60.186	29174	64.168	3600
3800	29862	62.325	46314	74.655	28043	45.423	37999	63.887	29598	60.652	30984	64.657	3800
4000	31605	62.772	49231	75.404	29704	45.849	40489	64.528	31329	61.097	32806	65.123	4000
4200	33354	63.198	52162	76.119	31380	46.257	43008	65.144	33068	61.520	34640	65.571	4200
4400	35109	63.607	55105	76.803	33071	46.651	45554	65.738	34813	61.927	36485	66.000	4400
4600	36869	63.998	58060	77.460	34776	47.030	48124	66.312	36564	62.316	38341	66.413	4600
4800	38634	64.374	61025	78.091	36493	47.396	50716	66.866	38320	62.689	40209	66.809	4800
5000	40403	64.735	64000	78.698	38223	47.749	53327	67.401	40080	63.049	42086	67.193	5000

* Abridged by permission from Gas Tables, by Joseph H. Keenan and Joseph Kaye, John Wiley & Sons, Inc., 1948.

TABLE 13·2

Enthalpy of Eight Gases at Low Pressure*

in B/mole

T, R	Methane CH$_4$	Ethane C$_2$H$_6$	Propane C$_3$H$_8$	n-Butane C$_4$H$_{10}$	n-Octane C$_8$H$_{18}$	Methanol CH$_3$OH	Ammonia NH$_3$	Hydrazine N$_2$H$_4$	T, R
0	0	0	0	0	0	0	0	0	0
537	4312	5137	6318	8356	15715	4912	4325	5059	537
600	4875	5982	7501	9929	18803	5603	4871	5886	600
700	5791	7422	9556	12669	24204	6756	5766	7309	700
800	6791	9042	11880	15734	30196	8052	6703	8971	800
1000	9012	12752	17259	22805	43941	10890	8710	12227	1000
1200	11545	17077	23493	30976	59757	14121	10888	15916	1200
1400	14370	21924	30458	37258	77243	17695	13227	19866	1400
1600	17461	27214	38055	49903	96145	21571	15715	24046	1600
1800	20794	32882	46176	60404	116312	25714	18342	28416	1800
2000	24334	38894	54944	71473	137490	30091	21098	32966	2000

* Methanol data from E. V. Ivash, J. C. M. Li, and K. S. Pitzer, *The Journal of Chemical Physics*, vol. 23, no. 10, October 1955, pp. 1814–1818. Ammonia and hydrazine data from K. A. Kobe and R. H. Harrison, *Petroleum Refiner*, vol. 33, no. 11, November 1954, pp. 161–164. Other data from *Selected Values of Properties of Hydrocarbons*, National Bureau of Standards Circular C461, 1947.

TABLE 13·3

Enthalpies and Internal Energies of Reaction at 77 F, Low Pressure*

in B/mole

Reaction	ΔH_R	ΔU_R
$H_2(g) + \frac{1}{2}O_2(g) \rightarrow H_2O(g)$	−103,968	−103,435
$H_2(g) + \frac{1}{2}O_2(g) \rightarrow H_2O(l)$	−122,891	−121,281
$C(s) + \frac{1}{2}O_2(g) \rightarrow CO(g)$	−47,517	−48,050
$C(s) + O_2(g) \rightarrow CO_2(g)$	−169,183	−169,183
$CO(g) + \frac{1}{2}O_2(g) \rightarrow CO_2(g)$	−121,666	−121,133
$S(s) + O_2(g) \rightarrow SO_2(g)$	−127,644	−127,644
$H_2O(g) + CO(g) \rightarrow H_2(g) + CO_2(g)$	−17,698	−17,698
$H_2(g) + CO_2(g) \rightarrow H_2O(g) + CO(g)$	+17,698	+17,698
$Fe_2O_3(s) + 3CO(g) \rightarrow 2Fe(s) + 3CO_2(g)$	−2,529	−2,529
$CH_4(g) + 2O_2(g) \rightarrow CO_2(g) + 2H_2O(g)$	−344,940	−344,940
$CH_4(g) + 2O_2(g) \rightarrow CO_2(g) + 2H_2O(l)$	−382,786	−380,655
$C_2H_6(g) + 3\frac{1}{2}O_2(g) \rightarrow 2CO_2(g) + 3H_2O(g)$	−613,868	−614,401
$C_2H_6(g) + 3\frac{1}{2}O_2(g) \rightarrow 2CO_2(g) + 3H_2O(l)$	−670,637	−667,973
$C_3H_8(g) + 5O_2(g) \rightarrow 3CO_2(g) + 4H_2O(g)$	−878,774	−879,840
$C_3H_8(g) + 5O_2(g) \rightarrow 3CO_2(g) + 4H_2O(l)$	−954,464	−951,267
$C_3H_8(l) + 5O_2(g) \rightarrow 3CO_2(g) + 4H_2O(g)$	−871,897	−874,028
$C_3H_8(l) + 5O_2(g) \rightarrow 3CO_2(g) + 4H_2O(l)$	−947,588	−945,457

* Data from *Selected Values of Properties of Hydrocarbons*, National Bureau of Standards Circular C461, 1947, and *Selected Values of Chemical Thermodynamic Properties*, National Bureau of Standards Circular 500, 1952.

If there is no work done and the reactants and products are both at the reference temperature, this first-law expression reduces to

$$Q_{\text{out}} = -Q = -\Delta H_R$$

For this reason, $-\Delta H_R$ is often called the *heat of reaction*. Since $-\Delta H_R$ is equal to a quantity of heat only under certain conditions, the term heat of reaction is somewhat misleading, but it is widely used. Heat of reaction is usually defined as $-\Delta H_R$ instead of $+\Delta H_R$ because a convention was established many years ago that the heat of reaction for an exothermic reaction should be a positive number. In some publications, however, $+\Delta H_R$ is called heat of reaction, so you must be careful about signs in reading tables headed "heats of reaction." If the tabulated heats of reaction for exothermic reactions are positive, then heat of reaction is being defined in the usual manner as $-\Delta H_R$.

If a reaction occurs in a closed system at constant pressure and the only work done is that involved in changing the volume of the system,

$$Q_{\text{out}} = -\Delta U - W = -\Delta U - \int p \, dV = -\Delta U - p \, \Delta V$$

$$= -\Delta U - \Delta p V = -\Delta H$$

and, if the reactants and products are at the reference temperature,

$$Q_{\text{out}} = -\Delta H_R$$

Consequently, $-\Delta H_R$ is often called the *heat of reaction at constant pressure*.

EXAMPLE 13·5. Determine the amount of heat transfer per pound of fuel during the complete combustion of ethane, C_2H_6, in an open steady-flow burner without excess air if the ethane enters at 140 F, the air enters at 40 F, and the products leave at 840 F.

Solution. The reaction equation is

$$C_2H_6 + 3\tfrac{1}{2}O_2 + 3\tfrac{1}{2}(3.77)N_2 \rightarrow 2CO_2 + 3H_2O + 3\tfrac{1}{2}(3.77)N_2$$

and the energy balance, if we neglect changes in kinetic energy, is

$$Q_{\text{out}} = -Q = H_1 - H_2 = \sum_{\text{reac}} N(h_1 - h_0) - \Delta H_R - \sum_{\text{prod}} N(h_2 - h_0)$$

$$= N_{C_2H_6}(h_1 - h_0)_{C_2H_6} + N_{O_2}(h_1 - h_0)_{O_2} + N_{N_2}(h_1 - h_0)_{N_2} - \Delta H_R$$
$$- N_{CO_2}(h_2 - h_0)_{CO_2} - N_{H_2O}(h_2 - h_0)_{H_2O} - N_{N_2}(h_2 - h_0)_{N_2}$$

Since the water leaving as a product at 840 F will be a vapor, the $-\Delta H_R$ value to be used from Table 13·3 is 613,868 B/mole of C_2H_6. Obtaining enthalpy values from Tables 13·1 and 13·2 for substitution into the energy balance,

$$Q_{\text{out}} = 1(5982 - 5137) + 3.5(3466 - 3725) + 13.1(3472 - 3730) - (-613,868)$$

$$- 2(12,137 - 4030) - 3(10,715 - 4258) - 13.1(9154 - 3730)$$

$$= 503,800 \text{ B/mole } C_2H_6 = 16,755 \text{ B/lb } C_2H_6$$

EXAMPLE 13·6.   Determine the enthalpy of reaction of $CO + \frac{1}{2}O_2 \to CO_2$ at 640 F.
Solution.   An *HT* diagram is first made.   It shows clearly the relationship

$$\Delta H_{R,640F} = H_{p,640} - H_{r,640} = (H_{p,640} - H_{p,77}) + (H_{p,77} - H_{r,77}) + (H_{r,77} - H_{r,640})$$

$$= (H_{p,640} - H_{p,77}) + \Delta H_{R,77} - (H_{r,640} - H_{r,77})$$

$$= (h_{640} - h_{77})_{CO_2} + \Delta H_{R,77} - (h_{640} - h_{77})_{CO} - \frac{1}{2}(h_{640} - h_{77})_{O_2}$$

Substituting values from Tables 13·1 and 13·3,

$$\Delta H_{R,640F} = (9803 - 4030) + (-121{,}666) - (7717 - 3730) - \frac{1}{2}(7850 - 3725)$$

$$= -121{,}942 \text{ B/mole CO}$$

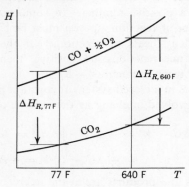

Example 13·6

Enthalpies of reaction for various reactions are frequently given more specific names such as *enthalpy of combustion, enthalpy of formation, enthalpy of hydration,* and so forth.   Similarly, the terms *heat of formation,* etc., are widely used.   *Heat of combustion* or heating value of a fuel is defined as the heat of reaction for the complete combustion of the fuel. Heat of formation is defined as the heat of reaction for the formation of a compound from its elements and is expressed in B/mole (or B/lb) of the compound.   (The heat of formation of an element is zero.)   The symbol $-\Delta H_f$ is often used for heat of formation and $-\Delta H_c$ for heat of combustion.

The value of the heat of combustion of any fuel containing hydrogen is called the higher heat of combustion or higher heating value (*hhv*) if the H_2O in the products is a liquid and the lower heat of combustion or lower heating value (*lhv*) if the H_2O formed is a gas.

EXAMPLE 13·7.   Verify the lower heat of combustion of ethane (C_2H_6) at 77 F as given in Table 13·4 with the tabulated higher heat of combustion as the starting point.
Solution A.   The lower and higher heats of combustion are given respectively by

$$-\Delta H_{lhv} = H_r - H_{p,H_2O(g)} = m_E h_E + m_O h_O - m_C h_C - m_W h_W(g)$$

$$-\Delta H_{hhv} = H_r - H_{p,H_2O(l)} = m_E h_E + m_O h_O - m_C h_C - m_W h_W(l)$$

where E, O, C, and W stand for ethane, oxygen, carbon dioxide, and water, respectively. Combining these two equations,

$$-\Delta H_{lhv} = -\Delta H_{hhv} - m_W[h_W(g) - h_W(l)] = -\Delta H_{hhv} - m_W[h_g - h_f]$$

$$= -\Delta H_{hhv} - m_W h_{fg}$$

Three moles of water are formed for each mole of ethane; so per pound of ethane the mass of water formed is $3(18.016)/1(30.068) = 1.798$ lb. The value of h_{fg} at 77 F is obtained from the steam tables so that

$$-\Delta H_{lhv} = -\Delta H_{hhv} - m_W h_{fg} = 22{,}304 - 1.798(1050.4) = 20{,}416 \text{ B/lb } C_2H_6$$

Solution B. In the steady-flow complete combustion of ethane with no work done and no change in kinetic or potential energy and the reactants and products both at 77 F, the heat removed is 22,304 B/lb of ethane if all the water formed is condensed to a liquid. If all the water leaves as a vapor, the heat removed is less by the latent heat of vaporization of the water. Thus, by this direct reasoning the difference between the higher and lower heats of combustion is

$$-\Delta H_{hhv} - (-\Delta H_{lhv}) = m_W h_{fg} = \frac{3(18.016)}{1(30.068)}(1050.4) = 1888 \text{ B/lb ethane}$$

and $-\Delta H_{lhv} = -\Delta H_{hhv} - m_W h_{fg} = 22{,}304 - 1888 = 20{,}416$ B/lb ethane

EXAMPLE 13·8. Starting from the higher heat of combustion of gaseous benzene as given in Table 13·4, determine the higher heat of combustion of liquid benzene at the same temperature, 77 F.

Solution. For liquid benzene,

$$-\Delta H_{hhv, C_6H_6(l)} = m_B h_B(l) + m_O h_O - m_C h_C - m_W h_W$$

and, for gaseous benzene,

$$-\Delta H_{hhv, C_6H_6(g)} = m_B h_B(g) + m_O h_O - m_C h_C - m_W h_W$$

where B, O, C, and W stand for benzene, oxygen, carbon dioxide, and water, respectively. Combining these two equations,

$$-\Delta H_{hhv, C_6H_6(l)} = -\Delta H_{hhv, C_6H_6(g)} - m_B h_B(g) + m_B h_B(l)$$

$$= -\Delta H_{hhv, C_6H_6(g)} - m_B[h_g - h_f]$$

$$= -\Delta H_{hhv, C_6H_6(g)} - m_B h_{fg}$$

If we want to express the heat of combustion per pound of benzene, then the mass in the last equation is unity. h_{fg} for benzene is taken from Table 13·4.

$$-\Delta H_{hhv, C_6H_6(l)} = 18{,}172 - 1\left(\frac{14{,}552}{78.108}\right) = 17{,}986 \text{ B/lb } C_6H_6$$

This calculation can also be carried out by more direct physical reasoning as was done in solution B of Example 13·7.

EXAMPLE 13·9. Liquid hydrazine, N_2H_4, which is used as a rocket fuel, is burned with one fourth of the stoichiometric amount of liquid oxygen in a steady-flow process. The hydrazine enters at 77 F ($h_{fg} = 18{,}400$ B/mole), and the liquid oxygen enters at -297 F ($h_f = -1830$ B/mole on the same scale as Table 13·1; $h_{fg} = 2930$ B/mole). The

TABLE 13-4

Properties of Substances at 77 F (25 C) and Low Pressure*

Name	Formula	Molecular Weight	Phase	h_{fg}, B/mole	Enthalpy of Combustion ΔH_c at 77 F, 1 atm — $H_2O(l)$ B/lb	$H_2O(l)$ B/mole	$H_2O(g)$ B/lb	$H_2O(g)$ B/mole	Enthalpy of Formation ΔH_f, B/mole	Absolute Entropy S (1 atm), B/mole-R	Formula
Hydrogen	H_2	2.018	gas	—	-60,958	-122,891	-51,571	-103,968	0	31.191	H_2
Water	H_2O	18.018	gas	18,926	—	—	—	—	-103,968	45.077	H_2O
Carbon	C	12.010	solid	—	-14,087	-169,183	-14,087	-169,183	0	1.3600	C
Carbon monoxide	CO	28.010	gas	—	-4,344	-121,665	-4,344	-121,665	-47,517	47.270	CO
Carbon dioxide	CO_2	44.010	gas	—	—	—	—	—	-169,183	51.028	CO_2
Nitrogen	N_2	28.016	gas	—	—	—	—	—	0	45.737	N_2
Oxygen	O_2	32.000	gas	—	—	—	—	—	0	48.971	O_2
Methane	CH_4	16.042	gas	—	-23,861	-382,786	-21,502	-344,940	-32,179	44.47	CH_4
Ethane	C_2H_6	30.068	gas	—	-22,304	-670,637	-20,416	-613,868	-36,401	54.81	C_2H_6
Propane	C_3H_8	44.094	gas	6,485	-21,646	-954,464	-19,929	-878,774	-44,647	64.47	C_3H_8
n-Butane	C_4H_{10}	58.120	gas	9,057	-21,293	-1,237,558	-19,665	-1,142,943	-53,627	74.05	C_4H_{10}
n-Pentane	C_5H_{12}	72.146	gas	11,361	-21,072	-1,520,293	-19,499	-1,406,752	-62,959	83.22	C_5H_{12}
n-Hexane	C_6H_{14}	86.172	gas	13,563	-20,928	-1,803,456	-19,391	-1,670,981	-71,881	92.39	C_6H_{14}
n-Heptane	C_7H_{16}	100.198	gas	15,713	-20,825	-2,086,655	-19,314	-1,935,204	-80,749	101.57	C_7H_{16}
n-Octane	C_8H_{18}	114.224	gas	17,835	-20,747	-2,369,859	-19,197	-2,199,547	-89,617	110.75	C_8H_{18}
Ethene	C_2H_4	28.052	gas	—	-21,625	-606,624	-20,276	-568,772	22,478	52.42	C_2H_4
Propene	C_3H_6	42.078	gas	—	-21,032	-884,998	-19,683	-828,228	8,776	63.76	C_3H_6
Acetylene	C_2H_2	26.036	gas	—	-21,460	-558,741	-20,734	-539,820	97,485	47.966	C_2H_2
Benzene	C_6H_6	78.108	gas	14,552	-18,172	-1,419,415	-17,446	-1,362,644	35,653	64.30	C_6H_6
Methanol	CH_3OH	32.042	gas	16,092	-10,257	-328,644	-9,075	-290,790	-86,321	56.8	CH_3OH
Ethanol	C_2H_5OH	46.068	gas	18,216	-13,159	-506,204	-11,926	-549,423	-100,835	67.4	C_2H_5OH
Hydrazine	N_2H_4	32.048	liquid	18,300	-8,346	-267,457	-7,165	-229,611	21,675		N_2H_4

* Data principally from *Selected Values of Properties of Hydrocarbons*, National Bureau of Standards Circular C461, 1947, and *Selected Values of Chemical Thermodynamic Properties*, National Bureau of Standards Circular 500, 1952.

products leave at 1540 F. The pressure is low enough so that the vapors can be treated as ideal gases. Assuming that the products consist of only N_2H_4, N_2, and H_2O, determine the amount of heat removed per pound of hydrazine.

Solution. The reaction is

$$N_2H_4(l) + \tfrac{1}{4}O_2(l) \rightarrow \tfrac{3}{4}N_2H_4(g) + \tfrac{1}{4}N_2(g) + \tfrac{1}{2}H_2O(g) \qquad (a)$$

but in order to use the data in Table 13·4, we consider the reaction

$$N_2H_4(l) + \tfrac{1}{4}O_2(g) \rightarrow \tfrac{3}{4}N_2H_4(l) + \tfrac{1}{4}N_2(g) + \tfrac{1}{2}H_2O(g) \qquad (b)$$

for which the enthalpy of reaction is one-fourth the lower enthalpy of combustion ($-lhv$) of hydrazine as listed in Table 13·4 because only one fourth of the hydrazine burns and the rest is unchanged. When using ΔH_R for reaction (b) in an energy balance for reaction (a), care must be taken to account for the change in phase of hydrazine and oxygen. The energy balance for reaction (a) is

$$Q = \Delta H_R + \sum_{\text{prod}} N(h_2 - h_0) - \sum_{\text{reac}} N(h_1 - h_0)$$

The h_0 terms must be evaluated for the same phases as those connected with ΔH_R; so, if we use ΔH_R for reaction (b) in the equation above,

$$Q = \Delta H_R + \tfrac{3}{4}[h_2(g) - h_0(l)]_{N_2H_4} + \tfrac{1}{4}[h_2(g) - h_0(g)]_{N_2} + \tfrac{1}{2}[h_2(g) - h_0(g)]_{H_2O}$$
$$- 1[h_1(l) - h_0(l)]_{N_2H_4} - \tfrac{1}{4}[h_1(l) - h_0(g)]_{O_2}$$

For hydrazine h_0 is for the liquid and for oxygen h_0 is for the gas because these are the phases for which we have a value of ΔH_R. For hydrazine we evaluate $h_0(l)$ by subtracting h_{fg} from the $h_0(g)$ value from Table 13·2. Thus, substituting values from Tables 13·1, 13·2, and 13·4,

$$Q = \tfrac{1}{4}(-229{,}611) + \tfrac{3}{4}[32{,}966 - (5059 - 18{,}400)] + \tfrac{1}{4}[14{,}534 - 3730]$$
$$+ \tfrac{1}{2}[17{,}439 - 4258] - 1[0] - \tfrac{1}{4}[-1830 - 3725]$$
$$= -11{,}988 \text{ B/mole } N_2H_4$$

The enthalpy of formation, which is defined as the enthalpy of reaction for the formation of a compound from its elements, is a very useful property because it reduces the amount of data needed on enthalpies of reaction. For an illustration of the calculation of ΔH_R from ΔH_f data, consider the reaction

$$CH_4 + 2O_2 \rightarrow CO_2 + 2H_2O$$

For this reaction the enthalpy of reaction is given by

$$\Delta H_R = H_p - H_r = h_{CO_2} + 2h_{H_2O} - h_{CH_4} - 2h_{O_2} \qquad (a)$$

where the enthalpies of the individual constituents are on a molar basis, are all at the same temperature, and are all evaluated on the same scale. Now suppose that we know the ΔH_f values of the constituents CH_4, CO_2, and H_2O. ($\Delta H_f = 0$ for O_2 as for all elements.) That is, for the reactions

$$C + O_2 \rightarrow CO_2$$

$$H_2 + \tfrac{1}{2}O_2 \rightarrow H_2O$$

$$C + 2H_2 \rightarrow CH_4$$

we know the ΔH_R values which are, by definition, ΔH_f values:

$$\Delta H_{f,CO_2} = h_{CO_2} - h_C - h_{O_2} \tag{b}$$

$$\Delta H_{f,H_2O} = h_{H_2O} - h_{H_2} - \tfrac{1}{2}h_{O_2} \tag{c}$$

$$\Delta H_{f,CH_4} = h_{CH_4} - h_C - 2h_{H_2} \tag{d}$$

Rearranging these last three equations, we have

$$h_{CO_2} = \Delta H_{f,CO_2} + h_C + h_{O_2} \tag{b}$$

$$h_{H_2O} = \Delta H_{f,H_2O} + h_{H_2} + \tfrac{1}{2}h_{O_2} \tag{c}$$

$$h_{CH_4} = \Delta H_{f,CH_4} + h_C + 2h_{H_2} \tag{d}$$

Now, if all these enthalpies are on a common scale—as those of equation (a) must be—we can substitute from these last three equations into equation (a) to get

$$\Delta H_R = \Delta H_{f,CO_2} + h_C + h_{O_2} + 2\Delta H_{f,H_2O} + 2h_{H_2} + h_{O_2}$$
$$- \Delta H_{f,CH_4} - h_C - 2h_{H_2} - 2h_{O_2}$$

Collecting terms,

$$\Delta H_R = \Delta H_{f,CO_2} + 2\Delta H_{f,H_2O} - \Delta H_{f,CH_4}$$

or
$$\Delta H_R = \Delta H_{f,CO_2} + \Delta H_{f,2H_2O} - \Delta H_{f,CH_4}$$

Thus we have expressed ΔH_R solely in terms of the ΔH_f values for the various constituents involved in the reaction. The procedure illustrated can be generalized so that for any reaction

$$\Delta H_R = \sum_{prod} \Delta H_f - \sum_{reac} \Delta H_f \tag{13.2}$$

In using this relationship remember that the enthalpy of formation of an element is zero. All the ΔH_f values must of course be for the same temperature.

Equation 13.2 makes possible the calculation of ΔH_R for complex reactions from data on the individual constituents. Another advantage of the formulation of ΔH_R in terms of ΔH_f values is that it applies to arbitrary mixtures of reactants and to incomplete reactions for which ΔH_R would not be tabulated. For example, if for some reason the burning of CH_4 is incomplete, we might have

$$CH_4 + 2O_2 \rightarrow 0.1CH_4 + 0.7CO_2 + 0.2CO + 1.8H_2O + 0.3O_2$$

For this reaction the enthalpy of reaction is not likely to be found tabulated, but it can be calculated by

$$\Delta H_R = \sum_{\text{prod}} \Delta H_f - \sum_{\text{reac}} \Delta H_f = 0.1\Delta H_{f,\text{CH}_4} + 0.7\Delta H_{f,\text{CO}_2}$$
$$+ 0.2\Delta H_{f,\text{CO}} + 1.8\Delta H_{f,\text{H}_2\text{O}} + 0.3(0) - \Delta H_{f,\text{CH}_4} - 2(0)$$

Table 13·4 gives the enthalpies of formation of several compounds.

By means of ΔH_f data it is possible to build tables of the enthalpies of different substances on a common scale. Tables 13·1 and 13·2 list h vs. T for several substances with $h = 0$ at $T = 0$ for each substance; that is, a common enthalpy scale is not employed. This is apparent because the enthalpy of a compound is much different from the enthalpy of its elements at the same temperature. This difference is known for many compounds and is of course ΔH_f. This means that, by arbitrarily assigning $h = 0$ at $T = 0$ (or some other temperature) *for elements* and adding a constant dependent on ΔH_f to all h values for each compound, we would have a single table giving for several substances h values which could be directly compared, added, and subtracted. Let us designate such h values by h^{abs} for purposes of this discussion. If h^{abs} vs. T tables were available, first-law analyses would be simplified. Also, ΔH_R and ΔH_f values could be obtained from them and the enthalpy information of Tables 13·1, 13·2, 13·3, and 13·4 could be presented in a single table. However, few data have been published in this form, partly because for certain calculations data in other forms are more useful. One disadvantage of h^{abs} vs. T data is that they depend on ΔH_f values which are more subject to refinement than the h vs. T data of a substance. Thus the data of Tables 13·1 and 13·2 can be used in conjunction with any ΔH_R or ΔH_f data, but refinements in the ΔH_f data on which an h^{abs} vs. T table is based would call for additive corrections to the whole table.

Even though presenting data in the form of h^{abs} vs. T or giving ΔH_f values at 0 R instead of at 77 F would simplify matters in this textbook, the data have been presented in more conventional forms because you must understand these in order to use effectively the standard sources of thermochemical data, several of which are listed in the references at the end of this chapter.

13·7   Internal energy of reaction

For any chemical reaction the difference between the internal energy of the products U_p and the internal energy of the reactants U_r, both at the same temperature, is called the *internal energy of* reaction ΔU_R. Thus,

$$\Delta U_R \equiv (U_p - U_r)_{T_p = T_r}$$

Calculations involving ΔU_R are made in the same manner as those involving ΔH_R. For example, we have for the internal energy change between reactants at state 1 and products at state 2

$$U_2 - U_1 = \sum_{\text{prod}} N(u_2 - u_0) + \Delta U_R - \sum_{\text{reac}} N(u_1 - u_0)$$

This relation is similar to equation 13·1 for the change in enthalpy.

For a process of a closed system, whether a chemical reaction occurs or not, the first law gives

$$Q - W = U_2 - U_1$$

If the process does involve a chemical reaction and *the reactants and products are at the reference temperature*, this becomes

$$Q - W = \Delta U_R$$

If the process occurs in a constant-volume container so that no work is done and $T_p = T_r$ (as in a bomb calorimeter), then

$$Q_{\text{out}} = -Q = -\Delta U_R$$

For this reason, $-\Delta U_R$ is often called the *heat of reaction at constant volume*. It was pointed out in the preceding article that $-\Delta H_R$ for a similar reason is often called the *heat of reaction at constant pressure*, although more general usage is to refer to $-\Delta H_R$ as simply the *heat of reaction*.

The relationship between ΔU_R and ΔH_R follows from the definition of enthalpy and is

$$\Delta H_R = \Delta U_R + \Delta(pV)_R$$

where $\Delta(pV)_R = (pV)_{\text{prod}} - (pV)_{\text{reac}}$ with the products and reactants at the same temperature. If the reactants and products may be treated as ideal gases, $\Delta(pV) = \Delta(mRT) = \Delta(NR_uT) = R_uT\,\Delta N$. This relationship may also be used if some of the reactants or products are solid or liquid and the rest ideal gases provided only ΔN for the gaseous constituents is used. This may be done because the molar volume of a solid or liquid is usually negligibly small compared to that of a gas at the same pressure; consequently the volume change of the entire system is very nearly equal to that of the gaseous constituents.

Since $\Delta(pV)$ may be greater than, less than, or equal to zero, the enthalpy of reaction may be greater than, less than, or equal to the internal energy of reaction. For example, for $H_2 + \frac{1}{2}O_2 \rightarrow H_2O(g)$, $\Delta(pV) < 0$ and $\Delta H_R < \Delta U_R$. At 77 F the values for this reaction are $\Delta H_R = -103,968$ B/mole of H_2 and $\Delta U_R = -103,435$ B/mole of H_2. Inequalities between negative numbers occasionally confuse people, because the inequality is different for the numbers and for their magnitudes only. For exothermic reactions, therefore, it is often convenient to make comparisons between the positive numbers $(-\Delta H_R)$ and $(-\Delta U_R)$. Thus

$$(-\Delta H_R) = (-\Delta U_R) - \Delta(pV)$$

and, for example, for $H_2 + \frac{1}{2}O_2 \rightarrow H_2O(g)$, $\Delta(pV) < 0$ and $(-\Delta H_R) > (-\Delta U_R)$; for $CH_4 + 2O_2 \rightarrow CO_2 + 2H_2O(g)$, $\Delta(pV) = 0$ and $(-\Delta H_R) = (-\Delta U_R)$; and, for $C_2H_6 + 3\frac{1}{2}O_2 \rightarrow 2CO_2 + 3H_2O(g)$, $\Delta(pV) > 0$ and $(-\Delta H_R) < (-\Delta U_R)$. To make sure that you know how to calculate ΔH_R from ΔU_R and vice versa for any reaction, you can test your reasoning by verifying the differences between the numerical values given in Table 13·3. One method of physical reasoning is to compare the amount of heat transferred out of a closed system during a constant-pressure process and during a constant-volume process between the same temperatures, the difference being the work of the constant-pressure process which is $\int p \, dV = p \, \Delta V = \Delta(pV)$.

13·8 Maximum adiabatic combustion temperature

Sometimes it is desired to know the temperature of the products of a combustion reaction which occurs adiabatically. For example, the combustion in a rocket motor or in a gas-turbine combustion chamber occurs nearly adiabatically. If no work or heat is removed from the system during the process, the final temperature is a maximum for the reaction which occurs. For a steady-flow adiabatic combustion reaction in which work $= 0$, $\Delta KE = 0$, and $\Delta PE = 0$, application of the first law shows that

$$H_{\text{prod}} = H_{\text{reac}}$$

so that the states 1 and 2 of the reactants and products are as shown in Fig. 13·6. Inspection of Fig. 13·6 shows that

$$0 = H_2 - H_1$$

can be expressed in terms of ΔH_R and the enthalpies of the constituents as

$$0 = \sum_{\text{reac}} N(h - h_0) - \sum_{\text{prod}} N(h - h_0) - \Delta H_R$$

Consider a combustion reaction for which ΔH_R and the initial properties of the reactants are known. The energy balance can be solved for $\sum_{\text{prod}} N(h - h_0)$. The number of moles of the products can be obtained from stoichiometric calculations. The enthalpy change of the products between the temperature at which ΔH_R is known and the end state of the adiabatic combustion process can then be determined. From the enthalpy at the end state, the temperature can be determined. If there are two or more products and enthalpy tables are being used, a trial-and-error or graphical solution is necessary. This is illustrated in the following example.

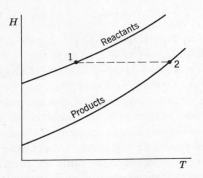

Fig. 13·6   Steady-flow adiabatic combustion.

EXAMPLE 13·10.   Calculate the maximum adiabatic combustion temperature for the steady-flow burning of methane, CH_4, at 77 F with 100 per cent excess air at 240 F.

Solution.   Since the *maximum* temperature is desired, complete combustion will be considered. Water in the products will be a vapor. The reaction equation is

$$CH_4 + 2(2)O_2 + 2(2)3.77N_2 \rightarrow CO_2 + 2H_2O(g) + 1(2)O_2 + 2(2)3.77N_2$$

The energy balance is

$$0 = N_{CH_4}(h_1 - h_0)_{CH_4} + N_{O_2}(h_1 - h_0)_{O_2} + N_{N_2}(h_1 - h_0)_{N_2} - N_{CO_2}(h_2 - h_0)_{CO_2}$$
$$- N_{H_2O}(h_2 - h_0)_{H_2O} - N_{O_2}(h_2 - h_0)_{O_2} - N_{N_2}(h_2 - h_0)_{N_2} - \Delta H_{thv}$$

Substituting enthalpy values from Table 13·1 and the enthalpy of reaction value from Table 13·3 or 13·4,

$$0 = 1(0) + 4(4879 - 3725) + 15.08(4865 - 3730) - 1(h_{2,CO_2} - 4030)$$
$$- 2(h_{2,H_2O} - 4258) - 2(h_{2,O_2} - 3725) - 15.08(h_{2,N_2} - 3730) + 344,940$$

Collecting terms and rearranging,

$$h_{2,CO_2} + 2h_{2,H_2O} + 2h_{2,O_2} + 15.08h_{2,N_2} = 442,916 \text{ B/mole } CH_4$$

Now it is necessary to find the temperature at which the sum of these enthalpies is 442,924 B/mole of CH_4. The sum is therefore calculated and tabulated for enough temperature values so that the temperature value sought can be obtained by interpolation.

T, R	h_{CO_2}	$2h_{H_2O}$	$2h_{O_2}$	$15.08h_{N_2}$	Total
2400	26,424	43,292	37,158	267,941	374,815
2600	29,187	47,680	40,622	292,793	410,282
2800	31,983	52,176	44,116	317,901	446,176

By interpolation the temperature sought is approximately 2780 R or 2320 F.

Actually the maximum adiabatic combustion temperature as calculated in Example 13·10 may not be reached, even though the process is adiabatic and the reactants are well mixed, for a reason which is explained qualitatively in the following article and is treated in more detail in Chapter 14.

13·9 Chemical equilibrium

In actual combustion, the maximum adiabatic temperature as calculated in Example 13·10 above is not attained for several reasons. One of these is

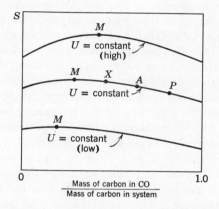

Fig. 13·7 Entropy of an isolated system.

that the reaction may not reach completion because the system reaches an equilibrium state in which both reactants and products are present instead of products alone. To illustrate this point, let us consider a reaction which occurs in a closed system instead of an open one. The qualitative conclusion is the same in either case, and the closed system affords a simpler brief explanation.

Consider a rigid thermally insulated tank which contains 12 lb of carbon and 32 lb of oxygen. All the carbon is combined with some oxygen so that the composition of the tank contents may vary from 44 lb of pure CO_2 to 28 lb of CO mixed with 16 lb of O_2. The entropy of the system will in general be different for each different composition. A plot of the entropy of the system versus composition is shown in Fig. 13·7. Since the tank is rigid and thermally insulated, there is no energy transfer across the system boundary as either work or heat, and the system is therefore an *isolated* system; its internal energy must be constant. For this reason the entropy–composition curve is labeled as a constant U curve. The value of the internal energy depends on the temperature and composition of the gas when the tank was filled or when the insulation was put on the tank; so several constant U curves are possible.

For any process of an *isolated* system,

$$\Delta S_{\text{isolated system}} \geq 0 \qquad\qquad (9\cdot4)$$

Therefore, if the gas mixture in the closed thermally insulated tank is represented by a point A on the figure, there can be no possible process of the isolated system which will carry the system to state P because such a process would violate the increase of entropy principle. A process which carries the system from point A to point X is possible (and irreversible). Further reasoning along this line tells us that, once the system exists in one of the states marked M (in each case the state of maximum entropy for a given internal energy), its state must remain fixed as long as the system is isolated. Furthermore, in any isolated system existing at states other than M states, there is always a tendency for the system to change toward the M state for its particular value of internal energy, although certain factors may prevent the system from undergoing the change toward the M state.

Now it is seen why the maximum adiabatic combustion temperature as calculated in Example 13·10 may not be attained: A state of equilibrium (state of maximum entropy if we are dealing with an isolated system) may be reached before the reaction is completed, and thus not all the reactants will react to form products, as was assumed in the calculation of the maximum adiabatic combustion temperature. The determination of the equilibrium composition and the temperature which is actually attained is treated in Chapter 14.

13·10   Second-law analysis of chemical reactions

We have seen in the preceding articles that the first law can be applied to chemically reacting systems, but we found it necessary to use new methods for evaluating ΔU and ΔH for use in first-law analyses because all our previous study of property relationships pertained to pure substances. In applying the second law to chemically reacting systems, we use the property entropy, and we realize immediately that up to this point we have usually calculated entropy changes only for pure substances. Now we consider the calculation of ΔS for processes involving chemical reactions.

First, let us review the calculation of ΔS for pure substances. We can of course make use of the definition

$$\Delta S \equiv \int_{\text{rev}} \frac{\delta Q}{T} \qquad\qquad (9\cdot1)$$

for any fixed quantity of matter whether a chemical reaction is involved or not; but the various relationships we have considered (such as the Maxwell equations) which relate entropy to other properties stem from the equation

$$T \, dS = dU + p \, dV \tag{9.3}$$

which holds only for pure substances. As an illustration of the fact that equation 9·3 holds only for pure substances, consider a system consisting initially of a mixture of several substances in a closed rigid thermally insulated vessel. Let this mixture be in mechanical and thermal equilibrium but not in chemical equilibrium; that is, the pressure and temperature are uniform throughout the system, and there is no relative motion among parts of the system, but the constituents are chemically reactive. The reaction may be occurring very slowly, or a catalyst may be needed to initiate it. (Remember that, if a catalyst is employed, it is entirely unaffected by the process.) In either case, allow the reaction to occur so that the system does reach a state of chemical equilibrium as well as mechanical and thermal equilibrium. This process in which the system goes from a nonequilibrium to an equilibrium state is irreversible, and it occurs in an isolated system; therefore

$$dS > 0 \quad \text{and consequently} \quad T \, dS > 0$$

Since the system is isolated, however, U and V are constant so that

$$dU = 0 \quad \text{and} \quad p \, dV = 0$$

Therefore　　　　　　$$T \, dS > dU + p \, dV$$

or, in other words, equation 9·3 does not hold for a process involving a chemical reaction.*

A reasonable suggestion for a means of determining ΔS for a chemical reaction is to make measurements during a reaction of $\int_{\text{rev}} \dfrac{\delta Q}{T}$ to determine a ΔS_R in the same way that ΔH_R is determined from measurements of Q under specified conditions; but finding and using a reversible path between end states involving different substances presents formidable difficulties. To avoid these difficulties we employ instead the *third law of thermodynamics*, an independent principle which cannot be deduced from the first and second laws or from any other principles of nature.

---

* Sometimes the range of application of equation 9·3 is defined by saying that the relationship holds only between states in which a system is in complete (chemical, mechanical, thermal) equilibrium. Another manner of stating the restriction on equation 9·3 is to limit it to states of systems in which $S = f(U, V)$. In the process described above, $S \neq f(U, V)$ because the entropy of the system changed during the process while U and V remained constant. The relative merits of these various statements are of little concern in this introductory textbook.

The third law of thermodynamics, like the second, can be stated in several forms which at first appear to be quite unrelated. The third law is mentioned here solely as the basis for determining entropies of various substances on a common scale; so for our purpose a suitable statement of the third law is the following: At absolute zero temperature the entropy of many pure crystalline substances is zero. There are some important restrictions on the third law as stated here,* but the result which is important to us at this point is that the third law makes possible the determination of absolute entropies based on $S = 0$ at $T = 0$. In Table 13·4 are given the absolute entropies of several substances, each in a standard state† of 1 atm and 77 F. These are on a common scale and can be directly added or compared. The symbol for absolute entropy in the standard state is S_0 (or s_0 on a per pound or per mole basis).‡ The absolute entropy of a substance in any other state x is given by

$$S_x = S_0 + \int_0^x dS$$

where the integral is evaluated by the methods already discussed for pure substances. For ideal gases,

$$s_x = s_0 + \int_0^x \frac{dh - v\, dp}{T} = s_0 + \int_0^x \frac{c_p\, dT}{T} - R \int_0^x \frac{dp}{p}$$

$$= s_0 + \phi_x - \phi_0 - R \ln \frac{p_x}{p_0}$$

The standard state used for solids, liquids, and *ideal* gases is often (always in this book) 1 atm and 77 F. For gases, this is sometimes a hypothetical state in which the substance actually cannot exist as a gas. For example, s_0 for $H_2O(g)$ is listed in Table 13·4. At 77 F, however, the

---

* For example, it must be pointed out just which substances the statement does apply to and which it does not.

† The term standard state is given various meanings in the thermodynamics literature. Often it refers not to a specific state but only to a specified pressure without regard to temperature, so that one encounters references to the standard-state entropy at 77 F, the standard-state entropy at 400 F, etc., and tables of standard-state entropy versus temperature are published. This use of the term standard state to refer to many different states at a given pressure is confusing, but it is widespread.

‡ Frequently the symbol $S°$ is used for absolute entropy in the standard state. This is especially convenient if standard state signifies only a specific pressure, because then a subscript can be added denoting the precise state. Since in this book standard state signifies a specific state, not just a pressure, the subscript 0 denotes the state fully. If you wish to use a different symbol for absolute entropy and entropy with respect to an arbitrary reference state, you might use the symbol S^{abs} (S_0^{abs} for the standard state), but this is usually regarded as unnecessary.

highest pressure under which water can exist as a gas is 0.4593 psia. The s_0 value in Table 13·4 is therefore equal to the absolute entropy of saturated water vapor at 77 F plus the entropy change of an isothermal compression of water vapor *as an ideal gas* from 0.4593 psia, 77 F, to 14.696 psia.

In the Keenan and Kaye *Gas Tables* (except for air) and Table 13·1 the ϕ values at 77 F are equal to the absolute entropy values at 77 F and 1 atm. Thus *in connection with these tables* the equation above for the entropy of an ideal gas in a state x is given by

$$s_x = \phi_x - R \ln \frac{p_x}{p_0}$$

where $p_0 = 1$ atm. Thus for ideal gases at 1 atm the tabulated ϕ values may be used directly as absolute entropy values. (Be careful: This applies only to ideal gases at 1 atm in connection with tables that have $\phi_0 = s_0$.)

Being able to calculate ΔS for processes involving chemical reactions makes it possible for us to apply the increase of entropy principle to determine whether a particular reaction is possible. Furthermore, we can now calculate the irreversibility of a chemical reaction.

EXAMPLE 13·11. Consider the adiabatic steady-flow burning of carbon monoxide with the stoichiometric amount of air. The air and the carbon monoxide are initially at 77 F, and the total pressure remains constant at 1 atm. *Assuming* that it is possible for 90 per cent of the carbon monoxide to be burned, is it possible for all of it to be burned under the conditions specified? In other words, with reference to the figure, is the process from state 2 to state 3 possible?

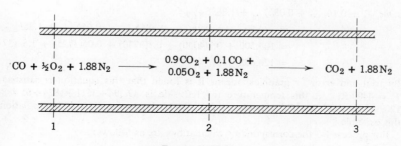

Example 13·11

Solution. An adiabatic steady-flow process is possible only if the entropy of the flowing material increases or remains constant; so we can answer the question by determining the entropy change of the gas mixture between states 2 and 3. In order to do this we must first determine T_2 and T_3. This can be done by means of the first law. For the adiabatic process 1-2-3 with no work done* and $\Delta KE = 0$, $H_1 = H_2 = H_3$. An

---

* Of course there is flow work, but recall the convention established in Art. 2·7 that the term *work* without modifiers stands for all other forms of work besides flow work.

HT diagram of the process is made to help in writing energy balances involving ΔH_R. For process 1-2 we have (recalling that ΔH_f for an element is zero)

$$\Delta H_{R,1\text{-}2} = \sum_{\text{prod}} \Delta H_f - \sum_{\text{reac}} \Delta H_f = 0.9(-169,183) + 0.1(-47,517) - 1(-47,517)$$

$$= -109,500$$

The energy balance is

$$H_2 = H_1 = H_1 - H_a + H_a = -\Delta H_{R,1\text{-}2} + H_a$$

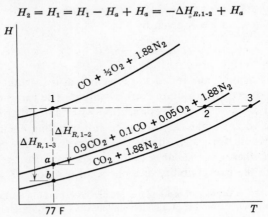

Example 13-11

Expressing H_2 and H_a in terms of the molar enthalpies of the individual constituents,

$$0.9h_{2,CO_2} + 0.1h_{2,CO} + 0.05h_{2,O_2} + 1.88h_{2,N_2}$$
$$= -\Delta H_{R,1\text{-}2} + 0.9h_{a,CO_2} + 0.1h_{a,CO} + 0.05h_{a,O_2} + 1.88h_{a,N_2}$$
$$= 109,500 + 0.9(4030) + 0.1(3730) + 0.05(3725) + 1.88(3730)$$
$$= 120,698$$

By trial and error or graphical means it is found that this equation is satisfied at $T_2 = 4400$ R. At this temperature the left side is $49,594 + 3511 + 1824 + 65,488 = 120,377$ B, which is sufficiently close to $120,698$ B, since we shall avoid interpolation in this example.

For process 1-3 the corresponding calculations are as follows:

$$\Delta H_{R,1\text{-}3} = -121,666 \text{ B} \qquad \text{(from Table 13·3)}$$
$$H_3 = H_1 = H_1 - H_b + H_b = -\Delta H_{R,1\text{-}3} + H_b$$
$$h_{3,CO_2} + 1.88h_{3,N_2} = -\Delta H_R + h_{b,CO_2} + 1.88h_{b,N_2} = 121,666 + 4030 + 1.88(3730)$$
$$= 132,708$$

This equation is satisfied at $T_3 = 4780$ R.

Now to see if the process from state 2 to state 3 is possible we calculate ΔS.

$$S_3 - S_2 = \sum_3 N\left(s_0 + \phi - \phi_0 - R_u \ln \frac{p}{p_0}\right) - \sum_2 N\left(s_0 + \phi - \phi_0 - R_u \ln \frac{p}{p_0}\right)$$

where s_0 is the absolute entropy of each constituent at 1 atm 77 F; p is the partial pressure of each constituent; and p_0 is the standard-state pressure of 1 atm. Since the mixture pressure is also 1 atm, $p/p_0 = p/p_m = x$, where x is the mole fraction. R_u is used in place of R because all specific properties are on a molar basis. If we use the Keenan and Kaye *Gas Tables* or Table 13·1, $\phi_0 = s_0$ for each constituent. Thus the expression for ΔS is simplified to

$$S_3 - S_2 = \sum_3 N(\phi - R_u \ln x) - \sum_2 N(\phi - R_u \ln x)$$

$$= [(\phi - R_u \ln x)_{CO_2} + 1.88(\phi - R_u \ln x)_{N_2}]_3 - [0.9(\phi - R_u \ln x)_{CO_2}$$

$$+ 0.1(\phi - R_u \ln x)_{CO} + 0.05(\phi - R_u \ln x)_{O_2} + 1.88(\phi - R_u \ln x)_{N_2}]_2$$

$$= \left[78.029 - 1.986 \ln \frac{1}{2.88} + 1.88 \left(62.652 - 1.986 \ln \frac{1.88}{2.88} \right) \right]$$

$$- \left[0.9 \left(76.803 - 1.986 \ln \frac{0.9}{2.93} \right) + 0.1 \left(63.607 - 1.986 \ln \frac{0.1}{2.93} \right) \right.$$

$$+ 0.05 \left(66.000 - 1.986 \ln \frac{0.05}{2.93} \right) + 1.88 \left(61.927 - 1.986 \ln \frac{1.88}{2.93} \right) \left. \right]$$

$$= -0.536 \text{ B/R per mole of CO at section 1}$$

(Obviously this is not a slide-rule calculation.) Process 2-3 would result in a decrease in the entropy of material flowing adiabatically through a steady-flow system; therefore in accordance with the increase of entropy principle, process 2-3 is impossible. The reaction $CO + \frac{1}{2}O_2 + 1.88N_2 \rightarrow CO_2 + 1.88N_2$ will not go to completion in a steady-flow adiabatic process at 1 atm with the reactants entering at 77 F.

Example 13·11 illustrates a method for determining if a process is possible and is another indication of the usefulness and scope of thermodynamics as a tool of the engineer and scientist. Some of the examples of irreversible and impossible processes discussed in earlier chapters were quite obvious: You could draw the correct conclusions intuitively, and the support of your conclusions by the second law seemed hardly necessary. But now in Example 13·11 we have a case in which the second law clearly leads us to a conclusion that cannot be reached intuitively or by deductions from other principles.

The extent to which a reaction will proceed could be determined by repeated calculations like those of Example 13·11, but a more direct method is presented in Chapter 14.

EXAMPLE 13·12. Assume that the reaction $CO + \frac{1}{2}O_2 + 1.88N_2 \rightarrow 0.9CO_2 + 0.1CO + 0.05O_2 + 1.88N_2$ occurs adiabatically at 1 atm in a steady-flow system which the reactants enter at 77 F. (This is process 1-2 of Example 13·11.) The lowest temperature in the surroundings is 40 F. (This means that the combustion air has been preheated if the atmosphere is at 40 F, or it could mean that a large body of water is available as an energy reservoir at 40 F.) Determine the irreversibility of the process and the stream availability of the products, both per mole of CO entering.

Solution. First we must avoid confusion by noting that in second-law analyses the subscript 0 usually denotes conditions at the dead state, and in chemical thermodynamics the same subscript denotes standard conditions. Here we encounter both conditions; so let the dead-state properties be denoted by the subscript d. Thus the lowest temperature in the surroundings is $T_d = 40$ F and $I = T_d \Delta S_{\text{isolated system}}$.

For an adiabatic steady-flow process the total change in entropy of the universe (or of an isolated system defined as the steady-flow system plus all parts of the surroundings which interact with it) is $S_2 - S_1$, where S_2 and S_1 are respectively the entropies of the material leaving and the material entering the system.

$$S_2 - S_1 = \sum_2 N\left(s_0 + \phi - \phi_0 - R_u \ln \frac{p}{p_0}\right) - \sum_1 N\left(s_0 + \phi - \phi_0 - R_u \ln \frac{p}{p_0}\right)$$

As noted in the solution of Example 13·11, this equation can be simplified to

$$S_2 - S_1 = \sum_2 N(\phi - R_u \ln x) - \sum_1 N(\phi - R_u \ln x)$$

Using $T_2 = 4400$ R as determined in Example 13·11, we have

$$\begin{aligned}
S_2 - S_1 = &\left[0.9\left(76.803 - 1.986 \ln \frac{0.9}{2.93}\right) + 0.1\left(63.607 - 1.986 \ln \frac{0.1}{2.93}\right)\right.\\
&\left. + 0.05\left(66.000 - 1.986 \ln \frac{0.05}{2.93}\right) + 1.88\left(61.927 - 1.986 \ln \frac{1.88}{2.93}\right)\right]\\
&- \left[1\left(47.272 - 1.986 \ln \frac{1}{3.38}\right) + 0.5\left(48.982 - 1.986 \ln \frac{0.5}{3.38}\right)\right.\\
&\left. + 1.88\left(45.743 - 1.986 \ln \frac{1.88}{3.38}\right)\right]
\end{aligned}$$

$$= 39.025 \text{ B/R per mole of CO entering}$$

$$I = T_d \Delta S_{\text{isolated system}} = 500(39.025) = 19,513 \text{ B/mole of CO entering}$$

If we neglect kinetic energy, the stream availability of the products is

$$Y_2 = (H_2 - T_d S_2) - (H_d - T_d S_d) = H_2 - H_d - T_d(S_2 - S_d)$$

where H_d and S_d are the enthalpy and entropy *of the products* (not of the reactants) at the dead state. (Recall that the stream availability is the maximum work which could be obtained as the fluid goes reversibly to the dead state while exchanging heat only with the atmosphere.) For the substitution of tabular values we rearrange the equation for stream availability,

$$Y_2 = \Sigma N(h_2 - h_d) - T_d \Sigma N\left(\phi_2 - \phi_d - R_u \ln \frac{p_2}{p_d}\right)$$

Since there is no change in the total pressure or the composition of the products between state 2 and the dead state, the partial pressure of each constituent remains constant, $p_2 = p_d$. Thus the equation for stream availability is

$$Y_2 = \Sigma N(h_2 - h_d) - T_d \Sigma N(\phi_2 - \phi_d)$$

$$= 0.9(55,105 - 3706) + 0.1(35,109 - 3472) + 0.05(36,485 - 3466)$$

$$+ 1.88(34,813 - 3472) - 500[0.9(76.803 - 50.408) + 0.1(63.607 - 46.775)$$

$$+ 0.05(66.000 - 48.483) + 1.88(61.927 - 45.246)]$$

$$= 81,158 \text{ B/mole of CO entering}$$

This is the maximum amount of work which can be obtained by any process which takes the products to the dead state while exchanging heat with only the energy reservoir at 40 F. The stream availability of the products is less than the heat of combustion for the reaction; so it is impossible, following the adiabatic combustion process, to produce work in an amount equal to the heat of combustion.

13·11 Summary

In this chapter mass balances and energy balances for processes involving chemical reactions have been discussed, and the second-law analysis of such processes has been considered briefly.

The oxygen for most combustion reactions comes from air. For nearly all combustion calculations the approximate composition of air can be taken as

$$1 \text{ mole } O_2 + 3.77 \text{ mole } N_2 = 4.77 \text{ moles air}$$

$$1 \text{ lb } O_2 + 3.31 \text{ lb } N_2 = 4.31 \text{ lb air}$$

Stoichiometric air is the quantity of air required to burn one pound, one mole, or one cubic foot of fuel completely with no oxygen appearing in the products of combustion.

Two combustion mass balance problems are encountered in engineering: One is the determination of the amount of air or other oxidizer required to burn a fuel completely and the composition of the resulting products; the other is the determination, from an analysis of the products of an actual combustion process, of how much air was actually supplied. The instrument frequently used for analyzing combustion products is the Orsat gas analyzer which measures the *volumetric* fractions of CO_2, O_2, and CO on a dry basis.

The first law of thermodynamics as applied to any system has the same form whether a chemical reaction occurs within the system or not, the only complication with a chemical reaction being to evaluate ΔU or ΔH for use in the first law. To assist in the evaluation of ΔH and ΔU we define the *enthalpy of reaction* ΔH_R as the difference between the enthalpy of the products and the enthalpy of the reactants at the same temperature (as long as the enthalpy of each is a function of temperature only), and we define *the internal energy of reaction* ΔU_R as the difference between the internal energy of the products and of the reactants at the same temperature (again assuming that the internal energy of each is a function of temperature only). The change in enthalpy for a process between the reactants at a state 1 and the products at a state 2 can be written as

$$H_2 - H_1 = \sum_{\text{prod}} N(h_2 - h_0) + \Delta H_R - \sum_{\text{reac}} N(h_1 - h_0) \qquad (13 \cdot 1)$$

where h_0 is in each case the enthalpy of a constituent at the temperature at which ΔH_R is measured. A similar expression can be written for $U_2 - U_1$. $-\Delta H_R$ is often called the *heat of reaction at constant pressure*, and $-\Delta U_R$ is often called the *heat of reaction at constant volume*.

Enthalpies of reaction for various reactions are often given more specific names such as enthalpy of combustion, enthalpy of formation (ΔH_f), enthalpy of hydration, and so forth. The enthalpy of formation is a valuable property because ΔH_R for any reaction can be expressed in terms of the ΔH_f values of the various constituents involved in the reaction in accordance with the relationship

$$\Delta H_R = \sum_{\text{prod}} \Delta H_f - \sum_{\text{reac}} \Delta H_f \qquad (13 \cdot 2)$$

The maximum adiabatic combustion temperature for any fuel–oxidizer combination can be calculated by means of the first law and data on ΔH_R and on the hT relationships of the constituents involved in the reaction. A reaction which appears possible from the standpoint of stoichiometric and first-law considerations may actually be impossible, however. This can be shown by means of the second law. Application of the second law to tell whether a given process is possible or to calculate the irreversibility of a process involves the determination of ΔS for the process. The entropy change for a process involving a chemical reaction can be determined by use of absolute entropy values which can be found on the basis of the third law of thermodynamics which, for our purposes here, can be stated as follows: At absolute zero temperature the entropy of many pure crystalline substances is zero. Absolute entropies of several substances at a specified standard state are given in Table 13·4 and are designated as s_0. The absolute entropy of a substance in any other state x is then

$$s_x = s_0 + \int_0^x ds$$

where the integral is evaluated by any of several methods which apply to entropy changes of pure substances.

REFERENCES

13·1 D. A. Mooney, *Mechanical Engineering Thermodynamics*, Prentice-Hall, 1953, chapter 22.
13·2 E. F. Obert, *Thermodynamics*, McGraw-Hill Book Co., 1948, chapter XI.
13·3 V. W. Young, *Basic Thermodynamics*, McGraw-Hill Book Co., 1952, chapter 19.
13·4 V. M. Faires, *Thermodynamics*, Macmillan Co., 3d ed., 1957, chapter 13.
13·5 L. E. Steiner, *Introduction to Chemical Thermodynamics*, McGraw-Hill Book Co., 1941, chapter V.

Brief reviews of the third law

13·6 B. F. Dodge, *Chemical Engineering Thermodynamics*, McGraw-Hill Book Co., 1944.
13·7 J. H. Potter, "The Third Law of Thermodynamics: A Half-Century Appraisal of the Nernst Heat Theorem," *Transactions ASME*, vol. 80, 1958, pp. 895–903.

For enthalpy of reaction and other data

13·8 *Selected Values of Chemical Thermodynamic Properties*, National Bureau of Standards Circular 500, 1952.
13·9 *Selected Values of Properties of Hydrocarbons*, National Bureau of Standards Circular C461, 1947.
13·10 *Handbook of Chemistry and Physics*, Chemical Rubber Publishing Co., published yearly. (Refer to "heat of formation" and "heat of reaction" in the index.)
13·11 *Mark's Mechanical Engineers' Handbook*, McGraw-Hill Book Co., 6th ed. 1958, pp. 4–71 to 4–73.

For data on thermodynamic properties of combustion gases

13·12 J. H. Keenan and J. Kaye, *Gas Tables*, John Wiley & Sons, 1948.
13·13 *Tables of Thermal Properties of Gases*, National Bureau of Standards Circular 564, 1955.
13·14 E. W. Geyer and E. A. Bruges, *Tables of Properties of Gases*, Longmans, Green & Co., 1948.

PROBLEMS

13·1 Calculate (*a*) the mass of water formed by burning completely 1000 cu ft of methane, measured at 14.0 psia, 40 F, with 20 per cent excess air, and (*b*) the dew point of the products which are at 14.0 psia, 515 F.

13·2 A gaseous mixture at 14.7 psia, 180 F, has a gravimetric analysis of 80 per cent CH_4, 14 per cent N_2, and 6 per cent H_2O. Determine (*a*) the dew point of this mixture, and (*b*) the minimum amount of air required to burn this mixture completely.

13·3 A gasoline with an ultimate analysis of 85 per cent carbon and 15 per cent hydrogen has a specific gravity of 0.72, a density of 6 lb/gal, and a higher heating value of 20,700 B/lb. For the complete combustion of this gasoline with 10 per cent excess air, determine (a) the air–fuel ratio and (b) the number of gallons of water formed per gallon of gasoline burned.

13·4 A gaseous fuel has the following volumetric analysis: CH_4 60 per cent, CO 20, O_2 10, N_2 10. Compute (a) the gravimetric analysis of this fuel by chemical compounds, (b) the ultimate analysis, (c) the specific volume at 14.7 psia, 100 F, (d) the volume of dry air at 14.7 psia, 100 F, required to burn 1 cu ft of this fuel with 30 per cent excess air, (e) the volumetric analysis of the dry products of complete combustion with 30 per cent excess air, (f) the mass of the total products per pound of fuel with 30 per cent excess air, (g) the mass of water vapor in the products per pound of fuel, (h) the mass of air supplied per pound of fuel, (i) the dew point of the products if dry air is supplied for combustion, and (j) the dew point of the products if the air supplied for combustion is at 14.7 psia, 100 F, 70 per cent relative humidity.

13·5 A gaseous fuel has the following volumetric analysis: CO 10 per cent, H_2 10, CH_4 20, C_2H_6 10, O_2 10, CO_2 10, N_2 30. Compute the same items as in Prob. 13·4.

13·6 Coke-oven gas has the following volumetric analysis: CO 6 per cent, H_2 42, CH_4 34, C_2H_4 2, C_2H_6 3, O_2 1, CO_2 2, N_2 10. Compute the same items as in Prob. 13·4.

13·7 A Mond producer gas has the following volumetric analysis: CO_2 12.0 per cent, CO 15.0, CH_4 3.0, H_2 26.0, N_2 44.0. Compute the same items as in Prob. 13·4.

13·8 A coal has the following gravimetric analysis: C 68 per cent, H 5, O 16, N 2, S 2, and ash 7. Calculate (a) the amount of air required to burn this coal completely with 30 per cent excess air, (b) the volumetric analysis of the dry products of complete combustion with 30 per cent excess air, (c) the mass of the total products per pound of fuel with 30 per cent excess air, (d) the mass of water vapor in the products per pound of fuel, (e) the mass of air supplied, (f) the dew point of the products if dry air is supplied for combustion, and (g) the dew point of the products if air at 14.7 psia, 100 F, 70 per cent relative humidity is supplied for combustion.

13·9 A hydrocarbon fuel is completely burned in air. How does the dew point of the products vary with (a) the fraction of hydrogen in the fuel? (b) the humidity ratio of the combustion air? (c) the barometric pressure?

13·10 The molecular weight of air is 28.966 lb/mole. Explain why this value is not obtained by calculating the molecular weight from the composition

$$1 \text{ mole } O_2 + 3.77 \text{ moles } N_2 = 4.77 \text{ moles air}$$

13·11 A liquid fuel has an ultimate analysis of 84 per cent carbon, 13 per cent hydrogen, and 3 per cent oxygen. When this fuel was burned, the Orsat analysis of the gaseous products was 11.5 per cent CO_2, 4.1 per cent O_2, and 0.9 per cent CO. The products were analyzed at 14.5 psia. Determine the amount of air supplied per pound of fuel.

13·12 Ethyl alcohol, C_2H_5OH, is burned in air, and a volumetric analysis of the dry products is given by CO_2 9.8 per cent, O_2 6.5, CO 0.6, HCHO 0.6, N_2 82.5. Air for combustion is supplied at 14.2 psia, 70 F. Determine per pound of ethyl alcohol (a) the mass of air supplied and (b) the mass of water formed.

13·13 A powdered substance has a gravimetric analysis of 60 per cent carbon, 30 per cent sulfur, 10 per cent ash. It is burned in air, and a modified Orsat analyzer which measures SO_2 as well as the usual constituents of the gaseous products gives the following:

CO_2 11.9 per cent, O_2 4.5, CO 3.0, SO_2 2.8. Assuming that all of the carbon and sulfur is burned, determine the amount of air supplied per pound of substance.

13·14 A gasoline with an ultimate analysis of 85 per cent carbon and 15 per cent hydrogen has a specific gravity of 0.72. This gasoline was burned in an automobile engine, and the products of combustion gave the following Orsat readings: CO_2 12.1 per cent, O_2 2.6, CO 1.1. Barometric pressure was 14.5 psia. The air supplied for combustion had a humidity ratio of 0.030 lb vapor per pound of dry air. Determine per pound of fuel (a) the amount of air supplied, and (b) the amount of water in the products of combustion.

13·15 A coal has the following gravimetric analysis: C 76 per cent, H 5, O 6, S 1, N 1, ash 5, free moisture 6. Volumetric analysis of the dry products of combustion by an Orsat shows: CO_2 12.7 per cent, CO 0.4, O_2 6.1. Assume that all ash is discharged to the ashpit and that the fraction of carbon in the refuse is 25 per cent. Calculate (a) the mass of air supplied per pound of fuel, (b) the per cent excess air, (c) the mass of carbon burned to CO per pound of fuel, (d) the dew point of the products if dry air at 14.7 psia, 100 F, is supplied, and (e) the dew point of the products if the air supplied for combustion is at 14.7 psia, 100 F, 70 per cent relative humidity.

13·16 Blast-furnace gas has the following volumetric analysis: CO_2 11 per cent, CO 29, H_2 3, CH_4 2, N_2 55. Heating value = 101 B/cu ft at 14.7 psia, 60 F. The volumetric analysis of the products of combustion is: CO_2 19.4 per cent, CO 1.0, O_2 4.5 N_2 75.1. Compute the same items as in Prob. 13·15.

13·17 Determine from the following test data the amount of water in the gaseous products: Coal ultimate analysis: C 70 per cent, H 5, O 10, N 4, S 3, ash 8. Higher heating value: 12,500 B/lb. Orsat analysis: CO_2 13.6 per cent, O_2 4.5, CO 1.1. Amount of coal fired during test: 5000 lb. Refuse collected: 500 lb with 20 per cent carbon. Combustion air conditions: 29.2 in. Hg, 90 F, humidity ratio of 0.030 lb/lb dry air. Products temperature: 510 F.

13·18 Prove that an Orsat analysis is a dry analysis, even though the gas sample contains saturated water vapor. Is there any change in the amount of water vapor in the sample each time it is returned to the measuring burette?

13·19 The heat of combustion of carbon is determined by means of a bomb calorimeter submerged in a water bath. In addition to a small amount of carbon, a considerable excess of air is placed in the bomb. How does the amount of air, assuming that in all cases there is enough for complete combustion, affect the value obtained for the heat of combustion?

13·20 The heat of combustion of a liquid hydrocarbon is to be measured by means of a bomb calorimeter. It is proposed to place a drop of liquid water in the bomb so that the amount of heat removed to return the bomb and its contents to their initial temperature will be the higher heat of combustion at constant volume, the reasoning being that part of the water drop will evaporate and make the air–vapor atmosphere in the bomb saturated so that all of the water formed by combustion will condense. Comment on this proposal.

13·21 Nitrogen is generally considered to be inert in combustion reactions. Still, oxides of nitrogen do exist. Therefore, why do we not burn the nitrogen in the air and thereby obtain some heating value from the air as well as from the fuel being burned?

13·22 Refer to Table 13·3. The sum of ΔH_R for $C + \frac{1}{2}O_2 \rightarrow CO$ and ΔH_R for $CO + \frac{1}{2}O_2 \rightarrow CO_2$ equals ΔH_R for $C + O_2 \rightarrow CO_2$. Is this a coincidence or is it a consequence of the first or second law? Prove your answer.

13·23 Determine the lower heat of combustion of hydrogen at 600 F.

13·24 Hydrogen is supplied to a burner at 100 F and is completely burned with 20 per cent excess air which is also supplied at 100 F. The products leave at 900 F. Determine the amount of heat released per pound of hydrogen.

13·25 Methane at 77 F is burned with 20 per cent excess air supplied at 77 F in a steady-flow process. The products leave at 800 F. Calcluate (a) the amount of heat transfer per pound of methane, and (b) the dew point of the products.

13·26 Determine the amount of heat released by the complete combustion of methane with 30 per cent excess air if the methane is supplied at 100 F, air is supplied at 200 F, and the products leave at 800 F.

13·27 Liquid benzene, C_6H_6, at 77 F is completely burned in an open burner with the stoichiometric amount of oxygen supplied at 300 F. Products leave the burner at 800 F. Determine the amount of heat released during the combustion.

13·28 Gaseous propane at 77 F is to be mixed with air at 77 F and burned adiabatically in a steady-flow system. Determine the air–fuel ratio required for a products temperature of 1500 R.

13·29 Verify the enthalpy of formation of butane, C_4H_{10}, as given in Table 13·4, from other data in that table.

13·30 Verify the higher heat of combustion (21,625 B/lb) of ethene gas at 77 F from the enthalpy of formation given in Table 13·4.

13·31 On the basis of data in Tables 13·1 and 13·3 construct a skeleton table of h^{abs} vs. T for CO_2, H_2, H_2O, and O_2, showing values at 0, 537 and 1000 R. Assign $h^{abs} = 0$ at $T = 0$ for elements.

13·32 Solve Prob. 13·29 but assign $h^{abs} = 0$ at $T = 0$ for CO_2 and H_2O.

13·33 State whether the heat of combustion at constant pressure is greater than, less than, or equal to the heat of combustion at constant volume for each of the following fuels: C, CO, C_3H_8, C_2H_2, C_2H_4.

13·34 An exothermic reaction occurs in a closed rigid thermally insulated vessel. The number of moles of products equals the number of moles of reactants. The specific heats are constant for both reactants and products, and they are higher for the products than for the reactants. Sketch a complete UT diagram for the reactants, the products, and the process.

13·35 Determine ΔU_R at 1000 R for the complete combustion of acetylene.

13·36 Write an equation in terms of properties tabulated in Tables 13·1 and 13·4 for the higher heating value at constant volume of a hydrocarbon at 1 atm and a temperature higher than 77 F.

13·37 Carbon monoxide is burned completely with 100 per cent excess air in a steady-flow process at 1 atm. The carbon monoxide and the air are supplied at 77 F. Calculate the maximum adiabatic combustion temperature for this reaction, assuming that the reaction goes to completion.

13·38 Determine the maximum adiabatic combustion temperature for the combustion of hydrogen supplied at 77 F with 100 per cent excess air also supplied at 77 F. Combustion occurs in a steady-flow system under a constant pressure of 1 atm. Assume that the reaction goes to completion.

13·39 Determine the maximum adiabatic combustion temperature for the steady-flow burning of propane, C_3H_8, with 100 per cent excess air with propane and air supplied at 1 atm, 77 F. Assume that the reaction goes to completion.

13·40 Refer to Prob. 13·25. All the heat released by the combustion process is absorbed by water which flows into the heat exchanger at 400 psia, 200 F, and leaves at 380 psia, 600 F. The lowest temperature in the surroundings is 77 F. Determine, per pound of methane, the irreversibility.

13·41 Determine the irreversibility of the process of Prob. 13·39.

CHAPTER 14

Chemical Equilibrium
in Ideal-Gas Reactions

In Chapter 13 it was demonstrated that the extent to which a chemical reaction can proceed under specified conditions is limited. In this chapter we take up the conventional manner of determining the extent to which a reaction can proceed by introducing a valuable parameter known as the *equilibrium constant*. You will see that all considerations of equilibrium are based on the second law. For simplicity, we confine our attention to chemical reactions in which all the constituents may be treated as ideal gases.

14·1 Criteria of equilibrium

A system is said to be in equilibrium (or in an equilibrium state) if no changes can occur in the state of the system without the aid of an external stimulus. A test to see if a system is in equilibrium is to isolate the system and observe whether any changes in its state occur. The pressure and temperature must be the same throughout a system in equilibrium, and there must be no velocity or concentration gradients within the system, because otherwise spontaneous changes would occur. These conditions alone insure that a system is in thermal and mechanical equilibrium, but there is still the possibility that the system is not in chemical equilibrium and a chemical reaction may occur. If the state of the system is such that no chemical reaction can occur without an external stimulus, then the system is in complete (mechanical, thermal, and chemical) equilibrium. When in such a state, the system is chemically homogeneous and invariant; so *it is a pure substance* and the relationship

$$T\,dS = dU + p\,dV \qquad \text{(pure substance only)}$$

applies.

For any isolated system,

$$dU = 0 \quad \text{and} \quad p\,dV = 0$$

but if a spontaneous chemical reaction occurs it is an irreversible process so that

$$dS_{\text{isolated system}} > 0$$

Therefore,

$$T \, dS > dU + p \, dV \qquad \text{(irreversible chemical reactions)}$$

for a process involving an irreversible chemical reaction, at least in an isolated system. Assuming that this relationship holds also for reactions in nonisolated systems (and this can be proved rigorously), we have the general relationship for all possible processes

$$T \, dS \geq dU + p \, dV \qquad\qquad (14\cdot1)$$

where the equality holds if no chemical reaction is possible and the inequality holds for chemical reaction processes, the only exception being the limiting case of a *reversible* chemical reaction for which the equality is true. For a system of constant U and constant V it is apparent that $T \, dS \geq 0$, or, using a brief notation,

$$(dS)_{U,V} \geq 0 \qquad\qquad (14\cdot2a)$$

For all processes at constant U and V, the entropy increases or remains constant; so, when a system is in complete equilibrium (i.e., no process is possible) at constant U and V, its entropy must be a maximum. This is one criterion of equilibrium.

Other criteria of equilibrium for different conditions can be obtained from equation 14·1 by rewriting it in terms of H, G, and A as we did in deriving the Maxwell equations (Art. 10·1). For example, if we would like to establish a criterion of equilibrium under the constraints of *constant pressure* and *constant temperature*, we notice that $T \, dS = d(TS)$ and $p \, dV = d(pV)$, so that equation 14·1 becomes

$$d(TS) \geq dU + d(pV) \qquad (p \text{ and } T \text{ constant})$$

$$d(U + pV - TS)_{p,T} \leq 0$$

Recalling the definition of the Gibbs function, we write this as

$$(dG)_{p,T} \leq 0 \qquad\qquad (14\cdot2b)$$

where the equality holds for the condition of complete equilibrium. This conclusion can also be reached by writing equation 14·1 as

$$T \, dS \geq dU + p \, dV = dH - V \, dp \qquad\qquad (14\cdot1)$$

and combining this with

$$dG = d(H - TS) = dH - T\,dS - S\,dT$$

to give $\quad\quad dG \leq V\,dp - S\,dT$

From this, $\quad\quad\quad\quad (dG)_{p,T} \leq 0 \quad\quad\quad\quad\quad\quad (14\cdot2b)$

Thus the Gibbs function of any system in complete equilibrium must be a minimum with regard to all states at the same pressure and temperature, for otherwise there would be some process for which $(dG)_{p,T} < 0$, and this process could occur, indicating that the system had not been in a state of complete equilibrium. This is a valuable criterion of equilibrium not only because many chemical reactions take place at constant pressure and temperature but also because it can be shown that, if a system is in such a state that no spontaneous process can occur at constant pressure and temperature, then no spontaneous process at all can occur. To illustrate this point, suppose that a system initially at the pressure and temperature of its surroundings is in such a state that some spontaneous process can occur which changes its pressure or temperature. This can certainly be followed by a spontaneous process which restores the system to the pressure and temperature of the surroundings. (The system can be allowed to expand or contract until its pressure again equals that of the surroundings, and heat can be transferred until there is temperature equality.) These two processes together constitute a spontaneous process between two states at the same pressure and temperature, so, *if no change to another state at the same pressure and temperature is possible, then no spontaneous process at all is possible.*

The $(dG)_{p,T} \leq 0$ criterion can be used to show that, when two or more phases of a pure substance coexist in equilibrium, the (specific) Gibbs function of each phase must be the same. Consider a mixture of liquid and vapor of a pure substance. The masses of the liquid and vapor are m_f and m_g, respectively, and g_f and g_g are the corresponding specific Gibbs functions. The Gibbs function of the system is

$$G = m_f g_f + m_g g_g$$

Now suppose that a mass dm evaporates at constant pressure so that the mass of the vapor changes by dm_g and the mass of the liquid changes by $dm_f = -dm_g$. The change in the Gibbs function of the system is

$$dG = m_f\,dg_f + m_g\,dg_g + g_f\,dm_f + g_g\,dm_g$$

g_f and g_g are each constant because the pressure and temperature of the system are constant; hence,

$$dG = 0 + 0 - g_f \, dm_g + g_g \, dm_g = (g_g - g_f) \, dm$$

But for this process at constant pressure and temperature in which the system is in equilibrium, $dG = 0$, hence

$$g_g = g_f$$

For any two phases (not just liquid and vapor) in equilibrium, the specific Gibbs functions are the same. At a triple point all three phases have the same g values.

The Clapeyron equation which was derived in Art. 10·2 from the Maxwell equations can be derived also from the fact that, for two phases of a pure substance existing together in equilibrium, the g values must be the same. Consider for the purpose of illustration a mixture of liquid and vapor. If the mixture is in equilibrium, then $g_f = g_g$. Let the temperature (and consequently the pressure) of the mixture change by an infinitesimal amount. The g values will change by dg_f and dg_g as the system goes to the new equilibrium state infinitesimally close to the original state, but, since the g values of the two phases must remain equal to each other, $dg_f = dg_g$. For each phase we can write $dg = v \, dp - s \, dT$; so, noting that dp and dT are the same for the two phases, we have

$$v_f \, dp - s_f \, dT = v_g \, dp - s_g \, dT$$

Rearranging,

$$\frac{dp}{dT} = \frac{s_g - s_f}{v_g - v_f} = \frac{s_{fg}}{v_{fg}}$$

From $T \, ds = dh - v \, dp$ we have $Ts_{fg} = h_{fg}$ which we substitute into the equation above to give the Clapeyron equation

$$\frac{dp}{dT} = \frac{h_{fg}}{Tv_{fg}} \qquad (10·11)$$

14·2   The equilibrium constant

We will now apply the equilibrium criterion $(dG)_{p,T} = 0$ to ideal-gas chemical reactions in order to determine the equilibrium state for any group of such constituents. The first step is the derivation of an expression for the Gibbs function of an ideal-gas mixture. Then we apply the equilibrium criterion, and finally we rearrange the resulting equation to show that for any reaction the relationship among the partial pressures of the constituents is a function of temperature only. We call this temperature function the equilibrium constant.

The Gibbs function of an ideal-gas mixture. If we assume that the expressions for the enthalpy and the entropy of a mixture of inert ideal gases apply also to a reactive mixture, we have

$$H_m = \Sigma Nh \tag{a}$$

and

$$S_m = \Sigma Ns(T, V_m) = \Sigma Ns(p_i, T) \tag{b}$$

where, as indicated, the entropy of each constituent is that of the constituent existing alone at the temperature and volume of the mixture. p_i is the partial pressure of a constituent. The entropy of each constituent in terms of the *mixture* pressure and temperature can be obtained by first writing

$$s(p_i, T) = s_b + \phi - \phi_b - R_u \ln \frac{p_i}{p_b}$$

where the subscript b refers to some reference (or *base*) state and $\phi - \phi_b = \int_{T_b}^{T} \frac{c_p \, dT}{T}$ as introduced in Art. 10·6. If we then add and subtract $R_u \ln x$ on the right side, we have

$$s(p_i, T) = s_b + \phi - \phi_b - R_u \ln \frac{p_i/x}{p_b} - R_u \ln x$$

But $p_i/x = p_m$, where p_m is the mixture pressure,* so

$$s(p_i, T) = s_b + \phi - \phi_b - R_u \ln \frac{p_m}{p_b} - R_u \ln x$$

$$= s(p_m, T) - R_u \ln x \tag{c}$$

Then we combine equations (*a*), (*b*), and (*c*) with the defining equation for Gibbs function to get

$$G_m = H_m - TS_m = \Sigma Nh - T\Sigma Ns(p_m, T) + T\Sigma NR_u \ln x$$

$$= \Sigma N[g(p_m, T) + R_u T \ln x] \tag{14·3}$$

Equation 14·3 gives the Gibbs function of the mixture in terms of the Gibbs functions of the constituents at the pressure and temperature *of the mixture* instead of in terms of the constituent partial pressures. The reason for deriving the equation in this form is that we will use it under the constraints of constant *mixture* pressure and constant temperature.

* The subscript m of p_m must be retained to avoid confusion between the mixture pressure and the constituent partial pressures, but no such subscript is needed on T to denote the mixture temperature because all constituents are at the same temperature and we are not concerned with any other temperature.

Application of the equilibrium criterion to an ideal-gas mixture.
Now we use equation 14·3 in the application of the equilibrium criterion
$(dG)_{p,T} = 0$ to a mixture of ideal gases, so that

$$(dG_m)_{p_m,T} = \Sigma N \, d[g(p_m, T) + R_u T \ln x]$$

$$+ \Sigma[g(p_m, T) + R_u T \ln x] \, dN = 0 \quad (d)$$

Under the conditions of constant mixture pressure and temperature,
however, the first summation term of equation (d) is zero because (1) for
each constituent $g(p_m, T)$ is constant and hence $dg(p_m, T) = 0$ and (2)

$$\Sigma N \, d \ln x = \Sigma N \frac{dx}{x} = \Sigma N \frac{dx}{N/N_m} = \Sigma N_m \, dx = N_m \Sigma \, dx$$

$$= N_m(dx_1 + dx_2 + \cdots)$$

$$= 0$$

because the sum of x_1, x_2, etc., is unity by definition. Thus equation (d)
becomes

$$(dG_m)_{p_m,T} = \Sigma[g(p_m, T) + R_u T \ln x] \, dN = 0 \qquad (e)$$

Let us now apply the equilibrium criterion in this form to an ideal-gas
chemical reaction

$$v_1 A_1 + v_2 A_2 \rightarrow v_3 A_3 + v_4 A_4 \qquad (f)$$

where v_1 moles of ideal gas A_1 react with v_2 moles of ideal gas A_2 to form
v_3 moles of ideal gas A_3 and v_4 moles of ideal gas A_4. The v's are the mole
numbers or stoichiometric coefficients which satisfy the reaction equation
and are independent of the amounts (moles) of constituents actually
present at any time which are represented by N_1, N_2, etc. In a mixture of
reacting gases the changes in the number of moles of the various constituents present (dN_1, dN_2, etc.) are not independent of each other. They
are proportional to the corresponding stoichiometric coefficients so that

$$-\frac{dN_1}{v_1} = -\frac{dN_2}{v_2} = \frac{dN_3}{v_3} = \frac{dN_4}{v_4} \qquad (g)$$

The two terms in equation (g) pertaining to the left-hand side of the
reaction equation (f) carry minus signs because all of the v's are positive,
and, as the reaction proceeds in the direction shown, N_1 and N_2 decrease
while N_3 and N_4 increase. Equation (e) can then be written as

$$\sum_{3,4} [g(p_m, T) + R_u T \ln x] v - \sum_{1,2} [g(p_m, T) + R_u T \ln x] v = 0 \qquad (h)$$

Definition of the equilibrium constant. The quantities within brackets in equation (h) can be expanded and rearranged as sums of partial pressure functions and temperature functions. For each constituent,

$$[g(p_m, T) + R_u T \ln x] = h - Ts(p_m, T) + R_u T \ln x$$

$$= h - T\left(s_b + \phi - \phi_b - R_u \ln \frac{p_m}{p_b}\right) + R_u T \ln x$$

$$= h - Ts_b - T\phi + T\phi_b + R_u T \ln \frac{1}{p_b} + R_u T \ln x p_m$$

$$= f(T) + R_u T \ln p_i \qquad (i)^*$$

Equation (h) becomes

$$[f_3(T) + R_u T \ln p_3]\nu_3 + [f_4(T) + R_u T \ln p_4]\nu_4$$
$$- [f_1(T) + R_u T \ln p_1]\nu_1 - [f_2(T) + R_u T \ln p_2]\nu_2 = 0$$

Rearranging,

$$\nu_3 \ln p_3 + \nu_4 \ln p_4 - \nu_1 \ln p_1 - \nu_2 \ln p_2$$

$$= \frac{1}{R_u T}[\nu_1 f_1(T) + \nu_2 f_2(T) - \nu_3 f_3(T) - \nu_4 f_4(T)] \qquad (j)$$

$$\ln \frac{p_3^{\nu_3} p_4^{\nu_4}}{p_1^{\nu_1} p_2^{\nu_2}} = F(\nu_1, \nu_2, \nu_3, \nu_4, T)$$

For any particular ideal-gas reaction (i.e., for fixed values of the ν's), we see then that

$$\frac{p_3^{\nu_3} p_4^{\nu_4}}{p_1^{\nu_1} p_2^{\nu_2}} = \text{function of } T$$

* At this point we are following general practice in making a step which can lead to much confusion later if it is not recognized. Logarithms are defined only for pure numbers (dimensionless quantities); so $\ln x$, where x is mole fraction, has meaning. However, when we expand

$$\ln x = \ln \frac{p}{p_m} = \ln p - \ln p_m$$

the individual terms on the extreme right-hand side are not defined. (If p has dimensions, notice the difficulty with dimensions in $y = \ln p$ and the equivalent expression $e^y = p$.)

In equation (i) above, the second term on the right-hand side is thus undefined except in combination with $R_u T \ln (1/p_b)$ which is part of $f(T)$. Later we define the equilibrium constant K_p in terms of a temperature function involving $f(T)$ in such a manner that K_p has dimensions, and then we proceed to treat $\ln K_p$ or $\log K_p$. This can be done only if we recognize that the logarithm of another quantity of identical dimensions is involved in any equation that includes $\ln K_p$ or $\log K_p$.

For a given group of ideal gases, the relationship among their partial pressures at equilibrium depends only on the temperature. For convenience in handling this temperature function, we define the equilibrium constant K_p *for ideal gases only** by

$$K_p \equiv \frac{p_3^{\nu_3} p_4^{\nu_4}}{p_1^{\nu_1} p_2^{\nu_2}}$$

This equilibrium constant has the dimensions of pressure to the $(\nu_3 + \nu_4 - \nu_1 - \nu_2)$ power. For more than two reactants and two products,

$$K_p \equiv \frac{\text{product of } p^\nu \text{ for all products}}{\text{product of } p^\nu \text{ for all reactants}}$$

Let us repeat for emphasis the conclusion reached in the preceding paragraph: If a mixture of ideal gases A_1, A_2, A_3, and A_4 which can undergo the reaction

$$\nu_1 A_1 + \nu_2 A_2 \rightarrow \nu_3 A_3 + \nu_4 A_4$$

is in equilibrium, the quantity

$$\frac{p_3^{\nu_3} p_4^{\nu_4}}{p_1^{\nu_1} p_2^{\nu_2}} = K_p$$

(where the p's are partial pressures) which we call the equilibrium constant is a function of temperature only. It does not depend on the amount of the various constituents initially present. Therefore, a knowledge of equilibrium constants for an ideal-gas reaction provides us with one relationship among the partial pressures of the constituents.

K_p for a given reaction can be measured at various temperatures by analyzing the equilibrium gas mixture. For an ideal-gas reaction in which the number of moles of products is different from the number of moles of reactants, the extent to which the reaction has proceeded when equilibrium is reached can be determined by measuring the total volume of the constituents at equilibrium. Several different methods of determining equilibrium constants experimentally and from other thermochemical data are used.†

---

* A more general definition of equilibrium constant is possible and is mentioned in Art. 14·4. So far in this book we have used broad definitions in place of restricted ones (e.g., the definitions of specific heat in Art. 3·5 and of partial pressure in Art. 12·2); so why do we here introduce a definition which is restricted to ideal gases when a broader one is possible? The answer to this question is that the purpose of this chapter is to give you some familiarity with chemical equilibrium calculations, and this can be done in a brief chapter if we consider the special case of an ideal gas. A more general approach to this particular subject, including the development of a more general definition of equilibrium constant, requires much more space and does not appreciably increase the understanding of chemical equilibrium calculations as an application of the second law.

† See references 14·4 and 14·6 at the end of the chapter.

K_p data for three ideal-gas reactions are given in Fig. 14·1. Other data can be found in the references listed at the end of the chapter.

One limitation of equilibrium calculations based on classical thermodynamics must be kept in mind: No conclusions can be reached regarding

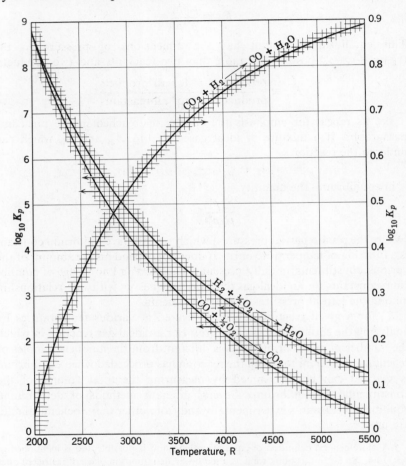

Fig. 14·1 Equilibrium constants for three reactions. Data from E. W. Geyer and E. A. Bruges, *Tables of Properties of Gases*, Longmans, Green & Co., Inc., 1948.

the rate at which a reaction occurs. Calculations may show that a system is not in a state of equilibrium, but the indicated reaction may occur so slowly that measurements made on the system even over a period of years will reveal no change in state. Such a condition is sometimes referred to as *frozen equilibrium.* A familiar example is that hydrogen and oxygen can exist together at room pressure and temperature for an indefinitely long period with no measurable reaction occurring, even though the equilibrium constant for the reaction $H_2 + \frac{1}{2}O_2 \rightarrow H_2O$ at room conditions shows that the equilibrium mixture is comprised almost entirely of H_2O. The reaction rate for the combining of hydrogen and oxygen at room conditions is so low that it can be taken as zero for virtually all purposes. The presence of a catalyst or a stimulus such as an electric spark speeds the reaction, however, and the reaction can be observed to proceed always in the direction indicated by equilibrium calculations.

We now take up several examples illustrating the use of the equilibrium constant. *Remember that we are treating only the special case of ideal-gas reactions.*

EXAMPLE 14·1.   For the reaction $\frac{1}{2}O_2 + \frac{1}{2}N_2 \rightarrow NO$, K_p at 6000 R is 0.1762. Determine K_p at this temperature for (*a*) the reaction $O_2 + N_2 \rightarrow 2NO$ and (*b*) the reaction $NO \rightarrow \frac{1}{2}O_2 + \frac{1}{2}N_2$.

Solution.   The equilibrium constant given is

$$K_{p1} = \frac{p_{NO}}{p_{O_2}^{1/2} p_{N_2}^{1/2}} = 0.1762$$

(*a*) For the reaction $O_2 + N_2 \rightarrow 2NO$, call the equilibrium constant K_{p2}:

$$K_{p2} = \frac{p_{NO}^2}{p_{O_2} p_{N_2}} = K_{p1}^2 = (0.1762)^2 = 0.0310$$

(*b*) For the reaction $NO \rightarrow \frac{1}{2}O_2 + \frac{1}{2}N_2$, the equilibrium constant K_{p3} is

$$K_{p3} = \frac{p_{O_2}^{1/2} p_{N_2}^{1/2}}{p_{NO}} = \frac{1}{K_{p1}} = \frac{1}{0.1762} = 5.67$$

EXAMPLE 14·2.   At 5000 R, $K_p = 6.60$ (with pressure in atmospheres) for the reaction $CO + \frac{1}{2}O_2 \rightarrow CO_2$. For an initial mixture of $CO + \frac{1}{2}O_2$, determine the composition of the equilibrium mixture at 5000 R and (*a*) 1 atm, (*b*) 5 atm.

Solution.   Let y be the fraction of the carbon in the system which is in CO under equilibrium conditions. Then the equilibrium mixture is

$$yCO + (1 - y)CO_2 + \tfrac{1}{2}yO_2*$$

The total number of moles of mixture is $y + 1 - y + \frac{1}{2}y = 1 + \frac{1}{2}y$. The partial pressures of the three constituents are

$$p_{CO} = x_{CO}p_m = \frac{y}{1 + \frac{1}{2}y} p_m = \frac{2y}{2 + y} p_m$$

$$p_{CO_2} = x_{CO_2}p_m = \frac{1 - y}{1 + \frac{1}{2}y} p_m = \frac{2 - 2y}{2 + y} p_m$$

$$p_{O_2} = x_{O_2}p_m = \frac{\frac{1}{2}y}{1 + \frac{1}{2}y} p_m = \frac{y}{2 + y} p_m$$

* This can also be expressed by saying that the actual reaction is

$$CO + \tfrac{1}{2}O_2 \rightarrow yCO + (1 - y)CO_2 + \tfrac{1}{2}yO_2$$

Substituting these values into the defining equation for K_p,

$$K_p = \frac{p_{CO_2}}{p_{CO}p_{O_2}^{1/2}} = \frac{2-2y}{2y\left(\dfrac{y}{2+y}\right)^{1/2}p_m^{1/2}}$$

$$K_p^2 = \frac{(1-y)^2}{y^2\left(\dfrac{y}{2+y}\right)p_m} = \frac{(1-y)^2(2+y)}{y^3p_m} = (6.60)^2$$

For $p_m = 1$ atm, the solution of this equation is $y = 0.297$; and, for $p_m = 5$ atm, $y = 0.190$.

(a) For $p_m = 1$ atm, $y = 0.297$, and the mole fractions are

$$x_{CO} = \frac{2y}{2+y} = 0.259$$

$$x_{CO_2} = \frac{2-2y}{2+y} = 0.612$$

$$x_{O_2} = \frac{y}{2+y} = 0.129$$

(b) For $p = 5$ atm, $y = 0.181$, and the mole fractions are

$$x_{CO} = \frac{2y}{2+y} = 0.173$$

$$x_{CO_2} = \frac{2-2y}{2+y} = 0.740$$

$$x_{O_2} = \frac{y}{2+y} = 0.087$$

A comparison of parts (a) and (b) shows that increasing the pressure causes the reaction $CO + \frac{1}{2}O_2 \to CO_2$ to proceed further to the right, which is the direction of decreasing volume.

EXAMPLE 14·3. Using the K_p data of Example 14·2, determine the equilibrium mixture at 5000 R for the burning of CO with the stoichiometric amount of air.

Solution. The complete reaction equation is

$$CO + \tfrac{1}{2}O_2 + \tfrac{1}{2}(3.77)N_2 \to CO_2 + \tfrac{1}{2}(3.77)N_2$$

If y stands for the fraction of the carbon which is in CO under equilibrium conditions, then the equilibrium mixture is

$$yCO + (1-y)CO_2 + \tfrac{1}{2}yO_2 + \frac{3.77}{2}N_2$$

The total number of moles of mixture is $2.885 + \frac{1}{2}y$. The partial pressures of the four constituents are

$$p_{CO} = x_{CO}p_m = \frac{y}{2.885 + \frac{1}{2}y}p_m = \frac{2y}{5.77 + y}p_m$$

$$p_{CO_2} = x_{CO_2}p_m = \frac{1 - y}{2.885 + \frac{1}{2}y}p_m = \frac{2 - 2y}{5.77 + y}p_m$$

$$p_{O_2} = x_{O_2}p_m = \frac{\frac{1}{2}y}{2.885 + \frac{1}{2}y}p_m = \frac{y}{5.77 + y}p_m$$

$$p_{N_2} = x_{N_2}p_m = \frac{1.885}{2.885 + \frac{1}{2}y}p_m = \frac{3.77}{5.77 + y}p_m$$

Substituting these values into the defining equation for K_p,

$$K_p \equiv \frac{p_{CO_2}}{p_{CO}p_{O_2}^{1/2}} = \frac{2 - 2y}{2y\left(\dfrac{y}{5.77 + y}\right)^{1/2}p_m^{1/2}}$$

$$K_p^2 = \frac{(1 - y)^2(5.77 + y)}{y^3 p_m} = (6.60)^2$$

For $p_m = 1$ atm, the solution of this equation is $y = 0.379$, so the mole fractions are

$$x_{CO} = \frac{2y}{5.77 + y} = 0.123$$

$$x_{CO_2} = \frac{2 - 2y}{5.77 + y} = 0.202$$

$$x_{O_2} = \frac{y}{5.77 + y} = 0.062$$

$$x_{N_2} = \frac{3.77}{5.77 + y} = 0.613$$

(Notice that the presence of nitrogen affects the extent to which the reaction proceeds, but it does not change the equilibrium constant. The presence of excess oxygen would cause the reaction to go further toward completion, but again this result would follow from the same equilibrium constant value which is independent of the amounts of the various constituents actually present.)

EXAMPLE 14·4.   Methane is burned with 80 per cent of stoichiometric air in a steady-flow process at 1 atm. Methane and air are both supplied at 77 F, and the products leave at 2540 F. Assuming that no CH_4, OH, NO, or free oxygen appears in the products, determine the amount of heat transferred per pound of methane.

Solution.   The reaction is

$$CH_4 + 0.8(2)O_2 + 0.8(2)3.77N_2 \rightarrow yCO_2 + (1 - y)CO$$
$$+ zH_2O + (2 - z)H_2 + 0.8(2)3.77N_2$$

Two unknowns, y and z, must be determined before an energy balance can be made. One relation between y and z is given by a mass balance for oxygen:

$$1.6 = y + \tfrac{1}{2}(1 - y) + \tfrac{1}{2}z$$

$$2.2 = y + z \qquad\qquad (A)$$

A second relationship between y and z can be found by means of the equilibrium constant for the reaction $CO_2 + H_2 \rightarrow CO + H_2O$, which is known as the *water gas reaction*:

$$K_p = \frac{p_{CO}p_{H_2O}}{p_{CO_2}p_{H_2}}$$

The partial pressures for substitution in this expression are obtained from the equilibrium mixture

$$yCO_2 + (1 - y)CO + zH_2O + (2 - z)H_2 + 6.03N_2$$

as

$$p_{CO} = \frac{(1 - y)p_m}{y + (1 - y) + z + (2 - z) + 6.03} = \frac{1 - y}{9.03}p_m$$

$$p_{H_2O} = \frac{z}{9.03}p_m$$

$$p_{CO_2} = \frac{y}{9.03}p_m$$

$$p_{H_2} = \frac{2 - z}{9.03}p_m$$

Thus, for $K_p = 3.42$ at 2540 F (from Fig. 14·1 as $\log_{10} K_p = 0.533$),

$$K_p = \frac{(1 - y)z}{y(2 - z)} = 3.42 \qquad\qquad (B)$$

Solving equations (A) and (B) gives

$$y = 0.566 \qquad z = 1.634$$

Thus the actual reaction equation is

$$CH_4 + 1.6O_2 + 6.03N_2 \rightarrow 0.566CO_2 + 0.434CO + 1.634H_2O + 0.366H_2 + 6.03N_2$$

The enthalpy of reaction at 77 F for this particular reaction is

$$\Delta H_R = \sum_{prod} \Delta H_f - \sum_{reac} \Delta H_f \qquad\qquad (13\cdot2)$$

$$= 0.566\Delta H_{f,CO_2} + 0.434\Delta H_{f,CO} + 1.634\Delta H_{f,H_2O} + 0 + 0 - \Delta H_{f,CH_4} - 0 - 0$$

$$= 0.566(-169,183) + 0.434(-47,517) + 1.634(-103,968) - 1(-32,179)$$

$$= -254,041 \text{ B/mole } CH_4$$

where the ΔH_f values are taken from Table 13·4.

The first law applied to this steady-flow reaction is

$$Q = \Delta H_R + \sum_{prod} N(h_2 - h_0) - \sum_{reac} N(h_1 - h_0)$$

Since the reactants enter at 77 F, the last term on the right-hand side is zero. Then

$$Q = \Delta H_R + 0.566(h_2 - h_0)_{CO_2} + 0.434(h_2 - h_0)_{CO} + 1.634(h_2 - h_0)_{H_2O}$$

$$+ 0.366(h_2 - h_0)_{H_2} + 6.03(h_2 - h_0)_{N_2}$$

$$= -254{,}041 + 0.566(34{,}807 - 4030) + 0.434(22{,}973 - 3730)$$

$$+ 1.634(28{,}386 - 4258) + 0.366(21{,}577 - 3640) + 6.03(22{,}762 - 3730)$$

$$= -67{,}611 \text{ B/mole } CH_4 = -4225 \text{ B/lb } CH_4$$

EXAMPLE 14·5.   Methane supplied at 1 atm, 77 F, is burned adiabatically in a steady-flow burner with the stoichiometric amount of air supplied at the same conditions. Assuming that the products contain no CH_4, OH, or NO, determine the temperature of the products.

Solution.   The reaction equation is

$$CH_4 + 2O_2 + 7.54N_2 \rightarrow yCO_2 + (1 - y)CO + zH_2O$$

$$+ (2 - z)H_2 + (1.5 - \tfrac{1}{2}y - \tfrac{1}{2}z)O_2 + 7.54N_2$$

The molar coefficients of the products in this equation were determined by C, O, and H mass balances. The products temperature and the values of y and z must be such that they satisfy an energy balance and also satisfy the equilibrium conditions which can be most readily expressed by means of equilibrium constants. There are three unknowns (y, z, and T), so three relationships are needed. The energy balance is one of these. Two others can be obtained by using equilibrium constants for two different reactions. Since our K_p vs. T and h vs. T data are in graphical or tabular form, the three relationships cannot be solved directly and simultaneously; so our procedure will be as follows: (1) Assume a value of T; (2) determine y and z from K_p data at the assumed T; (3) use the y and z values thus obtained and the assumed T value in an energy balance to see if the adiabatic condition is met; and (4) assume a new T value, and repeat the calculations until the y, z, and T values do satisfy the energy balance for adiabatic combustion.

Before assuming the first T value and carrying out numerical calculations, we will set up in convenient forms the relations to be used. The total number of moles of products is $y+(1-y)+z+(2-z)+(1.5-\tfrac{1}{2}y-\tfrac{1}{2}z)+7.54$ or $(12.04-\tfrac{1}{2}y-\tfrac{1}{2}z)$. The partial pressures of the products constituents are

$$p_{CO_2} = \frac{y}{12.04 - \tfrac{1}{2}y - \tfrac{1}{2}z} p_m$$

$$p_{CO} = \frac{1 - y}{12.04 - \tfrac{1}{2}y - \tfrac{1}{2}z} p_m$$

$$p_{H_2O} = \frac{z}{12.04 - \tfrac{1}{2}y - \tfrac{1}{2}z} p_m$$

$$p_{H_2} = \frac{2 - z}{12.04 - \tfrac{1}{2}y - \tfrac{1}{2}z} p_m$$

$$p_{O_2} = \frac{1.5 - \tfrac{1}{2}y - \tfrac{1}{2}z}{12.04 - \tfrac{1}{2}y - \tfrac{1}{2}z} p_m$$

$$p_{N_2} = \frac{7.54}{12.04 - \tfrac{1}{2}y - \tfrac{1}{2}z} p_m$$

We can use equilibrium constant data for any two reactions which involve constituents of the products mixture. Two such reactions for which equilibrium constant data are given in Fig. 14·1 are

$$CO_2 + H_2 \rightarrow CO + H_2O \qquad (1)$$

and

$$CO + \tfrac{1}{2}O_2 \rightarrow CO_2 \qquad (2)$$

The equilibrium constants for these reactions are

$$K_{p1} = \frac{p_{CO}p_{H_2O}}{p_{CO_2}p_{H_2}} \qquad K_{p2} = \frac{p_{CO_2}}{p_{CO}p_{O_2}^{1/2}}$$

Substituting the partial pressure values from above into these expressions for K_{p1} and K_{p2}, we have

$$K_{p1} = \frac{(1-y)z}{y(2-z)} \qquad K_{p2} = \frac{y(12.04 - \tfrac{1}{2}y - \tfrac{1}{2}z)^{1/2}}{(1-y)(1.5 - \tfrac{1}{2}y - \tfrac{1}{2}z)^{1/2}p_m^{1/2}}$$

These equations will be used to determine y and z at each temperature assumed. They can be combined to give

$$K_{p2} = \left(\frac{y}{1-y}\right)\left\{\frac{12.04 - y\left[\dfrac{1}{2} + \dfrac{K_{p1}}{1 + y(K_{p1} - 1)}\right]}{1.5 - y\left[\dfrac{1}{2} + \dfrac{K_{p1}}{1 + y(K_{p1} - 1)}\right]}\right\}^{1/2}\left(\frac{1}{p_m}\right)^{1/2} \qquad (M)$$

which can be solved for y graphically or by trial and error for various temperatures and mixture pressures.

The energy balance for this adiabatic steady-flow process is

$$Q = 0 = \Delta H_R + \sum_{\text{prod}} N(h - h_0) - \sum_{\text{reac}} N(h - h_0) \qquad (13·1, \text{ special case})$$

and ΔH_R can be expressed in terms of enthalpies of formation as

$$\Delta H_R = \sum_{\text{prod}} \Delta H_f - \sum_{\text{reac}} \Delta H_f \qquad (13·2)$$

Combining these two equations gives

$$Q = 0 = \sum_{\text{prod}} N(h - h_0 + \Delta H_f) - \sum_{\text{reac}} N(h - h_0 + \Delta H_f)$$

where each ΔH_f, unlike in equation 13·2, is on a per mole of constituent basis. For the reaction under consideration, recalling that $\Delta H_f = 0$ for elements and that the reactants enter at the reference temperature, we expand the last equation to

$$0 = y(h - h_0 + \Delta H_f)_{CO_2} + (1 - y)(h - h_0 + \Delta H_f)_{CO} + z(h - h_0 + \Delta H_f)_{H_2O}$$

$$+ (2 - z)(h - h_0)_{H_2} + \left(1.5 - \frac{y}{2} - \frac{z}{2}\right)(h - h_0)_{O_2} + 7.54(h - h_0)_{N_2} - \Delta H_{f,CH_4}$$

Substitution of h_0 and ΔH_f values from Tables 13·1 and 13·4 gives

$$0 = y(h_{CO_2} - 173,213) + (1 - y)(h_{CO} - 51,247) + z(h_{H_2O} - 108,226) + (2 - z)$$

$$\times (h_{H_2} - 3640) + \left(1.5 - \frac{y}{2} - \frac{z}{2}\right)(h_{O_2} - 3725) + 7.54(h_{N_2} - 3730) + 32,179 \qquad (N)$$

Now we are ready to determine the final temperature as that value which satisfies both equations (M) and (N). As a trial value, we select first 4000 R for which Fig. 14·1 shows $\log_{10} K_{p1} = 0.745$ and $\log_{10} K_{p2} = 2.14$ so that $K_{p1} = 5.55^+$ and $K_{p2} = 138^+$. For these values equation (M) is satisfied by $y = 0.913$, and then $z = 1.965$. Now, using these values of y and z and the h values at 4000 R from Table 13·1 or the *Gas Tables*, equation (N) becomes

$$Q = 0.913(49,231 - 173,213) + 0.087(31,605 - 51,247) + 1.965(40,489 - 108,226)$$

$$+ \ 0.035(29,704 - 3640) + (1.5 - 0.457 - 0.982)(32,806 - 3725)$$

$$+ \ 7.54(31,329 - 3730) + 32,179$$

$$= \ -4900 \quad \text{B instead of 0}$$

This means that, in order for the products to be at 4000 R, heat must be removed in the amount of 4900 B. The adiabatic combustion temperature must therefore be higher than 4000 R.

If we now select 4100 R as a trial value of temperature, we get $\log_{10} K_{p1} = 0.759$ and $\log_{10} K_{p2} = 1.98^+$ from Fig. 14·1, $y = 0.891$ and $z = 1.96$ from equation (M), and $Q = 8,530$ B from equation (N). We see, then, that 4100 R is too high.

As a third trial temperature we now select 4040 R, and carrying out the procedure outlined above shows that this value satisfies both equation (M) (mass balance) and equation (N) [energy balance which uses masses from equation (M)]. The accuracy of the K_p data as presented in Fig. 14·1 does not warrant more precise calculations.

Remember that this solution is based on the assumption that no CH_4, OH, or NO is in the products. For accurate results, at least the presence of OH at this temperature should be considered. (Adding OH to the products introduces another unknown coefficient. The additional relationship which is then needed can be the equilibrium constant equation for a reaction such as $H_2O \rightarrow \frac{1}{2}H_2 + OH$.)

14·3 The relationship between K_p and ΔH_R

It has been mentioned that there are methods of determining K_p values from other thermochemical data. An important relationship for this purpose as well as for others is the equation involving K_p and ΔH_R which we now derive.

If we combine equation (j) of the preceding article and the definition of K_p, we have

$$\ln K_p = \frac{1}{R_u T}[\nu_1 f_1(T) + \nu_2 f_2(T) - \nu_3 f_3(T) - \nu_4 f_4(T)] \tag{k}$$

for a reaction of the form

$$\nu_1 A_1 + \nu_2 A_2 \rightarrow \nu_3 A_3 + \nu_4 A_4$$

If we differentiate equation (j) or equation (k) with respect to temperature, we will have some terms $\dfrac{d}{dT}\left(\dfrac{f(T)}{T}\right)$; so let us examine these terms. From equation (i),

$$f(T) = h - T(\phi - \phi_b) - Ts_b - R_u T \ln p_b$$

and
$$\frac{f(T)}{T} = \frac{h}{T} - \phi + \phi_b - s_b - R_u \ln p_b$$

Then
$$\frac{d}{dT}\left(\frac{f(T)}{T}\right) = \frac{T(dh/dT) - h}{T^2} - \frac{d}{dT}\left[\int \frac{c_p\,dT}{T}\right] + 0$$

$$= \frac{1}{T}\frac{dh}{dT} - \frac{h}{T^2} - \frac{c_p}{T} = -\frac{h}{T^2}$$

where the last simplification is possible because *for an ideal gas h* is a function of T only so that $c_p = dh/dT$. (In general, of course, $c_p = (\partial h/\partial T)_p$.) Differentiation of equation (k) thus gives

$$\frac{d\ln K_p}{dT} = \frac{1}{R_u T^2}[-\nu_1 h_1 - \nu_2 h_2 + \nu_3 h_3 + \nu_4 h_4]$$

The term within the brackets is recognized as ΔH_R; so we have

$$\frac{d\ln K_p}{dT} = \frac{\Delta H_R}{R_u T^2} \tag{14·4}$$

This is a valuable equation, because, if the $K_p T$ variation is known, ΔH_R can be calculated. Notice that, for exothermic reactions ($\Delta H_R < 0$), K_p decreases as the temperature increases, and, for endothermic reactions ($\Delta H_R > 0$), K_p increases with increasing temperature. Equation 14·4 can also be written as

$$\frac{d\ln K_p}{d(1/T)} = -\frac{\Delta H_R}{R_u}$$

This form shows that, if ΔH_R varies only slightly with temperature, a plot of $\ln K_p$ vs. $1/T$ is nearly a straight line. (Caution: Data are usually given in terms of $\log_{10} K_p$ instead of in terms of the natural logarithm $\ln K_p$.)

14·4 The relationship between K_p and ΔG_R

An equation which is even more useful than equation 14·4 relates $\ln K_p$ (not its derivative) for a reaction to the Gibbs function change of reaction ΔG_R at a standard pressure of 1 atm. The definition of ΔG_R is analogous to that of ΔH_R and ΔU_R. The derivation of this valuable equation can start with equation (k) of the preceding article:

$$\ln K_p = \frac{1}{R_u T}[\nu_1 f_1(T) + \nu_2 f_2(T) - \nu_3 f_3(T) - \nu_4 f_4(T)] \tag{k}$$

Referring back to equation (*i*) in Art. 14·2, we see that $f(T)$ is defined as

$$f(T) \equiv h - Ts_b - T\phi + T\phi_b + R_u T \ln \frac{1}{p_b}$$

$$= (h - Ts)_{p=1 \, \text{atm}} = g_{1 \, \text{atm}}$$

It must not be inferred that equation (*k*) or the function $f(T)$ can be used only for a pressure of 1 atm. The steps above show only that $f(T)$ for each constituent *at any pressure* turns out to be the Gibbs function of the constituent at the same temperature and at 1 atm. Thus equation (*k*) becomes

$$\ln K_p = \frac{1}{R_u T} [\nu_1 g_1 + \nu_2 g_2 - \nu_3 g_3 - \nu_4 g_4]_{1 \, \text{atm}}$$

The quantity within the brackets is $-\Delta G_R$ at 1 atm and temperature T; so we have

$$\ln K_p = -\frac{\Delta G_{R,1 \, \text{atm}}}{R_u T} \tag{14·5}$$

$\Delta G_{R,1 \, \text{atm}}$ is often represented by the symbol ΔG_R° and is sometimes called the *standard free-energy* change, although the use of the name free energy for the Gibbs function is inadvisable because the same name has been used for the Helmholtz function as was pointed out in Art. 9·7. $\Delta G_{R,1 \, \text{atm}}$ can be calculated from ΔH_R and absolute entropy values, and it can also be found in tables of thermochemical data. (Caution in using various sources of thermochemical data: Usually, ΔG_R° or ΔG° refers only to a specified standard pressure; so that for any reaction, tables of ΔG_R° or ΔG° versus temperature are possible; but sometimes it refers to a specified pressure *and* a specified temperature so that there is but a single value for each reaction.)

This chapter is concerned only with ideal-gas reactions, but equation 14·5 actually applies to other reactions and in fact is widely used as a general definition of the equilibrium constant.

14·5 Summary

A more general form of the relation

$$T \, dS = dU + p \, dV \qquad \text{(pure substances)} \tag{9·3}$$

which holds only for pure substances is

$$T \, dS \geq dU + p \, dV \tag{14·1}$$

which holds even for systems which undergo chemical reactions. The equality holds for systems in complete (mechanical, thermal, and chemical) equilibrium, and the inequality holds for all other cases including those of irreversible chemical reactions.

From equation 14·1 we obtain equilibrium criteria such as

$$(dS)_{U,V} \geq 0 \quad \text{and} \quad (dG)_{p,T} \leq 0 \tag{14·2}$$

Referring to the second of these criteria, one interpretation is that, when a system is in complete equilibrium (i.e., no spontaneous process is possible), its Gibbs function must be a minimum with regard to all states at the same pressure and temperature. This is a valuable criterion of equilibrium, not only because many chemical reactions occur at constant pressure and temperature, but also because it can be shown that, if a system is in such a state that no spontaneous process can occur at constant pressure and temperature, then no spontaneous process at all can occur.

Application of one of the equilibrium criteria shows that for a mixture of ideal gases A_1, A_2, A_3, and A_4 which can undergo a reaction

$$\nu_1 A_1 + \nu_2 A_2 \rightarrow \nu_3 A_3 + \nu_4 A_4$$

the equilibrium mixture is such that

$$\frac{p_3^{\nu_3} p_4^{\nu_4}}{p_1^{\nu_1} p_2^{\nu_2}} = K_p$$

where the p's are partial pressures and K_p, called the equilibrium constant, is a function of temperature only. K_p does not depend on the amount of the various constituents initially present. Therefore, a knowledge of equilibrium constants for an ideal-gas reaction provides us with one relationship among the partial pressures of the constituents. Stoichiometric considerations give us other relationships; so we are able to determine the extent to which a reaction can proceed at a given temperature. Classical thermodynamics gives no information on reaction rates, however; so we cannot predict on this basis whether a reaction will proceed to the indicated extent within a given time interval.

Two valuable relationships between K_p and other thermochemical quantities are

$$\frac{d \ln K_p}{dT} = \frac{\Delta H_R}{R_u T^2} \tag{14·4}$$

and

$$\ln K_p = -\frac{\Delta G_{R,1\,\text{atm}}}{R_u T} \tag{14·5}$$

REFERENCES

14·1 C. O. Mackey, W. N. Barnard, and F. O. Ellenwood, *Engineering Thermodynamics*, John Wiley & Sons, 1957, chapter 9.

14·2 E. F. Obert, *Thermodynamics*, McGraw-Hill Book Co., 1948, chapter XI.

14·3 M. W. Zemansky, *Heat and Thermodynamics*, McGraw-Hill Book Co., 4th ed., 1957, chapter 18.

14·4 J. K. Roberts and A. R. Miller, *Heat and Thermodynamics*, Interscience Publishers, 4th ed., 1951, chapter XVIII.

14·5 P. J. Kiefer, G. F. Kinney, and M. C. Stuart, *Principles of Engineering Thermodynamics*, John Wiley & Sons, 2d ed., 1954, arts. 12-7 to 12-9.

14·6 R. R. Wenner, *Thermochemical Calculations*, McGraw-Hill Book Co., 1941, chapter VI.

14·7 E. W. Geyer and E. A. Bruges, *Tables of Properties of Gases*, Longmans, Green & Co., 1948.

PROBLEMS

14·1 Demonstrate that each of the following is a valid criterion of equilibrium:

$$(dU)_{S,V} \leq 0 \qquad (dS)_{H,p} \geq 0 \qquad (dA)_{T,V} \leq 0$$

14·2 At 5000 R, $K = 7.026$ (with pressure in atmospheres) for the reaction $CO + \frac{1}{2}O_2 \rightarrow CO_2$. For an initial mixture of 1 mole of CO and 1 mole of O_2, determine the composition of the equilibrium mixture at 5000 R and (a) 1 atm, (b) 5 atm.

14·3 A system comprised initially of H_2O is heated to 5000 R at a pressure of 14.7 psia. Determine the composition of the equilibrium mixture.

14·4 Solve Prob. 14·3 for an initial mixture of 1 mole of H_2O plus 1 mole of CO_2.

14·5 Determine the equilibrium mixture at 4000 R for a system initially comprised of 1 mole of CO_2 and 1 mole of H_2.

14·6 Solve Prob. 14·5 for an initial mixture of 1 mole of CO_2 and 2 moles of H_2.

14·7 What fraction of H_2O becomes dissociated (to H_2 and O_2) at 5000 R and (a) 1 atm (b) 10 atm?

14·8 At what temperature is 10 per cent of CO_2 dissociated at 14.7 psia?

14·9 Solve Prob. 14·8 if the CO_2 is initially mixed with an equal number of moles of air.

14·10 Determine the adiabatic flame temperature of a stoichiometric mixture of hydrogen and air reacting in a steady-flow system under a pressure of 1 atm if the initial mixture temperature is 77 F.

14·11 Solve Prob. 14·10 for a pressure of 5 atm.

14·12 Solve Prob. 14·10 for the mixture $CO + O_2$.

14·13 Solve Prob. 14·10 for a stoichiometric mixture of carbon monoxide and air.

14·14 Solve Prob. 14·10 for a mixture of carbon monoxide and 20 per cent excess air.

14·15 Solve Prob. 14·10 for a mixture of carbon monoxide and 80 per cent of the stoichiometric amount of air.

14·16 Determine the adiabatic flame temperature of a stoichiometric mixture of ethane, C_2H_6, and air initially at 1 atm, 77 F, in a steady-flow system. Assume that the products contain no constituents other than CO, CO_2, O_2, N_2, H_2, and H_2O.

14·17 Solve Prob. 14·16 if the fuel is propane, C_3H_8.

14·18 From the data of Fig. 14·1, determine ΔH_R at 3000 R for the reaction $CO + \frac{1}{2}O_2 \rightarrow CO_2$.

14·19 From the data of Fig. 14·1, determine ΔH_R at 3000 R for the reaction $CO_2 + H_2 \rightarrow CO + H_2O$.

CHAPTER **15**

Thermodynamic Aspects
of Fluid Flow

In the study of the flow of compressible fluids, the principles of both
fluid mechanics and thermodynamics must be applied, and there is no
sharp demarcation between the areas covered by these two engineering
sciences. This chapter is devoted to some of the thermodynamic aspects
of the flow of fluids, and in order to treat these we must touch briefly upon
some points which are usually considered to be in the realm of fluid
mechanics. This chapter shows that the application to flowing fluids of the
first law, the second law, the principles of mechanics, and some of our
knowledge of physical property relationships leads to many interesting and
useful results.

15·1 One-, two-, and three-dimensional steady flow

One-dimensional steady flow is flow in which the fluid properties
(pressure, temperature, velocity, etc.) depend on only one space coordinate.
In two-dimensional steady flow the properties depend on two space
coordinates, and in three-dimensional steady flow they depend on three.

One-dimensional flow exists if the velocity, temperature, etc. are uniform
across each cross section which is normal to the direction of flow. (See
Fig. 15·1a.) Properties may change from one cross section to another.
Also, the flow direction may change; that is, there may be bends in the
flow channel. Still for each value of the coordinate defined as distance in
the direction of flow there is a single value of velocity, a single value of
temperature, etc.; so the flow is one-dimensional.

In the actual flow of a fluid in a pipe, shear forces of the pipe wall on the
fluid cause a variation in velocity across any cross section, as shown in
Fig. 15·1b. If the pipe is circular and the flow is axially symmetric, the
flow is two-dimensional because the velocity (and any other property)
distribution can be completely described in terms of two space coordinates:
distance along the pipe and radius from the pipe center line. If the flow is
unsymmetrical, then it is three-dimensional.

As a further illustration of the difference between two- and three-dimensional flow, consider the flow across a long airplane wing as shown in Fig. 15·2. Over wing sections AA, BB, and CC in the uniform part of the wing far from the root and the tip the flow patterns are the same. They are independent of the distance l along the wing span; so this flow is two-dimensional. Across a tapered section of the wing and near the root or tip the flow is three-dimensional.

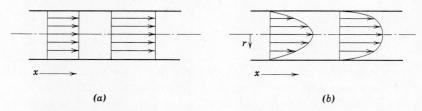

(a) (b)

Fig. 15·1   Velocity profiles for one- and two-dimensional flow in a circular pipe.

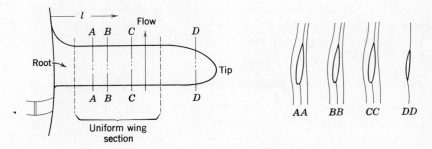

Fig. 15·2   Two- and three-dimensional flow.

To simplify analyses we frequently approximate two-dimensional flow by one-dimensional flow in which the uniform velocity across a cross section is given by

$$V = \frac{Mv}{A}$$

which is often called the average velocity at the section. Notice that the kinetic energy of a one-dimensional stream is not the same as that of a two-dimensional stream with the same average velocity. (See Prob. 15·1.) In many cases the difference can be neglected, but it is well to recognize that an approximation is being made because in cases where other energy changes are small compared to this difference, serious errors can result from the approximation.

15·2 Total enthalpy, total temperature, and total pressure

In the application of the first law of thermodynamics to flowing fluids the group $h + V^2/2g_c$ appears frequently. This group has been given the name of total enthalpy h_t, so that by definition,

$$h_t \equiv h + \frac{V^2}{2g_c}$$

Notice that this definition involves no assumption or restriction regarding the type of fluid or the type of process. Total enthalpy is useful because it simplifies energy balances. For example, the steady-flow energy balance applied to the adiabatic flow through a turbine,

$$w = h_1 - h_2 + \frac{V_1^2 - V_2^2}{2g_c}$$

becomes with the total enthalpy

$$w = h_{t1} - h_{t2}$$

The energy balance for adiabatic steady flow through a nozzle,

$$h_1 + \frac{V_1^2}{2g_c} = h_2 + \frac{V_2^2}{2g_c}$$

becomes $$h_{t1} = h_{t2}$$

The steady-flow energy balance applied to flow through a heat exchanger can be written in either of two forms:

$$q = h_2 - h_1 + \frac{V_2^2 - V_1^2}{2g_c}$$

$$q = h_{t2} - h_{t1}$$

Property diagrams of h_t vs. s are often more valuable than hs diagrams. For example, in the case of an adiabatic turbine, ordinate distances on an hs diagram represent work only if there is no change in kinetic energy; but on an $h_t s$ diagram ordinate distances represent work even if the kinetic energy change is appreciable.

Total enthalpy is often called stagnation enthalpy because the total enthalpy of a flowing fluid is equal to the enthalpy of the fluid if it were brought to rest adiabatically. The process of bringing the fluid to rest need not be reversible. A stagnation point is defined as a point in a fluid-flow field where the velocity is zero. Writing an energy balance between some

point 1 in a fluid stream and a stagnation point along the same streamline
gives

$$h_1 + \frac{V_1^2}{2g_c} = h_{\text{stagnation point}} = h_t$$

which is the same for any adiabatic no-work process, reversible or
irreversible.

The total temperature or stagnation temperature of a flowing fluid is
defined as the temperature which would result if the fluid were brought to
rest *reversibly* and adiabatically or, in other words, isentropically. (For an
ideal gas, total temperature could be defined as the temperature corresponding to the total enthalpy, but such a definition cannot be used for a
substance for which temperature and enthalpy are not uniquely related.)

The pressure which results when a flowing fluid is brought to rest
reversibly and adiabatically (isentropically) is called the total pressure or
the stagnation pressure.

The total pressure of a flowing fluid can be measured by means of a
pressure probe which opens directly upstream so that the flowing fluid is
brought to rest isentropically at the opening. Static pressure can be
measured by means of a pressure probe which moves with the fluid, or
where the fluid flows along a straight wall the static pressure can be
measured by means of a small opening in the wall. It is usually assumed
that static pressure is constant along a line normal to such a wall.

Total temperature can be measured by a probe which places the
temperature-sensitive element in contact with only the fluid which has been
brought to rest isentropically. Static temperature is measured by a
thermometer which moves with the fluid. (In both cases the usual
precautions must be taken in regard to radiation and other sources of
error.) A thermometer element placed in a wall along which a fluid flows
does not measure the static temperature.

When a fluid flows along a wall, shear forces reduce the fluid velocity to
zero right at the wall, establishing a velocity gradient between the wall and
the region where the flow is unaffected by the shear forces. The pressure is
usually considered to be constant along a line normal to a straight wall,
but the deceleration of the fluid layers near the wall causes an increase in
enthalpy of those layers, resulting in a temperature gradient which causes
heat transfer from one layer to the next. For a given velocity distribution,
the temperature distribution depends on the interrelationship of the
momentum transfer and heat-transfer characteristics of the flow. The
fluid temperature at the wall is called the *adiabatic wall temperature* if there
is no heat transfer between the fluid and the wall. (This condition requires
that the temperature gradient at the wall be zero.) For many gases, the
relationship of properties (including c_p, dynamic viscosity, and thermal

conductivity) is such that for adiabatic flow the total enthalpy is nearly constant from layer to layer across the stream. Let us call the adiabatic wall temperature which is calculated from the assumption of constant total enthalpy across the stream the *approximate adiabatic wall temperature*. This temperature corresponds to the total enthalpy and the static pressure of the main stream.

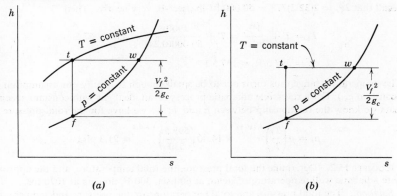

Fig. 15·3   Total or stagnation temperature and approximate adiabatic wall temperature.

Figure 15·3 shows the difference between the approximate adiabatic wall temperature and the total or stagnation temperature. Part (*a*) of Fig. 15·3 is for any fluid and part (*b*) is for the special case of an ideal gas. In both cases the state of a flowing fluid is represented by point *f*. The corresponding stagnation state is represented by point *t*. Process *f-t* is an isentropic deceleration to zero velocity. The approximate adiabatic wall state *w* is also the result of an adiabatic deceleration from V_f to zero velocity; so the enthalpy increases $h_w - h_f$ and $h_t - h_f$ are equal; therefore, $h_w = h_t$. However, process *f-w* is *irreversible* so that states *w* and *t* are not the same, the pressure at state *w* being equal to that at state *f*. Therefore, $T_w \neq T_t$ as a general case. For the case of an ideal gas, however, states of equal enthalpy are states of equal temperature (regardless of the pressure); so the approximate adiabatic wall temperature equals the stagnation temperature as shown in Fig. 15·3*b*.

EXAMPLE 15·1.   Determine the total pressure and the total temperature of air at 14.00 psia, 70 F, flowing with a velocity of 900 fps.

Solution.   The total pressure and total temperature are the pressure and temperature which correspond to the total enthalpy and the same entropy as the flowing fluid. From the definition of total enthalpy,

$$h_t - h = \frac{V^2}{2g_c}$$

For an ideal gas enthalpy is a function of temperature only; so we can determine T_t without reference to the value of entropy or any other property of the gas besides h_t. Applying Joule's law (i.e., h is a function of T only for an ideal gas) and assuming that c_p is constant in the temperature range involved,

$$c_p(T_t - T) = \frac{V^2}{2g_c}$$

Recall that $2g_c = 2(32.2)778 = 50,000$ ft²-lb$_m$/sec²-B, very nearly. Then

$$T_t = T + \frac{V^2}{2g_c c_p} = T + \frac{(900)^2}{50,000(0.24)} = 530 + 67.5$$

$$= 597.5 \text{ R} = 137.5 \text{ F}$$

(The temperature range thus turns out to be small enough to justify our assumption of a constant c_p.) For a reversible adiabatic process of an ideal gas with constant specific heats we know the relationship between p and T; so we have for the total pressure

$$p_t = p\left(\frac{T_t}{T}\right)^{k/(k-1)} = 14.00\left(\frac{597.5}{530}\right)^{1.4/0.4} = 21.3 \text{ pisa}$$

EXAMPLE 15·2. Determine the total pressure, the total temperature, and the approximate adiabatic wall temperature of steam at 60 psia, 300 F, flowing at 1070 fps.

Solution. The total pressure and total temperature are the pressure and temperature of the state defined by

$$h_t = h + \frac{V^2}{2g_c} = 1181.6 + \frac{(1070)^2}{50,000} = 1204.5 \text{ B/lb}$$

$$s_t = s = 1.6492 \text{ B/lb-R}$$

Interpolation on a Mollier chart or in the steam tables gives for this stagnation state

$$p_t = 79 \text{ psia} \quad \text{and} \quad T_t = 350 \text{ F}$$

The approximate adiabatic wall temperature T_w is the temperature of the state defined by

$$h_w = h_t = 1204.5 \text{ B/lb}$$

$$p_w = p = 60 \text{ psia}$$

From the chart or tables we obtain

$$T_w = 344^- \text{ F}$$

15·3   The dynamic equation for steady one-dimensional flow

Effective study of the thermodynamics of fluid flow requires attention to the mechanics or dynamics of flow. We now derive the basic dynamic equation for steady one-dimensional flow by starting with Newton's second law of motion,

$$F = \frac{1}{g_c}\frac{d}{d\tau}(mV) \tag{1·1}$$

where F is the resultant of all forces acting on a body which at any instant has a mass m and a velocity V. Equation 1·1 is a *vector* equation: F must be in the same direction as the change in momentum.* Applying it to any body of fixed mass m,

$$F = \frac{V\,dm}{g_c\,d\tau} + \frac{m\,dV}{g_c\,d\tau} = 0 + \frac{m\,dV}{g_c\,d\tau}$$

If dL is the distance traveled by the body in time $d\tau$, then $dV/d\tau = (dL/d\tau)(dV/dL) = V(dV/dL)$, and we have

$$F = \frac{mV}{g_c}\left(\frac{dV}{dL}\right)$$

Thus the resultant force on a mass m at any instant is proportional to the rate of change of velocity with distance. Let us consider now a fluid

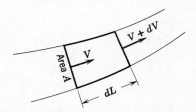

Fig. 15·4 An element of a fluid stream.

stream, directing our attention to an element of mass δm which has a length dL in the direction of flow. (See Fig. 15·4.) The mass and the length of the element are related by $\delta m = \rho A\,dL$, where A is the cross-sectional area of the element normal to the flow direction. An infinitesimal force dF causes this infinitesimal element to change velocity by dV as it moves a distance dL,

$$dF = \frac{(\delta m)V}{g_c}\left(\frac{dV}{dL}\right) = \frac{(\rho A\,dL)V}{g_c}\frac{dV}{dL} = \frac{\rho AV}{g_c}\,dV = \frac{M\,dV}{g_c}$$

For steady flow, $M = \rho AV = $ constant; so we can integrate to get the resultant force on a stream which changes velocity by ΔV:

$$F = \frac{M\,\Delta V}{g_c} \tag{15·1}$$

This is the basic dynamic equation for steady one-dimensional flow. The restriction to one-dimensional flow means that the velocity is uniform across any cross section of the flow. Remember that equation 15·1 is a

---

* Vector quantities are often designated by boldface type or overscores, **F** and **V** or $\bar{F}$ and $\bar{V}$. For our limited use of vectors this is unnecessary.

vector equation: the resultant force is in the same direction as ΔV, as shown in Fig. 15·5. The equation holds also for corresponding components of F and ΔV.

A convenient way of writing equation 15·1 for the resultant force on a fluid flowing steadily from a section 1 to a section 2 is

$$F \doteq \frac{MV_2}{g_c} - \frac{MV_1}{g_c}$$

The vector quantity MV/g_c is called the *momentum flux* at a section. For a steady-flow system with more than one stream entering or leaving, the

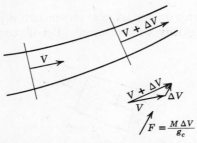

Fig. 15·5   The basic dynamic equation for steady one-dimensional flow. F is the resultant force and is in the same direction as ΔV.

resultant force is the vector difference between the sum of the momentum fluxes of streams leaving and the sum of the momentum fluxes of streams entering.

In applying the dynamic equation (equation 15·1) it is advisable to sketch the steady-flow system under consideration, showing all of the forces *on the fluid.** The sum of these forces is then equal to $M\,\Delta V/g_c$.

EXAMPLE 15·3.   Air at 20 psia, 100 F, enters a duct with a velocity of 500 fps. The duct entrance area is 2 sq ft. The air leaves the duct at 15 psia with a velocity of 800 fps through a cross-sectional area of 1.57 sq ft and in a direction 30 degrees different from the entrance direction. Determine the resultant force of the air on the duct.

Solution.   First a sketch of the open system and a diagram showing the forces on the fluid within the duct are made. The only external forces on the fluid are the force of the adjacent fluid at inlet p_1A_1 and outlet p_2A_2 and the force of the duct on the fluid F_d. We assign the positive directions of velocity and force as upward and to the right in the sketch. We do not know at first the direction of F_d; so we show it on the diagram in the

* Notice that such a diagram, although often called a "free-body diagram," is not the same as the free-body diagram made for a body of fixed mass where the sum of the forces acting on the body equals the time rate of change of momentum of the body. The time rate of change of momentum of a steady-flow system itself is always zero in accordance with the definition of steady flow.

positive directions. Then, if we observe the sign convention we have established, the signs of the components F_{d_x} and F_{d_y} which we solve for will indicate the actual direction of the force *on the fluid*.

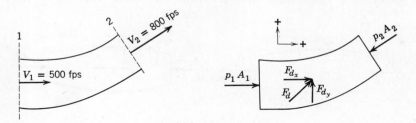

Example 15·3

Application of the dynamic equation (equation 15·1) requires a knowledge of the mass rate of flow; so we use the ideal-gas equation of state to determine the inlet air density,

$$\rho_1 = \frac{p_1}{RT_1} = \frac{20(144)}{53.3(560)} = 0.0965 \text{ lb/cu ft}$$

and then

$$M = \rho_1 A_1 V_1 = 0.0965(2)500 = 96.5 \text{ lb/sec}$$

Equating the sum of the x components of the forces to the x component of $M \, \Delta V / g_c$, we have

$$p_1 A_1 + F_{d_x} - p_2 A_2 \cos 30° = \frac{M}{g_c}(V_{2x} - V_{1x})$$

$$F_{d_x} = \frac{M}{g_c}(V_2 \cos 30° - V_1) - p_1 A_1 + p_2 A_2 \cos 30°$$

$$= \frac{96.5}{32.2}(800 \cos 30° - 500) - 20(144)2 + 15(144)1.57 \cos 30°$$

$$= -2241 \text{ lb}$$

Thus the x component of the force of the duct *on the fluid* is 2241 lb to the left.

Applying the dynamic equation now in the y direction,

$$F_{d_y} - p_2 A_2 \sin 30° = \frac{M}{g_c}(V_{2y} - V_{1y})$$

$$F_{d_y} = \frac{M}{g_c}(V_2 \sin 30° - 0) + p_2 A_2 \sin 30°$$

$$= \frac{96.5}{32.2}(800 \sin 30°) + 15(144)1.57 \sin 30°$$

$$= 2897 \text{ lb}$$

Adding F_{d_x} and F_{d_y} vectorially gives the resultant force of the duct *on the fluid* as 3663 lb in a direction (referring to directions in the sketch) upward and to the left, 37.8 degrees from the vertical. The resultant force of the fluid *on the duct* is of course opposite in direction.

EXAMPLE 15·4.   Air with a density of 0.0020 slug/cu ft enters a turbojet engine with a velocity of 500 fps relative to the engine.   Fuel is burned at one thirtieth of the mass rate of air flow.   Products of combustion leaving the engine have a density of 0.00080 slug/cu ft.   Inlet and outlet have equal cross-sectional areas of 2.0 sq ft, and the pressure is atmospheric at both inlet and outlet.   Determine the thrust developed by the engine.

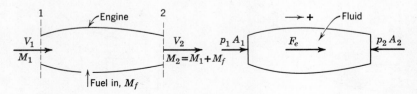

Example 15·4

Solution.   A diagram of the engine is made first.   It is unnecessary to show any internal features of the engine in the sketch because application of the dynamic equation involves only the *resultant* force on the fluid and conditions at the boundary of the open system.   Thrust is the net force of the fluid on the engine; so we find the equal-in-magnitude but opposite-in-direction force of the engine on the fluid by applying the dynamic equation in the axial direction, with the positive direction as shown above the sketch of the fluid.

$$F = p_1 A_1 - p_2 A_2 + F_e = \frac{1}{g_c}(M_2 V_2 - M_1 V_1 - M_f V_f)$$

where F is the resultant force on the fluid in the engine and F_e is the net force of the engine on the fluid.   Since $p_1 A_1 = p_2 A_2$, the resultant force happens to be equal to F_e.   Since the fuel is carried with the craft, its initial velocity has a zero component in the axial direction; so the last term on the right-hand side of the equation above is zero.   Also, $M_2 = (M_1 + M_f) = (M_1 + M_1/30) = \frac{31}{30}M_1$.   Thus the dynamic equation becomes

$$F = F_e = \frac{1}{g_c}(\tfrac{31}{30}M_1 V_2 - M_1 V_1) = \frac{M_1}{g_c}(\tfrac{31}{30}V_2 - V_1)$$

We calculate M_1 and V_2 for use in this equation by

$$M_1 = \rho_1 A_1 V_1 = 0.0020(2)500 = 2 \text{ slugs/sec}$$

$$V_2 = \frac{M_2}{\rho_2 A_2} = \frac{\tfrac{31}{30}M_1}{\rho_2 A_2} = \left(\frac{31}{30}\right)\frac{2}{0.00080(2)} = 1291 \text{ fps}$$

Substitution of these values into the dynamic equation gives

$$F_e = \frac{M_1}{g_c}(\tfrac{31}{30}V_2 - V_1) = 2[\tfrac{31}{30}(1291) - 500] = 1668 \text{ lb}$$

This is the force of the engine on the fluid.   It is positive; so, in accordance with the sign convention established at the beginning of this solution, this force is to the right for the diagrams as drawn.   The force of the fluid on the engine, the thrust, is therefore to the left and has a magnitude of 1668 lb.

15·4 Sonic velocity; Mach number

We shall see that in the study of gas flow an important property is the velocity of sound through the gas which is called also the *sonic velocity* or the *acoustic velocity*. We therefore derive now an expression for the sonic velocity in a gas.

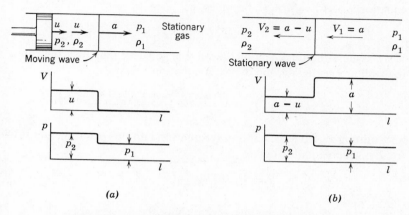

Fig. 15·6 Propagation of a pressure wave in a gas.

The plan of the derivation is to consider a pressure wave traveling through a gas and, from the viewpoint of an observer moving with the wave, to apply the continuity equation and the dynamic equation to the gas flowing through the wave in order to determine the relative velocity between the wave and the fluid ahead of it. We do this first for a pressure wave of any size (i.e., the pressure behind the wave may differ appreciably from that ahead of it) and then apply the restriction that the pressure difference across the wave is very small, as it is for a sound wave.

For a physical picture of the generation and propagation of a pressure wave in a gas, refer to Fig. 15·6. A gas fills a long tube of constant cross-sectional area. A piston in one end of the tube is moved as shown with a velocity u. The gas in a region near the piston face also moves with the velocity u. The boundary of this region in which the gas velocity is u is called the wave. Behind (i.e., to the left of) the wave the pressure is greater than it is ahead of it. Ahead of the wave the gas is unaffected by the motion of the piston or the approaching wave. The wave moves with a velocity a which is equal to or greater than u.

Our problem is to determine the wave velocity a in terms of properties of the fluid ahead of the wave. To simplify the derivation, however, let us use a frame of reference in which the wave is fixed, or, in other words, let us adopt the viewpoint of an observer moving with the wave. The resulting picture is shown in Fig. 15·6b which is the same as Fig. 15·6a with a uniform velocity a to the left imposed on the entire system. Thus the stationary wave is approached from the right by fluid with a velocity $V_1 = a$, and fluid leaves the wave to the left with a velocity $V_2 = a-u$. The flow is steady. Since the cross-sectional area is constant, the continuity equation $\rho_1 A_1 V_1 = \rho_2 A_2 V_2$ becomes

$$\rho_1 V_1 = \rho_2 V_2$$

If we assume the thickness of the wave is so small that shearing forces at the wall are negligible, the dynamic equation becomes

$$p_1 A_1 - p_2 A_2 = \frac{M \, \Delta V}{g_c} = \frac{\rho_1 A_1 V_1 (V_2 - V_1)}{g_c}$$

Substituting V_2 from the continuity equation into this equation and solving for V_1 (which equals a) gives

$$a = V_1 = \sqrt{g_c \frac{\rho_2}{\rho_1}\left(\frac{p_1 - p_2}{\rho_1 - \rho_2}\right)}$$

This is the velocity of the gas approaching the wave in Fig. 15·6b or the velocity of the wave in Fig. 15·6a. Such a wave is called a *shock wave*, and its velocity is higher for higher values of p_2/p_1*. The sonic velocity or velocity of sound, which we are interested in here, is the velocity of a pressure wave of very small amplitude. As p_2 approaches p_1 and ρ_2 approaches ρ_1, the quantity beneath the radical sign in the equation above becomes $g_c(dp/d\rho)$. Of course, the value of $dp/d\rho$ depends on the process because p and ρ can be varied independently. However, if we assume that the propagation of a sound wave is reversible and adiabatic,† and hence isentropic, we restrict $dp/d\rho$ to $(\partial p/\partial \rho)_s$ which has a single value at any state. Thus the sonic velocity, which is represented by the symbol c, is

$$c = \sqrt{g_c \left(\frac{\partial p}{\partial \rho}\right)_s} \qquad (15\cdot2)$$

This expression has been derived for a plane wave, but it also holds for cylindrical and spherical waves. c can be readily expressed in terms of the isentropic compressibility (defined in Art. 10·5) or the bulk modulus of the fluid. For ideal gases with constant specific heats, the $p\rho$ relationship for

* See pp. 286–287 of reference 15·1 or pp. 267–277 of reference 15·5 listed at the end of this chapter for the relationship between a and p_2/p_1 for the shock waves in ideal gases.

† For a discussion of this assumption, see M. W. Zemansky, *Heat and Thermodynamics*, McGraw-Hill Book Company, 4th ed., 1957, pp. 132–133.

isentropic processes is $p/\rho^k = $ constant, so that $(\partial p/\partial \rho)_s = kp/\rho$, and the *velocity of sound in an ideal gas* is

$$c = \sqrt{\frac{g_c k p}{\rho}} = \sqrt{k g_c p v} = \sqrt{k g_c RT}$$

In an ideal gas the sonic velocity, which is a property of the gas, is a function of temperature only. In the derivation above we have assumed that the propagation of a sound wave is isentropic, but we have placed no restriction on the type of process, if any, that the bulk of the gas may be undergoing. Of course, since c is a property, its value depends only on the state of the gas and not on the path followed in reaching that state.

In the study of gas flow a useful parameter is the ratio of the velocity of the gas at any point to the sonic velocity at the same point. This ratio is called the Mach* number and is designated by the symbol N_M:

$$N_M \equiv \frac{V}{c}$$

Flow with $N_M < 1$ is called subsonic and flow with $N_M > 1$ is called *supersonic*. The term *hypersonic* is used in connection with Mach numbers much greater than one, and the term *transonic* refers to flows in which the Mach number is close to one. Just how close to one the Mach number must be in order for a flow to be called transonic is not specified, and also the boundary between supersonic and hypersonic is not sharply defined; but notice that the value of $N_M = 1$ denotes clearly the boundary between subsonic and supersonic flow.

15·5   The basic relations

For the remainder of this chapter we will be concerned with the steady one-dimensional flow of fluids in which no work is done. In the analysis of such flow we have available five powerful tools:

1. The first law, which under the conditions stated can be expressed as

$$q = \Delta h + \Delta KE + \Delta PE$$

In connection with gases and vapors, ΔPE is nearly always negligible.

2. The continuity equation,

$$M = \rho_1 A_1 V_1 = \rho_2 A_2 V_2$$

---

* Ernst Mach (1838–1916) was an Austrian physicist and psychologist who is probably best known for his contributions to the philosophy of science.

3. The dynamic equation,

$$F = \frac{M \, \Delta V}{g_c}$$

4. The second law and its corollaries which indicate whether a conceivable process is possible.

5. Physical property relationships, either in the form of tabular or graphical data or in the form of equations of state and other property equations resulting from the first and second laws.

In analyzing fluid flow in which no work is done, these are the basic tools which you should use. Often you will find it convenient or even necessary to combine and restrict some of the basic relations to form equations which apply only to special cases. Always remember the restrictions on these special case equations and work as much as possible from the basic relations which are more general. In engineering practice, to be sure, it is the special cases which demand solution; but new special cases can be solved only by the application of the basic principles, and the great value of the basic principles is precisely that they apply not to just some special cases but to all special cases, including ones which are as yet unthought of.

15·6 Area variation for the isentropic flow of any fluid

We now develop an important conclusion regarding the variation of the cross-sectional flow area with respect to velocity change and pressure change for the isentropic flow of any fluid. For adiabatic flow with no work done and no change in potential energy, the first law can be expressed as

$$\Delta h + \Delta\left(\frac{V^2}{2g_c}\right) = 0$$

or in differential form

$$dh + \frac{V \, dV}{g_c} = 0 \tag{a}$$

For the case of an isentropic process, equation 9·3 can be written

$$T \, ds = 0 = dh - \frac{dp}{\rho} \tag{b}$$

Combining these two equations gives one that can also be developed from the dynamic equation. It is

$$dp = -\frac{\rho V \, dV}{g_c} \tag{c}$$

Differentiating the continuity equation, $\rho AV = $ constant, gives

$$\frac{d\rho}{\rho} + \frac{dA}{A} + \frac{dV}{V} = 0 \qquad (d)$$

Substituting from equation (c) into equation (d) gives

$$\frac{dA}{A} = \frac{g_c\, dp}{\rho}\left[\frac{1}{V^2} - \frac{d\rho}{g_c\, dp}\right] \qquad (e)$$

Since we are dealing with an isentropic process, $dp/d\rho = (\partial p/\partial \rho)_s$. Thus the second term within the brackets in equation (e) is $1/c^2$ so that we have

$$\frac{dA}{A} = \frac{g_c\, dp}{\rho V^2}\,[1 - N_M^2] \qquad (f)$$

Substituting from equation (c) into equation (f) gives

$$\frac{dA}{A} = -\frac{dV}{V}\,[1 - N_M^2] \qquad (g)$$

Inspection of equations (f) and (g) leads to the following conclusions:

1. When $N_M < 1$, $\quad \dfrac{dA}{dp} > 0 \quad$ and $\quad \dfrac{dA}{dV} < 0$

2. When $N_M > 1$, $\quad \dfrac{dA}{dp} < 0 \quad$ and $\quad \dfrac{dA}{dV} > 0$

3. When $N_M = 1$, $\quad \dfrac{dA}{dp} = 0 \quad$ and $\quad \dfrac{dA}{dV} = 0$

These results are shown graphically in Fig. 15·7. A flow channel we call a nozzle accelerates a fluid and a channel called a diffuser is used to decelerate a fluid. The conclusions reached above and illustrated in Fig. 15·7 mean that in order to accelerate a fluid which is flowing subsonically, a converging nozzle must be used. Once the speed of sound is reached by the fluid, however, further acceleration can occur only in a diverging section. Conversely, a diverging section is used to decelerate a fluid which is flowing subsonically, but, if the fluid were initially flowing supersonically, the diverging diffuser would have to be preceded by a converging diffuser for decelerating the fluid to the sonic velocity. This behavior of a supersonically flowing fluid seems strange at first because all our everyday experience is with subsonic flow. For a fluid flowing isentropically, the density and the velocity vary oppositely; and we see from the above and from the continuity equation $\rho A V = $ constant that for supersonic flow the density must vary more rapidly than velocity does with respect to area. This point warrants some reflection.

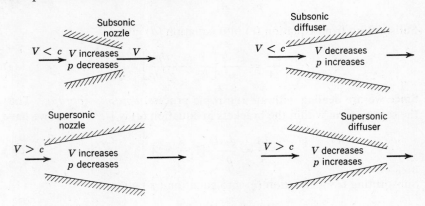

Fig. 15·7 Area–velocity–pressure variations for isentropic flow.

15·7 Adiabatic flow of ideal gases

For ideal gases, the simple equation of state and the resulting simple hT relation make the application of the basic principles to adiabatic flow quite simple. *We will consider in this article only steady-flow systems in which there is no work done and the change in potential energy is negligible.*

For the adiabatic flow of an ideal gas with no work done, the total enthalpy and consequently the total temperature also are constant along the flow. A simple and useful expression can be derived relating the temperature at any section where $N_M = 1$ to the total temperature of the gas. Let us denote the properties at a section where $N_M = 1$ by symbols such as h^* and T^*. Then from the definition of total enthalpy, recalling that the total enthalpy is constant in adiabatic flow, we have

$$h_t = h_t^* = h^* + \frac{V^{*2}}{2g_c}$$

Rearranging, substituting for V^* its equivalent $\sqrt{kg_cRT^*}$, and applying Joule's law, we have

$$c_p(T_t - T^*) = \frac{kg_cRT^*}{2g_c}$$

Use of the relationship $c_p = kR/(k-1)$ and rearrangement gives

$$\frac{T^*}{T_t} = \frac{2}{k+1} \tag{15·3}$$

If the velocity at some section of a flow path is negligibly small, the temperature at that section is the total temperature. In order to accelerate an ideal gas from rest to a sonic velocity by adiabatic expansion requires that the expansion proceed until the temperature has decreased in the ratio of $2/(k+1)$. This is true whether the expansion is reversible or irreversible. Since sonic velocity is proportional to the square root of the temperature and since T^* is less than T_t, notice that the sonic velocity at T^* is less than that in the gas at rest.

If the flow is reversible as well as adiabatic, and hence isentropic, the total pressure is also constant along the flow, and

$$\frac{p^*}{p_t} = \left(\frac{T^*}{T_t}\right)^{k/(k-1)} = \left(\frac{2}{k+1}\right)^{k/(k-1)} \tag{h}$$

For isentropic flow we have seen that, if a fluid enters a converging passage subsonically, it cannot reach a Mach number greater than one in the converging section. Therefore, for isentropic flow the pressure in a converging passage cannot be lower than a certain fraction of the total pressure as indicated by equation (h). For gases with $k = 1.4$, this fraction is 0.53. Let us investigate this point further.

Consider a converging nozzle as shown in Fig. 15·8. The upstream pressure p_1 and the temperature T_1, at a section where the velocity is negligibly small, are held constant. The pressure in the downstream region p_b can be varied. Designate the pressure in the minimum area section or throat as p_{th}. If $p_b = p_1$, there is no flow through the nozzle. If p_b is lowered slightly, flow occurs with $p_{th} = p_b$ and $V_{th} < c_{th}$. If p_b is lowered further, the pressure at the throat decreases to remain equal to p_b, and the mass rate of flow through the nozzle increases as shown in Fig. 15·8b until p_b and p_{th} reach the value of p^* at which time the velocity at the throat is sonic. Further reduction of p_b then has no effect on p_{th}, the velocity at the throat, or the mass rate of flow through the nozzle. Under these conditions the nozzle is said to be *choked* or to have reached *limiting flow* or *critical flow*. Whenever $p_b < p^*$, the pressure at the throat remains equal to p^*, and the drop in pressure from p^* to p_b occurs outside the nozzle just beyond the throat. This sudden expansion outside the nozzle is of course irreversible; it is only the flow within the nozzle which can be isentropic. Thus we can write $p_1v_1^k = p_{th}v_{th}^k$, but $p_1v_1^k \neq p_bv_b^k$.

In order to accelerate a fluid from a subsonic to a supersonic velocity, a converging–diverging nozzle, such as shown in Fig. 15·9, must be used. The flow in the converging section of such a nozzle is exactly the same as that in a converging nozzle alone; that is, for isentropic flow the velocity at the throat cannot exceed the sonic velocity, and the throat pressure cannot be lower than p^*. For flow rates less than the limiting flow rate,

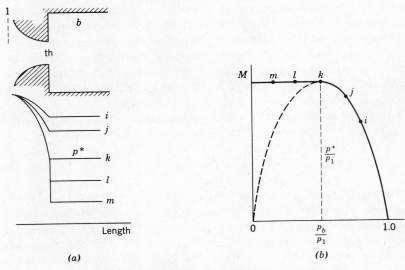

Fig. 15·8   Converging nozzle flow ($N_{M_1} < 1$).

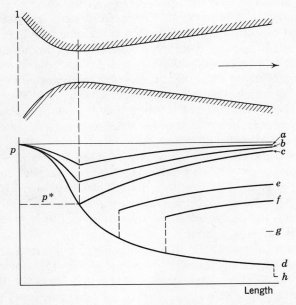

Fig. 15·9   Converging–diverging nozzle flow ($N_{M_1} < 1$). Solid lines are for isentropic processes; broken lines are for irreversible processes.

the throat pressure is not as low as p^*, the throat velocity is subsonic, and the diverging section of the nozzle is a subsonic diffuser. Back pressures such as shown by points a and b on Fig. 15·9 are possible. The exit state b corresponds to a higher flow rate than exit state a does. If the back pressure (still for the same inlet conditions) is lowered to point c, the pressure at the throat reaches p^*, and at the throat $N_M = 1$. For given inlet conditions the flow rate through the nozzle is then a maximum and the diverging section of the nozzle is a subsonic diffuser in which the gas is compressed isentropically. For this limiting flow rate there is one other back pressure besides c to which the nozzle can deliver the gas by means of an isentropic process.† This is the pressure represented by d which is the end point of an isentropic expansion in the diverging portion of the nozzle. The expansion to point d of course involves supersonic flow in the diverging portion of the nozzle.

The precise shape of a converging nozzle or the converging portion of a converging–diverging nozzle is not a critical matter in nozzle design, but the geometry of a supersonic nozzle must be determined carefully if it is to produce essentially one-dimensional isentropic flow. Design methods to give the variation of area with length of supersonic nozzles are outside the scope of this textbook.

For fixed inlet conditions, the limiting flow through a given converging–diverging nozzle can be isentropic only for two back pressures, one causing subsonic diffuser flow and the other causing supersonic nozzle flow in the diverging section. The question naturally arises: What happens if some back pressure between these two is applied to the nozzle exit? (Remember that the exit pressure is not simply a result of the inlet conditions or of the nozzle geometry but depends also on the geometry of the passage and the flow conditions farther downstream.) Referring to Fig. 15·9, suppose the back pressure is that represented by point e. In such a case, the flow proceeds past the throat just as it does in expanding toward point d, but at some point in the diverging section there is a sudden irreversible increase in pressure accompanied by a deceleration from supersonic to subsonic

---

† That two different pressures at each cross section of the diverging section are possible for isentropic flow can be seen by (1) combining the energy balance, the ideal-gas equation of state, $pv^k = $ constant, the continuity equation, and the definition of Mach number to give

$$\frac{A}{A^*} = \frac{1}{N_M}\left[\left(\frac{2}{k+1}\right)\left(1 + \frac{k-1}{2}N_M^2\right)\right]^{(k+1)/2(k-1)}$$

where A^* is the throat area, and (2) noting that two different values of N_M, one greater than unity and the other less than unity, satisfy this equation for any value of A greater than A^*. For the subsonic Mach number, $p > p^*$, and for the supersonic Mach number, $p < p^*$.

velocity. This discontinuity in the flow is called a *normal shock*. (The modifier *normal* indicates that the plane of the discontinuity is normal to the flow direction.) Downstream of the shock the gas is decelerated further isentropically as the passage acts as a subsonic diffuser. If the back pressure is lowered to f, the shock moves downstream to a new position. Further lowering of the back pressure to some value g causes the shock to move to the exit plane of the nozzle. Then the flow through the entire nozzle is isentropic to pressure d, but the shock at the exit plane causes the pressure to increase irreversibly there to pressure g. For back pressures between g

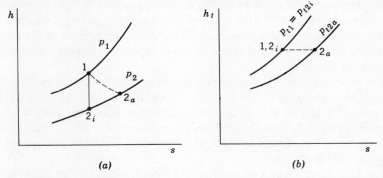

Fig. 15·10   Reversible and irreversible adiabatic expansions.

and d, the flow in the nozzle proceeds to the pressure d, but then just downstream from the exit plane there is an irreversible increase in pressure from d to g involving discontinuities called oblique shock waves across which the flow is no longer one-dimensional. If the back pressure is at some value h which is lower than d, the flow within the nozzle is the same as if the back pressure were d, but an irreversible expansion occurs just outside the nozzle exit.

If the adiabatic flow through a nozzle is irreversible, as it always is to some extent in an actual nozzle on account of friction, the entropy of the fluid must increase. Reversible adiabatic (isentropic) and irreversible adiabatic expansions from the same initial state and to the same final pressure are shown in Fig. 15·10. Point 2_i is the *i*sentropic (or *i*deal) exhaust state and point 2_a is the *a*ctual one. (Notice that on an hs diagram only lines of static pressure are uniquely determined because there exists only an hps relationship and not a unique hp_ts relationship. In a like manner, a single point on an h_ts diagram can represent several static pressures but only one total pressure; so total pressure lines instead of static pressure lines are shown on h_ts diagrams.) The total or stagnation enthalpy is constant for any adiabatic expansion in a nozzle; the total or stagnation pressure is constant only for an isentropic expansion and decreases in an irreversible adiabatic expansion.

Nozzle efficiency η_N is defined as the ratio of the kinetic energy at the nozzle outlet to the kinetic energy which would result at that point if the flow through the nozzle were isentropic between the same initial conditions and the same final pressure. Writing the definition and then extending it by means of the first law, we have

$$\eta_N \equiv \frac{V_{2a}^2/2g_c}{V_{2i}^2/2g_c} = \frac{h_{t1} - h_{2a}}{h_{t1} - h_{2i}}$$

Nozzle efficiencies of 0.95 and higher are easily obtained with converging nozzles. Similar efficiencies with converging–diverging nozzles can be obtained only by careful design. As nozzle sizes increase, fluid friction has relatively less effect on the flow, so nozzle efficiencies increase.

For various specialized studies of fluid flow and for repetitive calculations, it is often convenient to combine some of the basic equations to form equations which may be quite complex but which are suitable for the special purpose at hand. Some of the problems at the end of this chapter consist of the derivation of some of these. Many elements of such equations are published in *Gas Tables* by Keenan and Kaye and elsewhere. For an introductory study of compressible fluid flow and for illustrating the application of basic principles, it is well to avoid dependence on such equations. Notice that the following example problems are solved by the direct application of basic principles.

EXAMPLE 15·5. Helium flows isentropically through a channel of varying cross-sectional area. At one section where the area is 0.175 sq ft, the helium is at 6.0 psia, 90 F, and has a velocity of 5000 fps. Determine the velocity and the Mach number at a section where the pressure is 12.0 psia.

Analysis. Designate as section 1 that at which the pressure is 6.0 psia, and designate as section 2 that at which the pressure is 12.0 psia. Since the flow is isentropic, we can immediately calculate T_2 from $T_2/T_1 = (p_2/p_1)^{(k-1)/k}$ if we assume that the specific heats are constant. Then V_2 can be determined from an energy balance and the fact that $\Delta h = c_p \Delta T$. Finally we determine the sonic velocity at section 2 by $c_2 = \sqrt{kg_c RT_2}$ so that N_{M2} can be calculated.

Solution. Following the procedure outlined in the analysis,

$$T_2 = T_1 \left(\frac{p_2}{p_1}\right)^{(k-1)/k} = 550 \left(\frac{12.0}{6.0}\right)^{(1.67-1)/1.67} = 725 \text{ R}$$

$$\frac{V_2^2 - V_1^2}{2g_c} = h_1 - h_2 = c_p(T_1 - T_2)$$

$$V_2 = \sqrt{V_1^2 + 2g_c c_p(T_1 - T_2)} = \sqrt{(5000)^2 + 50{,}000(1.25)(550 - 725)}$$
$$= 3750 \text{ fps}$$

$$c_2 = \sqrt{kg_c RT_2} = \sqrt{1.67(32.2)386(725)} = 3880 \text{ fps}$$

$$N_{M2} = \frac{V_2}{c_2} = \frac{3750}{3880} = 0.967$$

EXAMPLE 15·6. Air at 100 psia, 140 F, enters a converging nozzle with negligible velocity. The nozzle discharges into a receiver where the pressure is 20 psia. Assuming isentropic flow, calculate the velocity at the nozzle exit.

Solution. We have seen that a fluid which enters subsonically cannot reach a Mach number greater than one in a converging section if the flow is isentropic. Therefore, the lowest temperature that can be reached by the air flowing through this converging nozzle is that corresponding to $N_M = 1$. This is of course the value we designate T^* and is given by

$$T^* = T_t\left(\frac{2}{k+1}\right) = 600\left(\frac{2}{2.4}\right) = 500 \text{ R} \qquad (15\cdot2)$$

in which we have made use of the fact that $T_t = T_1$ since the inlet velocity is negligibly small. The lowest pressure which can exist in the converging nozzle is then

$$p^* = p_t\left(\frac{T^*}{T_t}\right)^{k/(k-1)} = 100\left(\frac{500}{600}\right)^{3.5} = 53 \text{ psia}$$

Thus the receiver pressure is lower than p^*; so the pressure at the exit or throat of the converging nozzle is p^*, not the receiver pressure, and the velocity there is sonic:

$$V_2 = c_2 = \sqrt{kg_cRT_2} = \sqrt{kg_cRT^*} = \sqrt{1.4(32.2)53.3(500)} = 1097 \text{ fps}$$

(The same value of V_2 can be obtained by writing an energy balance between the inlet and the exit or throat.)

EXAMPLE 15·7. Air at 16.0 psia, 200 F, with a velocity of 600 fps is to be expanded isentropically until its Mach number is 1.5. The flow rate is 0.3 lb/sec. Determine the final pressure and cross-sectional area.

Analysis. Since the initial Mach number is obviously less than one and the final velocity is to be supersonic, a converging–diverging nozzle must be used. The final area can be found from the continuity equation, $A_2 = Mv_2/V_2$ if the final velocity and specific volume can be found. We know that $V_2 = 1.5c_2 = 1.5\sqrt{kg_cRT_2}$, and an energy balance will give us another relationship between V_2 and T_2; so we can solve for these two quantities. The final specific volume can be found from $v_2 = v_1(T_1/T_2)^{1/(k-1)}$ for the isentropic process, but, since the final pressure is also sought anyway, we might as well calculate $p_2 = p_1(T_2/T_1)^{k/(k-1)}$ and then determine v_2 by means of the ideal-gas equation of state.

Solution. The energy balance is

$$\frac{V_2^2 - V_1^2}{2g_c} = h_1 - h_2 = c_p(T_1 - T_2)$$

if we assume that c_p is constant. Since $N_{M2} = 1.5$, we have $V_2 = 1.5c_2 = 1.5\sqrt{kg_cRT_2}$ which when substituted into the energy balance above gives

$$\frac{(1.5)^2 kg_cRT_2 - V_1^2}{2g_c} = c_p(T_1 - T_2)$$

Solving for T_2,

$$T_2 = \frac{c_pT_1 + V_1^2/2g_c}{1.125kR + c_v} = \frac{c_pT_1 + V_1^2/2g_c}{c_p[1.125(k-1)+1]} = \frac{T_1 + V_1^2/2g_cc_p}{1.125k - 0.125}$$

$$= \frac{660 + (600)^2/50,000(0.24)}{1.125(1.4) - 0.125} = 476 \text{ R}$$

(This value of T_2 justifies our use of $c_p = 0.24$ B/lb-F and $k = 1.4$. See Figs. 4·4 and 4·9.) Solving the energy balance for V_2, we have

$$V_2 = \sqrt{V_1^2 + 2g_c c_p(T_1 - T_2)} = \sqrt{(600)^2 + 50{,}000(0.24)(660 - 476)}$$

$$= 1603 \text{ fps}$$

(This value can also be obtained from $V_2 = 1.5c_2 = 1.5\sqrt{kg_c RT_2}$.) Following the procedure outlined in the analysis,

$$p_2 = p_1\left(\frac{T_2}{T_1}\right)^{k/(k-1)} = 16\left(\frac{476}{660}\right)^{3.5} = 5.10 \text{ psia}$$

$$v_2 = \frac{RT_2}{p_2} = \frac{53.3(476)}{5.10(144)} = 34.5 \text{ cu ft/lb}$$

$$A_2 = \frac{Mv_2}{V_2} = \frac{0.3(34.5)}{1603} = 0.00646 \text{ sq ft}$$

15·8   Adiabatic flow of vapors

The basic principles listed in Art. 15·5 and the isentropic flow relationships derived in Art. 15·6 apply of course to the flow of vapors or nonideal gases. The method of analysis for vapor flow is similar to that for ideal-gas flow except that for vapors no simple equation of state or hT relation is available, and therefore tabulated or graphical property data must be used. The hs or Mollier diagram which was discussed in Art. 10·7 is useful in this respect for nozzle flow calculations. For steam, convenient hv charts are available.†

For limited ranges of pressure and temperature, the c_p and k values of vapors may sometimes be considered as constant so that relationships derived for ideal gases, such as equations 15·2 and (h) of the preceding article, can be used for vapors. For example, the mean value of k for slightly superheated steam at pressures less than about 200 psia is around 1.3, so that equation (h) of the preceding article gives $p^*/p_t = 0.55$, and this figure is frequently used in predicting whether a converging or a converging–diverging nozzle should be used for a given expansion of steam. The same value of p^*/p_t is used for slightly wet steam because it has been observed experimentally that steam expanding isentropically (or nearly so) in a nozzle can expand for some distance into the wet region on an hs diagram before condensation actually begins. This delay of condensation is known as *supersaturation*, and steam which is represented by a point within the wet region, as far as its enthalpy and entropy are concerned, and

† See reference 15·6 listed at the end of this chapter.

yet contains no liquid is called *supersaturated steam*. It is said to be in a metastable state, and we do not treat such states in this book.*

Nozzle efficiency as defined in the preceding article is used in connection with both vapor and ideal-gas nozzles. For vapor nozzles the term *reheat fraction* is also used and may be defined as $(1 - \eta_N)$. The frictional effect in a converging–diverging nozzle occurs principally between the throat and exit of the nozzle; hence the flow from the entrance to the throat may be safely assumed to be isentropic even in actual nozzles.

EXAMPLE 15·8. A nozzle expands steam at a rate of 2.0 lb/sec from 200 psia, 600 F, to 40 psia. The initial velocity is negligible. Assuming that the flow is isentropic, compute the velocity and the area at sections along the nozzle where the pressure is 150, 100, 80, and 40 psia.

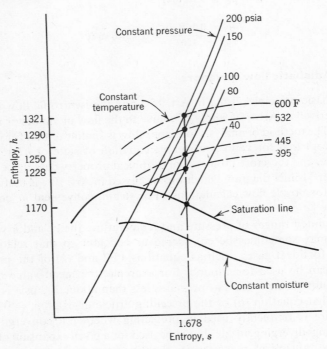

Example 15·8

Solution. Since an isentropic process is assumed, the four state points we are interested in can be found at the intersections of the constant-entropy line from the initial state with the proper pressure lines on a Mollier chart. A skeleton sketch of the chart is shown.

* For a discussion of metastable states, see J. H. Keenan, *Thermodynamics*, John Wiley & Sons, 1941, chapter XXV.

Since the initial kinetic energy is negligible, application of the first law shows that the kinetic energy at any section equals the decrease in enthalpy between the inlet and that section. Thus the velocities are given by

$$V = \sqrt{2g_c(h_1 - h)} = \sqrt{50,000(h_1 - h)} = 223.8\sqrt{h_1 - h}$$

$$V_{150} = 223.8\sqrt{1321 - 1290} = 1246 \text{ fps}$$

$$V_{100} = 223.8\sqrt{1321 - 1250} = 1886 \text{ fps}$$

$$V_{80} = 223.8\sqrt{1321 - 1228} = 2160 \text{ fps}$$

$$V_{40} = 223.8\sqrt{1321 - 1170} = 2750 \text{ fps}$$

The specific volumes are found from the steam tables.

$$v_{150} = 3.81 \text{ cu ft/lb}$$

$$v_{100} = 5.24 \text{ cu ft/lb}$$

$$v_{80} = 6.17 \text{ cu ft/lb}$$

$$v_{40} = 10.5 \text{ cu ft/lb}$$

The areas are found by use of the continuity equation, $A = Mv/V$:

$$A_{150} = \frac{2(3.81)144}{1246} = 0.88 \text{ sq in.}$$

$$A_{100} = \frac{2(5.24)144}{1886} = 0.80 \text{ sq in.}$$

$$A_{80} = \frac{2(6.15)144}{2160} = 0.82 \text{ sq in.}$$

$$A_{40} = \frac{2(10.5)144}{2750} = 1.10 \text{ sq in.}$$

These figures show that the nozzle area is a minimum at some section between the 150-psia section and the 80-psia section.

EXAMPLE 15·9.   Determine the flow rate through a properly designed nozzle which steam enters at 200 psia, 500 F, with negligible velocity and leaves at 20 psia if the throat area is 0.2 sq in.

Solution.   The ratio p_2/p_1, where p_2 is the outlet pressure, is so low that undoubtedly the exit velocity is supersonic, and therefore limiting flow exists. Using the value of 0.55 for p^*/p_t and noting that $p_1 = p_t$ because the entrance velocity is negligible, we have at the throat

$$p_{\text{th}} = p^* = 0.55p_1 = 0.55(200) = 110 \text{ psia}$$

At this pressure and $s_{\text{th}} = s_1 = 1.6240$ B/lb-R, the steam is superheated; so from a Mollier chart or steam tables we have $h_{\text{th}} = 1213$ B/lb, and from the tables we have

$v_{\text{th}} = 4.32$ cu ft/lb. Applying the first law and then the continuity equation gives

$$V_{\text{th}} = \sqrt{2g_c(h_1 - h_{\text{th}})} = \sqrt{50{,}000(1269 - 1213)} = 1673 \text{ fps}$$

$$M = \frac{A_{\text{th}}V_{\text{th}}}{v_{\text{th}}} = \frac{0.2(1673)}{4.32(144)} = 0.538 \text{ lb/sec}$$

EXAMPLE 15·10.   A nozzle is to be designed to expand steam at a rate of 0.2 lb/sec from 100 psia, 500 F, to 20 psia. Inlet velocity is to be very low. For a nozzle efficiency of 0.9, determine the exit area.

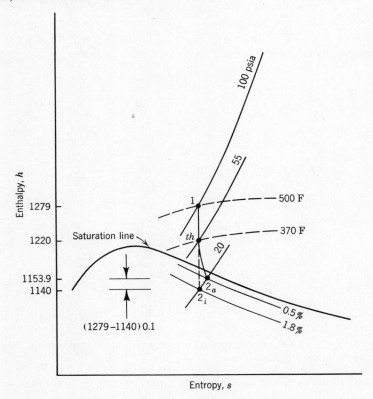

Example 15·10

Solution.   A skeleton *hs* diagram is made first, and values read from a Mollier chart are placed on it. Point 2_a, the actual end state, is located by first finding $(h_1 - h_{2i}) = 1279 - 1140 = 139$ B/lb and then locating point 2_a by the fact that the actual enthalpy decrease is 0.9 of the ideal enthalpy decrease. The actual exit velocity is

$$V_{2a} = \sqrt{2g_c(h_1 - h_{2a})} = \sqrt{2g_c(h_1 - h_{2i})\eta_N}$$

$$= \sqrt{50{,}000(1279 - 1140)0.9} = 2500 \text{ fps}$$

From the steam tables at 20 psia and 1153.9 B/lb ($x = 0.997$), $v_{2a} = 20.0$ cu ft/lb. (Notice that this is larger than v_{2i}.) The area is then found from the continuity equation

$$A_2 = \frac{Mv_{2a}}{V_{2a}} = \frac{0.2(20)144}{2500} = 0.23 \text{ sq in.}$$

15·9 Flow through orifices

Up to this point in our discussion of nozzle and diffuser flow we have treated only one-dimensional flow in which the fluid completely fills the flow channel. In the flow through an orifice as shown in Fig. 15·11 the fluid stream continues to contract after passing through the orifice until a

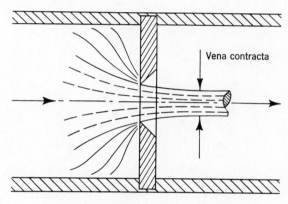

Vena contracta

Fig. 15·11   Flow through an orifice.

minimum area section called the *vena contracta* is reached at which the pressure is also a minimum. The size and location of the vena contracta can be predicted by means discussed in books on fluid mechanics and fluid metering. Mention of orifice flow is made here only as a reminder that a flowing fluid does not always fill the flow channel provided for it.

15·10 The Fanno line; flow in pipes

Consider the adiabatic steady flow of a fluid in a constant-area passage with no work done. The flow in an insulated pipe meets such conditions. Application of the first law and the continuity equation gives

$$h_t = h + \frac{V^2}{2g_c} = h + \left(\frac{M}{A}\right)^2 \frac{v^2}{2g_c} = \text{constant} \qquad (15\cdot4)$$

Thus the relationship between h and v (and consequently between any two properties if we are dealing with a pure substance) is fixed; so the states which satisfy equation 15·4 can be plotted on an hs diagram. Figure 15·12 shows three such plots for the same total enthalpy but different values of M/A (lines A, B, and C) and one plot for a higher total enthalpy (line D). These lines are called *Fanno lines** and each one is the locus of states through which a fluid passes in adiabatic pipe flow for given entrance conditions. A limiting case Fanno line is the constant-enthalpy line E which inspection of equation 15·4 shows to be the limiting case as M/A approaches zero or the case for incompressible flow ($v =$ constant).

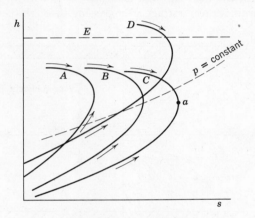

Fig. 15·12 Fanno lines.

We know from the increase of entropy principle that for adiabatic flow the entropy of the fluid cannot decrease; therefore, the processes represented by the Fanno lines in Fig. 15·12 can proceed only in the directions shown by the arrows on the lines. Let us investigate the conditions at a maximum entropy point on a Fanno line such as point a in Fig. 15·12. The energy balance in differential form is

$$dh + \frac{V\,dV}{g_c} = 0$$

From the continuity equation we have $\rho V =$ constant so that $dV = -V\,d\rho/\rho$, and making this substitution in the energy balance gives

$$dh - \frac{V^2\,d\rho}{g_c\rho} = 0$$

* Fanno, a student at the Eidgenössiche Technische Hochschule, Zürich, described these lines in a thesis submitted in 1904.

Then substituting for dh from the $T\,ds$ equation,

$$T\,ds = dh - v\,dp \qquad (9\cdot3)$$

gives

$$T\,ds + v\,dp - \frac{V^2\,d\rho}{g_c\rho} = 0$$

$$T\,ds + \frac{dp}{\rho} - \frac{V^2\,d\rho}{g_c\rho} = 0$$

At a maximum entropy point, $ds = 0$, so that this last equation can be simplified and solved for V as

$$V = \sqrt{g_c\left(\frac{\partial p}{\partial \rho}\right)_s} = c \qquad (15\cdot2)$$

Thus the limiting state such as a on Fig. 15·12 is one for which the velocity equals the sonic velocity. Further consideration of Fig. 15·12 shows that the upper part of each Fanno line (i.e., the part above the maximum entropy point) represents states of subsonic flow, and the lower part corresponds to supersonic flow. Therefore, for subsonic adiabatic flow in a pipe the pressure and enthalpy decrease and the velocity increases in the direction of flow, but the velocity cannot exceed the velocity of sound; and for supersonic adiabatic flow in a pipe the pressure and enthalpy increase and the velocity decreases in the direction of flow, the limiting velocity again being the velocity of sound which in this case is approached from above. In both cases, of course, the entropy of the fluid must increase in the direction of flow. If a pipe carrying a fluid at subsonic velocities discharges into a region where the pressure is lower than that corresponding to the point of maximum entropy on the Fanno line p_a, then the expansion from p_a to the receiver pressure must occur outside the end of the pipe, because inside the pipe only states on the Fanno line which can be reached without a decrease in entropy can be attained. Likewise, if the flow in the pipe is supersonic and the receiver pressure is higher than p_a, then the pressure at the end of the pipe will be p_a, and the increase in pressure from p_a to the receiver pressure will occur just outside the end of the pipe. (*Caution:* The limiting pressure in a pipe where the flow is irreversible is not the same as the limiting pressure in a converging nozzle under isentropic flow conditions. In both cases, however, the total enthalpy is constant and the limiting velocity is sonic.)

The variation of pressure, enthalpy, velocity, etc. of the fluid as a function of pipe length can be predicted only if information is available on friction factors or fluid shearing stresses. These matters are treated in books on fluid mechanics.

15·11   The Rayleigh line;   conditions across a normal shock

Consider frictionless flow (i.e., no fluid shearing forces) in a constant-area passage with no work done. There may be heat transfer. The dynamic equation applied to an element of fluid between sections 1 and 2 is

$$p_1 A - p_2 A = \frac{M}{g_c}(V_2 - V_1) \qquad \text{(15·1, expanded)}$$

Dividing both sides of this equation by the area and substituting from the continuity equation $V = Mv/A$, we have

$$p_1 - p_2 = \frac{1}{g_c}\left(\frac{M}{A}\right)^2 (v_2 - v_1)$$

or
$$p + \frac{1}{g_c}\left(\frac{M}{A}\right)^2 v = \text{constant}$$

This is the equation of a *Rayleigh* line* which can be plotted on various property diagrams because at least for pure substances a *pv* relationship completely determines the relationships among other properties. Figure 15·13 shows a Rayleigh line and, for comparison, one of the Fanno lines possible for the same value of M/A. The Fanno line is a line of constant total enthalpy, so obviously the total enthalpy varies along a Rayleigh line. This means that a fluid can follow a Rayleigh line only if there is heat transfer. As in the case of the Fanno line, it can be shown that the maximum entropy point on a Rayleigh line corresponds to $N_M = 1$, the lower part of the line is for supersonic flow, and the upper part is for subsonic flow. The direction in which a process proceeds along a Rayleigh line depends on the direction of heat transfer as indicated in Fig. 15·13. The process is not adiabatic, so of course there is no restriction on the entropy change of the fluid alone.

A combination of Fanno and Rayleigh lines is useful in determining the change in state which occurs across a normal shock which was mentioned in Art. 15·7 as a flow discontinuity in which the pressure rises suddenly and the velocity changes from supersonic to subsonic. Referring to Fig. 15·14, fluid in state 1 approaches the shock at a supersonic velocity. The thickness of the shock is very small so that between section 1 just upstream of the shock and section 2 just downstream of it the area is virtually the same, even though the shock may occur in a diverging passage. If the process is

---

* Lord Rayleigh (1842–1919) was an English physicist who is perhaps now best known for his work in acoustics, but he also made notable contributions in the fields of optics, hydrodynamics, electromagnetic phenomena, and gas properties. He received a Nobel prize in 1904.

also adiabatic, then states 1 and 2 must lie on the same Fanno line. Again because the shock is so thin, wall friction forces can be neglected (i.e., they are very small compared to the difference in pressure forces acting on a fluid element which contains the shock). Therefore, states 1 and 2 are connected by a frictionless (but not necessarily reversible) constant-area flow and hence lie on the same Rayleigh line. The only point on the *hs*

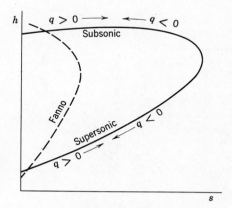

Fig. 15·13 Rayleigh line.

diagram of Fig. 15·14 that lies on both the same Fanno line and the same Rayleigh line as point 1 is the point 2 at the other intersection of the two lines. Thus the conditions just downstream of a shock can be determined by plotting the Fanno and Rayleigh lines through the state of the fluid just upstream of it. For an ideal gas the equation of state is simple enough so that the Fanno and Rayleigh line equations can be solved directly for the Mach number, pressure, and temperature ratios across a shock. For vapors an empirical *hpv* relation can often be formulated which makes possible the direct solution of the two equations.* It is found that for a supersonic upstream velocity the downstream velocity is always subsonic.

Figure 15·14 shows $s_2 > s_1$ as expected for an irreversible adiabatic process. It is possible to show that for all flows which satisfy both the Fanno and Rayleigh line conditions the entropy of the subsonic state is always higher than that of the supersonic state. Therefore, since the shock is an adiabatic process, it can occur in only one direction: from a supersonic state to a subsonic state. This is another illustration of the value of

* For the ideal-gas case, see pp. 116–119 of reference 15·4 listed at the end of this chapter. For the case of vapors, see J. H. Keenan, *Thermodynamics*, John Wiley & Sons, 1941, pp. 335–336.

the second law in showing whether a conceivable process is possible. From inspection of the Fanno and Rayleigh lines we conclude that two states satisfy the requirements of the first law, the dynamic equation, and the continuity equation, but the second law is needed to tell us in which direction between these two states a process can occur.

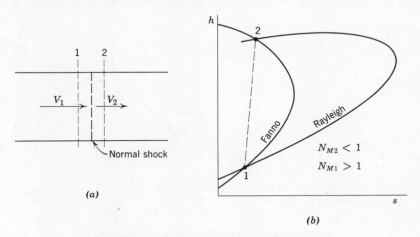

Fig. 15·14 State change across a normal shock.

15·12 Summary

This chapter deals with the thermodynamic aspects of the steady one-dimensional flow of fluids. A useful property in such studies is the total enthalpy which is defined as

$$h_t \equiv h + \frac{V^2}{2g_c}$$

The total temperature and total pressure of a flowing fluid are defined as the temperature and pressure which would result if the fluid were brought to rest isentropically. They are also called the stagnation temperature and stagnation pressure.

The basic dynamic equation for steady one-dimensional flow is

$$F = \frac{M \, \Delta V}{g_c} \tag{15·1}$$

where F is the resultant force on a stream which undergoes a velocity change ΔV and which has a flow rate M. This is a vector equation: F and ΔV are in the same direction.

The velocity of sound in a fluid is given by

$$c = \sqrt{g_c \left(\frac{\partial p}{\partial \rho}\right)_s}$$ (15·2)

which for an ideal gas becomes

$$c = \sqrt{\frac{g_c k p}{\rho}} = \sqrt{k g_c p v} = \sqrt{k g_c R T}$$

A useful parameter in the study of gas flow is the Mach number N_M, which is defined by

$$N_M \equiv \frac{V}{c}$$

Application of the first and second laws, the continuity equation, and the dynamic equation shows that for the isentropic flow of any fluid the pressure, velocity, and cross-sectional area variations depend on the Mach number as follows:

1. When $N_M < 1$, $\quad \dfrac{dA}{dp} > 0 \quad$ and $\quad \dfrac{dA}{dV} < 0$

2. When $N_M > 1$, $\quad \dfrac{dA}{dp} < 0 \quad$ and $\quad \dfrac{dA}{dV} > 0$

3. When $N_M = 1$, $\quad \dfrac{dA}{dp} = 0 \quad$ and $\quad \dfrac{dA}{dV} = 0$

Further application of the basic relations reveals that, if a fluid enters a converging nozzle subsonically, the Mach number at the outlet cannot exceed unity, regardless of how far the receiver pressure is lowered. A converging–diverging nozzle must be used to accelerate a fluid from a subsonic to a supersonic velocity and a converging–diverging diffuser must be used to decelerate a fluid isentropically from a supersonic to a subsonic velocity. When $N_M = 1$ at the throat of a converging–diverging passage, there are for isentropic flow only two possible pressures for the fluid at each other section of the passage, one for subsonic and the other for supersonic flow.

The Fanno line is the locus of states of a fluid which flows adiabatically through a constant-area channel with no work done. The Rayleigh line is the locus of states of a fluid which flows frictionlessly through a constant-area passage with no work done but with heat transfer allowed. The Fanno and Rayleigh lines are useful in several types of analyses, one of which is the determination of the change of state across a normal shock.

A normal shock is a flow discontinuity which occurs only if the velocity is initially supersonic and which results in a deceleration to a subsonic velocity and an abrupt pressure rise.

REFERENCES

15·1   R. C. Binder, *Fluid Mechanics*, Prentice-Hall, 3d ed., 1955, chapters 17 and 18.

15·2   N. A. Hall, *Thermodynamics of Fluid Flow*, Prentice-Hall, 1951, chapters 4, 6, 7, 8, and 9.

15·3   C. O. Mackey, W. N. Barnard, and F. O. Ellenwood, *Engineering Thermodynamics*, John Wiley & Sons, 1957, chapter 7.

15·4   A. H. Shapiro, *The Dynamics and Thermodynamics of Compressible Flow*, Ronald Press, 1953, vol. I, chapters 3, 4, and 5.

15·5   M. J. Zucrow, *Aircraft and Missile Propulsion*, John Wiley & Sons, vol. I, 1958, chapters 3, 4, and 5.

15·6   F. O. Ellenwood and C. O. Mackey, *Thermodynamic Charts*, John Wiley & Sons, 2d ed., 1944.

15·7   J. H. Keenan and J. Kaye, *Gas Tables*, John Wiley & Sons, 1948.

PROBLEMS

15·1   Water flows steadily through a circular pipe with a velocity distribution given by $u = u_{max}(1 - r/r_0)^2$, where u is the velocity at any radius r, u_{max} is the velocity at the pipe axis, and r_0 is the pipe radius. Determine the ratio of the kinetic energy per pound of this stream to that of a one-dimensional flow in the same pipe with the same flow rate.

15·2   Determine the stagnation temperature and the stagnation pressure for air at 5 psia, 0 F, moving at 1000 fps.

15·3   Determine the stagnation temperature and the approximate adiabatic wall temperature of steam at 600 psia, 500 F, flowing with a velocity of 1000 fps.

15·4   Air at 20 psia, 100 F, flows in a stream of 4 sq ft cross-sectional area with a velocity of 500 fps into a system of vanes which turns the stream through an angle of 30 degrees without changing the magnitude of the velocity or the pressure. Determine the force of the stream on the vane system.

15·5   A jet of water having a cross-sectional area of 0.1 sq ft strikes a flat plate which is normal to the jet. The force on the plate is 100 lb. If the jet velocity is doubled, what will be the magnitude of the force on the plate? What is the magnitude of the higher velocity?

15·6   Air flows through a long straight section of 4-in.-diameter pipe at a rate of 600 lb/min, entering at 100 psia, 80 F, and leaving at 18.4 psia, −7 F. Determine the force of the air on the pipe.

15·7   On a certain day when sea-level atmospheric temperature is 60 F, the temperature decreases with altitude at a rate of 5 F per 1000 ft. How long does it take for a sound wave to travel from sea level to an altitude of 10,000 ft?

15·8   Determine the Mach number of the steam flow of Prob. 15·3.

15·9 A vertical pipe contains water. A pressure gage on the pipe reads 10 psi higher than another gage located 30 ft above the first. Is there upward flow, downward flow, no flow, or flow of indeterminate direction in the pipe?

15·10 In a throttling process, the final enthalpy equals the initial enthalpy. The flow through a pressure-reducing valve is often considered to be a throttling process, even though there is actually a change in velocity of the fluid if the inlet and outlet lines are the same size. Determine the change in enthalpy for the adiabatic flow of steam through a pressure-reducing valve in a 6-in.-diameter line if steam enters at 600 psia, 600 F, with a velocity of 200 fps and leaves at 100 psia.

15·11 Refer to Example 15·5. Determine the cross-sectional area at section 2.

15·12 Refer to the definition of nozzle efficiency in Art. 15·7. What would you propose as an analogous definition of diffuser efficiency? Compare your definition with those you find in the literature.

15·13 Figure 15·9 is for subsonic entrance to a converging–diverging nozzle. Sketch the pressure distributions in a similar manner for supersonic entrance to such a passage.

15·14 An airplane is flying through air at 12.8 psia, 59 F, at a velocity of 600 fps. Determine the Mach number at a point on the plane where the air velocity relative to the plane is 300 fps.

15·15 Derive the following equation for the stagnation pressure of an ideal gas:

$$p_t = p \left(1 + \frac{k-1}{2} N_M^2 \right)^{k/(k-1)}$$

15·16 Air at 120 psia, 180 F, with negligible velocity enters a converging nozzle which discharges to a region where the pressure is 14.6 psia. The flow is adiabatic. The nozzle throat has a cross-sectional area of 0.60 sq in. Determine the flow rate.

15·17 Air at 300 psia, 400 F, expands isentropically in a nozzle to 100 psia. If the discharge rate is 2 lb/sec, compute the areas at sections where the pressures are 250, 200, 150, and 100 psia. Neglect the entrance velocity.

15·18 Air at 150 psia, 300 F, enters a nozzle with negligible velocity and expands isentropically to 20 psia. For a flow rate of 0.5 lb/sec determine the cross-sectional area and the Mach number at a section in the nozzle where the pressure is 60 psia.

15·19 Air is to be expanded isentropically through a nozzle and discharged at 14.7 psia, 100 F, with a Mach number of 2.0 through a cross-sectional area of 5.42 sq in. Determine the initial pressure and temperature if the initial velocity is very low.

15·20 Air flows through the test section of a wind tunnel at 10 psia, 40 F, with a Mach number of 1.15. At the outlet of the diffuser which follows the test section, the air is at 19 psia, 160 F. The flow is adiabatic. Determine the velocity leaving the diffuser. Is the flow reversible?

15·21 Air at 30 psia, 200 F, enters a horizontal converging tube with a velocity of 200 fps. The tube tapers from a cross-sectional area of 0.5 to 0.3 sq ft and is insulated. The pressure at the outlet is 10.0 psia. Calculate the temperature and velocity of the air at the outlet.

15·22 Determine the inlet and throat areas of a nozzle which is to discharge air at 5.0 psia, 40 F, at a Mach number of 2.0 through an exit area of 0.5 sq ft. The inlet velocity is to be 500 fps. Assume that the flow is isentropic.

15·23 Air at 14.0 psia, 60 F, flows through a tube at 1800 fps. If the flow is reversible and adiabatic, does the velocity increase, decrease, remain constant, or vary indeterminately in a diverging section following the tube?

15·24 Air at 40 psia, 240 F, enters a nozzle with a velocity of 600 fps and expands reversibly and adiabatically to 20 psia. The nozzle discharge area is 1.44 sq in. Determine the flow rate.

15·25 There is a fable about a traveler who was turned out of a peasant's house because he blew on his hands to warm them and blew on his soup to cool it, and the peasant would not allow any person enchanted enough to be able to blow hot and cold from the same mouth to stay in his house. Explain how it is possible to blow either "hot or cold."

15·26 Derive the following equation for the velocity at any section of a channel through which an ideal gas flows isentropically. The subscript 1 refers to any other section of the channel.

$$V = \sqrt{\frac{2g_c k R T_1}{k-1}\left[1 - \left(\frac{p}{p_1}\right)^{(k-1)/k}\right] + V_1^2}$$

15·27 Derive the following equation for the mass rate of flow for an ideal gas flowing isentropically from an initial condition of negligible velocity:

$$M = A\sqrt{\frac{2g_c k}{k-1}\frac{p_1}{v_1}\left[\left(\frac{p}{p_1}\right)^{2/k} - \left(\frac{p}{p_1}\right)^{(k+1)/k}\right]}$$

15·28 Derive the following equation for p^* of an ideal gas flowing isentropically:

$$\frac{p^*}{p} = \left[\frac{2}{k+1} + N_M^2\left(\frac{k-1}{k+1}\right)\right]^{k/(k-1)}$$

15·29 Solve Prob. 15·19 for adiabatic flow with a nozzle efficiency of 90 per cent. Also calculate the irreversibility of the process if the sink temperature is 60 F.

15·30 A nozzle is to expand steam adiabatically from 100 to 80 psia. The steam enters the nozzle with negligible velocity in a dry saturated condition. Should this be a converging nozzle, a converging–diverging nozzle, either type, or neither type?

15·31 Steam flows isentropically through a nozzle from 300 to 25 psia. If the initial temperature of the steam is 520 F and the flow rate is 0.5 lb/sec, compute the areas at the throat and outlet. Neglect the entrance velocity.

15·32 Determine the areas at the throat and outlet of a nozzle which discharges 4200 lb of steam per hour. The steam is initially at 85 psia, 500 F, and is discharged to a vacuum of 14 in. of mercury. The barometric pressure is 30 in. of mercury. The entrance velocity is 375 fps. Assume reversible adiabatic flow conditions.

15·33 Determine the throat area of a nozzle which is to discharge dry saturated steam at 100 psia with a velocity of 2580 fps at a rate of 16.2 lb/sec. Assume that the flow is isentropic.

15·34 A nozzle with an efficiency of 90 per cent is used to expand steam adiabatically from 300 psia, 550 F, to 60 psia at a rate of 2000 lb/hr. The initial velocity is negligible. The lowest temperature in the surroundings is 70 F. Compute the nozzle discharge area and the irreversibility of the process per pound of steam.

15·35 Sketch hs and $h_t s$ diagrams for an ideal gas flowing adiabatically through (a) a long pipe line, (b) a nozzle, (c) a diffuser.

15·36 Air at 55 psia, 263 F, enters an 8-in.-diameter pipe at 100 fps and leaves at 243 F. The flow is adiabatic. Calculate the Mach number at the outlet.

15·37 At one section in a long well-insulated pipe line 2 in. in inside diameter air at 60 psia, 120 F, has a velocity of 350 fps. Determine the minimum pressure that can exist in the pipe.

15·38 For an atmospheric condition of 14.7 psia, 70 F, determine the change in stream availability between the two specified sections in Prob. 15·36.

15·39 Air flows through a well-insulated 4-in.-diameter pipe at a rate of 600 lb/min. At one section the air is at 100 psia, 80 F. Determine the minimum pressure and the maximum velocity that can occur in the pipe.

15·40 Plot the Fanno line for the flow of Prob. 15·39.

15·41 At one section in an insulated pipe, steam at 400 psia, 500 F, has a velocity of 400 fps. Plot the Fanno line for this flow, and determine the minimum pressure and the maximum velocity that can occur in the pipe.

15·42 State whether each of the following increases, decreases, remains constant, or varies indeterminately across a normal shock: pressure, temperature, density, velocity, Mach number, entropy, stream availability.

15·43 Air at 14.0 psia, 60 F, with a Mach number of 2.0 enters a normal shock. Determine the downstream pressure, temperature, and velocity and the irreversibility of the process if the sink temperature is taken as 60 F.

CHAPTER 16

Compression and Expansion Processes: Fluid Machines

Machines which compress flowing fluids or which produce work from the expansion of flowing fluids are components of many engineering systems. These machines may generally be classified either as turbo- or dynamic machines or as positive displacement machines. In turbomachines work is done on or by a fluid by means of a rotor which exerts a torque on the fluid, causing a change in angular momentum of the fluid as it passes through the rotor. Examples of turbomachines are centrifugal and axial-flow pumps, fans, blowers, compressors, and turbines. The designation *pump* is generally used in connection with liquids. *Fans* move gases against such small pressure differences that density changes are negligible. Machines that move gases against somewhat greater pressure differences are called *blowers*, and *compressors* are used for still greater pressure differences. There are no sharply defined lines of demarcation among these designations. Examples of positive-displacement machines are reciprocating and rotary engines, pumps, blowers, and compressors. Gear pumps and vane pumps are rotary machines.

In this chapter we first review the application of the first and second laws to all types of compression and expansion processes and define some performance parameters. Then with the help of the principles of mechanics we consider the energy transfer between a fluid and a rotor for various types of turbomachinery. In conclusion, we look briefly at some performance features of reciprocating machines.

16·1 Steady-flow compression processes

To any steady-flow system we can apply (1) the first law for determining energy quantities, (2) the relationship $w_{in} = \int v \, dp + \Delta KE + \Delta PE$ for determining work if the process is reversible, and (3) the second law and its corollaries to determine the possibility of a process and its irreversibility.

These are the tools we now use in analyzing steady-flow compression and expansion processes.

For given end states it is generally desirable to reduce to a minimum the work input to a compressor. This of course means that the actual process should approximate as closely as possible a reversible process between the two specified states. Often, however, the purpose of a compressor is to bring a fluid not to a specified final state but only to a specified final pressure. This is usually the case when the compressed fluid is to be stored before it is used further. Therefore, we should first investigate the various

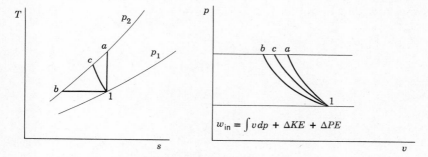

Fig. 16·1 Reversible compression paths.

types of reversible processes between an initial state and some given final pressure to see which involves the least work. Figure 16·1 shows on pv and Ts diagrams for a gas three different reversible compression paths between a state 1 and the same final pressure p_2. Process 1-a is a reversible adiabatic compression, process 1-b is a reversible isothermal compression, and process 1-c is a reversible compression with some heat removed from the gas but not enough to hold the temperature constant. Process 1-c might be a polytropic process: one for which pv^n = constant. If it is, then $k > n > 1$ because the cases of $n = k$ and $n = 1$ are the reversible adiabatic (process 1-a) and reversible isothermal (process 1-b) cases, respectively.

For a reversible steady-flow process,

$$w_{in} = \int v \, dp + \Delta KE + \Delta PE \qquad (1·10)$$

and the integral term is represented by an area on a pv diagram. Inspection of the pv diagram of Fig. 16·1 shows that, for equal changes in kinetic and potential energy, the work required to compress a gas reversibly from a state 1 to a final pressure p_2 is reduced as the compression path approaches the isothermal. (The question might be raised as to the advisability of cooling the gas during compression to a temperature lower than T_1. If a coolant at a sufficiently low temperature is available for doing this, it would be better, as shown by the solution of Prob. 16·3, to cool the gas before it enters the compressor; therefore we generally consider the compressor inlet temperature to be the minimum temperature attainable by means of heat transfer to a coolant.)

In an actual machine, the amount of heat which can be transferred during the compression process is limited by both the small surface area available for heat transfer and the short length of time required for the gas to pass through the machine. Consequently, the ideal process which may be simulated in an actual cooled compressor is a polytropic process with n closer to k than to 1.

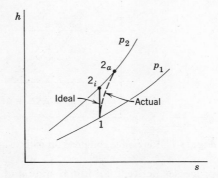

Fig. 16·2 Reversible and irreversible adiabatic compression.

Sometimes no cooling is desired during a compression process, even though the work input for given pressure limits is increased. This is the case in a simple gas-turbine power plant where immediately after compression the gas is to be heated by means of fuel. For this application a reversible adiabatic compression is the most desirable from the standpoint of over-all plant efficiency. (See Chapter 17.)

Comparisons between actual and ideal compressor performance are expressed by compressor efficiencies. We have seen above that the ideal compression process may be either reversible isothermal, polytropic, or isentropic, so care must be taken to use the proper ideal process as a basis of comparison in any particular case. We will introduce here only one compressor efficiency, the *adiabatic compressor efficiency*, which is defined by

$$\eta_C \equiv \frac{\text{work of } \textit{reversible adiabatic } \text{compression from state 1 to } p_2}{\text{work of } \textit{actual adiabatic } \text{compression from state 1 to } p_2}$$

Slightly different definitions are also in use. For the ideal compression the kinetic energy change is often considered to be negligible. Referring to Fig. 16·2 and applying the first law, we have

$$\eta_C = \frac{\text{input work}_i}{\text{input work}_a} = \frac{h_{2i} - h_1}{h_{2a} - h_1 + \dfrac{V_{2a}^2 - V_1^2}{2g_c}} = \frac{h_{2i} - h_1}{h_{t2a} - h_1}$$

If there is no change in kinetic energy, then

$$\eta_C = \frac{h_{2i} - h_1}{h_{2a} - h_1}$$

Following a practice which is rather general, especially in the gas-turbine

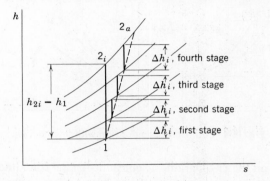

Fig. 16·3 Multistage compression.

literature, we shall in this book use the term *compressor efficiency*, without modifiers, to mean *adiabatic compressor efficiency* as defined above. Remember that this parameter is useful only in connection with adiabatic compressors.

Multistage compressors consist of two or more compressors, each of which is called a *stage*, in series. If each stage operates adiabatically, and there is no heat transfer from the gas as it passes from one stage to another, the entire compressor operates adiabatically. Then we can apply the definition of (adiabatic) compressor efficiency to individual stages and to the entire compressor. It should be noticed, however, that, if the efficiency of each stage is the same (and not 100 per cent), the efficiency of the entire compressor is less than that of the stages. This can be seen by reference to Fig. 16·3 which shows the actual adiabatic compression path through a four-stage compressor. Let $\Delta KE = 0$ for each stage, and therefore for the compressor. If each stage has the same efficiency, the ratio $\Delta h_i / \Delta h_a$ is the same for each stage. For the entire compressor the efficiency is $(h_{2i}-h_1)/(h_{2a}-h_1)$. Notice that $h_{2a}-h_1 = \Sigma\,\Delta h_a$, but, on account of the divergence of constant-pressure lines on the diagram in the direction of increasing entropy, $h_{2i}-h_1 < \Sigma\,\Delta h_i$; therefore, the efficiency of the entire compressor is less than that of the individual stages.

Multistaging of compressors is sometimes used to allow for cooling between the stages to reduce the total work input. Gas can be cooled more effectively in heat exchangers called intercoolers between stages than during the compression process. Figure 16·4 shows a polytropic compression process 1-a. If $\Delta KE = 0$, the work done on the gas is represented by the

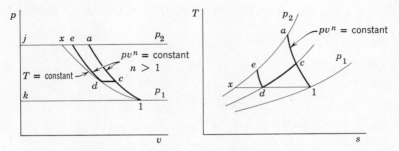

Fig. 16·4 Multistage compression with intercooling.

area 1-a-j-k-1 on the pv diagram. A constant-temperature line is shown as 1-x. If the polytropic compression from state 1 to p_2 is divided into two parts, 1-c and d-e, with constant pressure cooling to $T_d = T_1$ between them, the work done is represented by area 1-c-d-e-j-k-1. The area c-a-e-d-c represents the work saved by means of the two-stage compression with intercooling to the initial temperature.

Inspection of Fig. 16·4 indicates that for specified values of p_1 and p_2 there is an optimum pressure for intercooling. (This conclusion is suggested by reflection on extreme cases. If the process proceeds for a very short distance along the polytropic path before intercooling, or if it proceeds almost to a before intercooling, the work saved in either case is small compared to that saved with an interstage pressure such as shown in Fig. 16·4.) Call the optimum interstage pressure p_i, so that, for two stages with $\Delta KE = 0$,

$$w_{\text{in}} = \int_1^{p_i} v\,dp + \int_{p_i}^{p_2} v\,dp$$

Expansion of this equation for the case of $pv^n = $ constant and then the setting of $dw/dp_i = 0$ to find the conditions for minimum work shows that, if the intercooling brings the gas to its initial temperature, the minimum work input is required when $p_2/p_i = p_i/p_1$, or when the work is the same for the two stages. Further analysis shows that no matter how many stages there are, minimum work input is required when the total work is divided equally among the stages. The pressure ratio is then the same for each stage.

Another means of reducing the work required to compress a gas is to inject a liquid into the gas being compressed. As it evaporates, the liquid takes energy from the gas and thereby reduces the gas temperature rise.

EXAMPLE 16·1.   A compressor operates with inlet air at 14 psia, 70 F, and a pressure ratio (i.e., ratio of discharge pressure to inlet pressure) of 3. Kinetic energy changes are negligible. The compressor efficiency is 70 per cent. Determine the irreversibility per pound of air.

Analysis. We will calculate the irreversibility as $i = T_0 \Delta s$. Since no information to the contrary is given, we will assume that the temperature of the inlet air is the temperature of the surrounding atmosphere which can be considered the sink temperature. In order to calculate Δs, we must determine the end states of the process. The final state can be determined from the initial state and the work done, since the process is adiabatic. The work done can be obtained from the ideal (isentropic) work and the compressor efficiency. The ideal work can be obtained by means of the first law and the ideal-gas enthalpy–temperature relationship after the ideal end state temperature is calculated. For the small temperature range likely to be encountered we will use constant values of $c_p = 0.24$ B/lb-F and $k = 1.4$. (The calculations can also be made using air tables, but for the limited temperature range involved there is but a slight gain in accuracy.)

Solution. Following the procedure outlined in the analysis above,

$$T_{2i} = T_1 \left(\frac{p_2}{p_1}\right)^{(k-1)/k} = 530(3)^{0.286} = 725 \text{ R}$$

$$\text{Input work}_i = h_{2i} - h_1 = c_p(T_{2i} - T_1) = 0.24(725 - 530) = 46.8 \text{ B/lb}$$

$$\text{Input work}_a = \frac{\text{input work}_i}{\eta_C} = \frac{46.8}{0.7} = 66.9 \text{ B/lb}$$

$$T_{2a} - T_1 = \frac{h_{2a} - h_1}{c_p} = \frac{\text{input work}_a}{c_p} = \frac{66.9}{0.24} = 278 \text{ F degrees}$$

$$T_{2a} = T_1 + 278 = 530 + 278 = 808 \text{ R}$$

$$\Delta s = s_{2a} - s_1 = \int_1^{2a} ds = \int_1^{2a} \frac{dh}{T} - \int_1^{2a} \frac{v \, dp}{T} = c_p \ln \frac{T_{2a}}{T_1} - R \ln \frac{p_2}{p_1}$$

$$= 0.24 \ln \frac{808}{530} - \frac{53.3}{778} \ln 3 = 0.0266 \text{ B/lb-R}$$

$$i = T_0 \Delta s = 530(0.0266) = 14.1 \text{ B/lb}$$

This result means that, of the 66.9 B/lb of energy added to the air as work, 14.1 B/lb can never be reconverted into work. For the reversible process used as a standard of comparison and involved in the definition of compressor efficiency, only 46.8 B/lb of work is required, and of course it can all be reconverted into work by reversing the process. The difference between the actual work and the ideal work is greater than the irreversibility because some of the additional work required by the actual process can be reconverted into work after the actual process has occurred.

16·2   Steady-flow expansion processes

The process in a turbine or expansion engine is usually adiabatic because the heat addition process in a steady-flow power plant is usually separate from the expansion process. Furthermore, the expansion machine is insulated to prevent heat loss to the surroundings which would reduce the work output. The ideal process used as a basis of comparison is therefore the reversible adiabatic or isentropic process between the same initial state and the same final total pressure.

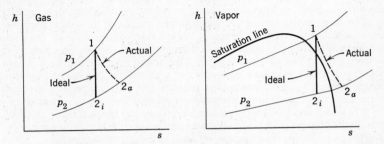

Fig. 16·5 Reversible and irreversible adiabatic expansion.

Adiabatic turbine efficiency, which we will call simply *turbine efficiency* or the efficiency of a turbine, is defined as

$$\eta_T \equiv \frac{\text{work of } \textit{actual adiabatic} \text{ expansion}}{\substack{\text{work of } \textit{reversible adiabatic} \text{ expansion between same} \\ \text{initial state and same final total pressure}}}$$

This term is also used in connection with positive-displacement expansion machines such as steam engines and compressed-air motors. It has also been called engine efficiency, and slightly different definitions are occasionally found. Applying the first law, we have

$$\eta_T = \frac{\text{work}_a}{\text{work}_i} = \frac{h_1 - h_{2a} + \dfrac{V_1^2 - V_{2a}^2}{2g_c}}{h_1 - h_{2i} + \dfrac{V_1^2 - V_{2i}^2}{2g_c}} = \frac{h_{t1} - h_{t2a}}{h_{t1} - h_{t2i}}$$

where state 2_i is one for which the entropy is the same as at state 1 and the total pressure is the same as at the actual exhaust condition. If there is no change in kinetic energy, then

$$\eta_T = \frac{h_1 - h_{2a}}{h_1 - h_{2i}}$$

Actual and ideal expansion paths are shown in Fig. 16·5 for an ideal gas and for a vapor.

The efficiency of a multistage turbine can be higher than the efficiency of any of its stages. For an illustration of this point, refer to Fig. 16·6 which shows the adiabatic expansion path through a four-stage turbine. Let $\Delta KE = 0$ for each stage and therefore for the entire turbine. If each stage has the same efficiency, the ratio $\Delta h_a / \Delta h_i$ is the same for each stage. For the entire turbine, $h_1 - h_{2a} = \Sigma \Delta h_a$, but, on account of the divergence of

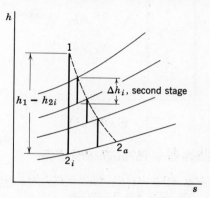

Fig. 16·6   Multistage expansion.

constant-pressure lines on the diagram in the direction of increasing entropy, $h_1 - h_{2i} < \Sigma \Delta h_i$; consequently, the efficiency of the entire turbine is higher than that of the individual stages. This paradoxical behavior is sometimes referred to as the *reheat effect*, although this term is a misnomer because the entire process under consideration is adiabatic.

EXAMPLE 16·2.   Determine the exhaust temperature of an air turbine which operates adiabatically between 70 psia, 1540 F, and 15 psia with an efficiency of 80 per cent and no change in kinetic energy.

Solution. An hs diagram showing the actual process and the corresponding ideal process is made first. To avoid the trouble of finding mean specific heats for these expansions we will use the Keenan and Kaye *Gas Tables* (or Table A·8 in the appendix). To determine the ideal exhaust condition,

$$p_{r2i} = p_{r1}\frac{p_2}{p_1} = 174.00(\tfrac{15}{70}) = 37.3$$

$$h_{2i} = f(p_{r2i}) = 329.7 \text{ B/lb}$$

Then from the definition of turbine efficiency,

$$h_1 - h_{2a} = \eta_T(h_1 - h_{2i})$$

$$h_{2a} = h_1 - \eta_T(h_1 - h_{2i})$$

$$= 504.7 - 0.8(504.7 - 329.7) = 364.7 \text{ B/lb}$$

From the tables,

$$T_{2a} = f(h_{2a}) = 1483 \text{ R} = 1023 \text{ F}$$

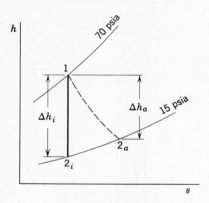

Example 16·2

16·3 Incompressible flow through machines

Consider the steady flow of an incompressible ($\rho = $ constant) fluid through a machine. The first law becomes

$$q - w = u_2 - u_1 + p_2v - p_1v + \Delta KE + \Delta PE \qquad (a)$$

If the process is also reversible,

$$-w = \int v\,dp + \Delta KE + \Delta PE \qquad (1\cdot10)$$

$$= (p_2 - p_1)v + \Delta KE + \Delta PE \qquad (b)$$

Comparison of equations (a) and (b) shows that, for reversible incompressible steady flow $q - \Delta u = 0$. If the process is irreversible, then $q - \Delta u \neq 0$, but the heat transfer and internal energy change are usually small and difficult to measure in comparison with the other energy quantities in equations (a) and (b); therefore the quantity ($q - \Delta u$) in incompressible flow is occasionally given a name such as "friction loss" or "head loss due to friction" and is measured indirectly by measuring all the other quantities in an energy balance such as equation (a).

Incompressible flow analyses are not restricted to liquids. A gas or vapor can be treated as incompressible if its density changes very little during a process.* For example, atmospheric air flowing through a fan and undergoing an over-all pressure change of a few inches of water can be treated as incompressible because its density change is so small. The greater the density change is, the greater are the errors which result from treating the flow as incompressible.

It must also be remembered that liquids are not entirely incompressible: Their densities are affected by pressure, and for large pressure differences isentropic pumping may cause appreciable changes in temperature. For water, Fig. 3 of the Keenan and Keyes steam tables (*Thermodynamic Properties of Steam*) is an *hs* diagram for compressed liquid which is convenient for determining enthalpy and temperature changes in isentropic processes.

Pump and fan efficiencies for incompressible flow are defined just as compressor efficiency is except that for incompressible flow the kinetic energy change is always the same for the actual and the ideal processes. Thus

$$\eta_p \equiv \frac{\text{input work}_i}{\text{input work}_a} = \frac{v\,\Delta p + \Delta KE + \Delta PE}{v\,\Delta p + \Delta KE + \Delta PE + \Delta u - q}$$

For an actual pump (or fan) the numerator is evaluated by measurements of pressure, velocity, elevation, etc. and the denominator is obtained by power and flow rate measurements from which the actual work input can be calculated. (The shaft input work to a pump exceeds the work done on the fluid at least by the work required to overcome bearing and shaft seal friction.)

The term *head* which is frequently used in connection with pumps, fans, and hydraulic turbines refers to an energy quantity per unit mass or per unit weight. When energy is expressed on a unit weight basis, units such as ft-lb$_f$/lb$_f$ can be reduced to a unit of length alone, so expressions like "a velocity head of 40 ft" (meaning kinetic energy of 40 ft-lb$_f$/lb weight) are common. For most engineering analyses, treating the weight of a given mass of substance as constant is satisfactory, but in a varying gravitational field (as in a high-altitude vehicle) it is much simpler to use a mass basis instead of a weight basis.

An important phenomenon in the flow of liquids is *cavitation*. Changes in the velocity of a liquid flowing through a passage are accompanied by pressure changes. If the pressure is lowered to the saturation pressure

---

* It has been suggested that such flows be referred to as *uncompressed* rather than *incompressible*. This terminology has not been widely adopted, but it is mentioned for its descriptive value.

corresponding to the liquid temperature, vapor bubbles form. If these bubbles are then carried by the stream to a region where the pressure is higher than the vapor pressure, they collapse. This alternate formation and collapse of vapor bubbles in a flowing liquid is called *cavitation*. When the bubbles collapse on a solid wall of a flow passage such as a pump rotor, very high impact pressures are exerted on minute areas of the wall and serious damage to the wall may result. Also, the vapor bubbles may disrupt the liquid flow to the detriment of the over-all performance of the machine.

16·4   Energy transfer between a fluid and a rotor

In order to understand the performance of turbomachines, it is necessary to understand the mechanism of energy transfer between a fluid and a rotor. A working knowledge of this subject cannot be obtained from a

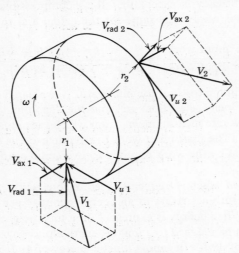

Fig. 16·7   Flow entering and leaving a rotor.

discussion as limited in scope as the one in this article, but we derive the general equations for the torque and the work transfer between a fluid and a rotor for steady one-dimensional flow in order to give you a picture of the general mechanism which is involved. Flow through a rotor is usually two- or three-dimensional, but for simplicity we restrict our attention here to one-dimensional flow which in many cases is a satisfactory approximation.

Consider the flow of a fluid through a rotating rotor as shown in the general diagram of Fig. 16·7. Some particular types of rotors are shown in

Fig. 16·8 to illustrate that the general diagram of Fig. 16·7 applies to various rotor types which differ markedly from each other. (In none of these rotors is the flow one-dimensional except as an approximation.) The linear velocity of any point on the rotor is u. The radius to any point is r, and the angular velocity of the rotor is ω, so that $u = r\omega$. The fluid velocity V at any point has three mutually perpendicular components:

V_{rad}, the radial component.
V_{ax}, the axial component (parallel to the rotor axis of rotation).
V_u, the tangential component.

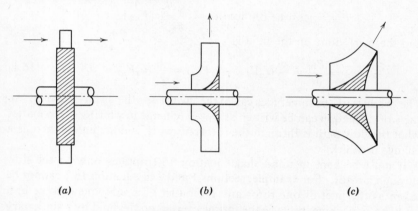

(a)   (b)   (c)

Fig. 16·8   Types of rotors.

The torque of the fluid on the rotor is equal and opposite in sign to the torque of the rotor on the fluid. The net torque on the fluid is equal to the time rate of change of angular momentum of the fluid. The angular momentum with respect to the axis of rotation of a mass m of fluid entering is mr_1V_{u1}, and that of a mass m of fluid leaving is mr_2V_{u2}. For this mass m the change in angular momentum is $m(r_2V_{u2}-r_1V_{u1})$, and for steady flow the rate of change of angular momentum is $M(r_2V_{u2}-r_1V_{u1})$. Thus, for the steady flow of a fluid the basic relation of mechanics,

$$\text{Torque} = \frac{1}{g_c}\frac{d}{d\tau}(mrV_u)$$

becomes $$\text{Torque on fluid} = \frac{1}{g_c}M(r_2V_{u2} - r_1V_{u1})$$

This is the basic dynamic equation for the steady one-dimensional flow through a rotor. (Remember that one-dimensional means that properties are uniform in any cross section normal to the direction of flow; it does not restrict the flow to a constant direction.) The fluid pressure does not appear in the torque equation because the pressure does not vary circumferentially. It is important to notice that, no matter what the path inside the rotor is, the net torque depends only on the flow rate, the inlet and outlet radii, and the tangential components of the fluid velocity at inlet and outlet. The inlet and outlet velocities depend on the flow rate, the rotor speed, and the rotor geometry, but this dependence is not a simple one because the velocities at inlet and outlet are not necessarily tangent to the rotor vanes or blades.

The power delivered to the fluid by a rotor is

$$P_{\text{in}} = (\text{torque on fluid})\omega = \frac{M\omega}{g_c}(r_2 V_{u2} - r_1 V_{u1})$$

and the work done on the fluid is

$$w_{\text{in}} = \frac{P_{\text{in}}}{M} = \frac{\omega}{g_c}(r_2 V_{u2} - r_1 V_{u1}) = \frac{1}{g_c}(u_2 V_{u2} - u_1 V_{u1}) \qquad (16\cdot1)$$

The product uV_u is sometimes called the "whirl" or the "whirl velocity," so the work equation can be written as $w_{\text{in}} = (\text{change in whirl})/g_c$. No matter what the flow path is through the rotor, no work is done unless there is a change in whirl.

It must be kept in mind that equation 16·1 applies only to the flow through a rotor. For example, sections 1 and 2 in equation 16·1 cannot be taken as the inlet of one rotor and the outlet of a subsequent rotor in a multistage machine, because the torque exerted on the fluid by a stationary part of the machine does no work on the fluid. The change in the product uV_u between the inlet and outlet of an entire machine, in fact, is often zero.

In addition to the above equation for work which was derived from dynamic considerations, the first law may be used to determine the work done on a fluid by a rotor. If the process is reversible, we can also use the expression

$$w_{\text{in}} = \int v\, dp + \Delta KE + \Delta PE \qquad (1\cdot10)$$

This equation and the first law can also be applied to the flow through a rotor with the frame of reference fixed to the rotor. In such a frame of reference, or from the viewpoint of an observer moving with the rotor, there is no work done, and of course the velocities used must be velocities relative to the rotor. The first law and equation 1·10 become

$$q = h_2 - h_1 + \frac{V_{r2}^2 - V_{r1}^2}{2g_c} + \Delta PE$$

and

$$0 = \int v\, dp + \frac{V_{r2}^2 - V_{r1}^2}{2g_c} + \Delta PE$$

where V_r designates a velocity relative to the rotor. The flow through a rotor is usually adiabatic, and the change in potential energy across the rotor is zero or negligible except in the case of some large hydraulic turbines.

The continuity equation can also be applied to the flow through a rotor if relative velocities are used in connection with flow areas in the rotor. Thus the basic relations (in addition to physical property relationships) which are useful in analyzing the one-dimensional steady flow through turbomachine rotors and in designing such rotors are (1) the torque and work equations derived in this article, (2) the first law, (3) equation 1·10, and (4) the continuity equation. From these basic relations many special forms useful for particular phases of analysis and design can be derived. These are treated in books on pumps, compressors, turbines, and turbo-machines in general.

16·5 Dynamic compressors

A fundamental difference between the flow through turbines and the flow through pumps and compressors must be recognized. In all flows of a fluid through a passage, shearing forces at the wall retard the fluid near the wall in a region called the boundary layer. In turbines, the pressure generally decreases in the direction of flow and thus the pressure gradient, acting oppositely to the wall shearing forces, tends to prevent the retardation of fluid in the boundary layer. In pumps and compressors, however, there is an adverse pressure gradient (i.e., pressure increases in the direction of flow) which acts with the wall shearing forces to reduce the fluid velocity near the wall. These two actions together may reduce the velocity to zero near the wall and then the adverse pressure gradient may cause the flow to reverse direction near the wall. This phenomenon is called *separation* and is highly detrimental to the performance of fluid machines. The design of pumps and compressors is therefore greatly influenced by the necessity to limit the magnitude of adverse pressure gradients which tend to cause separation.

Both centrifugal and axial-flow compressors are comprised of two parts: a rotor which does work on the fluid, increasing its kinetic energy and its pressure, and a stator which at least serves as a diffuser to reduce the velocity of the fluid and increase its pressure. The stator may also serve to redirect the fluid into following rotors or into a collector which leads to the machine outlet. Work is done on a fluid passing through a compressor only by the rotor, but in the stator or diffuser there is a decrease in kinetic energy, so the enthalpy increases in both the rotor and the stator. The fraction of the over-all increase in enthalpy which occurs in the rotor is called the *degree of reaction*.

Figure 16·9 shows hs and h_ts diagrams for one stage, including rotor and stator, of either a centrifugal or axial-flow compressor operating isentropically. Process 1-2 occurs in the rotor, and process 2-3 occurs in the stator or stationary diffuser. In a centrifugal compressor the stationary diffuser may have vanes which form diverging passages or it may be a vaneless

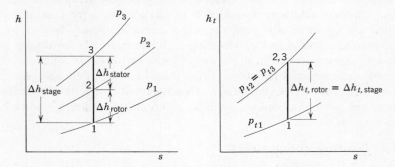

Fig. 16·9 Isentropic compression in a single stage.

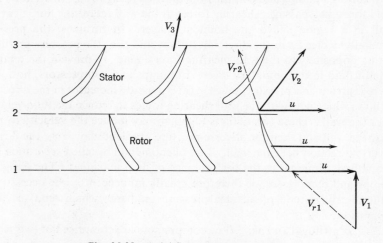

Fig. 16·10 Axial-flow compressor stage.

annular passage through which the fluid spirals outward with decreasing velocity and increasing pressure. In an axial-flow compressor the stator of each stage is comprised of a row of vanes which form diverging flow passages. Details can be found in the specialized literature.

To illustrate the application of the basic dynamic equation to an axial-flow machine, a developed view of an axial-flow compressor stage is shown in Fig. 16·10. The cylindrical surfaces to which the rotor and stator blades are attached are flattened into the plane of this figure. Velocity vectors relative to the moving blades are shown as broken lines. Since the inlet and outlet of the rotor blade passages are at the same distance from the rotor axis of rotation, $u_2 = u_1$. The work done by the rotor on the fluid is then, from equation 16·1,

$$w_{in} = \frac{1}{g_c}(u_2 V_{u2} - u_1 V_{u1}) = \frac{u}{g_c}(V_{u2} - V_{u1})$$

The work per stage is proportional to the change in the tangential component of velocity across the rotor. The more the fluid stream is turned by the rotor blades, the greater the work and the pressure ratio per stage. The amount of turning which can be accomplished is limited by the occurrence of separation, so for high pressure ratios axial-flow compressors need many stages.

16·6 Turbines

The flow through turbines is usually adiabatic or very nearly so. A stage consists of at least one stationary row of blades or nozzles and at least one row of moving blades which are a part of the rotor. The *degree of reaction* is defined as the fraction of the total decrease in enthalpy which occurs across the rotor. A turbine with a zero degree of reaction is called an impulse turbine or sometimes a pure impulse turbine. In such a turbine the fluid is expanded to the stage exhaust pressure in stationary nozzles; then the pressure remains constant and kinetic energy decreases as the fluid does work on the rotor blades. The blades on the rotor of an impulse turbine form flow passages of approximately constant cross-sectional area, since changes in area would involve changes in pressure.

Both axial-flow and radial-flow turbines are in use, the latter usually in the smaller sizes. Many different types of flow paths through turbines are used for various reasons, but the basic dynamic equation for turbomachines (equation 16·1) and the other basic relations listed in Art. 16·4 apply in all cases.

To illustrate the application of the basic dynamic equation to an axial-flow turbine stage, Fig. 16·11 shows a developed view of such a stage. Fluid enters the stationary nozzles with a low velocity V_1, is expanded, and leaves with a higher velocity V_2. Relative to the moving blades, this nozzle exit velocity is V_{r2}. Within the moving blade passages, the fluid is further expanded so that its velocity relative to the rotor blades increases from V_{r2} to V_{r3}. The absolute velocity decreases across the rotor; that is, $V_3 < V_2$. The work done *by* the fluid is

$$w = \frac{1}{g_c}(uV_{u2} - uV_{u3}) = \frac{u}{g_c}(V_{u2} - V_{u3}) = \frac{u}{g_c}(V_{ru2} - V_{ru3})$$

Figure 16·12 is a diagram of an impulse stage. If there are no frictional effects, the pressure and the relative velocity do not change across the rotor.

For given inlet conditions and exhaust pressure, maximum work is obtained from the fluid passing through a turbine stage if the kinetic energy (based on absolute velocity) of the fluid leaving the stage is a minimum. Inspection of the velocity vector diagrams in Figs. 16·11 and 16·12 shows

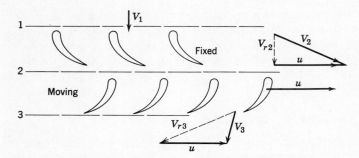

Fig. 16·11   Axial-flow turbine stage.

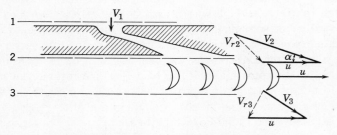

Fig. 16·12   Axial-flow impulse turbine stage.

that for a given blade shape (or a given degree of reaction) the leaving kinetic energy can be minimized by the proper selection of the ratio u/V_{u2} or $u/(V_2 \cos \alpha)$. For an impulse stage the optimum value of this ratio is 0.5. The optimum value increases as the degree of reaction increases. The blade speed u of a turbine is limited by centrifugal stresses in the rotor. Therefore, maintaining the optimum value of $u/V_2 \cos \alpha$ limits the pressure or enthalpy decrease across a stage. This is the reason for multistaging of turbines. Several ingenious arrangements of fixed nozzles and moving and stationary blades are in use for increasing the allowable enthalpy drop across a single stage. Descriptions of these can be found under the headings of *reentry stages* and *Curtis stage* in books on turbines, several of which are listed at the end of this chapter.

16·7 Reciprocating machines

In analyzing the processes which occur in the cylinder of a reciprocating machine, we deal with a closed system when the cylinder valves are closed and with transient flow in an open system the rest of the time. As pointed out in Art. 1·15, the flow through a reciprocating machine can be treated as steady if the properties at various points within the system vary cyclically; but it is often difficult to arrive at average values of the properties. Furthermore, in designing a reciprocating machine it is necessary to analyze the processes which occur in a cylinder. A convenient diagram in such analyses is a pV diagram such as the one shown in Fig. 16·13 for an

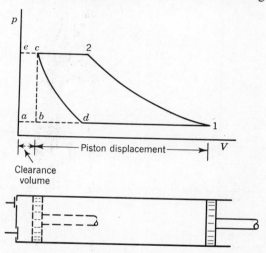

Fig. 16·13 pV diagram for an ideal reciprocating gas compressor.

ideal reciprocating gas compressor. This compressor is ideal in that the pressure and temperature are uniform throughout the cylinder, the valves act instantaneously, and there is no pressure drop across the valves while gas is flowing through them. The abscissa is the volume of gas within the cylinder. The mass of gas in the cylinder varies, so p and V do not define the state of the gas. Therefore, gas at a given pressure and temperature may be represented by many different points on the pV diagram.

For the compressor operation illustrated by Fig. 16·13, all valves are closed as the piston travels from point 1 to point 2, so path 1-2 is a closed-system process. When the piston reaches point 2, the pressure inside the cylinder is sufficient to open the discharge valve against the pressure of the gas in the discharge line. As the piston moves from point 2 to point c, gas is pushed out of the cylinder at constant pressure and constant temperature. Point c is the end of the piston stroke. The remaining volume in the cylinder V_c is called the *clearance volume*. The volume swept by the piston during its entire stroke $(V_1 - V_c)$ is called the *piston displacement*, and the volume V_1 is called the *cylinder volume*. The per cent clearance is defined as the ratio of the clearance volume to the piston displacement. As the piston moves back to the right from point c, the gas which was trapped in the clearance volume at the discharge pressure expands. The intake valve

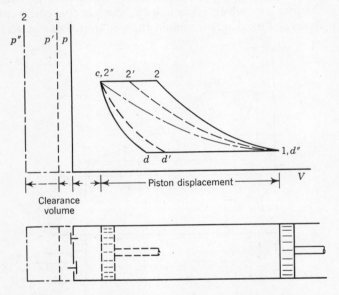

Fig. 16·14   Influence of clearance volume on volumetric efficiency.

does not open until the pressure inside the cylinder reaches the intake pressure. This occurs at point d. From point d to point 1 gas is being drawn into the cylinder.

The volume of gas, measured at p_1, which is drawn in is less than the piston displacement. Volumetric efficiency η_{vol} is defined as

$$\eta_{vol} \equiv \frac{\text{mass of gas drawn in per stroke}}{\substack{\text{mass of gas at intake line pressure and} \\ \text{temperature required to fill piston displacement}}}$$

If p_1 equals the intake line pressure, $\eta_{vol} = (V_1 - V_d)/(V_1 - V_c)$. In an actual compressor, p_1 is lower than the pressure in the intake line on account of the throttling of the gas through the intake valve. (For an air compressor, the intake line pressure may be lower than the ambient pressure on account of pressure drop through intake filters.)

If the compression 1-2 and the expansion c-d are both polytropic with the same value of n in $pv^n =$ constant, the amount of clearance has no effect on the amount of work done per pound of gas delivered.

Increasing the clearance decreases the volumetric efficiency of a reciprocating compressor. The compressor of Fig. 16·14 has a fixed stroke and piston displacement, but the cylinder can be extended to increase the

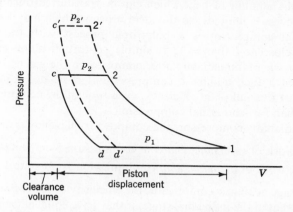

Fig. 16·15   Influence of discharge pressure on volumetric efficiency.

clearance volume. As the clearance volume increases, the pressure axis of the pV diagram must be moved to the left. Three different values of clearance volume are illustrated. For the minimum clearance shown, the pV diagram is 1-2-c-d-1. If the clearance is increased, the pressure axis must be moved to the left to a position such as shown for the axis marked p'. The pV diagram is then 1-2'-c-d'-1. The volume of gas inducted per stroke has decreased from $(V_1 - V_d)$ to $(V_1 - V_{d'})$, so the volumetric efficiency has decreased. If the clearance is increased further, a value will be reached for which the pressure of the gas in the cylinder reaches the discharge pressure just at the end of the stroke. Thus no gas is delivered and, if the processes are reversible, the gas expands along the same path during the return stroke of the piston and no gas is drawn in. The pressure axis for this case is marked p''. Points 2″ and c on the pV diagram coincide, and so do points d'' and 1. The volumetric efficiency is zero. The delivery of constant-speed compressors is sometimes regulated by changing the clearance. This is done by valves which open and close auxiliary chambers connected to the clearance volume of the cylinder.

Inspection of Fig. 16·15 shows that, for constant suction pressure, increasing the discharge pressure decreases the volumetric efficiency. With discharge pressure p_2, gas is inducted along the line d-1; but, with the higher discharge pressure $p_{2'}$, the induction process is shortened to d'-1.

16·8 Summary

Minimum work is required to compress a gas from a given initial state to a given final pressure if the compression is isothermal. In actual machines, the amount of heat which can be transferred during the compression process is limited; so the ideal process which may be simulated in an actual compressor is a polytropic process with the polytropic exponent n closer to k than to 1. In simple gas-turbine plants and in other applications where immediately after compression the gas is to be heated by means of a fuel, adiabatic compression is most desirable from the standpoint of over-all plant efficiency, even though the compression work is greater than for isothermal compression.

For an adiabatic compressor, the compressor efficiency is defined as

$$\eta_C \equiv \frac{\text{work of } \textit{reversible adiabatic} \text{ compression from state 1 to } p_2}{\text{work of } \textit{actual adiabatic} \text{ compression from state 1 to } p_2}$$

In a multistage adiabatic compressor, the efficiency of the entire machine is lower than that of the individual stages if they have equal efficiencies of less than 100 per cent.

If isothermal compression is impossible or impractical, as it usually is, a reduction in the work required for given pressure limits can be achieved by cooling the gas at constant pressure between stages. For polytropic compression with the same value of n in each stage and intercooling to the initial temperature, minimum total work is required when the pressure ratio is the same for each stage.

Adiabatic turbine efficiency, which we call simply *turbine efficiency* or the efficiency of a turbine, is defined as

$$\eta_T \equiv \frac{\text{work of } \textit{actual adiabatic} \text{ expansion}}{\begin{array}{c}\text{work of } \textit{reversible adiabatic} \text{ expansion between}\\ \text{same initial state and same final total pressure}\end{array}}$$

The efficiency of a multistage turbine can be higher than the efficiency of any of its stages.

The basic dynamic equation for the steady, one-dimensional flow of a fluid through a turbomachine rotor is

$$\text{Torque on fluid} = \frac{1}{g_c}M(r_2 V_{u2} - r_1 V_{u1})$$

where r is the radial distance from the axis of rotation, V_u is the tangential component of the fluid velocity, and subscripts 1 and 2 refer to inlet and outlet of the rotor. The work done on the fluid is

$$w_{in} = \frac{1}{g_c}(u_2 V_{u2} - u_1 V_{u1}) \tag{16.1}$$

where u is the linear velocity of a point on the rotor.

The degree of reaction of a turbomachine stage is defined as the fraction of the enthalpy change in a stage which occurs in the rotor.

In analyzing the performance of a reciprocating machine, it must be remembered that the piston and the cylinder walls enclose a closed system part of the time and form most of the boundary of an open transient-flow system at other times during a cycle.

The work done by an ideal reciprocating compressor is the same per pound of gas delivered regardless of the amount of clearance in the machine, but the amount of gas delivered per stroke is decreased as the clearance increases. Increasing the discharge pressure also decreases the amount of gas delivered per stroke.

REFERENCES

16·1 S. A. Moss, C. W. Smith, and W. R. Foote, "Energy Transfer between a Fluid and a Rotor for Pump and Turbine Machinery," *Transactions ASME*, vol. 64, August 1942, pp. 567–597.

16·2 J. F. Lee, *Theory and Design of Steam and Gas Turbines*, McGraw-Hill Book Co., 1954.

16·3 B. H. Jennings and W. L. Rogers, *Gas Turbine Analysis and Practice*, McGraw-Hill Book Co., 1953.

16·4 H. A. Sorensen, *Gas Turbines*, Ronald Press, 1951.

16·5 V. W. Young, *Basic Thermodynamics*, McGraw-Hill Book Co., 1952, arts. 9:9 to 9:11 (on reciprocating machines).

16·6 V. M. Faires, *Thermodynamics*, Macmillan Co., 3d ed., 1957, chapter 19 (on steam engines).

PROBLEMS

16·1 Air at 30 psia, 300 F, is to be produced from air at 14.5 psia, 70 F, by isentropic compression and constant-pressure heating. Calculate the work required per pound of air if (*a*) the isentropic compression precedes the heating, and (*b*) the isentropic compression follows the heating.

16·2 Solve Prob. 16·1 with the compression for each case being adiabatic with an efficiency of 70 per cent.

16·3   An ideal gas with constant specific heats is to be compressed from p_1 and T_1 to a state at p_2 and the same temperature. Consider two methods for doing this: (a) isentropic compression from state 1 to p_2 followed by constant-pressure cooling to the initial temperature, and (b) constant-pressure cooling from state 1 to a temperature T_c, isentropic compression to p_2, and then constant-pressure cooling to the initial temperature. Sketch the processes on a Ts diagram and calculate (in terms of p_1, p_2, T_1, T_c, and properties of the gas) the amount of work that can be saved by the proper choice of method.

16·4   Air is compressed from 14.7 psia, 70 F, to 50 psia, 250 F, in a centrifugal compressor at a rate of 50 lb/min. The rise in temperature of the cooling water flowing through the jacket is 7 F for a flow rate of 50 lb/min. Compute the power required to operate the compressor. Neglect the change in kinetic energy.

16·5   An air compressor uses a lubricating oil having a flash point of 350 F. If air is taken in at 15 psia, 60 F, and compressed polytropically with an exponent of 1.35, what is the maximum allowable discharge pressure if the maximum allowable temperature is 50 F below the flash point of the oil?

16·6   An ideal centrifugal compressor compresses air polytropically, with $n = 1.35$, at a rate of 5 lb/sec from 15 psia, 40 F, to 45 psia. Inlet velocity is negligibly small while the discharge velocity is 600 fps. Heat is removed from the air being compressed at a rate of 20 B/sec. Calculate the compressor power requirement.

16·7   An ideal centrifugal air compressor takes in 10,000 cfm of air at 15 psia, 40 F, with negligible velocity. It compresses the air polytropically with $n = 1.35$ and discharges it at 30 psia with a velocity of 600 fps. Calculate the power input to the compressor.

16·8   Determine the total amount of work required by a compressor which draws in air at 14.0 psia, 80 F, and compresses it isentropically to raise the pressure to 42 psia in a 20-cu-ft insulated tank which initially contains air at 14.0 psia, 80 F.

16·9   The temperature of the air entering an axial-flow compressor is 520 R. If the pressure ratio is 3 and the compression is adiabatic, compute the discharge temperature of the air for the following compressor efficiencies: (a) 100 per cent, (b) 90 per cent, and (c) 80 per cent.

16·10   Determine the power required to compress air adiabatically at a rate of 12,000 cfm (measured at the inlet) from 14.5 psia, 75 F, to 35 psia with an efficiency of 72 per cent.

16·11   Air is compressed adiabatically from 14.5 psia, 80 F, to 85 psia, 500 F. Kinetic energy changes are negligible. Determine the compressor efficiency.

16·12   Determine the irreversibility of the steady-flow adiabatic compression of air initially at 14.7 psia, 80 F, through a pressure ratio of 5 if the compressor efficiency is 74 per cent.

16·13   A two-stage compressor draws in 300 cfm of air at 14.3 psia and compresses it polytropically with $n = 1.3$ to 143 psia. The intercooler cools the air to its initial temperature before it enters the second stage. How much work does two-stage compression save in comparison with compression in a single stage with the same value of n?

16·14   Is it true that for a turbine operating on an ideal gas with constant specific heats the work output for a given pressure ratio is proportional to the inlet gas absolute temperature? Prove your answer.

16·15 Air enters a turbine at 88.2 psia, 1660 R. If the final pressure is 14.7 psia, compute the exhaust temperature of the gases for the following turbine efficiencies: (a) 100 per cent, (b) 90 per cent, and (c) 80 per cent.

16·16 Solve Prob. 16·15, using constant specific heats, and compare your results with those of Prob. 16·15.

16·17 Determine the irreversibility of an adiabatic expansion of air from 73.5 psia, 1600 F, through a pressure ratio of 5 if the turbine efficiency is 78.5 per cent and the lowest temperature in the surroundings is 80 F.

16·18 Air enters a turbine at 83.0 psia, 1540 F, and expands adiabatically to 14.6 psia, 940 F, with negligible change in kinetic energy. Determine the turbine efficiency.

16·19 Determine the mass rate of flow through a turbine which takes in air at 75 psia, 1600 F, and exhausts at 15 psia if the flow is adiabatic with a turbine efficiency of 75 per cent and the power output is 1500 hp.

16·20 A three-stage gas turbine operating on air is to produce equal work per stage. Determine the intermediate stage pressures if the inlet conditions are 90 psia, 1800 F; the exhaust pressure is 15 psia; and the adiabatic efficiency for all parts of the expansion is 75 per cent.

16·21 Prove that, if a turbine discharges wet steam at the sink temperature, the product of $(1 - \eta_T)$ and the isentropic enthalpy drop between the initial condition and the exhaust pressure is equal to the irreversibility.

16·22 Determine the efficiency of a turbine which expands steam at a rate of 20,000 lb/hr from 200 psia, 440 F, to 5 psia, 90.5 per cent quality if the power output is 1560 hp.

16·23 Steam is supplied to a turbine at 200 psia, 600 F, and is exhausted at 14.7 psia. The flow is adiabatic, the power output of the turbine is 10,000 kw, and the turbine efficiency is 65 per cent. The lowest temperature in the surroundings is 80 F. Determine (a) the steam rate in lb/kwhr, and (b) the amount of energy made unavailable during the turbine expansion in B/lb.

16·24 Devise a single-stage turbine which can be made to rotate in either direction, the change in direction of rotation to be brought about by the movement of a single lever or valve. Explain its operation clearly by means of sketches or diagrams as well as words.

16·25 Two air streams are available for power production by expansion to 15 psia. One is at 30 psia, 600 F, and the other is at 30 psia, 1200 F. The flow rates are the same. For maximum power output, should the two streams be mixed and then expanded through a single turbine, or should each be expanded through a separate turbine without mixing? Prove your answer.

16·26 The water flow rate through a centrifugal pump running at 1200 rpm is 2 cfs. The inlet and discharge lines are 6 in. in diameter and are at the same elevation. The inlet pressure is 8 in. of mercury vacuum, and the discharge pressure is 20 psig. Power input to the pump is 20 hp. Barometric pressure is 29.0 in. of mercury. Determine the pump efficiency.

16·27 A fan draws air at 14.0 psia, 80 F, from a room at a rate of 6000 cfm and discharges it through a duct of 2.0-sq-ft cross-sectional area at a static gage pressure of 3.0 in. of water. The fan efficiency is 60 per cent. Determine the power input.

16·28 Consider a steam-turbine impulse stage. Steam enters the nozzle at 60 psia, 460 F, with a velocity of 500 fps and expands adiabatically through the nozzle to 40 psia, 400 F. The nozzle angle is 20 degrees. The blade velocity is 500 fps, and the symmetrical blades are so shaped that the steam enters the blades tangentially to the blade surface. The steam flow rate is 10,000 lb/hr. Sketch a complete vector diagram, and, neglecting friction in the blade passage, calculate (a) the kinetic energy of the steam leaving the turbine, and (b) the power output of the turbine.

16·29 Consider an ideal single-stage impulse turbine. Steam enters the nozzles at 100 psia, 400 F, with a velocity of 500 fps, and the exhaust pressure is 30 psia. Flow is frictionless and adiabatic. The blades are symmetrical, and the blade speed is 1000 fps. Steam leaving the nozzles makes an angle of 20 degrees with the line of blade motion. The flow rate is 100 lb/min. Sketch a complete accurate vector diagram for the stage, and calculate (a) the power output and (b) the kinetic energy of the steam leaving the blades. What change, if any, should be made in the blade speed to increase the stage efficiency?

16·30 An ideal reciprocating compressor draws in 200 cfm of air at 15 psia, 40 F, and compresses it polytropically with $n = 1.35$ to 75 psia. Cooling water which removes heat from the air flows at a rate of 10.2 lb/min and undergoes a temperature rise of 10 Fahrenheit degrees. Calculate the compressor power input.

16·31 A single-acting reciprocating compressor compresses air reversibly and adiabatically. The piston displacement is 1.0 cu ft, and there is 4.0 per cent clearance. The speed is 60 rpm. Suction pressure is 14.0 psia; discharge pressure is 70.0 psia. Ambient temperature is 60 F. Neglect pressure drop across the valves. Sketch a pV diagram and determine the volume of ambient air compressed per minute.

16·32 A single-stage air compressor having a clearance of 3 per cent takes in air at 14.2 psia, 60 F, and compresses it to 200 psia. If the mass of air compressed per minute is 50 lb, and n for both compression and expansion processes is 1.35, compute (a) the power required, (b) the piston displacement if the compressor operates at 100 rpm, and (c) the heat transferred to the water jacket.

16·33 Compute the power and the cylinder volume required to compress 500 cfm of ambient air to 120 psia. The atmospheric pressure is 14.7 psia, and the suction pressure is 14 psia. The clearance is 2.5 per cent, and the value of n during compression and expansion is 1.3. The compressor is double-acting and operates at 50 rpm.

16·34 Consider an ideal reciprocating gas compressor which operates with polytropic compression and with polytropic expansion of the clearance gas, but the polytropic exponents are not the same for the two processes. If the cylinder walls are generally cooler than the gas, for which process will the n be greater? In such a case, how does increasing the clearance affect the work done per pound of gas delivered?

CHAPTER 17

Gas Power Cycles

Nearly all systems which convert heat or the stored (chemical or nuclear) energy of a fuel into work use fluid working substances. One of the many ways in which such systems may be classified is according to whether the working fluid changes phase. In this chapter we consider power cycles in which a gas is the working substance, and in the next chapter we treat power cycles in which the working substance is alternately vaporized and condensed.

17·1 Air-standard analyses

An ideal system is simpler than the corresponding actual system in that it is described in terms of only a few characteristics instead of the many needed to describe the actual system fully. Depending on the nature and degree of simplification, several ideal systems can be devised to correspond to the same actual system. Likewise, an actual process or cycle can be simulated by several different ideal processes or cycles.

The processes which occur in a reciprocating internal-combustion engine and to a lesser degree those which occur in gas-turbine power plants are so complex that considerable simplification is required to make possible an elementary analysis. A common procedure in the study of gas power cycles is to use an *air-standard analysis*. In an air-standard analysis two idealizations are always made: (1) The working substance is air which behaves like an ideal gas, and (2) the combustion process is replaced by a heat-addition process. The second of these idealizations must accompany the first because the combustion of a fuel in the system would of course involve substances other than air in the system. In most actual gas turbines and all reciprocating internal-combustion engines, air is drawn in at ambient conditions, and gases at relatively high temperature are discharged. The system is an open one, and the same working fluid is not used repeatedly. In an air-standard analysis, however, the cycle is usually completed by a heat-rejection process which restores the fluid (which is taken to be air alone) to its initial state. Thus the same fluid is used repeatedly, and there is no exchange of mass with the surroundings.

A *cold air-standard analysis* involves the further simplification that the specific heats of air are constant at their room-temperature values. The cold air-standard analysis leads to very simple relations for quantities such as thermal efficiency, and these relations are often valuable as qualitative indications of cycle characteristics. For other purposes, more accurate quantitative results can so readily be obtained by means of an air-standard analysis using property values from air tables that there is little reason for the use of the cold air-standard analysis.

Sufficient data are published on the products of combustion of hydrocarbon fuels so that it is not difficult to eliminate the use of air as the ideal-gas power-cycle working substance. In the interest of brevity in this chapter, however, we will treat only air-standard power cycles.

17·2 The simple gas-turbine cycle

In the simple gas-turbine power plant shown in Fig. 17·1, air is drawn into the compressor and compressed adiabatically. Then fuel is mixed with the compressed air and burned in a combustion chamber. The air–fuel ratio is quite high in order to limit the temperature of the gas entering the turbine. The gases expand adiabatically to the ambient pressure in the turbine. Usually more than half the turbine power output is required to drive the compressor, and the rest of the turbine power output is the net power of the gas-turbine plant. An actual plant also requires auxiliary equipment such as starting motors, fuel pumps, lubricating oil pumps, ignition systems, and control and safety equipment.

The air-standard ideal-gas turbine cycle is called the Brayton* cycle or Joule cycle. Flow, *pv*, and *Ts* diagrams are shown in Fig. 17·2. Notice that the compression and expansion processes are isentropic, and the heat addition and heat rejection occur in reversible constant-pressure processes. (In sketching *Ts* and *hs* diagrams of gas-turbine cycles, show clearly the divergence of constant-pressure lines with increasing entropy to insure that the diagram indicates the Δh of the turbine expansion to be greater in magnitude than the Δh of compression. Otherwise, the turbine cannot drive the compressor and deliver work to the surroundings.)

Application of the first law to an air-standard gas-turbine cycle numbered

* George B. Brayton (1830–1892), American engineer, invented a breech-loading gun, a riveting machine, and a sectional steam generator in addition to the internal-combustion engine for which he is best remembered. The Brayton engine, developed around 1870, was a reciprocating oil-burning engine with fuel injection directly into the cylinder, and a compressor which was separate from the power cylinder. The Brayton cycle, which is now used only for gas turbines, was thus first used with reciprocating machines.

as in Fig. 17·2 shows the turbine work, compressor work, net work, and cycle efficiency to be given by

$$w_T = h_3 - h_4 + \frac{V_3^2 - V_4^2}{2g_c} = h_{t3} - h_{t4}$$

$$w_{\text{in},C} = h_2 - h_1 + \frac{V_2^2 - V_1^2}{2g_c} = h_{t2} - h_{t1}$$

$$w_{\text{cycle}} = w_T - w_{\text{in},C} = h_{t3} - h_{t4} - (h_{t2} - h_{t1})$$

$$\eta = \frac{w_{\text{cycle}}}{q_{2\text{-}3}} = \frac{h_{t3} - h_{t4} - (h_{t2} - h_{t1})}{h_{t3} - h_{t2}} = 1 - \frac{h_{t4} - h_{t1}}{h_{t3} - h_{t2}}$$

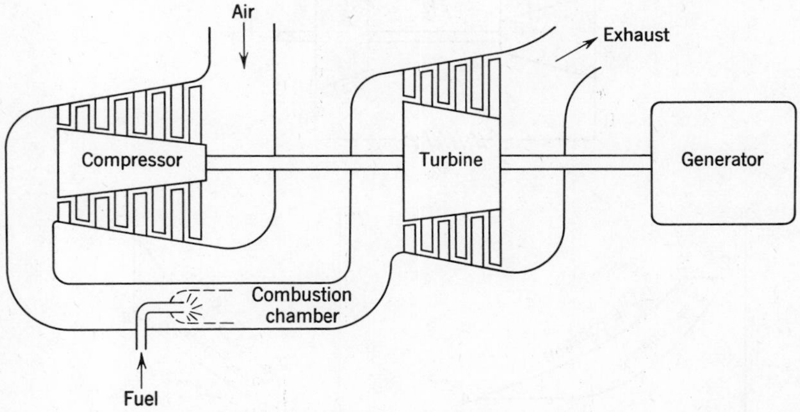

Fig. 17·1 Simple gas-turbine power plant.

For the *special case of constant specific heats* (i.e., the cold air-standard analysis), the last equation can be reduced to show that the thermal efficiency of the cycle is a function of the pressure ratio p_2/p_1 only.

The *back-work ratio*, defined as

$$\text{Back-work ratio} \equiv \frac{\text{compression work}_{\text{in}}}{\text{gross work of prime mover}} = \frac{w_{\text{in},C}}{w_T} = \frac{w_T - w_{\text{cycle}}}{w_T}$$

$$= 1 - \frac{w_{\text{cycle}}}{w_T}$$

is high for a gas-turbine cycle.* Consequently, the efficiency of the cycle

---

* Back-work ratio is sometimes defined as $w_{\text{in},C}/w_{\text{cycle}}$. As it is defined and used in this book, the limiting values are 0 and 1.

is reduced appreciably by relatively small reductions in compressor and turbine efficiencies. For example, suppose that the gross power output of a turbine is 9000 hp and the compressor requires an input power of 6000 hp so that the net power produced by the plant is 3000 hp. A reduction of 10 per cent in the compressor efficiency from 0.80 to 0.72 would increase the compressor power requirement to 6670 hp and would thereby reduce the plant power output by 22.3 per cent. (The plant thermal efficiency would not be decreased by 22.3 per cent because a decrease in compressor efficiency raises the compressor outlet temperature and thus decreases the amount of heat input required for the cycle.) The efficiencies of the turbine

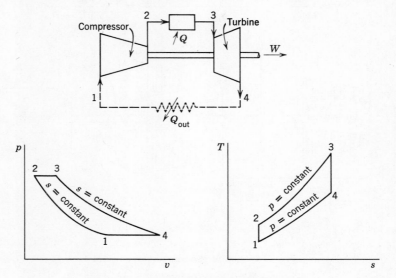

Fig. 17·2   Air-standard gas-turbine cycle.

and compressor in a gas-turbine plant are consequently of great importance. The practical development of gas-turbine power plants was delayed many years by the low efficiencies of the available compressors and turbines.

hs and *Ts* diagrams of a gas-turbine cycle with irreversible adiabatic compression and expansion are shown in Fig. 17·3. For an adiabatic steady-flow process, the entropy change of the universe equals the entropy change of the matter flowing through the steady-flow system. Therefore, for the compression process $1\text{-}2_a$,

$$i = T_0 \, \Delta s_{\text{universe}} = T_0(s_{2a} - s_1)$$

and this can be represented by an area on the *Ts* diagram as can the irreversibility of the adiabatic turbine expansion. Remember that the irreversibility of a process is the decrease caused by the process in the amount of energy of the universe which can be converted into work.

In an actual gas-turbine plant, frictional effects in the passages between components and in the combustion chamber also add to the irreversibility of the cycle.

Increasing the turbine inlet temperature helps to offset the effects of various irreversibilities in the cycle, but this temperature is limited by the loss of strength of turbine construction materials with increasing temperature. Notice that this temperature limitation is more stringent in a steady-flow machine like a turbine, where the gas temperature at each point is

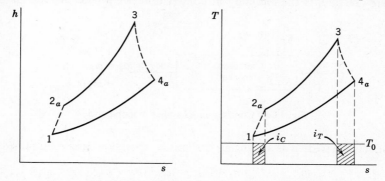

Fig. 17·3 Air-standard gas-turbine cycle with irreversible compression and expansion.

constant, than it is in a reciprocating engine, where the metal parts which are at one instant in contact with gases at the maximum temperature are for much of the cycle in contact with relatively cool gases. For this reason, much higher maximum gas temperatures can be used in reciprocating engines than in gas turbines.

In order to limit the maximum temperature in a gas-turbine cycle, high air–fuel ratios are used. Therefore, the products of combustion can be treated as air with little loss of accuracy. Because the back-work ratio is so high, however, the small increase of mass flowing through the turbine resulting from the addition of fuel may increase the net work of the cycle by an appreciable amount. A cycle analysis which considers the mass of the fuel added but still treats the combustion products as air is called an *air-standard analysis with mass of fuel considered*. The air–fuel ratio required to produce a given temperature with a fuel of given enthalpy of combustion can be found by starting with an energy balance for adiabatic combustion in a steady-flow burner,

$$-Q = 0 = \sum_{\text{reac}} m(h - h_0) - \sum_{\text{prod}} m(h - h_0) - \Delta H_R \qquad (13·1)$$

This energy balance is based on the assumption that the change in kinetic energy is negligible. Designating the air entering by 2, the fuel entering by f, and the products leaving by 3, as shown in Fig. 17·4,

$$0 = m_2(h_2 - h_0)_{\text{air}} + m_f(h_f - h_0)_{\text{fuel}} - m_3(h_3 - h_0)_{\text{prod}} - \Delta H_R$$

This can be rearranged to

$$\frac{m_2}{m_f} = \frac{\Delta H_R/m_f + (h_3 - h_0)_{\text{prod}} - (h_f - h_0)_{\text{fuel}}}{(h_2 - h_0)_{\text{air}} - (h_3 - h_0)_{\text{prod}}}$$

where $\Delta H_R/m_f$ is the enthalpy of combustion per pound of fuel. If the

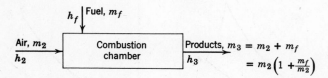

Fig. 17·4   Combustion-chamber mass balance.

products are treated as air, the air–fuel ratio expression can be simplified to

$$\frac{m_2}{m_f} = \frac{\Delta H_R/m_f + h_3 - h_0 - (h_f - h_0)_{\text{fuel}}}{h_2 - h_3}$$

where all of the h's except those marked for fuel can be taken from air tables.

EXAMPLE 17·1.   A Brayton cycle operates with air entering the compressor at 14.0 psia and 80 F, a pressure ratio of 5, and a turbine inlet temperature of 1800 F. Changes in kinetic energy are negligible. Determine the compressor work, the turbine work, and the cycle thermal efficiency based on (*a*) an air-standard analysis using air tables, and (*b*) a cold air-standard analysis.

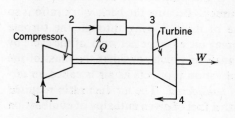

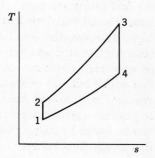

Example 17·1

Solution. A sketch of the system and a *Ts* diagram are made first. For either analysis, the work and heat quantities can be found from the first law if the enthalpy changes across the compressor, turbine, and heat exchanger 2-3 are determined.

(*a*) Use of air tables:

$$p_{r2} = p_{r1}\frac{p_2}{p_1} = 1.386(5) = 6.93 \qquad h_2 = 204.6 \text{ B/lb}$$

$$p_{r4} = p_{r3}\frac{p_4}{p_3} = 286.6(\tfrac{1}{5}) = 57.3 \qquad h_4 = 371.8 \text{ B/lb}$$

Applying the first law to the compressor, the turbine, and the heat exchanger 2-3, respectively,

$$w_{\text{in},c} = h_2 - h_1 = 204.6 - 129.1 = 75.5 \text{ B/lb}$$

$$w_T = h_3 - h_4 = 577.5 - 371.8 = 205.7 \text{ B/lb}$$

$$q_{2\text{-}3} = h_3 - h_2 = 577.5 - 204.6 = 372.9 \text{ B/lb}$$

Then the cycle thermal efficiency is

$$\eta = \frac{w_{\text{cycle}}}{q_{2\text{-}3}} = \frac{w_T - w_{\text{in},c}}{q_{2\text{-}3}} = \frac{205.7 - 75.5}{372.9} = 0.349$$

(*b*) Cold air-standard analysis:

$$T_2 = T_1\left(\frac{p_2}{p_1}\right)^{(k-1)/k} = 540(5)^{0.286} = 855 \text{ R}$$

$$w_{\text{in},c} = h_2 - h_1 = c_p(T_2 - T_1) = 0.24(855 - 540) = 75.5 \text{ B/lb}$$

$$T_4 = T_3\left(\frac{p_4}{p_3}\right)^{(k-1)/k} = 2260(1/5)^{0.286} = 1428 \text{ R}$$

(As a matter of interest, notice that $T_2/T_1 = T_3/T_4$ in the cold air-standard cycle.)

$$w_T = h_3 - h_4 = c_p(T_3 - T_4) = 0.24(2260 - 1428) = 199.6 \text{ B/lb}$$

$$q_{2\text{-}3} = h_3 - h_2 = c_p(T_3 - T_2) = 0.24(2260 - 855) = 337 \text{ B/lb}$$

$$\eta = \frac{w_{\text{cycle}}}{q_{2\text{-}3}} = \frac{w_T - w_{\text{in},c}}{q_{2\text{-}3}} = \frac{199.6 - 75.5}{337} = 0.368$$

Discussion. The compressor work is the same in both analyses because the compressor operates in a temperature range where c_p is very nearly constant at 0.24 B/lb-F. Using the same value of c_p in the higher temperature range up to 1800 F introduces some inaccuracy, however. The cold air-standard analysis gives a work output which is too low and a cycle thermal efficiency which is too high in comparison with the more accurate results based on the variable specific heat data of the air tables.

EXAMPLE 17·2. Solve Example 17·1*a* on the basis of an air-standard analysis with the mass of fuel considered. The fuel is added at 77 F and has a lower heating value of 19,000 B/lb at 77 F.

Solution. The compressor work is unchanged by the consideration of the mass of fuel added. We determine the air–fuel ratio by means of the expression developed from an energy balance just prior to Example 17·1, using a base temperature of 77 F,

$$\frac{m_a}{m_f} = \frac{\Delta H_R/m_f + h_3 - h_0 - (h_f - h_0)_{\text{fuel}}}{h_2 - h_3} = \frac{-19,000 + 577.5 - 128.3 - 0}{204.6 - 577.5}$$

$$= 49.7 \text{ lb air/lb fuel}$$

From the solution of Example 17·1, the turbine work is 205.7 B/lb of air (i.e., combustion products treated as air) passing through the turbine. Per pound of air flowing through the compressor,

$$w_T = 205.7 \left(\frac{B}{\text{lb air to turbine}}\right) \frac{50.7}{49.7} \left(\frac{\text{lb air to turbine}}{\text{lb air to compressor}}\right)$$

$$= 209.8 \text{ B/lb air compressed}$$

Using a thermal efficiency based on the lower heating value,

$$\eta = \frac{w_T - w_{\text{in,}c}}{(-\Delta H_R/m_f)(m_f/m_a)} = \frac{209.8 - 75.5}{19,000/49.7} = 0.352$$

17·3 The regenerative gas-turbine cycle

In a simple gas-turbine cycle, the turbine exhaust temperature is nearly always appreciably higher than the temperature of the air leaving the compressor and entering the combustion chamber. Obviously, the amount of fuel needed can be reduced by the use of a heat exchanger in which the hot turbine exhaust gas is used to preheat the air between the compressor and the combustion chamber. This heat exchanger is called a *regenerator*. In the ideal case the flows through the regenerator are at constant pressure.

An air-standard regenerative cycle is shown in Fig. 17·5. Application of the first law to the regenerator, assuming that kinetic energy changes are negligible and that no heat is lost to the surroundings, shows that $h_3 - h_2 = h_5 - h_6$. Since $q_{2\text{-}3} = -q_{5\text{-}6}$, the two crosshatched areas on the Ts diagram of Fig. 17·5 are equal in magnitude. If, as shown in the Ts diagram, heat is transferred across a finite temperature difference in the regenerator, then the increase of entropy principle shows that, for this irreversible steady-flow process, $s_3 - s_2 + s_6 - s_5 > 0$, or $|\Delta s_{2\text{-}3}| > |\Delta s_{5\text{-}6}|$. The irreversibility of the regenerator process is $i = T_0(s_3 - s_2 + s_6 - s_5)$. Another way to look at the irreversibility of the regenerator is to observe that the magnitude of the unavailable portion of the heat removed from the hot gas is $T_0(s_5 - s_6)$. In other words, this part of the heat removed from the hot gas could not be converted into work even by an externally reversible engine. As the heat is added to the cold gas in the regenerator, the unavailable part of it is $T_0(s_3 - s_2)$. The difference between $T_0(s_3 - s_2)$ and $T_0(s_5 - s_6)$ is therefore the amount of *energy made unavailable* by the irreversible transfer of heat in the regenerator, and this is the same as the irreversibility of the process.

For maximum thermal efficiency of a regenerative cycle, T_3 in Fig. 17·5 should be as high as possible, its limiting value being T_5. The extent to which this limit is approached in any particular cycle is expressed by the regenerator *effectiveness* which with reference to Fig. 17·5 is defined as

$$\text{Effectiveness} \equiv \frac{T_3 - T_2}{T_5 - T_2}$$

Increasing the effectiveness of a regenerator calls for more heat-transfer surface area which increases the cost and the space requirements of the unit. The use of regenerators of very high effectiveness cannot be justified

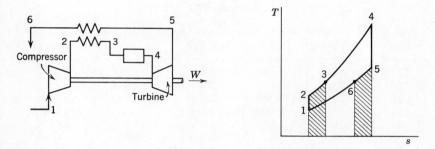

Fig. 17·5 Air-standard regenerative cycle.

economically because the fixed costs (i.e., costs which are largely independent of plant output such as depreciation, interest, taxes, insurance, maintenance, etc.) exceed the savings in fuel cost which result from the higher plant thermal efficiency. Consequently, effectiveness values rarely exceed about 0.7 in actual plants.

EXAMPLE 17·3. In a regenerative air-standard gas-turbine cycle, air enters the compressor at 14.7 psia, 80 F, and leaves it at 73.5 psia, 500 F. The temperature of air entering the combustion chamber is 800 F, entering the turbine is 1600 F, and leaving the turbine is 1060 F. The lowest temperature in the surroundings is 80 F. Neglect the mass of fuel. Assuming no pressure drop in the regenerator or "combustion chamber," and neglecting changes in kinetic energy, calculate (*a*) the compressor efficiency, (*b*) the turbine efficiency, (*c*) the cycle thermal efficiency, (*d*) the irreversibility of the compressor process, (*e*) the irreversibility of the turbine expansion, and (*f*) the irreversibility of the regenerator. (*g*) How much of the heat added to the cycle is available energy? (*h*) How much of the heat rejected from the cycle is available energy?

Solution. First a flow diagram and a *Ts* diagram are made. Points 2_i and 5_i are the *isentropic* end states of the compression and expansion processes which are needed in the calculation of compressor and turbine efficiencies. At various stages in the solution, property values will be obtained; so for convenience a table of these values is made, showing both the specified values and the calculated values which are entered as soon as they are obtained. Air tables are used.

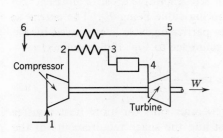
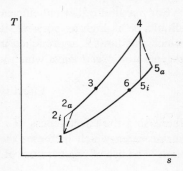

Example 17·3

Point	p, psia	T, F	h, B/lb	p_r	ϕ
1	14.7	80	129.1	1.382	0.6008
2_i	73.5		204.6	6.93	
2_a		500	231.1		0.7403
3		800	306.6		0.8088
4		1600	521.4	196.2	0.9403
5_i	14.7		334.4	39.2+	
5_a		1060	374.5		0.8568
6			299.0		0.8026

The solution of the first three parts involves the application of (1) the definitions of the three efficiencies, and (2) the first law.

(a) $p_{r2i} = p_{r1}\dfrac{p_2}{p_1} = 1.386\dfrac{73.5}{14.7} = 6.93$ $h_{2i} = 204.6$ B/lb

$$\eta_C = \frac{w_{in,i}}{w_{in,a}} = \frac{h_{2i} - h_1}{h_{2a} - h_1} = \frac{204.6 - 129.1}{231.1 - 129.1} = 74.0 \text{ per cent}$$

(b) $p_{r5i} = p_{r4}\dfrac{p_5}{p_4} = 196.2\dfrac{14.7}{73.5} = 39.24$ $h_{5i} = 334.4$ B/lb

$$\eta_T = \frac{w_a}{w_i} = \frac{h_4 - h_{5a}}{h_4 - h_{5i}} = \frac{521.4 - 374.5}{521.4 - 334.4} = 78.5 \text{ per cent}$$

(c) $\eta = \dfrac{w_{cycle}}{q_{3\text{-}4}} = \dfrac{w_T - w_{in,c}}{h_4 - h_3} = \dfrac{521.4 - 374.5 - (231.1 - 129.1)}{521.4 - 306.6}$

= 20.9 per cent

The compressor, the turbine, and the entire regenerator (including both fluid streams) operate steadily and adiabatically, so for each one the irreversibility per pound of fluid is given by $i = T_0 \, \Delta s$, where Δs is the entropy change of the fluid flowing through the device. (See equation (b) of Art. 11·3.)

(d) Compressor:

$$i = T_0(s_{2a} - s_1) = T_0\left[\phi_{2a} - \phi_1 - R\ln\frac{p_2}{p_1}\right]$$

$$= 540\left[0.7403 - 0.6008 - 0.0685\ln\frac{73.5}{14.7}\right]$$

$$= 15.8\ \text{B/lb}$$

(e) Turbine:

$$i = T_0(s_{5a} - s_4) = T_0\left[\phi_{5a} - \phi_4 - R\ln\frac{p_5}{p_4}\right]$$

$$= 540\left[0.8568 - 0.9403 - 0.0685\ln\frac{14.7}{73.5}\right]$$

$$= 14.5\ \text{B/lb}$$

(f) Regenerator:

$$h_6 = h_{5a} - (h_3 - h_{2a}) = 374.5 - (306.6 - 231.1) = 299\ \text{B/lb}$$

$$i = T_0[\Delta s_{2\text{-}3} + \Delta s_{5\text{-}6}] = T_0\left[\phi_3 - \phi_2 - R\ln\frac{p_3}{p_2} + \phi_6 - \phi_5 - R\ln\frac{p_6}{p_5}\right]$$

$$= 540[0.8088 - 0.7403 - 0 + 0.8026 - 0.8568 - 0]$$

$$= 7.71\ \text{B/lb}$$

(g) Of the heat added:

$$q_{\text{unav}} = T_0(s_4 - s_3) = T_0(\phi_4 - \phi_3 - R\ln 1) = 540(0.9403 - 0.8088)$$

$$= 71.0\ \text{B/lb}$$

$$q_{\text{av}} = q - q_{\text{unav}} = 214.8 - 71.0 = 143.8\ \text{B/lb}$$

(h) For the heat rejected:

$$q_{\text{out}} = h_6 - h_1 = 299.0 - 129.1 = 169.9\ \text{B/lb}$$

$$q_{\text{unav}} = T_0(s_6 - s_1) = T_0(\phi_6 - \phi_1) = 540(0.8026 - 0.6008) = 109\ \text{B/lb}$$

$$q_{\text{out,av}} = q_{\text{out}} - q_{\text{out,unav}} = 169.9 - 109 = 60.9\ \text{B/lb}$$

The energy flow diagram shows graphically that the unavailable energy rejected from the cycle exceeds the unavailable energy added to the cycle by the sum of the irreversibilities in the cycle.

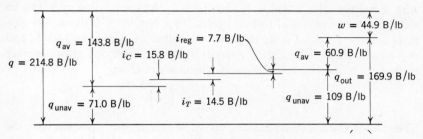

Example 17·3

17·4 Intercooling and reheating in gas-turbine cycles

The net work of a gas-turbine cycle is given by

$$w_{\text{cycle}} = w_T - w_{\text{in},C}$$

and can be increased either by decreasing the compressor work or by increasing the turbine work. These are the purposes of *intercooling* and *reheating*, respectively.

It was shown in Art. 16·1 that intercooling between stages reduces the work input required to compress a gas from a given initial state to a

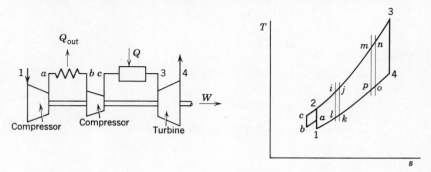

Fig. 17·6 Air-standard gas-turbine cycle with intercooling.

specified final pressure. Therefore, if a simple gas-turbine cycle is modified by having the compression accomplished in two or more adiabatic processes with intercooling between them, the back-work ratio is reduced and consequently the net work of the cycle is increased with no change in the work of the turbine.

Several different lines of reasoning can be used to show that the thermal efficiency of an ideal simple gas-turbine cycle is lowered by the addition of an intercooler. One line of reasoning is based on a Ts diagram like Fig. 17.6 in which the ideal simple gas-turbine cycle is 1-2-3-4-1, and the cycle with the intercooler added is 1-a-b-c-2-3-4-1. Any reversible cycle can be simulated by a number of Carnot cycles. (See Art. 9·1.) If the simple gas-turbine cycle 1-2-3-4-1 is divided into a number of cycles like i-j-k-l-i and m-n-o-p-m, these little cycles approach Carnot cycles as their number increases. Notice that, *if the specific heats are constant,*

$$\frac{T_3}{T_4} = \frac{T_m}{T_p} = \frac{T_i}{T_l} = \frac{T_2}{T_1} = \left(\frac{p_2}{p_1}\right)^{(k-1)/k}$$

Thus all the Carnot cycles making up the simple gas-turbine cycle have the same efficiency. Likewise, all of the Carnot cycles into which the cycle *a-b-c*-2-*a* might similarly be divided have a common value of efficiency which is *lower* than the Carnot cycles which comprise cycle 1-2-3-4-1. Thus the addition of an intercooler, which adds *a-b-c*-2-*a* to the simple cycle, lowers the efficiency of the ideal gas-turbine cycle. We have based our reasoning here on constant specific heats (the cold air-standard analysis), but the same conclusion can be reached for variable specific heats.

The addition of an intercooler to a regenerative gas-turbine cycle increases the cycle thermal efficiency because the heat required for the process *c*-2 in Fig. 17·6 can be obtained from the hot turbine exhaust gas passing through the regenerator instead of from burning additional fuel

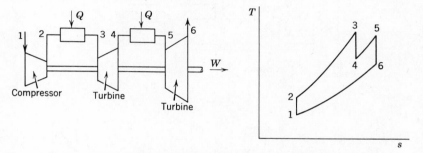

Fig. 17·7   Air-standard gas-turbine cycle with reheat.

(or, in the case of the air-standard cycle, from adding more heat from outside the cycle). The use of an intercooler consequently calls for a larger regenerator.

The turbine work, and consequently the net work of the cycle, can be increased without changing the compressor work or the maximum temperature in the cycle by dividing the turbine expansion into two or more parts with constant-pressure heating (i.e., combustion in an actual cycle, heat transfer in an air-standard cycle) before each expansion. This cycle modification is known as *reheating*. Flow and *Ts* diagrams of an ideal simple gas-turbine cycle modified by a single reheat are shown in Fig. 17·7. By reasoning similar to that used in connection with intercooling, it can be seen that the thermal efficiency of a simple cycle is lowered by the addition of reheat but that a combination of regeneration and reheating can increase the thermal efficiency.

Notice that reheating increases the turbine exhaust temperature so that regeneration can bring the temperature of the air entering the combustion chamber closer to the turbine inlet temperature than is possible without reheat. As the number of reheats is increased, the exhaust temperature increases, making regeneration even more valuable.

Diagrams of an intercooled–regenerative–reheat cycle are shown in Fig. 17·8. If the number of intercools, the number of reheats, and the regenerator effectiveness are increased, this cycle approaches the Ericsson cycle discussed in Art. 7·8. With adiabatic compression and expansion, the costs of equipment for multiple intercools and reheats exceed the fuel-cost savings, but the advantages of approaching isothermal compression and isothermal turbine expansion (as by burning fuel in the turbine in an actual cycle) are apparent.

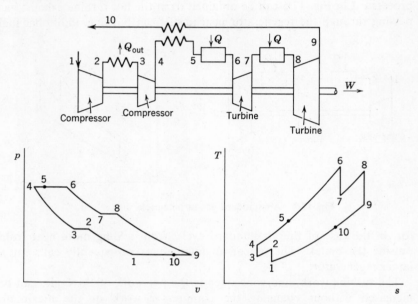

Fig. 17·8 Intercooled–regenerative–reheat cycle.

17·5 Gas-turbine jet propulsion

Powered aircraft and water craft are propelled by accelerating fluid rearward by exerting a force on it. The equal-magnitude and opposite-direction force of the fluid on the craft drives the craft. A propeller accelerates slightly a large mass of fluid while an aircraft jet engine causes a relatively small mass of air to undergo a large change in velocity. In both cases the action is in accordance with the basic dynamic equation for steady flow which for the one-dimensional case is

$$F = \frac{M \, \Delta V}{g_c} \tag{15·1}$$

where F is the resultant force on the fluid which flows at a rate M. (See Example 15·4.)

From among the various jet-propulsion engines which are in use or have been proposed, we will select the gas-turbine jet engine or turbojet engine to illustrate the application of the principles that have already been introduced.

Figure 17·9 shows the flow, pv, and Ts diagrams of a turbojet engine. Air enters the engine at state 1 and is compressed to state 2. It then flows into the combustion chamber, where it is mixed with fuel and combustion occurs, or where, in the air-standard cycle, heat is added. The gas then

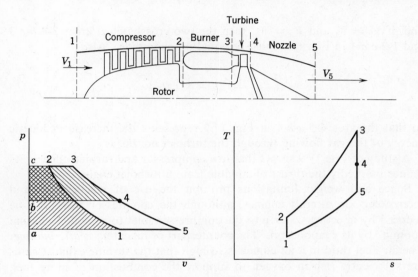

Fig. 17·9   Turbojet engine.

expands adiabatically through the turbine which drives only the compressor, so that *the turbine work equals the compressor work input.* In order for the turbine to produce enough work to drive the compressor it is necessary for it to expand the gas only to a pressure p_4, which is higher than the ambient pressure p_1 ($= p_5$). The gas is then expanded isentropically (in the ideal case) through a nozzle from state 4 to state 5. The gas leaves the engine at a velocity V_5 which is appreciably higher than V_1, and consequently a thrust is developed.

If the flow through the turbojet engine is reversible and steady, we can apply to any process the relationship developed from the principles of mechanics,

$$\int v \, dp = w_{\text{in}} - \Delta KE - \Delta PE \tag{1·10}$$

In dealing with a gas flowing through a jet engine, ΔPE is negligibly small.

Equation 1·10 shows the physical significance of areas on a pv diagram as in Fig. 17·9. For example,

$$w_{in,1\text{-}2} = w_{3\text{-}4}$$

for an air-standard analysis. Therefore,

$$\int_1^2 v\,dp + \frac{V_2^2 - V_1^2}{2g_c} = -\int_3^4 v\,dp + \frac{V_3^2 - V_4^2}{2g_c}$$

and, if $V_2 = V_1$ and $V_3 = V_4$, then the two crosshatched areas 3-4-b-c-3 and 1-2-c-a-1 in Fig. 17·9 must be equal in magnitude. Also,

$$\frac{V_5^2 - V_4^2}{2g_c} = -\int_4^5 v\,dp$$

so that the area 4-5-a-b-4 in Fig. 17·9 represents the increase in kinetic energy of the gas flowing through the turbojet nozzle.

A study of Fig. 17·9 shows that low compressor and turbine efficiencies reduce markedly the thrust obtainable from a turbojet engine.

Space and weight limitations prohibit the use of regenerators and intercoolers on aircraft engines, although the compressor work can be reduced by injecting water into the compressor inlet to provide "internal cooling" by its evaporation. The counterpart of reheating is *afterburning*. The air–fuel ratio in a jet engine is so high that the turbine exhaust gases are sufficiently rich in oxygen to support the combustion of more fuel. Such burning of fuel (or, in the air-standard cycle, addition of heat) raises the temperature of the gas before it expands in the turbojet nozzle, increasing the kinetic energy change in the nozzle and consequently increasing the thrust.

This brief discussion of turbojet engines has not touched on the performance characteristics of the individual components—compressor, combustion chamber, and turbine—and the important problem of matching these characteristics over a wide operating range. Another major problem is the prediction of the system behavior under transient conditions. For example, a change in fuel flow changes the turbine inlet temperature, which changes the turbine power output and hence the shaft speed. A change in shaft speed changes the flow rate and the pressure ratio, which in turn cause further changes in the turbine inlet temperature. Such problems must be thoroughly analyzed in designing an engine. They are mentioned here as a reminder that the design of jet engines involves much more than a thermodynamic analysis of steady-flow cycles.

17·6   The air-standard Otto cycle

The air-standard Otto* cycle is comprised of four reversible processes of air in a closed system: adiabatic compression, constant-volume heat addition, adiabatic expansion, and constant-volume heat rejection. pv and Ts diagrams of an Otto cycle are shown in Fig. 17·10. The *compression ratio r* of the cycle is defined by

$$r \equiv \frac{V_1}{V_2} = \frac{v_1}{v_2}$$

Compression ratio is thus a volume ratio which is fixed by the geometry of the engine.

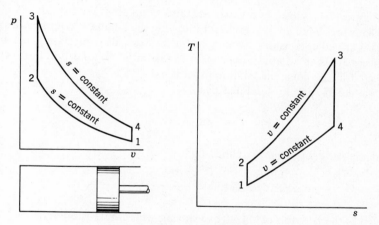

Fig. 17·10   Air-standard Otto cycle.

A first-law analysis of this cycle is very simple because no work is done during the two heat-transfer processes (2-3 and 4-1) and both processes which involve work (1-2 and 3-4) are adiabatic; so for each process one term is zero in the first-law formulation

$$Q = \Delta U + W \tag{2·7}$$

A cold air-standard analysis is of course even simpler and yields results such as $T_2/T_1 = T_3/T_4$ and $\eta = 1 - r^{1-k}$. The latter result shows that the cold air-standard Otto-cycle thermal efficiency is a function of compression

---

* Nikolaus A. Otto (1832–1891) and his partner Eugen Langen built a gas engine in 1867 in Deutz, Germany, and began commercial manufacture of it. In 1876 Otto produced a successful four-stroke cycle engine which was far superior to any internal-combustion engine previously built. The four-stroke cycle had been worked out in principle in 1862 by a Frenchman, Alphonse Beau de Rochas.

ratio only. The thermal efficiency of an air-standard (i.e., variable specific heats) Otto cycle depends on the temperature limits as well as on the compression ratio.

The qualitative effects on efficiency and on work per cycle of varying the compression ratio, temperature limits, and pressure limits are similar for an air-standard Otto cycle and for an actual spark-ignition engine, and this is why the air-standard analysis is of value. The differences between the air-standard and the actual cycles are so great, however, that close quantitative agreement is not to be expected.

17·7   The air-standard Diesel cycle

Figure 17·11 shows pv and Ts diagrams of an air-standard Diesel* cycle. All four processes are reversible. Following the adiabatic compression 1-2, heat is added at constant pressure as the air expands from state 2 to state 3. Process 3-4 is an adiabatic expansion to the initial volume, and heat is then rejected in the constant volume process 4-1.

The *cutoff ratio* r_c is defined by

$$r_c \equiv \frac{V_3}{V_2} = \frac{v_3}{v_2}$$

and the *per cent cutoff* is defined by

$$\text{Per cent cutoff} \equiv \frac{V_3 - V_2}{V_1 - V_2} = \frac{v_3 - v_2}{v_1 - v_2}$$

i.e., it is the fraction of the stroke during which heat is added.

The thermal efficiency of a cold air-standard Diesel cycle is a function of the compression ratio and cutoff ratio only, but other factors are pertinent with variable specific heats.

In actual compression-ignition engines only air is compressed in the cylinder, and, since there is no fuel in the cylinder, the compression ratio can be high enough to raise the air temperature above the fuel ignition temperature without causing ignition. Then, as the piston moves away from the cylinder head, fuel is injected and burned. The pressure variation during the first part of the expansion stroke depends on the rate at which fuel is injected and burned. In low-speed engines at least part of the fuel may be burned at approximately constant pressure as it is injected. In

---

* Rudolph Diesel (1858–1913) was born in Paris of German parents and educated in Munich. In 1893 he published a book, *The Theory and Construction of a Rational Heat Motor,* and obtained a patent on a compression–ignition engine. By 1899 he had developed this new type of engine to the point where he was able to begin commercial production in his factory at Augsburg.

high-speed engines, ignition lag delays the start of combustion until most or all of the fuel is in the cylinder; so the ideal picture of the pressure being held constant by a regulated injection of fuel as the gas expands is quite

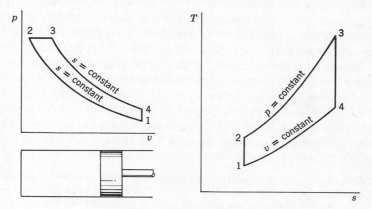

Fig. 17·11   Air-standard Diesel cycle.

unrealistic. Once again the differences between an actual cycle and a corresponding ideal one must be remembered so that conclusions based on one will not be blindly applied to the other.

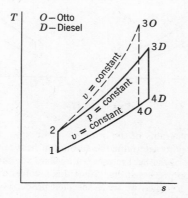

Fig. 17·12   Comparison of Otto and Diesel cycles.

Performance comparisons among various gas power cycles are readily made by using Ts diagrams to aid in reasoning which is based on the first and second laws and ideal-gas properties. As one example, let us determine which has the higher thermal efficiency, an air-standard Otto cycle or an air-standard Diesel cycle with the same compression ratio and the same heat input. Superimposed Ts diagrams of the two cycles are shown in Fig. 17·12. Since the two cycles have the same compression ratio, process 1-2 is common to them. After one of the cycle Ts diagrams is sketched, the relative locations of points $3O$ (Otto) and $3D$ are determined by the fact that equal heat inputs means equal areas under the constant-volume line 2-$3O$ and the constant-pressure line 2-$3D$. Thus points $3O$ and $4O$ are at a lower entropy than points $3D$ and $4D$. Since both cycles reject heat in a constant-volume process ending at state 1, the relative location of points $4O$ and $4D$ on the Ts diagram shows that less heat is rejected by the Otto cycle. The heat inputs are the same; so the work of the Otto exceeds the work of the Diesel cycle. Consequently the Otto cycle has the higher thermal efficiency. *Caution:* This conclusion applies to cycles which have the same compression ratio and the same heat input. Comparisons can be made in a similar manner for various other conditions.

EXAMPLE 17·4.   In an air-standard Diesel cycle, compression starts at 14.5 psia, 120 F. At the end of compression the pressure is 550 psia. The mass of air in the system is 0.15 lb, and the amount of heat added per cycle is 42 B. Calculate for this cycle (a) the compression ratio, (b) the work, and (c) the amount of heat rejected which is available energy.

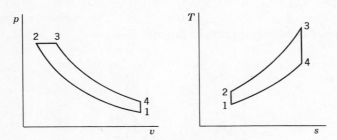

Example 17·4

Solution. pv and Ts diagrams of the cycle are made first. Since in order to solve part (c) it will be necessary to determine the amount of heat rejected and since part (b) can also be solved by use of the heat rejected, it appears advisable to determine state 4 at which the heat-rejection process starts. Since this involves calculations "around the cycle," we make a table in which we write specified property values immediately and calculated values as soon as they are obtained:

Point	p, psia	T, R	p_r	v_r	u, B/lb	h, B/lb	ϕ
1	14.5	580	1.7800	120.70	98.90		
2	550	1575	67.5	8.648	281.1	389.1	0.86710
3	550	2581		1.9202		669.1	1.00411
4		1255		16.38	219.3		

The manner in which the calculated values are obtained for the table is shown in the following:

$$p_{r2} = p_{r1}\frac{p_2}{p_1} = 1.7800\left(\frac{550}{14.5}\right) = 67.5$$

(From p_{r2}, values of v_r, T, u, and h at state 2 can be determined from the air tables.)

(a)   Compression ratio $= \dfrac{v_1}{v_2} = \dfrac{v_{r1}}{v_{r2}} = \dfrac{120.70}{8.648} = 13.97$

(b) Applying the first law to process 2-3 and noting that for a reversible constant-pressure process of a closed system $q = \Delta u + w = \Delta u + \int p\,dv = \Delta u + \Delta pv = \Delta h$,

$$h_3 = h_2 + \frac{Q}{m} = 389.08 + \frac{42}{0.15} = 389.1 + 280.0 = 669.1 \text{ B/lb}$$

(Knowing h_3, we take from the air tables values of T and v_r at state 3.)

$$v_{r4} = v_{r3}\frac{v_4}{v_3} = v_{r3}\frac{v_1}{v_3} = v_{r3}\frac{T_1 p_3}{T_3 p_1} = 1.9202\left(\frac{580}{2581}\right)\frac{550}{14.5} = 16.38$$

(Knowing v_{r4}, we take from the air tables values of T, u, and ϕ for state 4.)

$$W = \oint \delta Q = Q_{2\text{-}3} - Q_{\text{out},4\text{-}1} = Q_{2\text{-}3} - m(u_4 - u_1) = 42 - 0.15(219.3 - 98.9)$$
$$= 42 - 18.1 = 23.9 \text{ B}$$

(c) $Q_{av,4\text{-}1} = Q_{4\text{-}1} - Q_{unav,4\text{-}1} = Q_{4\text{-}1} - T_0(S_1 - S_4) = Q_{4\text{-}1} - T_0(S_2 - S_3)$

$$= Q_{4\text{-}1} - T_0 m\left(\phi_2 - \phi_3 - R\ln\frac{p_2}{p_3}\right)$$

$$= -18.1 - 580(0.15)(0.86710 - 1.00411 - 0) = -6.2 \text{ B}$$

where we have used the lowest temperature in the cycle as T_0 since no other information was provided. The negative sign indicates that 6.2 B of available energy is *removed* from the system. The physical interpretation is that, if the 18.1 B of heat rejected by the Diesel cycle were transferred into a series of Carnot engines (or other externally reversible engines) rejecting heat at 580 R, 6.2 B out of the 18.1 B could be converted into work by the Carnot engines. A shortcoming of a Diesel cycle in comparison with a Carnot cycle is that some of the heat rejected by the former *can* be converted into work while the Carnot cycle rejects only heat which *cannot* be converted into work.

17·8   The dual cycle and others

Neither the air-standard Otto nor the air-standard Diesel cycle closely approximates the pressure–volume variation of the working substance in an actual engine. For some analyses it is profitable to use an air-standard cycle in which the pressure–volume variation does simulate that in an actual engine. One such cycle, called the dual cycle, involves two heat-addition processes: one at constant volume and one at constant pressure as shown in Fig. 17·13. The relative amounts of heat added in the two processes can be adjusted to make the air-standard cycle more like an actual one.

A further refinement is to have heat addition first at constant volume, then at constant pressure, and then at constant temperature in an air-standard cycle. Such cycles can be analyzed and evaluated by the same fundamental methods used for the simpler ones. Remember, however, that the most highly refined air-standard cycle is still much different from

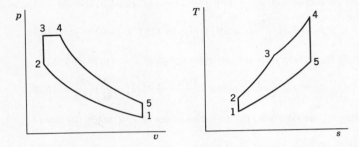

Fig. 17·13 Air-standard dual cycle.

what occurs in an actual internal-combustion engine. An ideal system can be more confusing than helpful if the differences between it and the corresponding actual system are not kept in mind.

17·9 Compound power plants

As mentioned in Art. 17·2, reciprocating engines can employ much higher maximum gas temperatures than turbines. Since adiabatic expansions are used in most gas power cycles, the higher temperatures are accompanied by higher pressures. On the other hand, reciprocating engines are poor in contrast with turbines for expanding gas to low pressures with resulting large volumes because the engine size increases more rapidly than the power output. Either method of increasing the mass flow rate through a reciprocating engine—increasing engine size or increasing speed—augments the design difficulties which stem from increased inertia loads on the reciprocating parts. In contrast, turbines are readily adaptable to handling large gas volumes. To capitalize on the advantages and minimize the drawbacks of each type of prime mover, *compound power plants* or *compound engines* are used in which the high-pressure and high-temperature processes occur in a reciprocating engine and the low-pressure expansion occurs in a turbine.

Three different arrangements of compound engines are shown in Fig. 17·14. In the first one, exhaust gases from the reciprocating engine drive a turbine which supplies part of the net power output of the plant. The compressor for supercharging the engine is driven from the engine shaft. Figure 17·14*b* shows the exhaust gas turbine driving only the compressor or supercharger and the reciprocating engine supplying all the plant power output. The turbine and compressor are mounted on a single shaft with no mechanical connection to the engine. In the arrangement of Fig. 17·14*c*,

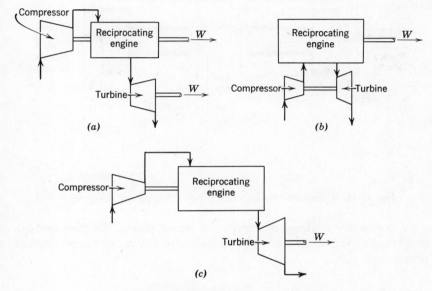

Fig. 17·14   Compound power plants.

the reciprocating engine drives only the compressor, and the turbine provides the plant power output. If the air–fuel ratio of the reciprocating engine is sufficiently high, some fuel can be burned in a combustion chamber between the engine and the turbine to raise the turbine inlet temperature and thereby increase the plant power output. In addition to the thermodynamic advantage of a compound engine, there are some mechanical advantages of a turbine, instead of a reciprocating engine, driving the plant load.

In the compound power plant shown in Fig. 17·14*c*, the reciprocating engine and compressor comprise a gas generator, the sole function of which is to supply gas for driving the turbine. The gas generator can consist of a conventional engine geared to a centrifugal or axial-flow compressor, or, since there is no work output, it can be a free-piston engine–compressor. A schematic diagram of a compound power plant using a free-piston gas generator is shown in Fig. 17·15. The air in the bounce cylinders is compressed during the power stroke of the opposed pistons and then expands to move the pistons toward each other to compress the air in the combustion chamber and start a new cycle of operation.

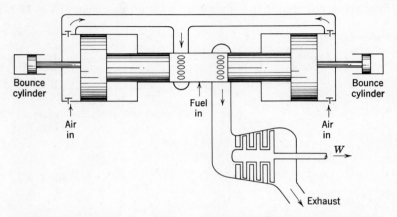

Fig. 17·15 Compound power plant using a free-piston gas generator.

In elementary analyses of compound power plants, the flow through reciprocating engines can often be treated as steady, using mean values of properties.

17·10 Summary

In an *air-standard* cycle analysis, the working substance is air which behaves like an ideal gas, and the combustion process of an actual power cycle is replaced by a heat-addition process. A *cold air-standard* analysis involves the further simplification that the specific heats of air are constant at their room-temperature values.

The air-standard ideal gas-turbine cycle is the *Brayton cycle* which consists of isentropic compression, reversible constant-pressure heating, isentropic expansion through a turbine, and reversible constant-pressure heat rejection to complete the cycle.

The *back-work ratio* of a power cycle, which is defined as

$$\text{Back-work ratio} \equiv \frac{\text{compression work}_{\text{in}}}{\text{gross work of prime mover}}$$

is high for a gas-turbine cycle. Consequently, the efficiency of a gas-turbine cycle is reduced appreciably by relatively small reductions in compressor and turbine efficiencies.

The addition of a *regenerator* increases the thermal efficiency of a simple gas-turbine cycle. Intercooling and reheating increase the power output, and when used in conjunction with regeneration they increase the efficiency.

In a gas-turbine jet-propulsion engine (turbojet engine), the turbine drives the compressor, and the exhaust gas from the turbine expands through a nozzle to leave at a high velocity in a rearward direction. The change in momentum of the gas passing through the engine results in a forward thrust on the engine, and thus on the aircraft of which the engine is a part. In a jet engine, the counterpart of reheating is *afterburning* which increases the thrust by increasing the enthalpy drop and hence the velocity change across the jet nozzle.

The air-standard *Otto cycle* is comprised of four reversible processes of air in a closed system: adiabatic compression, constant-volume heat addition, adiabatic expansion, and constant-volume heat rejection. The *compression ratio* of a reciprocating engine is defined as the ratio of the maximum to the minimum volume of the working substance in the cylinder.

The air-standard *Diesel cycle* is also comprised of four reversible processes of air in a closed system: adiabatic compression, constant-pressure heat addition, adiabatic expansion to the initial volume, and constant-volume heat rejection. For a Diesel cycle the *cutoff ratio* is defined as the ratio of the cylinder volume after heat addition to that before heat addition. The *per cent cutoff* is the fraction of the stroke during which heat is added.

Other air-standard cycles such as the dual cycle, in which the heat addition is divided between a constant-volume and a constant-pressure process, are used in analyses where it is desired to simulate the pressure–volume variation of actual engine operation more closely than can be done with an air-standard Otto or Diesel cycle.

Compound power plants or compound engines are combinations of reciprocating engines and turbines designed to capitalize on the advantages and minimize the drawbacks of each type of prime mover.

REFERENCES

17·1 P. J. Kiefer, G. F. Kinney, and M. C. Stuart, *Principles of Engineering Thermodynamics*, John Wiley & Sons, 2d ed., 1954, chapter 14.

17·2 E. F. Obert, *Thermodynamics*, McGraw-Hill Book Co., 1948, chapter XIII.

17·3 V. W. Young, *Basic Thermodynamics*, McGraw-Hill Book Co., 1952, chapter 12.

17·4 M. J. Zucrow, *Aircraft and Missile Propulsion*, John Wiley & Sons, vol. II, 1958.

17·5 G. M. Dusinberre, *Gas Turbine Power*, International Textbook Co., 1952.

17·6 B. H. Jennings and W. L. Rogers, *Gas Turbine Analysis and Practice*, McGraw-Hill Book Co., 1953.

17·7 H. A. Sorensen, *Gas Turbines*, Ronald Press, 1951.

17·8 L. C. Lichty, *Internal Combustion Engines*, McGraw-Hill Book Co., 6th ed., 1951.

PROBLEMS

17·1 An air-standard gas turbine operates on the Brayton cycle between pressure limits of 14.7 and 70 psia. The inlet air temperature to the compressor is 60 F, and the air entering the turbine is at a temperature of 1500 F. Air enters the compressor at a rate of 50,000 cfm. Compute the power output and the cycle thermal efficiency.

17·2 Solve Prob. 17·1 using a temperature of 1250 F for the air entering the turbine.

17·3 Solve Prob. 17·1 using a temperature of 1000 F for the air entering the turbine. What effect does the temperature of the air entering the turbine have on the work and efficiency of the cycle?

17·4 Solve Prob. 17·1 using an upper pressure limit of 100 psia. What effect does increasing the pressure have on the work and efficiency of the cycle?

17·5 Air enters the compressor of a simple gas-turbine cycle at 14.7 psia, and discharges at 103 psia, 386 F. The temperatures of the gases entering and leaving the turbine are 1600 and 716 F, respectively. If such data are possible, compute the net work per pound of air and the efficiency of the cycle.

17·6 A simple gas-turbine cycle operates at a pressure ratio of 5. The inlet temperature to the compressor is 530 R. If the turbine and compressor efficiencies are 0.85 and 0.84, respectively, compute the cycle efficiency for a turbine inlet temperature of 1560 R. Assume that the compression and expansion are adiabatic.

17·7 Solve Prob. 17·6 using a pressure ratio of 6 and an inlet turbine temperature of 1400 R.

17·8 Consider a simple air-standard gas-turbine cycle operating with compressor inlet conditions of 14.7 psia, 70 F. The pressure ratio is 5, and the maximum temperature is 1500 F. $\eta_o = 0.80$, and $\eta_T = 0.80$. What reduction in compressor efficiency would have the same effect on the cycle efficiency as a reduction of the turbine efficiency to 0.75?

17·9 For equal pressure and temperature limits, rank in order of decreasing efficiency cold air-standard simple gas-turbine cycles using as working fluids helium, air, and carbon dioxide.

17·10 An air-standard gas turbine operates on a regenerative cycle with a regenerator effectiveness of 100 per cent. The inlet temperature to the compressor is 60 F. Compute the air-standard cycle efficiency for the following conditions: (*a*) inlet temperature to the turbine equals 1200 F, pressure ratio equals 5; (*b*) inlet temperature to the turbine equals 1600 F, pressure ratio equals 5; and (*c*) inlet temperature to the turbine equals 1200 F, pressure ratio equals 10.

17·11 The following data apply to a regenerative air-standard gas-turbine cycle with adiabatic compression and expansion. Atmospheric temperature is 80 F.

Location	Pressure, psia	Temperature, F
Entering compressor	14.5	80
Leaving compressor	85.0	500
Entering combustion chamber	84.9	620
Entering turbine	83.0	1540
Leaving turbine	14.6	940
Leaving plant	14.5	

Determine (*a*) the effectiveness of the regenerator, (*b*) the turbine efficiency, and (*c*) the irreversibility of the turbine expansion.

17·12 For fixed inlet temperatures, sketch a curve of regenerator irreversibility versus regenerator effectiveness. Does the maximum irreversibility correspond to the least desirable value of effectiveness from the standpoint of cycle thermal efficiency? Explain.

17·13 Solve Prob. 17·10*a* if the regenerator effectiveness is (*a*) 75 per cent, (*b*) 50 per cent.

17·14 Solve Prob. 17·10*a* if there is a leak in the high-temperature end of the regenerator which allows 5 per cent of the entering air to flow into the exhaust line.

17·15 Solve Prob. 17·10*a* if there is a frictional pressure drop of 3 psi in each gas stream passing through the regenerator.

17·16 A gas-turbine plant is used to supply compressed air by having the turbine drive only the compressor, and the air stream from the compressor is divided into two parts: that which goes to the combustion chamber and turbine, and that which is the compressed air delivered by the plant. Inlet conditions are 14.0 psia, 70 F, and the compressor discharge pressure is 70 psia. The fuel lower heating value is 17,300 B/lb. The turbine inlet temperature is 1500 F, and the exhaust products can be treated as air. All velocities are negligible except for the turbine exhaust velocity of 500 fps. Determine the mass ratio of compressed air delivered to air drawn in.

17·17 In the gas-turbine plant shown in the figure, the compressor is driven by one

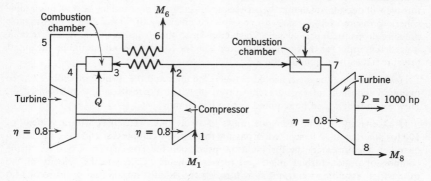

Problem 17·17

turbine, and the other turbine delivers 1000 hp as the power output of the plant. The compressor and the turbines operate adiabatically. The compressor efficiency is 80 per cent; the efficiency of each turbine is 80 per cent. Air drawn into the compressor is at 14.7 psia, 60 F. Both turbines exhaust at 14.7 psia. The inlet condition for each turbine is 61 psia, 1280 F. High-pressure air leaves the regenerator at 600 F. Neglect pressure drop in the heat exchangers and changes in kinetic energy. Treat the working fluid as air. Calculate the amount of heat added in each combustion chamber in B/hr.

17·18 The following data apply to an air-standard intercooled regenerative cycle: air temperatures entering and leaving the low-pressure stage of the compressor equal 80 and 208 F; air temperatures entering and leaving the high-pressure stage of the compressor equal 140 and 280 F; air temperature leaving the regenerator equals 645 F; gas temperatures entering and leaving the turbine equal 1600 and 770 F. The initial pressure is 14.7 psia, and the pressure ratio is 6. Cooling water enters the intercooler at 70 F and discharges at 80 F. Compute (a) the net work of the cycle per pound of air, (b) the thermal efficiency, and (c) the amount of water required per pound of air in the intercooler.

17·19 The following temperatures are for the intercooled regenerative air-standard cycle with reheat as shown in Fig. 17·8: $T_1 = 80$ F, $T_2 = 245$ F, $T_3 = 160$ F, $T_4 = 349$ F, $T_5 = 700$ F, $T_6 = 1600$ F, $T_7 = 1082$ F (at 46.5 psia), $T_8 = 1600$ F, and $T_9 = 1082$ F. The initial pressure is 14.7 psia, and the over-all pressure ratio is 10. Cooling water enters the intercooler at 70 F and discharges at 78 F. Compute (a) heat transferred to the water in the intercooler per pound of air, (b) mass of cooling water per pound of air, (c) heat supplied per pound of air in the first combustion chamber, (d) heat supplied per pound of air in the second combustion chamber, (e) work per pound of air required to compress the air, (f) net work per pound of air for the complete unit, and (g) thermal efficiency of the cycle.

17·20 Consider an air-standard reheat cycle with the high-pressure turbine driving the compressor and the low-pressure turbine supplying the net plant power output of 5000 hp. Air enters the plant at 14.7 psia, 60 F, and the compressor pressure ratio is 6. The inlet temperature to each turbine is 1500 F. The compressor efficiency is 0.85, and each turbine efficiency is 0.82. Determine the mass rate of flow and the cycle thermal efficiency.

17·21 As an emergency power supply it is proposed to use a turbine driven by compressed air from a storage tank in which the air is initially at 100 psia, 70 F. The turbine will operate adiabatically between the decreasing pressure in the tank and atmospheric pressure of 14.7 psia with an expected efficiency of 50 per cent until the tank pressure drops to 20 psia. Neglect heat transfer to the air in the tank. What size tank is needed in order for the turbine to deliver 5 hp for 10 min? Would doubling the initial pressure halve the required volume?

17·22 Suppose the air is heated between the tank and the turbine of Prob. 17·21 to maintain a constant turbine inlet temperature of 900 F. What size tank would be needed? How much heat would be required during the 10 min?

17·23 An ideal turbojet engine draws in air at 14.0 psia, 80 F, with a velocity of 500 fps at a rate of 32 lb/sec. After passing through the compressor and the combustion chamber, the air enters the turbine at 60 psia, 1600 F. The velocity is 500 fps at the compressor outlet, turbine inlet, and turbine exhaust. Calculate the velocity of the exhaust jet, assuming isentropic flow through the exhaust nozzle to a pressure of 14.0 psia.

17·24 Determine the maximum thrust obtainable from an air-standard turbojet engine which takes in air at 10 psia, 40 F, with a velocity of 800 fps (the craft speed) at a rate of 70 lb/sec. The compressor total pressure ratio is 3, compressor outlet and turbine inlet and outlet velocities are 500 fps, and the maximum temperature in the cycle is 1800 F. Assume that the total pressure is constant from the compressor outlet to the turbine inlet. The exhaust pressure is 10 psia.

17·25 Solve Prob. 17·24 with an afterburner raising the temperature to 1800 F at the entrance to the jet nozzle.

17·26 In a prop-jet aircraft engine, the gas turbine drives a propeller and also the compressor, and the exhaust gases from the turbine are expanded through a nozzle to form an exhaust jet which provides additional thrust. Determine the required compressor pressure ratio for an air-standard prop-jet engine which provides 1000 lb of thrust in addition to 1000 hp to a propeller if air at 8 psia, 0 F, is drawn in with a velocity of 600 fps. The velocity is also 600 fps at the compressor outlet, turbine inlet, and turbine exhaust. The maximum temperature is 1600 F, and the flow rate is not to exceed 20 lb/sec. Assume that all processes are reversible.

17·27 In a ramjet engine, air at 10 psia, 40 F, enters the diffuser at 1500 fps (the craft speed) through a cross-sectional area of 0.8 sq ft and is decelerated to 300 fps relative to the engine. Fuel at 0.02 times the air flow rate is burned to bring the temperature to 1600 F, and the combustion products which can be treated as air are then expanded through a nozzle to the ambient pressure and leave at 2500 fps. Calculate the thrust.

17·28 What effects do you believe a heavy rain would have on the performance of a turbojet aircraft engine in flight?

17·29 Derive the following expression for the cold air-standard Otto-cycle thermal efficiency: $\eta = 1 - r^{1-k}$, where r is the compression ratio.

17·30 At the beginning of compression in a cold air-standard Otto cycle, the working substance is at 14 psia, 90 F, and has a volume of 1 cu ft. At the end of compression, the pressure is 140 psia, and 10 B is added during the constant-volume process. Calculate (a) the thermal efficiency, (b) the amount of heat added which is available energy, and (c) the amount of heat rejected which is available energy. (In the absence of other information, the sink temperature should be taken as equal to the lowest temperature in the cycle).

17·31 Solve Prob. 17·30 on an air-standard basis.

17·32 For the conditions of Prob. 17·30, calculate (a) the percentage increase of stroke necessary to allow the adiabatic expansion to proceed until the initial pressure (14 psia) is reached, causing the heat-rejection process to be at constant pressure instead of at constant volume, and (b) the thermal efficiency of the modified cycle described in (a).

17·33 Solve Prob. 17·32 with the adiabatic expansion proceeding to the initial temperature (90 F) so that the heat-rejection process is isothermal.

17·34 In a cold air-standard Otto cycle, the cylinder volume is 0.10 cu ft, and the compression ratio is 7. At the beginning of the compression stroke, the working fluid is at 14.0 psia, 80 F. Heat added during one cycle amounts to 1.41 B, and the pressure at the end of the heat addition is 427 psia. The sink temperature is 80 F. Calculate the fraction of the heat rejected which is available energy.

17·35 Consider a cold air-standard Otto cycle having a compression ratio of 9. At the beginning of compression, the air is at 14.0 psia, 40 F; during the heat-addition process, the pressure of the air is doubled. Calculate the efficiency and the back-work ratio (how do you think it should be defined?) of this cycle and the efficiency of a Carnot cycle operating between the same over-all temperature limits. What would be the minimum over-all volume ratio for a Carnot cycle with the same temperature limits and the same maximum specific volume?

17-36   In a cold air-standard Otto cycle with a compression ratio of 6, the working fluid is 0.10 lb of air which is at 14.0 psia, 40 F, at the beginning of the compression stroke. The maximum temperature in the cycle is 1740 F. Heat is received from a constant-temperature reservoir at 1740 F and is rejected to the atmosphere at 40 F. How much energy is made unavailable by the operation of one cycle?

17-37   Solve Example 17·4 on a cold air-standard basis.

17-38   Refer to Fig. 17·11. For the cold air-standard Diesel cycle, determine the compression ratio which results in $T_3 - T_4 = T_2 - T_1$.

17-39   A cold air-standard Diesel cycle has a compression ratio of 16 and a cutoff ratio of 2. The cylinder volume is 0.5 cu ft, and at the beginning of the compression stroke the air is at 14.0 psia, 40 F. The lowest temperature in the surroundings is 40 F. How much of the heat added is available energy?

17-40   State clearly the differences between a pv diagram as used with air-standard cycles and an indicator diagram for an actual engine.

17-41   In the closed system pv diagram which is shown, paths 1-2 and a-b-c-d are reversible adiabatic paths. All processes shown are reversible. (a) Sketch the corresponding Ts diagram. (b) Four cycles are possible: 1-2-a-d-1; 1-2-a-c-1; 1-2-b-c-1; and 1-2-b-d-1. Rank these cycles in order of thermal efficiency.

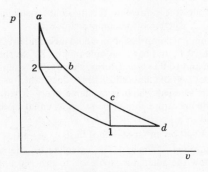

Problem 17-41

17-42   The compression ratio for an engine operating on the cold air-standard dual cycle is 7, the cylinder diameter is 10 in., and the stroke is 12 in. The air at the start of compression is at 14.7 psia, 70 F. At the end of the constant-volume process, the pressure is 800 psia. If heat is added at constant pressure during 3 per cent of the stroke, compute (a) the net work of the cycle, (b) the thermal efficiency, (c) the amount of heat added which is available energy, and (d) the amount of heat rejected which is available energy.

17-43   For the same temperature limits and equal amounts of heat added, which air-standard cycle has the higher thermal efficiency, Otto or Diesel?

17-44   A compound power plant consists of a high-speed multicylinder Diesel engine which drives only a centrifugal compressor and a turbine which operates on the gases which leave the Diesel engine. Air enters the compressor at 14.7 psia, 70 F. The compressor operates adiabatically with an efficiency of 80 per cent and a pressure ratio of 3. Air from the compressor is supplied to the Diesel engine. The air–fuel ratio is high because a high amount of excess air is used for scavenging and cooling. The pressure in the engine exhaust line is 43.5 psia. The brake specific fuel consumption of the Diesel engine alone when operating at 3 atm is 0.50 lb/bhp-hr. The lower heating value of the fuel is 18,000 B/lb. Twenty per cent of the lower heating value of the fuel is transferred to cooling water, which is used to cool the hottest parts of the engine cylinders. Gases leaving the engine expand adiabatically to 14.7 psia through a turbine which has an efficiency of 80 per cent. The turbine output is 1000 hp. Calculate the specific fuel consumption of the plant. (*Note*: In view of the high air–fuel ratio, treat the engine exhaust products as air. Assume that the flow through the entire plant is steady.)

CHAPTER **18**

Vapor Power Cycles

This chapter treats power cycles that use working fluids which are alternately vaporized and condensed. The usual such working fluid is water, and the cycles are called steam cycles, even though the water is in the liquid phase during part of the cycle. The chief purpose of this chapter is to illustrate further the application of thermodynamic principles to engineering systems. Steam power plants are engineering systems of widespread importance because they generate a major and increasing fraction of the electric power produced in the world and because continual improvements in plant performance and reliability have made possible a decreasing real cost of electric power even while the real cost of fuel and labor have been increasing. Also, steam power generation is often combined with the use of steam for space heating or process heating such as sugar cooking or paper drying. Steam power cycles are essentially the same whether heat is supplied from the burning of a fuel in a furnace or from the fission process in a nuclear reactor.

18·1 The Carnot cycle using steam

The second law leads to the facts that the efficiency of a Carnot cycle depends only on the temperature limits and not on the working substance and that no cycle can have a higher efficiency than a Carnot cycle operating between the same temperature limits. (See Chapter 8.) Therefore, from the standpoint of efficiency, a steam power cycle might well be designed to simulate a Carnot cycle; however, consideration of several other points shows why this is not done.

Ts diagrams of steady-flow steam Carnot cycles for two different temperature ranges are shown in Fig. 18·1. In the first one, the maximum cycle temperature is below the critical temperature, the heat-addition process converts liquid water completely to dry saturated steam, and the working fluid is always in a saturated state. In the second cycle shown, the maximum temperature is above the critical temperature, the heat-rejection process is a complete condensation of dry saturated vapor to

596

saturated liquid, and the working fluid passes also through compressed liquid and superheated vapor states.

Referring to the Carnot cycle which is entirely within the wet region (Fig. 18·1a), process 1-2 is of course a constant-pressure as well as constant-temperature process which can be simulated very closely in a boiler. In fact, it is easier to control a constant-temperature process with a two-phase working substance by controlling the pressure than it is to maintain an isothermal process of a gas. The isentropic expansion process 2-3 can be

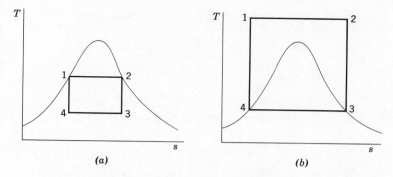

Fig. 18·1   Carnot cycles using steam as the working fluid.

simulated quite closely by a well-designed engine or turbine. Constant-temperature (and hence constant-pressure) condensation as in process 3-4 can be accomplished in an actual condenser except that controlling the final quality is difficult, and, if the final quality is not correct, i.e., if state 4 is not located correctly, an isentropic compression will not end at state 1. Also it may be difficult to compress the two-phase mixture isentropically. Another difficulty in using this cycle is that heat cannot be added to an evaporating fluid at a constant temperature higher than the critical temperature, but for maximum thermal efficiency heat should be added at the highest possible temperature. For steam, the critical temperature of 705.4 F is well below the temperature limit set by the strength characteristics of construction materials.

The Carnot cycle of Fig. 18·1b eliminates the difficulties of the first one but presents some new ones. The isentropic compression 4-1 involves extremely high pressures. Also, the isothermal heat-addition process 1-2 involves a pressure variation which introduces a control problem not encountered when the temperature can be held constant simply by maintaining a constant pressure as in heat addition to a two-phase mixture.

In summary, the Carnot cycle is not suitable as a model for the design of steam power-plant cycles on account of the difficulty of carrying out the required processes in actual machines, especially while utilizing the maximum possible temperature for heat addition.

18·2 The Rankine cycle

Flow, pv, and Ts diagrams of a Rankine cycle, which is the ideal simple steam power-plant steady-flow cycle, are shown in Fig. 18·2. Dry saturated steam enters the prime mover, which may be either an engine or a turbine,

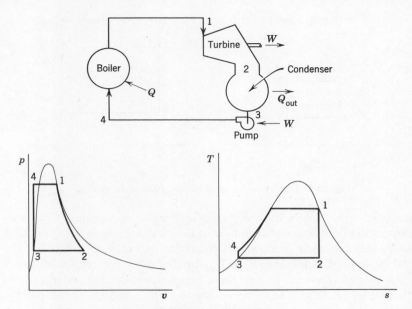

Fig. 18·2 Rankine cycle.

and expands isentropically to pressure p_2 at which the steam is condensed to a saturated liquid, state 3. In the condenser, heat is transferred from the condensing steam to water, frequently from a lake or river, which is circulated through many tubes which provide a large heat-transfer surface.* The saturated liquid leaving the condenser is then pumped isentropically into the boiler at pressure $p_4 (= p_1)$ where at constant pressure it is first heated to the saturation temperature and then evaporated to state 1 to complete the cycle. The temperature rise which results from isentropic

---

* Your study of this chapter will be more rewarding if you refer to a handbook or book on steam power plants or applied thermodynamics for physical descriptions, including pictures, of the various cycle components mentioned.

compression of liquid water is very small, so the length of line 3-4 in the
Ts diagram of Fig. 18·2 is greatly exaggerated.

In order to use higher temperatures without increasing the maximum
pressure of the cycle, the steam after leaving the boiler is heated further at
constant pressure in a superheater. The combination of boiler and
superheater is called a steam generator. Flow and Ts diagrams of a
Rankine cycle with superheat are shown in Fig. 18·3. Comparison of the
Ts diagrams of Figs. 18·2 and 18·3 shows that for given pressure limits the
thermal efficiency is increased by superheating.

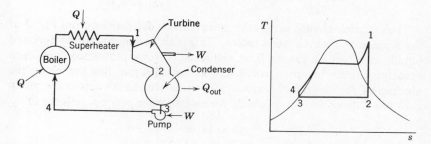

Fig. 18·3 Rankine cycle with superheat.

If the steam-generator pressure is higher than the critical pressure, there
is of course no constant-temperature heat-addition process in a Rankine
cycle. pv, Ts, and hs diagrams for such a cycle are shown in Fig. 18·4.

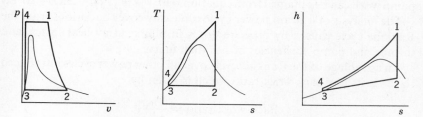

Fig. 18·4 Supercritical-pressure Rankine cycle.

Inspection of Ts diagrams shows that, for given temperature limits, the
Rankine cycle efficiency is always lower than that of the Carnot cycle
because not all the heat is added at the highest temperature.

Performance calculations for a Rankine cycle are simple because no
work is done in the two heat-transfer processes and the two processes
involving work are adiabatic. Also, the changes in kinetic and potential
energy across each cycle component are usually negligible. The first law

applied to each piece of steady-flow equipment thus gives

steam generator: $\qquad q_{4\text{-}1} = h_1 - h_4 \qquad (p_1 = p_4)$

turbine: $\qquad\qquad\quad w_T = h_1 - h_2 \qquad (s_2 = s_1)$

condenser: $\qquad\quad\ q_{\text{out},2\text{-}3} = h_2 - h_3 \qquad (p_3 = p_2;\ h_3 = h_f)$

pump: $\qquad\qquad\quad\ w_{\text{in},P} = h_4 - h_3 \qquad (s_4 = s_3)$

The cycle thermal efficiency is

$$\eta = \frac{w_{\text{cycle}}}{q_{4\text{-}1}} = \frac{w_T - w_{\text{in},P}}{q_{4\text{-}1}} = \frac{(h_1 - h_2) - (h_4 - h_3)}{(h_1 - h_4)}$$

The enthalpy change across the pump can be determined from Fig. 3 of the Keenan and Keyes steam tables. This is an hs diagram for compressed liquid, modified by having h_f at the same entropy subtracted from each enthalpy value. In other words, the saturated liquid line lies along the abscissa of the diagram. Another way to determine Δh across the pump is to use $T\,ds = dh - v\,dp$ which, *for an isentropic process*, reduces to

$$\Delta h = \int v\,dp$$

and then to make the approximation

$$\int v\,dp \approx v\,\Delta p$$

This approximation is quite accurate because the specific volume of liquid water is nearly independent of pressure. (The same expression for reversible pump work can be obtained from equation 1·10, $w_{\text{in}} = \int v\,dp + \Delta KE + \Delta PE$.)

The analysis of a steam power cycle can easily cover deviations from the Rankine cycle caused by pressure drops in piping, stray heat losses, and turbine and pump efficiencies of less than unity.

An advantage of the Rankine cycle over all other power cycles introduced so far is its low back-work ratio which is given by

$$\text{Back-work ratio} = \frac{w_{\text{in},P}}{w_T}$$

where w_T and $w_{\text{in},P}$ are respectively the turbine work and the pump work input.

EXAMPLE 18·1. Consider a Rankine cycle which operates with throttle (i.e., turbine inlet) conditions of 1000 psia, 800 F, and a condenser pressure of 1 psia. The sink temperature (lowest temperature of available cooling water) is 70 F. Determine (a) the thermal efficiency, (b) the back-work ratio, and (c) the fraction of the heat added which is available energy.

Solution. A Ts diagram and a flow diagram are made first, and then property values from the steam tables are entered on the flow diagram. The enthalpy change across the pump can be read from Fig. 3 of the Keenan and Keyes steam tables as 3.0 B/lb, or it can be calculated by

$$h_4 - h_3 = \int_3^4 v\, dp \approx v(p_4 - p_3) = 0.01614(1000 - 1)\tfrac{144}{778} = 3.0 \text{ B/lb}$$

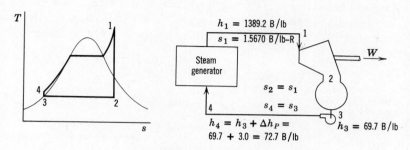

$h_1 = 1389.2$ B/lb
$s_1 = 1.5670$ B/lb-R

Steam generator

$s_2 = s_1$
$s_4 = s_3$

$h_4 = h_3 + \Delta h_P =$
$69.7 + 3.0 = 72.7$ B/lb

$h_3 = 69.7$ B/lb

Example 18·1

h_2 can be determined from $p_2 = 1$ psia and $s_2 = s_1 = 1.5670$ B/lb-R as follows:

$$x_2 = \frac{s_2 - s_f}{s_{fg}} = \frac{1.5670 - 0.1326}{1.8456} = 0.778$$

$$h_2 = h_f + x_2 h_{fg} = 69.7 + 0.778(1036.3) = 875.9 \text{ B/lb}$$

or this value can be determined from an hs (Mollier) chart or hv chart for steam. Having obtained all the h and s values needed, we can now complete the solution.

(a)
$$\eta = \frac{w_{cycle}}{q_{4\text{-}1}} = \frac{w_T - w_{in,P}}{q_{4\text{-}1}} = \frac{h_1 - h_2 - \Delta h_P}{h_1 - h_4}$$

$$= \frac{1389.2 - 875.9 - 3.0}{1389.2 - 72.7} = \frac{513.3 - 3.0}{1316.5} = 0.388$$

(b)
$$\text{Back-work ratio} = \frac{w_{in,P}}{w_T} = \frac{3.0}{513.3} = 0.00585$$

(Notice how low this value is compared with those for gas-turbine cycles.)

(c) Of the heat added,

$$q_{av} = q - q_{unav} = q - T_0(s_1 - s_4) = 1316.5 - 530(1.5670 - 0.1326)$$
$$= 556.3 \text{ B/lb}$$

$$\frac{q_{av}}{q} = \frac{556.3}{1316.5} = 0.422$$

18·3   The regenerative steam power cycle

If we investigate the Rankine cycle for the purpose of devising improvements, we are struck by the fact that some heat is added to the working fluid at a very low temperature. We know from our study of the second law that this impairs the efficiency of the cycle, so we look for a means of raising the temperature of the condensate leaving the pump without transferring heat to it from outside the cycle. Isentropic compression of liquid water as in the Carnot cycle of Fig. 18·1*b* is clearly out of the question. A more promising method is regeneration similar to that of the Stirling and Ericsson cycles (Art. 7·8) whereby heat is transferred from the vapor expanding in the turbine (or engine) to the liquid flowing between the pump and the steam generator. In order for this heat transfer to be

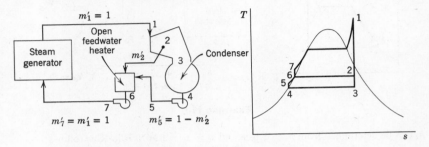

Fig. 18·5 Regenerative cycle with one open feedwater heater.

reversible, a counterflow arrangement is required, which allows heat to be transferred across only an infinitesimal temperature difference at each section of the heat exchanger which would be built into the turbine. Disadvantages of this scheme are the difficulties of building an effective heat exchanger into a turbine and the increased moisture content of the expanding steam which causes erosion of turbine blades.

A more satisfactory solution is to extract or "bleed" steam from the turbine at various points in the expansion process and to transfer the energy of this bled steam to water flowing from the pump to the steam generator. This energy transfer occurs in *feedwater heaters*.

Flow and *Ts* diagrams of a steam power cycle using one *open feedwater heater* (also called a *direct-contact heater*) are shown in Fig. 18·5. In an open feedwater heater, the bled steam and the condensate pumped from the condenser are mixed, and, under optimum operating conditions, saturated liquid leaves the heater. The heater operates at the bleed-point pressure (or slightly below it in an actual plant on account of frictional pressure drop in the bleed line), so another pump is needed to force the water into the steam generator.

For energy and mass balances on regenerative cycles it is convenient to define the mass ratio m' for any point a in the cycle as

$$m'_a \equiv \frac{M_a}{M_1}$$

where M_a is the mass rate of flow at point a, and M_1 is the mass rate of flow leaving the steam generator. Typical units of m' are lb/lb of steam generated or lb/lb of throttle steam. By definition, $m_1' = 1$. Thus an energy balance on the open feedwater heater of Fig. 18·5 for which $W = 0$, $Q = 0$, $\Delta KE = 0$, and $\Delta PE = 0$ is

$$M_2 h_2 + M_5 h_5 = M_6 h_6$$
$$M_2 h_2 + (M_1 - M_2)h_5 = M_1 h_6$$

and this can also be written as

$$m_2' h_2 + (1 - m_2')h_5 = h_6$$

If the states of the fluid at points 2, 5, and 6 are known, this equation can be solved for m_2', the fraction of the throttle flow which is bled to the open feedwater heater. Notice that on a Ts diagram for a regenerative cycle, as shown in Fig. 18·5, the state of the fluid at each point in the cycle is correctly shown but the mass of fluid is not the same at all points. Therefore, the area beneath the path of a reversible process represents heat transfer *per pound of fluid undergoing that process*, and care must be taken to account for variations in mass when comparing areas.

In addition to its function of raising the temperature of feedwater to reduce the amount of heat which is added to the cycle at low temperature, an open feedwater heater in an actual cycle also serves as a *deaerator* to remove air and other noncondensable gases which would cause corrosion. This deaeration is based on the fact that the solubility of gases in water decreases with increasing temperature, so that, if the water is brought to its saturation temperature and provision is made for letting the non-condensable gases escape, they can be removed from the system.

Flow and Ts diagrams of a steam power cycle using one *closed feedwater heater* are shown in Fig. 18·6. The feedwater (which is the condensate from the condenser) is pumped through many tubes in the feedwater heater, and the bled steam condenses (and is first desuperheated, if necessary) on the outside of the tubes. The two fluid streams do not mix in the closed feedwater heater. In the ideal case, the condensate leaving at 8 is saturated liquid, and the feedwater leaving at 6 is at a temperature only infinitesimally lower than T_8. In practice, in order to limit the amount of heat-transfer surface area needed, the difference $(T_8 - T_6)$, called the *terminal temperature difference*, is usually of the order of 5 or 10 Fahrenheit degrees.

The solid lines in Fig. 18·6 show the heater drain being pumped into the feedwater line between the heater and the steam generator. The drain after being pumped to state 9 is mixed with the feedwater at state 6 to form feedwater at state 7. A magnified portion of the Ts diagram in Fig. 18·6 shows these processes. Another method of handling the heater drain is shown by the broken lines in Fig. 18·6. It is throttled through a trap or valve into the condenser. (A trap operates in such a manner that liquid which enters it is throttled to the lower pressure on the discharge side, but vapor which enters the trap is not allowed to pass. The same function is

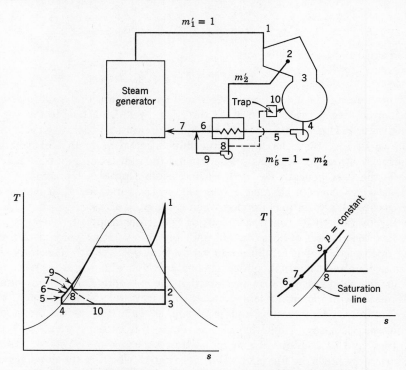

Fig. 18·6 Regenerative cycle with one closed feedwater heater. An alternate method of handling the heater drain is shown by the broken lines.

performed by a valve in the drain line which is controlled by a float to maintain a constant liquid level in the lower part of a heater.) Application of the first law to the trap results in $h_8 = h_{10}$.

A mass and energy balance on the closed feedwater heater gives

$$M_2 h_2 + M_5 h_5 = M_2 h_8 + M_5 h_6$$
$$M_2 h_2 + (M_1 - M_2)h_5 = M_2 h_8 + (M_1 - M_2)h_6$$
$$m_2' h_2 + (1 - m_2')h_5 = m_2' h_8 + (1 - m_2')h_6$$

A significant advantage of closed heaters is that they do not require for each heater a separate pump to handle the feedwater flow, but a drawback of closed heaters is that they do not bring the feedwater to the heater saturation temperature as open heaters do.

EXAMPLE 18·2.   Consider an ideal steam power cycle which operates with throttle conditions of 1000 psia and 800 F, an open feedwater heater at 90 psia, and a condenser pressure of 1 psia. Determine the thermal efficiency.

Solution.   Flow and Ts diagrams should be made first, and for this solution we will refer to those of Fig. 18·5. The following enthalpy values are obtained from the steam tables as in Example 18·1, or more quickly by following an isentropic line on a Mollier (hs) or hv chart:

$$h_1 = 1389.2 \text{ B/lb} \qquad h_2 = 1150.9 \text{ B/lb} \qquad h_3 = 875.9 \text{ B/lb}$$

From the steam tables,

$$h_4 = h_{f,1\,\text{psia}} = 69.7 \text{ B/lb} \qquad h_6 = h_{f,90\,\text{psia}} = 290.6 \text{ B/lb}$$

The first law shows that h_5 and h_7 exceed h_4 and h_6, respectively, by the pump work in each case. Using the approximation $\int v\,dp \approx v\,\Delta p$ for the reversible pump work input,

$$h_5 = h_4 + v\,\Delta p = 69.7 + 0.01614(90 - 1)\tfrac{144}{778} = 69.7 + 0.3 = 70.0 \text{ B/lb}$$

$$h_7 = h_6 + v\,\Delta p = 290.6 + 0.01766(1000 - 90)\tfrac{144}{778} = 290.6 + 3.0 = 293.6 \text{ B/lb}$$

The amount of steam bled per pound of throttle steam m_2' can be found by making an energy balance on (i.e., by applying the first law to) the open feedwater heater. We assume that there is no heat transfer with the surroundings and that the changes in kinetic and potential energy are negligible. Then

$$m_2' h_2 + (1 - m_2')h_5 = h_6$$

$$m_2' = \frac{h_6 - h_5}{h_2 - h_5} = \frac{290.6 - 70.0}{1150.9 - 70.0} = 0.204 \text{ lb/lb throttle}$$

Applying the first law to the steady-flow turbine with $q = 0$ and $\Delta KE + \Delta PE = 0$, we have for the work *per pound of steam entering the turbine*

$$w_T = h_1 - m_2' h_2 - (1 - m_2')h_3 \qquad (a)$$

(This energy balance has been written from the general form $w = \sum_{\text{in}} m'h - \sum_{\text{out}} m'h$. Slightly different physical reasoning gives

$$w_T = h_1 - h_2 + (1 - m_2')(h_2 - h_3) \qquad (b)$$

or

$$w_T = m_2'(h_1 - h_2) + (1 - m_2')(h_1 - h_3) \qquad (c)$$

Any one of these three forms is satisfactory here, but for complex systems, with multiple inlets and outlets, form (a) is the simplest to apply.) Substituting values already determined into equation (a),

$$w_T = 1389.2 - 0.204(1150.9) - 0.796(875.9) = 457 \text{ B/lb throttle}$$

Then

$$\eta = \frac{w_{\text{cycle}}}{q_{7-1}} = \frac{w_T - w_{\text{in},4-5} - w_{\text{in},6-7}}{h_1 - h_7} = \frac{457 - (0.796)0.3 - 3.0}{1389.2 - 293.6} = 0.414$$

Discussion.   Comparing this result with that of Example 18·1 for a Rankine cycle with the same throttle and exhaust conditions shows that the use of a single feedwater heater increases the efficiency by $(0.414 - 0.388)/0.388 = 6.7$ per cent. Other things being equal, the feedwater heater is justified if its total annual cost is less than 6.7 per cent of the annual fuel cost for the simple Rankine cycle.

Modern high-pressure steam power plants use several stages of regenerative feedwater heating. A flow diagram with three closed heaters and one open heater is shown in Fig. 18·7, and some plants use twice as many. The gain in efficiency resulting from the addition of a heater drops as the number of heaters increases. The number of heaters to be used in a plant is determined by an economic study. Roughly speaking, the number of heaters is increased until the addition of one more heater would increase

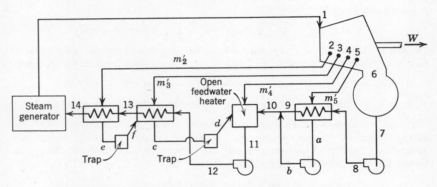

Fig. 18·7 Cycle with four stages of regenerative feedwater heating.

the fixed charges more than it would decrease fuel costs. Consequently, more heaters will be used in a plant that operates near full capacity most of the time than in one of the same capacity which is lightly loaded much of the time.

The steam flow distribution required for several heaters can be determined by starting at the highest-pressure heater and making mass and energy balances on each one in turn.

In passing, it should be mentioned that in actual plants there are many features not discussed here which affect the steam and energy distribution in the cycle. For example, steam may be used for soot blowing and for atomizing fuel oil; water is lost through blowdown, and make-up water must be added; steam may be used to drive auxiliaries; and there are numerous components such as shaft seals and oil coolers which have small but significant effects on the plant energy balance. For analyzing these various effects there are no more powerful tools than the first and second laws of thermodynamics which, on account of their generality, can be studied and learned in connection with some systems and then applied to quite different ones.

EXAMPLE 18·3.   Consider a regenerative steam power cycle as shown on the following page. The flow through the turbine is adiabatic but not isentropic. Assume that the pumps operate isentropically. Pressure, temperature, and enthalpy values are shown on the diagram. The sink temperature is 70 F. Determine the efficiency of the cycle and the irreversibilities, per pound of throttle steam, of the processes in the turbine, closed feedwater heater (including trap), and open feedwater heater. Make an energy flow diagram showing the results.

Solution.   Energy and mass balances on the closed heater and then on the open heater are made to determine m_2' and m_3'.

$$m_2' h_2 + h_8 = m_2' h_{10} + h_9$$

$$m_2' = \frac{h_9 - h_8}{h_2 - h_{10}} = \frac{370 - 219.5}{1286 - 376} = 0.165 \text{ lb/lb throttle}$$

$$m_3' h_3 + (1 - m_2' - m_3') h_6 + m_2' h_{11} = h_7$$

$$m_3' = \frac{h_7 - h_6 - m_2'(h_{11} - h_6)}{h_3 - h_6} = \frac{218.8 - 69.8 - 0.165(376 - 69.8)}{1155 - 69.8}$$

$$= 0.091 \text{ lb/lb throttle}$$

Applying the first law to the turbine, and noting that $m_4' = 1 - m_2' - m_3'$,

$$w_T = h_1 - m_2' h_2 - m_3' h_3 - m_4' h_4$$

$$= 1389 - 0.165(1286) - 0.091(1155) - 0.744(1005) = 324 \text{ B/lb throttle}$$

Then
$$\eta = \frac{w_T - m_4' w_{in,5\text{-}6} - w_{in,7\text{-}8}}{q_{9\text{-}1}} = \frac{w_T - m_4' \Delta h_{5\text{-}6} - \Delta h_{7\text{-}8}}{h_1 - h_9}$$

$$= \frac{324 - (0.744)0.1 - 0.7}{1389 - 370} = 0.317$$

For each piece of adiabatic steady-flow equipment, $i = T_0 \Delta s$, where $\Delta s = \sum\limits_{out} m's - \sum\limits_{in} m's$. For the turbine,

$$i = T_0[m_4' s_4 + m_3' s_3 + m_2' s_2 - s_1]$$

$$= 530[0.744(1.798) + 0.091(1.686) + 0.165(1.618) - 1.567] = 101 \text{ B/lb throttle}$$

To find s_{11}, we notice that $p_{11} = 30$ psia and $h_{11} = h_{10} = 376$ B/lb because the flow through the trap is a throttling process. Then

$$x_{11} = \frac{h_{11} - h_f}{h_{fg}} = \frac{376 - 218.8}{945.3} = 0.166$$

$$s_{11} = s_f + x_{11} s_{fg} = 0.3680 + 0.166(1.3313) = 0.589 \text{ B/lb-R}$$

Then for the closed feedwater heater and its trap,

$$i = T_0[s_9 + m_2' s_{11} - s_8 - m_2' s_2] = T_0[s_9 - s_8 + m_2'(s_{11} - s_2)]$$

$$= 530[0.578 - 0.368 + 0.165(0.589 - 1.618)] = 21.2 \text{ B/lb throttle}$$

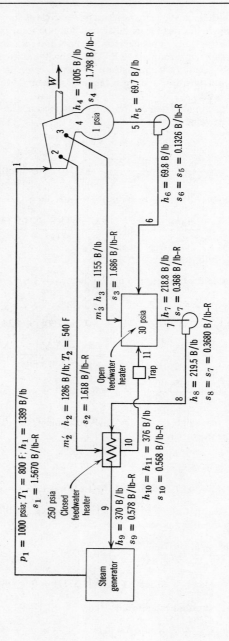

Example 18-3

For the open feedwater heater,

$$i = T_0[s_7 - m_3's_3 - m_4's_6 - m_2's_{11}]$$
$$= 530[0.368 - 0.091(1.686) - 0.744(0.1326) - 0.165(0.589)]$$
$$= 10.1 \text{ B/lb throttle}$$

Other data needed for making the energy flow diagram are the unavailable part of the heat added,

$$q_{unav,9-1} = T_0(s_1 - s_9) = 530(1.567 - 0.578) = 524 \text{ B/lb throttle}$$

the amount of heat rejected per pound of throttle steam,

$$q_{out,4-5} = m_4'(h_4 - h_5) = 0.744(1005 - 69.7) = 695 \text{ B/lb throttle}$$

and the unavailable part of the heat rejected,

$$q_{out,unav,4-5} = m_4'T_0(s_4 - s_5) = 0.744(530)(1.798 - 0.1326)$$
$$= 656 \text{ B/lb throttle}$$

The energy flow diagram shows that the difference between the unavailable energy rejected by the cycle and that added to the cycle is accounted for completely by the sum of the irreversibilities of the cycle components.

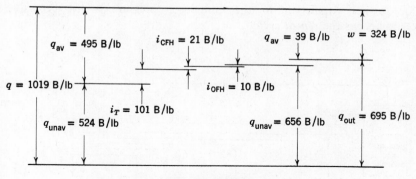

$q_{av} = 495$ B/lb $i_{CFH} = 21$ B/lb $q_{av} = 39$ B/lb $w = 324$ B/lb

$q = 1019$ B/lb $i_{OFH} = 10$ B/lb

$i_T = 101$ B/lb

$q_{unav} = 524$ B/lb $q_{unav} = 656$ B/lb $q_{out} = 695$ B/lb

Example 18·3

18·4 The reheat cycle

The thermal efficiency of a Rankine cycle is increased by increasing the steam-generator pressure or the maximum temperature. For a given maximum temperature, which is usually determined by the strength characteristics of construction materials, increasing the steam-generator pressure causes a decrease in the quality of the steam leaving the prime mover. This is undesirable if the prime mover is a turbine because moisture content of more than 10 to 12 per cent causes serious erosion of turbine blades. (Notice that the exhaust quality in Examples 18·1 and 18·2 is only

0.778, far below the erosion limit of 0.88 to 0.9. Of course, an actual turbine with an efficiency less than 100 per cent has a higher exhaust quality than the corresponding ideal turbine with isentropic expansion.) One way to prevent the exhaust moisture content from exceeding the

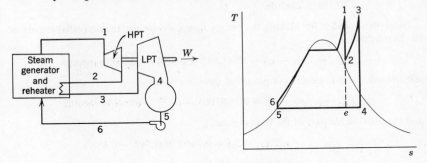

Fig. 18·8 Reheat cycle.

limiting value is to remove the steam from the turbine after part of its expansion, add heat to it at constant pressure, and return it to the turbine for further expansion to the condenser pressure. This procedure characterizes the *reheat cycle*.

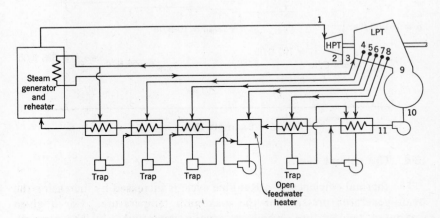

Fig. 18·9 Reheat–regenerative cycle.

Flow and *Ts* diagrams of a reheat cycle are shown in Fig. 18·8. Expansion 1-2 occurs in the high-pressure turbine (HPT), process 2-3 is the constant-pressure reheating, and expansion 3-4 occurs in the low-pressure turbine (LPT). Point *e* is the exhaust state without reheating.

Whether adding reheat to a Rankine cycle increases the cycle thermal efficiency depends on the cycle conditions. Inspection of a reheat-cycle Ts diagram shows that, the higher the reheat pressure and the higher the final reheat temperature, the higher the cycle thermal efficiency is. For the cycle of Fig. 18·8, the thermal efficiency is

$$\eta = \frac{w_{\text{HPT}} + w_{\text{LPT}} - w_{\text{in},P}}{q_{6\text{-}1} + q_{2\text{-}3}}$$

In practice, reheat equipment is economically justifiable only in high-capacity plants; consequently, several stages of regeneration are used in any cycle which involves reheating, and a reheat cycle without regeneration, as shown in Fig. 18·8, is not used. A flow diagram of a reheat–regenerative cycle is shown in Fig. 18·9. For very high-pressure cycles, double reheating is used.

18·5 Cycles for heating and power

In all the cycles discussed so far in this chapter, the useful energy output is work or power, and the heat rejected is considered to be of no value, especially since it is largely unavailable energy. There are many instances, however, where energy in the form of heat is needed, and, since there is no intention of producing power from it, its value is not lessened by the fact that its available fraction is small. Where this heat can be supplied by steam, as in building heating and the heating required by many industrial processes, the functions of heating and power production can often be combined very effectively.

As an example, consider a plant which needs 10^7 B of heat from steam per hour at 30 psia with a minimum temperature in the heating system of 150 F. Figure 18·10a shows how this heating load can be met by 9550 lb of dry saturated steam per hour at 30 psia with condensate returned to the boiler at 150 F. The pump is needed to overcome frictional pressure drop in the system. Its work input is negligibly small in comparison with 10^7 B/hr. An alternative method of meeting this heating load is shown in Fig. 18·10b where dry saturated steam is generated at 100 psia, expanded through a turbine which has an efficiency of 50 per cent, and then gives up 10^7 B/hr as it condenses and is subcooled to 150 F at 30 psia. Analysis of this cycle shows that the same heating load is carried and also 177 hp or 450,000 B/hr of power is produced with an additional heat input of only 450,000 B/hr. Thus power is produced in an amount equivalent to the additional rate of heat input; so this *by-product power* is much cheaper than that from any cycle devised for power only.

The power output and heat output of the cycle in Fig. 18·10b are tied together because the same steam flow passes through the turbine and the heating system. Such a cycle is satisfactory where the steam flow can be controlled only by the heating needs, and whatever power produced can always be used, probably to supplement in varying amounts power which

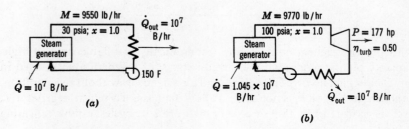

Fig. 18·10 (a) Cycle for heating only. (b) Cycle for heating and by-product power.

is obtained from other sources. Where varying heat and power loads must be carried by a single plant, a cycle such as shown in Fig. 18·11 is used. When the power load is zero, all the steam passes through the pressure-reducing valve (PRV), and none through the turbine. When the heating load is zero, all of the steam expands through the turbine and into the

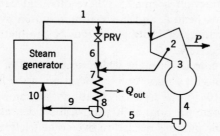

Fig. 18·11 Cycle for heating and power.

condenser. For meeting both heating and power demands, the steam flow distribution is determined as follows: Assuming that all steam to the heating system comes from the turbine extraction point* (state 2), the flow

* As used here, a turbine extraction point differs from a turbine bleed point in that the pressure at an extraction point is held constant under all flow conditions by an automatic valve arrangement in the turbine while a bleed point is simply an opening which takes steam from a section of the turbine at which the pressure may vary slightly as the flow rate changes.

rate in the extraction line is determined from an energy balance on the heating system as

$$M_2 = \frac{\dot{Q}_{\text{heating}}}{h_2 - h_8}$$

Then the power produced by this steam flowing through the turbine from the throttle to the extraction point is determined from an energy balance on that part of the turbine,

$$P = M_2(h_1 - h_2)$$

If this power is less than the total required, the remainder is produced by additional steam which expands all the way through the turbine to the condenser. If this power obtained from the flow M_2 is greater than the total required, then the flow M_2 into the turbine and through the extraction line must be reduced to the value which produces the required amount of power, even though it is inadequate for the heating load. The deficit in energy to the heating system is then made up by steam passed through the pressure-reducing valve. Remember that $h_6 = h_1$ and $h_2 = h_1 - w$, so that $h_6 > h_2$.

In short, the steam distribution problem is to determine the values of M_2, M_3, and M_6 such that their sum is a minimum and they satisfy the first-law equations

$$P = M_2(h_1 - h_2) + M_3(h_1 - h_3)$$

$$\dot{Q} = M_2(h_2 - h_8) + M_6(h_6 - h_8)$$

where P and $\dot{Q}$ are the power required and the heating load, respectively. For the minimum total steam flow, M_3 or M_6 must be zero.*

When M_3 is zero, all the heat added in the steam generator is being utilized; when M_6 is zero, the maximum amount of by-product power is being obtained for a given heating load. When $M_3 = M_6 = 0$, the heating and power loads are said to be balanced, and this is the most economical condition. Loads are usually variable, so a plant cannot be operated with balanced loads all the time; however, the plant designer must select operating conditions which give the closest approach to balanced conditions in the long run.

18·6 Binary vapor cycles

The only working fluid we have considered and the one which is used almost exclusively in practice for vapor power cycles is water. No better

---

* In an actual turbine, changes in flow rate affect the efficiency so that h_2 and h_3 vary somewhat as the total flow rate and the flow distribution are changed. Also, it may not be advisable from an operating viewpoint to reduce M_3 to zero.

fluid has been found, but water is quite undesirable in some respects. Let us list the desirable characteristics of a vapor-cycle working fluid.

1. Critical temperature well above the highest temperature which can be used in a cycle as fixed by construction material limitations. This would make it possible to vaporize the fluid, and thus add a considerable amount of heat to it, at the maximum temperature.

2. Saturation pressures at the maximum and minimum cycle temperatures within a range that involves neither very high pressures which introduce strength problems nor very low pressures which introduce problems of sealing against infiltration of the atmosphere.

3. A high ratio of h_{fg} to c_p of the liquid so that most of the heat added in a Rankine cycle is added at the maximum temperature. This reduces the need for regeneration.

4. Chemical inertness and stability throughout the cycle temperature range.

5. Triple point below the expected minimum ambient temperature. This insures that the fluid will not solidify at any point in the cycle or while being handled outside the cycle.

6. Saturated vapor line (on a property diagram) which is close to a turbine expansion path. This would prevent excessive moisture in the turbine exhaust, thus eliminating the need for reheating, and still permit all or nearly all the heat rejection to occur at the minimum temperature.

7. Cheapness and ready availability.

8. Nontoxicity.

No fluid has all these desirable characteristics. Water is better than any other in an over-all evaluation, but it is poor in regard to desirable characteristics 1 and 2. The critical temperature of water is 705.4 F, approximately 500 F below the temperature limit set by material strength properties. Also, the saturation pressure of water is quite high even at moderate vaporization temperatures (1543 psia at 600 F and 2208 psia at 650 F, for example). Thus water is especially poor at the high-temperature end of the operating range.

Since no single working fluid better than water has been found, searches have been made for a combination of fluids such that one is well suited to the high-temperature part and the other to the low-temperature part of the cycle. The most successful combination to date is mercury and water.

Flow and Ts diagrams for a mercury–water *binary vapor cycle* are shown in Figs. 18·12 and 18·13. The mercury is vaporized in a boiler at, say, 100 psia for which the saturation temperature is 907 F. It is then expanded in a turbine to a pressure of 2 psia for which the saturation temperature is about 505 F. (Expanding the mercury to a condenser temperature of 100 F would require maintaining a condenser pressure of 0.005 mm Hg!) Heat removed from the mercury to condense it is used to boil water at 540 psia and 475 F. The steam is then superheated and expanded through a turbine

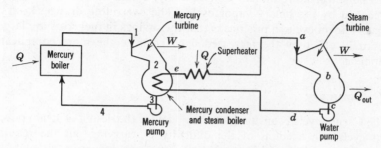

Fig. 18·12 Mercury–water binary vapor cycle.

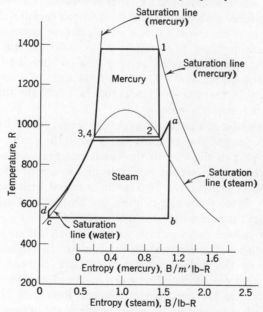

Fig. 18·13 *Ts* diagram of mercury–water binary vapor cycle.

to a pressure determined by the temperature of available cooling water. Thus the Rankine cycle using mercury as a working substance rejects heat to the Rankine cycle using water. (In practice, the water cycle is a regenerative one.) Since h_{fg} for water at the steam-generation temperature is several times as large as h_{fg} for mercury, several pounds of mercury must circulate per pound of water in the binary vapor cycle.

Inspection of the Ts diagram of Fig. 18·13 shows that the binary vapor cycle approaches a Carnot cycle more closely than a steam cycle can for the same temperature limits. Consequently, higher thermal efficiency can be reached by the binary vapor cycle. The overriding drawback of the mercury–steam cycle in practice is that the savings in fuel costs are largely or entirely offset by the increased fixed costs of the more complicated equipment.

18·7 Summary

The Carnot cycle is unsuitable as a model for the design of steam power-plant cycles on account of the difficulty of carrying out the required processes in actual machines. Actual cycles can, however, simulate the *Rankine cycle* which is comprised of four reversible processes: constant-pressure heat addition which takes the fluid from a compressed liquid state to a saturated or superheated vapor state, isentropic expansion in a prime mover, constant-pressure heat rejection to condense the vapor to a saturated liquid, and isentropic pumping to a compressed liquid state at the steam-generation pressure. The back-work ratio of a Rankine cycle is low so that cycle thermal efficiency suffers relatively little from low prime-mover or pump efficiency.

The efficiency of a steam power cycle can be increased by *regeneration* which involves the *bleeding* of some vapor from the prime mover after it has expanded part of the way to the condenser pressure and using it in *feedwater heaters* to preheat the liquid on its way to the steam generator. In open feedwater heaters, the bled steam is mixed with the feedwater in the heater; in closed feedwater heaters, the bled steam condenses on the outside of tubes through which the feedwater flows.

In order to reduce the moisture content which causes erosion in the low-pressure stages of turbines, *reheating* is used. In a reheat cycle, steam is removed from the turbine after part of its expansion is completed, heated at constant pressure, and returned to the turbine for the remainder of the expansion to the condenser pressure. Reheating is used only in conjunction with regeneration because economic studies always show that regeneration should be added to a Rankine cycle before reheating.

Whenever power and heat at a relatively low temperature are both to be produced, a combination steam cycle, often using an *extraction turbine*, is much more economical than separate power and heating cycles.

Water has some serious shortcomings as a vapor-power-cycle working fluid, but no better fluid has been found. A *binary vapor cycle* uses two fluids: One with good high-temperature characteristics is used in a Rankine cycle which rejects heat into another Rankine cycle (or regenerative cycle) which uses a second fluid with good low-temperature characteristics.

It must be remembered that modifications which improve the efficiency of a power plant can be economically justified only if the saving in fuel costs exceeds the additional fixed costs which result from the modifications.

REFERENCES

18·1 P. J. Kiefer, G. F. Kinney, and M. C. Stuart, *Principles of Engineering Thermodynamics*, John Wiley & Sons, 2d ed., 1954, chapter 13.

18·2 D. A. Mooney, *Mechanical Engineering Thermodynamics*, Prentice-Hall, 1953, chapters 14 and 15.

18·3 F. T. Morse, *Power Plant Engineering*, D. Van Nostrand Co., 3d ed., 1953.

18·4 G. A. Gaffert, *Steam Power Stations*, McGraw-Hill Book Co., 4th ed., 1952, chapter XXIII.

18·5 P. J. Potter, *Power Plant Theory and Design*, Ronald Press, 2d ed., 1959.

18·6 *Steam, Its Generation and Use*, Babcock & Wilcox Co., 1955, chapter 10.

18·7 *Combustion Engineering*, Combustion Engineering, Inc., 1947, chapter 13.

18·8 C. A. Meyer, G. J. Silvestri, and J. A. Martin, "Availability Balance of Steam Power Plants," *Journal of Engineering for Power, Transactions ASME*, vol. 81, series A, January 1959, pp. 35–42.

PROBLEMS

18·1 Determine the efficiency of a steam power plant operating on a Carnot cycle if the fluid states at the beginning and end of the isothermal expansion are saturated liquid and dry saturated vapor, respectively, at a pressure of 200 psia. The pressure during the heat rejection is 10 psia.

18·2 A Rankine cycle has steam entering the turbine at 400 psia, 700 F, and an exhaust pressure of 1 psia. Determine the efficiency of the cycle.

18·3 Solve Prob. 18·2 for an exhaust pressure of 1 in. of mercury absolute.

18·4 Determine the efficiency and the back-work ratio of a Rankine cycle which operates between 5000 psia and 1 psia with a turbine throttle temperature of 1100 F.

18·5 Solve Example 18·1 with a turbine efficiency of 0.75 and a pump efficiency of 0.60.

18·6 Solve Example 18·1, allowing for a 30 psi drop in pressure between the steam-generator outlet and the turbine (i.e., the steam-generator outlet pressure is 1030 psia), a turbine efficiency of 0.70, a pump efficiency of 0.65, and a pump discharge pressure of 1300 psia to allow for pressure drops in the piping and in the steam generator.

18·7 For a throttle temperature of 1150 F, an exhaust pressure of 0.5 psia, and a turbine efficiency of 0.80, what is the maximum throttle pressure which can be used if the moisture in the exhaust is not to exceed 10 per cent?

18-8 Steam enters a turbine at 5000 psia, 1100 F, and expands to 1 psia. At the section of the turbine where the quality reaches 90 per cent, 90 per cent of the liquid present is separated mechanically from the steam flow and removed from the turbine. Calculate the amount by which the ideal turbine work is changed.

18-9 Consider any type of steam power cycle operating with fixed conditions at the steam-generator inlet and outlet and a fixed condenser pressure. The turbine exhaust is always wet (i.e., not superheated). Demonstrate that an increase in irreversibility i anywhere in the cycle always results in an increased heat rejection in the condenser.

18-10 Mechanical design limitations are similar for both gas and steam turbines. What reasons can you give for the fact that steam power plants are built in much larger capacities than gas-turbine power plants?

18-11 Steam is supplied to a turbine at 200 psia, 600 F, and exhausted at 14.7 psia. Assume reversible adiabatic flow. To what pressure must the incoming steam be throttled in order to reduce the work per pound to two thirds of that obtained without throttling? Assume that the flow through the turbine is still reversible and adiabatic and that the exhaust pressure is unchanged.

18-12 Prove that the constant-pressure lines in the wet region of an hs diagram for steam are straight. Also prove that they are or are not parallel.

18-13 Liquid sodium leaving a nuclear reactor is at 20 psia, 700 F. It goes to a heat exchanger where it is cooled to 600 F before returning to the reactor. The sodium flow rate in this circuit (the *primary circuit*) is 100,000 lb/hr. In the heat exchanger, heat is transferred to liquid sodium in an *intermediate circuit*, which in turn transfers heat to a boiler which produces dry saturated steam at 1000 psia. The steam expands adiabatically through a turbine to 1 psia. The turbine efficiency is 0.60. Sketch a flow diagram showing all three (primary, intermediate, and steam) circuits. Assuming (1) negligible pressure drops due to friction, (2) negligible work required by sodium pumps, (3) negligible stray heat losses, and (4) the specific heat of sodium to be constant at 0.30 B/lb-F, determine (a) the net amount of power available from the plant, (b) the irreversibility, in B/hr, of the process of transferring energy from the primary sodium circuit through the intermediate circuit to the water.

18-14 Dry saturated steam at a pressure p_1 enters a turbine at a rate of M_1 lb/hr. Partway through the turbine, M_2 lb/hr of dry saturated steam at a pressure p_2 is added. All of the steam is exhausted at a pressure p_3. The expansion in the turbine is adiabatic. The sink temperature is T_3. A throttling calorimeter is used to measure the quality of the exhaust steam. Write equations in terms of flow rates and properties at 1, 2, and 3 for (a) the turbine power output, (b) the irreversibility of the turbine process, and (c) the minimum possible exhaust quality if no measurement of it had been made. (Of course, without the measurement of x_3 or h_3, parts (a) and (b) could not be solved.)

18-15 Solve Example 18-2 if a closed heater is used and the condensate in the heater is trapped into the condenser. (a) Assume that the feedwater is heated to the saturation temperature of the heater. (b) Assume that the feedwater leaves the heater 20 Fahrenheit degrees colder than the saturation temperature of the heater.

18-16 Calculate the irreversibility per pound of throttle steam of the operation of the feedwater heater of (a) Example 18-2, (b) Prob. 18-15.

18-17 A regenerative steam power-plant cycle uses one open and one closed feedwater heater. The closed heater operates at a higher pressure than the open one. There are three ways that the condensate drain from the closed heater can be handled: (a) It can be pumped into the feedwater line between the closed heater and the boiler. (b) It can be trapped into the open heater. (c) It can be trapped into the condenser. From the standpoint of cycle efficiency, which method is the best? Which is the worst? Explain your reasoning.

18·18 An ideal regenerative cycle operates with throttle conditions of 400 psia, 700 F; a single open feedwater heater at 35 psia; and a condenser pressure of 1 in. mercury absolute. Determine its efficiency.

18·19 An ideal regenerative cycle operates with throttle conditions of 400 psia, 700 F; one open feedwater heater at 20 psia; one closed feedwater heater (with its drain trapped to the open heater) at 100 psia; and a condenser pressure of 1 in. mercury absolute. The terminal temperature difference of the closed feedwater heater is 8 Fahrenheit degrees. Determine the thermal efficiency of the cycle.

18·20 Solve Prob. 18·18, assuming that the turbine efficiency between the throttle and any point in the turbine is 0.65 and the boiler feed pump efficiency is 0.70.

18·21 Consider a regenerative steam cycle with one open heater. If the turbine expansion is adiabatic but irreversible, the values of several flow and energy quantities in the cycle may be different from their values with an isentropic turbine expansion. Explain clearly how and why each of the following values is affected: (a) the mass of steam bled, (b) the heat rejected in the condenser per pound of throttle steam, and (c) the heat rejected in the condenser per pound of steam entering the condenser.

18·22 An ideal reheat cycle has throttle conditions of 2000 psia, 836 F, and reheats at 550 psia to 900 F. The exhaust pressure is 1 psia. Compute the thermal efficiency of the cycle. Per pound of throttle steam, how much unavailable energy is rejected by the cycle if the sink temperature is 70 F?

18·23 Solve Prob. 18·22 for a high-pressure turbine efficiency of 0.85 and a low-pressure turbine efficiency of 0.80.

18·24 Determine the efficiency and the required flow rate of an ideal reheat cycle which is to produce 150,000 kw at the turbine coupling if the throttle conditions are 2400 psia, 1100 F; reheat is at 300 psia to 1050 F; and the condenser pressure is 1 psia.

18·25 Solve Prob. 18·24 if a closed feedwater heater with a terminal temperature difference of 5 Fahrenheit degrees is supplied with steam from the high-pressure turbine exhaust. The heater drain is pumped into the feed line.

18·26 Determine the efficiency and the required flow rate from the steam generator for an ideal reheat–regenerative cycle which is to produce 150,000 kw at the turbine coupling if the throttle conditions are 2400 psia, 1100 F; reheat is at 300 psia to 1050 F; there are closed feedwater heaters at 800 psia, 300 psia, 120 psia, and 8 psia; there is an open feedwater heater at 35 psia; and the condenser pressure is 1 psia. The drain from each closed heater is trapped into the next lower heater except that the drain from the 8-psia heater is pumped into the open heater.

18·27 Consider a reheat cycle as shown in Fig. 18·8 with the two turbines on the same shaft driving a single generator. The load on the generator is suddenly reduced from full load to zero. Steam flow through the turbines must be stopped immediately or they will overspeed, but some flow of steam must be maintained through the superheater and reheater to keep them from overheating before the furnace or reactor cools. Make a sketch showing what valves are needed in the system to take care of this emergency, each one's normal position, and its action when the turbine load is suddenly dropped.

18·28 Comment on the advisability of extracting steam for regenerative feedwater heating from the line between a reheater and the following turbine.

18·29 Steam is to be supplied to a turbine at 5000 psia, 1100 F, and exhausted to a condenser at 1 psia. For isentropic expansion it is desired to have no moisture entering a reheater and not more than 10 per cent moisture entering the condenser. These conditions call for a double reheat arrangement. If reheat temperatures are not to exceed 1000 F and it is desired to have the same enthalpy drop across each turbine, determine the reheat pressures to be used.

18·30 A steam accumulator is an energy-storage device which consists of an insulated tank which normally contains both liquid water and steam. Steam is admitted below the liquid surface, and steam is withdrawn from the highest point in the tank. A certain accumulator contains 100 cu ft of vapor and 500 cu ft of liquid at 200 psia. For how long a period, with no steam entering, can steam at 50 psia be withdrawn through a pressure-reducing valve at a steady rate of 4000 lb/hr? (*Suggestion*: As an approximation, use a constant mean enthalpy value for the steam leaving.)

18·31 An accumulator is filled with 200 cu ft of steam and 400 cu ft of liquid water at 50 psia. The accumulator is charged from a line in which steam is at 200 psia, 500 F. If steam is supplied to the accumulator at a steady rate of 4000 lb/hr, how long will it take to charge it to 200 psia?

18·32 If a steam accumulator is alternately charged with dry saturated steam at 200 psia and discharged to pressures as low as 50 psia with only dry saturated vapor leaving, is it necessary to add or remove water periodically to keep the accumulator operating? Explain.

18·33 Verify the numerical values given in the second paragraph of Art. 18·5 which refer to Fig. 18·10.

18·34 Steam enters an extraction turbine at 200 psia, 500 F; extraction occurs at 20 psia, $h = 1140$ B/lb; and steam entering the condenser is at 1 psia, $h = 1005$ B/lb. Part of the extracted steam goes to an open feedwater heater which operates at 20 psia, and the rest goes to a heating system which provides 30 million B/hr and from which condensate at 152 F is pumped into the open heater. Saturated liquid leaves the open heater. The turbine power output is 3500 kw. Determine (*a*) the efficiency of the turbine between the throttle and the extraction point, (*b*) the irreversibility of the turbine expansion upstream of the extraction point, and (*c*) the flow rate of steam into the turbine.

18·35 A plant is designed to supply a power load of 5000 kw and a heating load of 45 million B/hr. Steam is generated at 650 psia, 850 F, and is expanded in a turbine exhausting to a condenser at a pressure of 2 in. mercury absolute. Assume that expansion is isentropic and that the condensate leaves the condenser as saturated water. The heating load is supplied by steam at 22 psia which is condensed and subcooled to 120 F and returned to the boiler at that temperature. Two types of plant can be used, (1) power produced by a condensing turbine and heating steam supplied by throttling high-pressure steam, (2) power produced by an automatic extraction turbine and heating steam supplied by bleeding 22 psia steam from the turbine. Compute for each type (*a*) pounds of steam required per hour, (*b*) heat input to boiler, B/hr, and (*c*) heat rejected in condenser, B/hr.

18·36 In a manufacturing plant, steam for heating purposes is obtained at 20 psia by drawing steam through a pressure-reducing valve from a line where it is dry and saturated at 100 psia. The heating load is 20 million B/hr. Condensate leaves the heating system at 20 psia, 180 F. It is proposed to use a turbine in place of the pressure-reducing valve in order to obtain some "by-product" power while still carrying the same heating load. Assuming a turbine efficiency of 60 per cent, determine (a) the amount of power which can be obtained with the proposed arrangement, and (b) the change in steam flow rate, in lb/hr, which will be required if the proposal is adopted.

18-37 A steam plant is to produce 7500 hp at the turbine coupling and supply a heating load of 70 million B/hr by means of steam extracted at 30 psia which is condensed and subcooled to 200 F in the heating system. Condenser pressure is 1 psia and the condenser flow rate must not be less than 5000 lb/hr. Determine the optimum steam-generator pressure for balanced operation under these conditions, and calculate the amount of heat which must be added in B/hr. A throttle pressure below 300 psia should be accompanied by a throttle temperature of 600 F; 300 to 600 psia, by 700 F; and over 600 psia, by 800 F.

CHAPTER 19

Refrigeration

The purpose of a refrigerating system is to remove heat continuously from a body which is at a temperature lower than that of the surroundings. If the refrigerator operates cyclically (so that there is no net change in its stored energy), the energy transfers are as shown in Fig. 19·1a. A

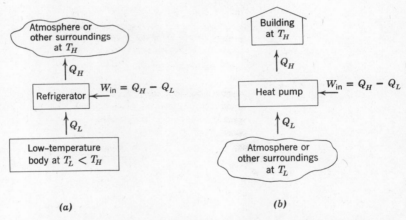

Fig. 19·1 Refrigeration cycle application (a) as a refrigerator and (b) as a heat pump.

consequence of the first law is that $W_{in} = Q_H - Q_L$ and a consequence of the second law is that $W_{in} > 0$. The same cycles of operation and the same energy transfers are involved in the heat-pump application, where heat is removed from the atmosphere or some other part of the surroundings for the purpose of supplying heat to a building or other body at a higher temperature, as shown in Fig. 19·1b.

The purpose of this chapter is to introduce a few refrigeration or heat-pump systems as further illustrations of the use of the first law, the second law, and physical property relationships.

622

19·1   The reversed Carnot cycle

The reversed Carnot cycle (or the Carnot refrigerator cycle) has been described in Art. 7·7 and discussed further in Chapter 8. Figure 19·2 shows a TS diagram for a reversed Carnot cycle. The heat absorbed at temperature T_L during process 1-2 is represented by area 1-2-b-a-1; the heat rejected at T_H during process 3-4 is represented by area 3-4-a-b-3; and the net work input is therefore represented by the difference between these two areas which is area 1-2-3-4-1.

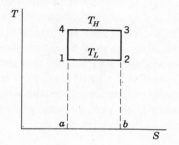

Fig. 19·2   Reversed Carnot cycle.

The Carnot cycle is used as a standard of comparison for heat-engine cycles because its efficiency is the maximum for given temperature limits. In a similar manner, the reversed Carnot cycle is used as a standard of comparison for refrigeration because for given temperature limits its coefficient of performance is the maximum. (See Prob. 8·2.) Coefficient of performance β of any refrigerator is defined as

$$\beta \equiv \frac{Q_L}{W_{\text{in}}}$$

where Q_L is the heat absorbed from the low-temperature body. (See Art. 2·10 for the introduction of coefficient of performance.) Application of the first law and the important relationship

$$\frac{Q_H}{Q_L} = \frac{T_H}{T_L} \tag{8·3}$$

which results from the second law (and which applies only to externally reversible cycles) to the Carnot refrigerator shows that its coefficient of performance is given by

$$\beta_{\text{Carnot}} = \frac{T_L}{T_H - T_L}$$

19·2   Definition of the ton of refrigeration

A widely used unit of the rate of heat absorption by a refrigeration system is the *ton of refrigeration*, which is defined as a heat absorption rate of 200 B/min. The name of this unit is derived from the fact that this rate of heat removal will freeze approximately one ton of water at 32 F into ice at 32 F in 24 hr. (It would be exactly one ton if the latent heat of fusion were 144 B/lb instead of 143.35 B/lb.)

The capacity or rating of a refrigeration system is usually expressed in tons. Thus a 10-ton system is one which can absorb 2000 B/min *when operating under design conditions*. This does not mean that the rate of heat absorption by this system at any instant actually is 2000 B/min, because many factors other than the system design affect the actual performance. (This is analogous to the fact that the power delivered by a 10-hp electric motor is not 10 hp just because the motor is running.)

In addition to coefficient of performance, the power required per ton of refrigeration is a widely used performance parameter for refrigeration systems.

19·3   The reversed Brayton cycle

Actual refrigeration cycles using gaseous working substances are not based on the reversed Carnot cycle, on account of the difficulties involved in carrying out the isothermal heat-absorption and heat-rejection processes. An ideal cycle which can be more easily simulated in practice is the reversed Brayton cycle. Flow, pv, and Ts diagrams of a reversed Brayton cycle are shown in Fig. 19·3. T_H and T_L are the temperatures of those parts of the surroundings to which heat can be rejected and from which heat is to be removed, respectively. The usual working fluid is air. The air is compressed isentropically to a temperature above T_H, and then it is cooled reversibly* at constant pressure until its temperature is T_H or slightly higher than T_H. The air is then expanded isentropically through an engine which supplies some of the power requirement of the compressor. The temperature of the air passing through the engine drops to a value lower than T_L. Therefore, heat can be absorbed from part of the surroundings at T_L as the air flows at constant pressure through a heat exchanger to state 1 to complete the cycle. Application of the first law to each of the four pieces of equipment

---

* Remember that *reversible*, without a modifier, means *internally reversible*. (See Art. 7·3.) The direct transfer of heat from the gas undergoing process 2-3 across a finite temperature difference to the surroundings at T_H is of course externally irreversible.

in the steady-flow cycle, assuming that $\Delta KE + \Delta PE = 0$, gives

$$w_{\text{in},C} = h_2 - h_1$$
$$q_{\text{out},2\text{-}3} = h_2 - h_3$$
$$w_{\text{eng}} = h_3 - h_4$$
$$q_{4\text{-}1} = h_1 - h_4$$

There is a net work input to the cycle because the work input to the compressor is greater than the engine work. This can be seen from either the pv or the Ts diagram of Fig. 19·3 and is of course in accordance with the second law.

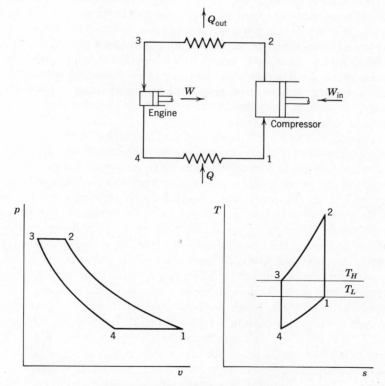

Fig. 19·3 Reversed Brayton cycle.

Notice that the engine of the reversed Brayton cycle cannot be successfully replaced by a throttling valve if the air in the cycle behaves as an ideal gas, because for an ideal gas the Joule–Thomson coefficient is zero, and there is consequently no temperature change across a throttling valve. For information on how closely air at low temperatures approximates an ideal gas, refer to the *Ts* diagram for air in the appendix, Chart A·1. For an ideal gas, constant-enthalpy lines coincide with constant-temperature lines.

In the temperature ranges normally encountered in refrigeration cycles. the specific heats of air can be treated as constant with very little loss in accuracy.

Recall that for any process the irreversibility is given by

$$I = T_0 \, \Delta S_{\text{isolated system}}$$

where T_0 is the temperature of the atmosphere. If some other energy reservoir such as the water of a river or lake is used instead of the atmosphere as a source or absorber of heat,* then its temperature is used as T_0. In the case of a refrigeration cycle, it is not strictly correct to refer to T_0 as "the lowest temperature in the surroundings" unless it is understood that the temperature of the body being cooled is excluded from consideration because that body is certainly not an energy reservoir which can absorb or reject very large amounts of heat without experiencing a temperature change. If it were, there would probably be no need for a refrigerating system to remove heat from it.

A drawback of an air refrigeration system is that the low density of air at moderate pressures calls for either very high pressures or very high volume flow rates in order to obtain moderate refrigerating capacity. The early solution to this problem was to use very high pressures in order to limit the physical size of the equipment. Consequently, the early systems were called "dense air refrigerating machines." Such machines have been completely displaced by vapor-compression systems, which are cheaper to build on account of the lower pressures and smaller volumes involved, and cheaper to operate because their coefficients of performance are higher for any specified temperature range. The major application for air refrigerating systems is now aircraft cabin or cockpit cooling where cool air must be supplied and low system weight is desirable. Small high-speed compressors and turbines which are low in weight but handle large volumes of air are used. An example of an aircraft cooling system is shown in Fig. 19·4. Some air is bled from the jet-engine compressor, cooled in a heat exchanger, and then compressed further by a small compressor which is driven by the turbine. The air is cooled in a heat exchanger between the compressor discharge and the turbine inlet. The cool air leaving the turbine is then ducted to the cabin. Many variations of this cycle are possible. A major problem with such systems in high-speed aircraft is cooling the air before

* In a power cycle, heat is rejected to the atmosphere or to the water of a river, lake, or ocean. A heat pump for heating a building, however, takes heat *from* these same energy reservoirs.

it enters the turbine, because the ambient air experiences a considerable temperature rise when it is brought into the craft and slowed down (relative to the craft).

The chief disadvantage of the reversed Brayton cycle from a thermo-dynamic standpoint is illustrated by a Ts diagram: The constant-pressure

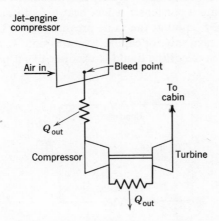

Fig. 19·4 Aircraft cooling system.

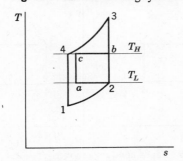

Fig. 19·5 Comparison of reversed Brayton and reversed Carnot cycles.

heat-transfer processes result in an operating temperature range much greater than the minimum range established by the temperatures of those parts of the surroundings with which heat is exchanged. In Fig. 19·5, 1-2-3-4-1 is a reversed Brayton cycle which absorbs the same amount of heat (the area beneath 1-2 equals the area beneath a-2) as the Carnot cycle a-2-b-c-a, which exchanges heat with the same energy reservoirs at T_H and T_L. The area within each diagram represents the work input, and it is apparent that the coefficient of performance of the reversed Brayton cycle is much lower than that of the reversed Carnot cycle.

19·4 Vapor-compression refrigeration

Flow, Ts, and ph diagrams of a conventional vapor-compression refrigerating system are shown in Fig. 19·6. Wet vapor enters the compressor at 1 and is compressed reversibly and adiabatically to state 2. The vapor then flows into a condenser where heat is removed to condense the vapor to a saturated liquid at the same pressure, state 3. The refrigerant then expands through a valve or capillary tube to state 4. For the throttling process, $h_4 = h_3$. Some of the liquid is vaporized as it passes through the

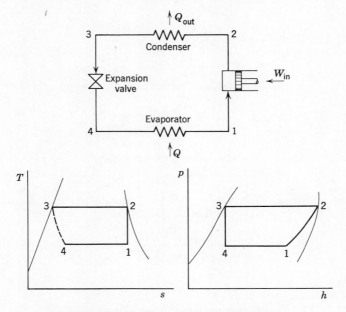

Fig. 19·6 Vapor compression refrigeration cycle.

expansion valve; so a low-quality mixture enters the evaporator. In the evaporator, heat is absorbed from the body being refrigerated to evaporate most of the liquid. Thus the cycle is completed when the refrigerant leaves the evaporator and enters the compressor in state 1.

Notice that three of the four processes in the ideal vapor-compression refrigeration cycle are reversible but that process 3-4 is irreversible. An engine is not used in place of the expansion valve in *actual* cycles because the work obtained by expanding a saturated liquid in an engine is much too small to justify the addition of the engine and its related equipment. Therefore, an engine is not used in the *ideal* cycle because doing so would increase the differences between the actual cycle and the corresponding ideal cycle.

The *ph* diagram, which also is called a Mollier diagram,* is convenient in analyzing vapor-compression refrigeration cycles because (1) three of the four processes appear on it as straight lines, and (2) for the evaporator and condenser processes the heat transfer is proportional to the lengths of the process paths. Such a diagram for ammonia is in the appendix, Chart A·4. On Chart A·4 the pressure scale is logarithmic. The *ph* diagram of Fig. 19·6 has a linear pressure scale.

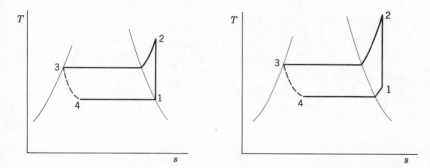

Fig. 19·7   Dry compression cycles.

The cycle shown in Fig. 19·6 is called a *wet compression* cycle because it involves the compression of a liquid–vapor mixture. Notice on the *Ts* diagram how closely it approximates a reversed Carnot cycle. In fact, replacing the expansion valve throttling process by an isentropic expansion would make the two cycles identical.

If the vapor entering the compressor is dry and saturated or superheated, as in Fig. 19·7, the cycle is said to involve *dry compression*. Notice that dry compression, especially with superheated vapor entering the compressor, makes part of the cycle resemble a reversed Brayton cycle and reduces the coefficient of performance for given evaporation and condensation temperatures. Nevertheless, dry compression is usually favored over wet compression because it results in higher compressor efficiency, higher compressor volumetric efficiency, and less danger of damage to the compressor caused by slugs of liquid entering it.

In a dry compression cycle, the temperature of the vapor being compressed exceeds the condensation temperature, so it is possible to cool the compressor by the same coolant used in the condenser. Doing so decreases the work required by the compressor.

* This name is used for several different thermodynamic diagrams.

For a given condensation temperature, the refrigerating capacity of a vapor-compression system is increased by subcooling the condensate before it reaches the expansion valve. In actual systems the incoming (coldest) coolant is sometimes used for this purpose before it is used for condensing the refrigerant.

Many factors must be considered in the selection of a refrigerant for a vapor-compression system. One of the most important properties is the

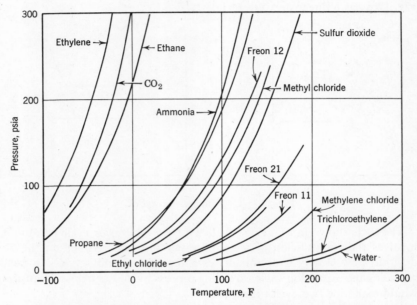

Fig. 19·8 Saturation pressure–temperature curves for some refrigerants.

saturation pressure–temperature relationship which establishes the operating pressure range for any particular application. Saturation curves for several refrigerants are shown in Fig. 19·8. Also, for given temperature limits the coefficient of performance which can be obtained varies markedly from one refrigerant to another. Tables showing the relative performance obtainable with various refrigerants are published in virtually all engineering handbooks which include chapters or sections on refrigeration.

Many modifications of the basic vapor-compression cycle are possible for the purpose of increasing the coefficient of performance. In an actual plant where costs must be watched closely, various refinements are used only if the saving in power costs is greater than the additional costs incurred by adding the refinements. Details of these cycle variations can be found in the literature on refrigeration. Here, simply as an example of such a variation, we will describe the use of multistage compression with intercooling by means of a flash chamber.

For a fixed condensation temperature, lowering the evaporator temperature increases the compressor pressure ratio. For a reciprocating compressor, a high pressure ratio across a single stage means low volumetric efficiency. Also, with dry compression the high pressure ratio results in a

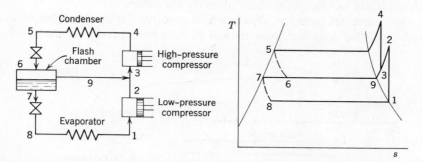

Fig. 19·9 Two-stage vapor compression cycle with flash chamber intercooler.

high compressor discharge temperature which may cause decomposition of the refrigerant. Multistage compression with intercooling is obviously called for, but effective intercooler temperatures may be well below the temperature of available cooling water which is used for the condenser. Therefore, several methods of using the refrigerant as an intercooling medium have been devised. One of these methods employs a flash chamber as shown in Fig. 19·9.

Liquid from the condenser in Fig. 19·9 expands through the first expansion valve into the flash chamber where the pressure is the same as the compressor interstage pressure. The refrigerant entering the flash chamber is a liquid–vapor mixture in state 6. The liquid fraction, which alone is in state 7 as shown on the Ts diagram, flows through the second expansion valve into the evaporator. The vapor from the flash chamber, which is in state 9, is mixed with the vapor (state 2) from the low-pressure compressor to form vapor in state 3 which enters the high-pressure compressor. The ratio M_9/M_7 can be determined from an energy balance on the flash chamber. State 3 can then be determined by an energy balance on the mixing point between the compressors.

For very wide temperature ranges, binary vapor cycles are used in which the condenser for the lower-temperature fluid is the evaporator for the higher-temperature fluid. Three- and four-fluid cycles have also been used.

Control systems for refrigerating units range from very complex ones used in large industrial installations to the simple on–off control of household refrigerators. One aspect of the control problem should be noted: The heat absorbed is (1) the product of the mass rate of flow through the evaporator and the specific enthalpy increase in the evaporator and also (2) proportional to the temperature difference between the evaporating refrigerant and the surroundings of the evaporator. Therefore, no one of these three variables (M, Δh in the evaporator, and ΔT for heat transfer) can be changed without affecting the others.

One other refrigeration system which involves the compression of a vapor will be described even though it does not operate on the usual

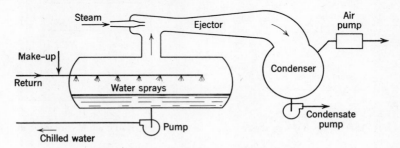

Fig. 19·10   Steam Jet refrigeration system.

vapor-compression refrigeration cycle. This is the *steam-jet system* or *vacuum system*. For refrigeration at temperatures above 32 F, water is a satisfactory refrigerant. Its chief drawback is the high specific volume of water vapor at low temperatures which calls for large compressors. Centrifugal compressors have been used for this service, but steam-jet ejectors for the same flow rate and pressure ratio are cheaper and involve less maintenance expense, even though they use large quantities of steam. The application of a steam-jet ejector to a system for chilling water is shown in Fig. 19·10. Water to be chilled is sprayed into the flash chamber where part of it evaporates. The pressure is kept low by the steam ejector which removes the vapor formed. The flash chamber is thermally insulated; so the latent heat of the spray water which evaporates is taken from the spray water which does not evaporate. Thus the liquid is chilled. Make-up water must be supplied continually because some of the spray water is carried away as vapor. The ejector discharges into a condenser where the pressure is determined by the temperature of available cooling water. This pressure is usually below atmospheric, so a pump or ejector must be used to remove air and other noncondensable gases from the condenser. The steam-jet or vacuum system is well-suited to air-conditioning applications where ample supplies of steam and condenser cooling water are available.

19·5   Absorption refrigeration

A vapor-compression refrigeration system requires a power input in order to compress the refrigerant vapor from the evaporator pressure to the condenser pressure. Pumping a liquid through the same pressure difference at the same mass flow rate requires less power, so it is worthwhile to seek means for having the refrigerant in a liquid phase as its pressure is raised. To condense the pure refrigerant at the evaporator pressure would defeat the purpose of the refrigeration system; however, a workable arrangement is the absorption refrigeration cycle in which the refrigerant

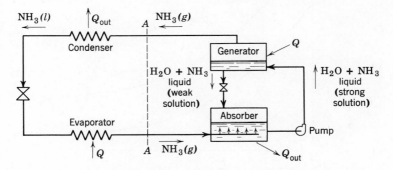

Fig. 19·11   Elementary absorption refrigeration cycle.

is dissolved in a liquid at the evaporator pressure, the liquid is pumped to the condenser pressure, and the refrigerant is then separated at the condenser pressure from the liquid.

Figure 19·11 is a flow diagram of an elementary absorption cycle which uses ammonia as the refrigerant, and water (or a water–ammonia mixture) as the liquid in which the refrigerant is carried from the low pressure to the high pressure. Ammonia enters the condenser as a vapor, is condensed, and enters the expansion valve as a liquid. It partially flashes to vapor when it expands through the valve, and it is further vaporized as it absorbs heat in the evaporator. Thus the part of the flow diagram to the left of line *A-A* in Fig. 19·11 is identical with that of a vapor-compression cycle. Looking to the right of line *A-A*, we see that in place of a compressor are an absorber, a pump, a generator, and a return line for liquid. Vapor from the evaporator is absorbed in water in the absorber. This dissolving process is exothermic, so heat must be removed from the absorber in order to keep its temperature constant. Also, at a given pressure the amount of ammonia which can be dissolved in water increases as the temperature is decreased; so the absorber temperature must be kept as low as possible by means of cooling water. The strong ammonia–water solution is then pumped to the generator, which is at the condenser pressure. Heat is added to the solution in the generator to drive some of the ammonia out of solution (an endothermic process). Ammonia vapor, or a vapor mixture which is very rich in ammonia, then goes to the condenser, and the weak

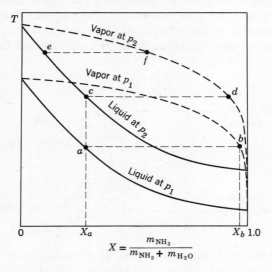

Fig. 19·12   Aqua–ammonia equilibrium diagram.

ammonia–water solution left in the generator passes through a valve back to the absorber. The liquid which travels through the absorber–pump–generator–valve cycle is simply a transport medium for the refrigerant, carrying it from the evaporator pressure to the condenser pressure in the liquid phase.

An understanding of the operation of an absorption cycle requires some knowledge of the characteristics of binary mixtures such as ammonia and water. A skeleton *equilibrium diagram* for aqua ammonia, as the ammonia–water mixture is called, is shown in Fig. 19·12. At any pressure, the boiling temperature of aqua ammonia liquid depends on the concentration X which is the mass of ammonia per unit mass of mixture. When $X = 0$, the boiling temperature is the saturation temperature of water; when $X = 1.0$, it is the saturation temperature of ammonia at the specified pressure. An important fact is that, when liquid and vapor exist together in equilibrium, the concentration is not the same in the two phases. In Fig. 19·12, the solid curves represent saturated liquid states at two pressures, p_1 and p_2; and the broken curves represent saturated vapor states at the same pressures. p_2 is greater than p_1. Points a and b represent states of saturated liquid and saturated vapor, respectively, which can exist together in equilibrium. Notice that the concentration of ammonia is higher in the vapor than in the liquid.

In an absorption cycle, saturated liquid in state a might leave the absorber and enter the pump. Leaving the pump, the concentration is the same, and the temperature is very nearly the same, but the pressure is p_2. In order to evaporate any of the liquid, its temperature must be raised to bring the liquid to state c. This is done in the generator. Then, as more heat is added, some of the liquid is evaporated to form vapor in state d. Since X_d is greater than X_c, the formation of the ammonia-rich vapor reduces the concentration of ammonia in the liquid. Evaporation then ceases if the pressure and temperature are held constant, because the liquid at a lower concentration is not at its boiling point. If more heat is added so that evaporation continues, the temperature of the two phases increases, and the states of the liquid and vapor change toward e and f, respectively. Liquid e flows from the generator back to the absorber, and vapor f flows to the condenser.

Equilibrium diagrams like Fig. 19·12 are adequate for mass balance analyses of absorption systems, but, for energy balance or first-law analyses, enthalpy data are also needed. These cannot be conveniently presented on a diagram like Fig. 19·12, so other property diagrams have been devised. One which relates p, T, h, X' (concentration in the liquid), and X'' (concentration in the vapor) for aqua ammonia is included in the appendix as Chart A·5.

Actual absorption systems always involve some modifications not shown in Fig. 19·11. The pump delivers cold liquid from the absorber to the generator where the temperature must be high, and hot liquid flows from the generator back to the absorber which must be kept cold; so a heat exchanger is always used to transfer heat from the weak solution to the strong solution. Also, carrying water vapor into the condenser must be avoided because it will freeze in the expansion valve and evaporator; therefore, a device called a *rectifier* is placed between the generator and the condenser. Its function is to remove traces of water from the refrigerant ahead of the condenser.

Absorption cycles are generally used in industrial applications only where heat which would otherwise be wasted is available. In all cases the choice between a compression cycle and an absorption cycle depends on the relative costs of power and heat.

The advantage of an absorption cycle over a compression cycle is the large reduction in power input. An ingenious method of reducing to zero the required power input of an absorption cycle was devised by two undergraduates at the Royal Institute of Technology in Stockholm, Carl G. Munters and Baltzar von Platen. It is usually referred to as the Servel system. The basic feature is that the total or mixture pressure is constant throughout the system. Condensation of the refrigerant ammonia occurs where the ammonia exists alone under the system pressure; but

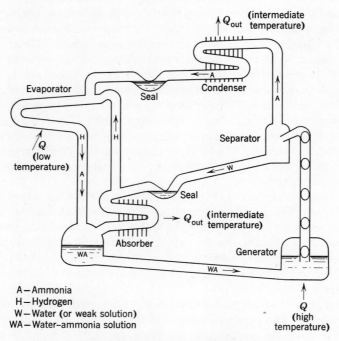

Fig. 19.13 Simplified flow diagram of Servel refrigerator.

evaporation occurs where the ammonia is mixed with hydrogen so that the ammonia behaves as though it existed alone at a pressure approximately (exactly, if it were an ideal gas) equal to its partial pressure in the mixture. Thus the ammonia is condensed at one temperature and evaporated at a lower one, even though the total pressure is the same in the condenser and the evaporator. Refrigeration is achieved without the use of a mechanical pump or compressor.

A highly simplified flow diagram of a Servel refrigerator is shown in Fig. 19·13. A water–ammonia solution flows down into the generator where heat is added to vaporize part of the mixture, the vapor formed being very rich in ammonia. The formation of vapor in the dome of the generator forces liquid up the tube toward the separator until the liquid level in the generator drops to the end of the tube. Then some vapor from the dome passes into the tube, the liquid level rises as more mixture enters the generator, and the process is repeated. The result is that alternate ammonia-rich bubbles and slugs of weak liquid solution flow up to the separator from which the ammonia passes to the condenser, and the water (or weak solution) flows by gravity to the absorber. In the condenser, heat is removed from the ammonia, which exists alone at the total pressure of the system, to condense it. The liquid drains from the condenser through a U-tube liquid seal or trap, which allows only liquid to pass, and into the evaporator. The total pressure is the same in both the condenser and the evaporator; so the liquid seal does not blow out. Hydrogen is present in the evaporator, however, so the ammonia passing through the liquid seal from the condenser evaporates at a low partial pressure and the corresponding low saturation temperature, thus absorbing heat from the region which is to be refrigerated. The cold ammonia–hydrogen mixture flows down from the evaporator and back up through the absorber, where the ammonia is absorbed by water which is flowing from the separator through a liquid seal, which prevents the entry of hydrogen into the separator and condenser. The ammonia is thereby carried back to the generator to complete its cycle and the hydrogen is left in the evaporator and absorber circuit. Heat must be removed from the absorber to keep its temperature constant, just as in the ammonia-absorption cycle discussed earlier.

In analyzing a Servel system, notice that there are three fluids, each of which flows in a different circuit. The refrigerant ammonia passes through the generator, separator, condenser, evaporator, and absorber, and back to the generator. The water is a transport medium which carries ammonia from the absorber, where the ammonia partial pressure is low, to the separator, where it is high. The function of the hydrogen is to circulate through the evaporator and absorber to hold down the ammonia partial pressure.

19·6 The liquefaction of gases

The liquefaction of a gas is an important step in most very low-temperature refrigeration systems, and also in the preparation of pure oxygen and nitrogen from air.

As pointed out in Art. 10·3, a gas can be cooled by throttling if its Joule–Thomson coefficient, $(\partial T/\partial p)_h$, is positive, and this means that its initial temperature must be less than its maximum inversion temperature. Further information on the conditions necessary for gas liquefaction by throttling can be obtained from a Ts diagram such as Fig. 19·14. (A Ts

diagram for air is included in the appendix as Chart A·1.) A throttling process between pressures p_1 and p_2 will not result in liquefaction if it begins at state a, b, or c, but it will if it starts from a state such as d.

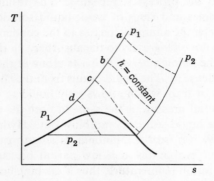

Fig. 19·14   Throttling processes from gaseous states.

Flow and Ts diagrams for an ideal Hampson–Linde gas liquefaction system are shown in Fig. 19·15. After multistage compression, the gas is cooled from state 2 to state 3 at constant pressure in an aftercooler, which is cooled either by water or by a refrigerating system. The gas is further

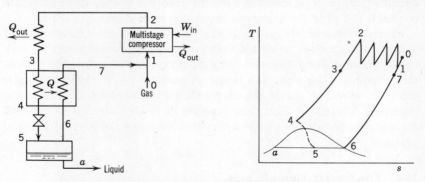

Fig. 19·15   Hampson–Linde system for liquefying gases.

cooled to state 4 in a regenerative heat exchanger, which is supplied with very cold gas from elsewhere in the cycle. After expansion through a throttle valve, the fluid is in the liquid–vapor mixture state 5 and is mechanically separated into liquid (state a) and vapor (state 6) parts. The liquid is drawn off as the desired product, and the vapor flows through the regenerative heat exchanger to cool high-pressure gas flowing toward the throttle valve. The area under line 6-7 on the Ts diagram equals that under

3-4 after adjustment for the smaller mass flow rate for process 6-7. The gas at state 7 is mixed with an amount of gas from outside equal to the amount of liquid removed, and this mixture in state 1 enters the compressor.

From a thermodynamic viewpoint, better performance of a gas lique-faction plant could be obtained by replacing the highly irreversible throttling process by expansion in an engine. The operation of an engine at very low temperatures presents difficulties, however, especially if liquefaction occurs in the engine. A compromise solution is the Claude system for liquefying gases. Simplified flow and Ts diagrams are shown in

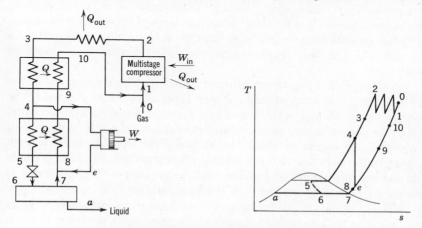

Fig. 19·16 Claude system for liquefying gases.

Fig. 19·16. From state 1 to state 4 the Claude system processes are the same as those of the Hampson–Linde system. After the gas is cooled to state 4' by the compressor aftercooler followed by a regenerative heat exchanger, most of it is expanded through an engine and then is mixed with vapor from the separator and flows back toward the compressor through a heat exchanger, which precools appreciably the small fraction of the flow which is directed toward the throttle valve instead of the engine. Thus in the ideal Claude system the cooling of a gas by isentropic expansion is utilized but the presence of liquid in the engine is avoided. In studying the Ts diagram of Fig. 19·16, remember that the flow rates are different at points 3, 5, 7, and 9.

19·7 Summary

In this chapter several refrigeration systems have been described in sufficient detail so that you can analyze their performance by means of the principles which have been introduced earlier.

The reversed Carnot cycle serves as a standard of performance for refrigerating cycles but it is unsuitable for actual systems.

The reversed Brayton cycle employs a gas as working fluid and is widely applied in aircraft cooling. Shortcomings of a gas as a refrigerant are its low specific heat, its low density at moderate pressures, and the difficulty of executing isothermal heat absorption and rejection processes which are necessary if the performance of any refrigerating system is to approach that of a reversed Carnot cycle.

Vapor-compression refrigeration systems employing many different refrigerants are widely used. In large commercial or industrial applications, the basic cycle is modified in various ways to improve performance. For air conditioning, water is sometimes used as the refrigerant in a variation of the basic vapor-compression cycle known as the vacuum system.

An absorption refrigeration system requires very little power input, but it takes large amounts of heat. Power input is saved by dissolving the refrigerant in a liquid at the evaporator pressure, pumping it in the liquid phase to the condenser pressure, and then driving the refrigerant out of solution. An ingenious method of reducing the work input of a small absorption system to zero is known as the Servel system. The total pressure throughout the system is constant, and the pressure of the refrigerant is varied by alternately mixing with it and separating from it an inert gas.

Several methods of producing very low temperatures or liquefying gases are based on the adiabatic expansion of a high-pressure gas either through a throttling valve or in an engine. In this chapter the Hampson–Linde and the Claude systems were described briefly.

A ton of refrigeration is defined as the heat absorption by a refrigerator at a rate of 200 B/min.

REFERENCES

19·1 P. J. Kiefer, G. F. Kinney, and M. C. Stuart, *Principles of Engineering Thermodynamics*, John Wiley & Sons, 2d ed., 1954, chapter 15.

19·2 H. J. Stoever, *Engineering Thermodynamics*, John Wiley & Sons, 1951, chapter 12.

19·3 C. O. Mackey, W. N. Barnard, and F. O. Ellenwood, *Engineering Thermodynamics*, John Wiley & Sons, 1957, chapter 15.

19·4 B. F. Dodge, *Chemical Engineering Thermodynamics*, McGraw-Hill Book Co., 1944, chapter X.

19·5 D. A. Mooney, *Mechanical Engineering Thermodynamics*, Prentice-Hall, 1953, chapter 24.

19·6 R. C. Jordan and G. B. Priester, *Refrigeration and Air Conditioning*, Prentice-Hall, 2d ed., 1956.

19·7 *ASHRAE Guide and Data Book*, published periodically by the American Society of Heating, Refrigerating, and Air Conditioning Engineers.

PROBLEMS

19·1 Ten tons of refrigeration are to be supplied by a reversed Carnot engine. The condenser temperature is 85 F, and the refrigeration temperature is −5 F. Compute the power required to operate the refrigeration machine and the coefficient of performance.

19·2 A dense air refrigerating machine operates between 50 and 200 psia. The air temperatures entering the compressor and expansion cylinder are 33 and 96 F, respectively. If the expansion is reversible adiabatic and the compression is polytropic with $n = 1.35$, determine (a) the power required for a capacity of 2000 B extracted from the cold room per minute, and (b) the coefficient of performance.

19·3 A reversed Brayton cycle operates between 100 and 200 psia. Air leaves the cold heat exchanger at 40 F and enters the air engine at 100 F. Refrigerating capacity is one ton. Determine the coefficient of performance.

19·4 Air at 10 psia, 40 F, is to be supplied to the cockpit of an aircraft at a rate of 0.2 lb/sec by bleeding air at 50 psia, 400 F, from the aircraft jet-engine compressor, cooling it in a heat exchanger, and expanding it isentropically through a turbine which exhausts into the cockpit. Neglecting friction and changes in kinetic energy, determine (a) the heat-transfer rate in the heat exchanger, and (b) the power output of the turbine.

19·5 For an aircraft cabin cooling system, a turbine is to exhaust air at 10 psia, 40 F, at a rate of 4.0 lb/sec. The turbine drives a compressor which takes in air at 10 psia, 120 F. The air discharged from this compressor is mixed with air at the same state bled from the main jet-engine compressor. It is then cooled to 140 F before entering the cooling-system turbine. Assume that compression and expansion are reversible and adiabatic. Neglect pressure drops in the heat exchanger and ducting, and neglect changes in kinetic energy. Determine the pressure and the flow rate of air to be bled from the main engine compressor.

19·6 Explain how a reversed Brayton cycle can be modified to approach a reversed Carnot cycle by means of multistage compression with intercooling and also multistage expansion. Sketch flow, pv, and Ts diagrams for the modified cycle.

19·7 Comment on the advisability of using a reversed regenerative gas-turbine cycle for refrigeration.

19·8 An ideal vapor-compression refrigerating cycle operates between temperature limits of 40 and 100 F. Dry saturated vapor leaves the compressor, and saturated liquid enters the expansion valve. For a refrigerating capacity of 5 tons, calculate the required power input if the refrigerant is (a) ammonia, (b) water, (c) Freon 12, (d) propane.

19·9 Solve Prob. 9·8 with an isentropic expansion in an engine replacing the throttling through the expansion valve.

19·10 Calculate the slope of an isentropic line on a pressure–enthalpy diagram of a pure substance. Check your result qualitatively by the ammonia ph chart in the appendix, Chart A·4.

19·11 In a vapor-compression refrigeration system the condenser temperature is 80 F and the evaporator temperature is 10 F. Saturated liquid enters the expansion valve, and dry saturated vapor enters the compressor which operates reversibly and adiabatically. For a refrigeration effect of one ton, determine the flow rate and the power input if the refrigerant is (a) ammonia, (b) Freon 12.

19·12 A refrigerating plant uses 14,220 lb/hr of cooling water in the condenser. The average inlet and outlet water temperatures are 55 and 81 F, respectively. The power required to drive the compressor is 20 hp. Calculate the coefficient of performance and the capacity of the plant in tons of refrigeration as indicated by these figures.

19·13 For a condensing temperature of 70 F and adiabatic dry compression, plot the minimum compressor discharge temperature against evaporator temperature for a range of 10 to −60 F of the latter for (a) ammonia, (b) Freon 12. What conclusions do you draw from these plots?

19·14 Derive the relationship between coefficient of performance and horsepower per ton of refrigeration. For refrigerating machines used in ice making and food preservation, a rule of thumb for the power required is 1 hp/ton. What is the corresponding coefficient of performance?

19·15 An ideal Freon 12 compression refrigerating cycle operates between 12 and 100 psia. Dry saturated vapor enters the compressor, and Freon 12 at 100 psia, 60 F, enters the expansion valve. Compression is adiabatic. The refrigerating capacity is 10 tons. Determine the power input.

19·16 A 5-ton Freon 12 compression refrigeration machine operates at rated capacity with pressures in the evaporator and condenser of 35.7 and 90 psia, respectively. Dry saturated vapor enters the compressor, and vapor leaving the compressor is at 100 F. Heat removed from the Freon being compressed amounts to 1.0 B/lb. Liquid entering the expansion valve is at 70 F. Determine the power input.

19·17 In an ammonia compression refrigeration cycle, the evaporator and condenser pressures are 20 and 180 psia, respectively. Dry saturated vapor enters the compressor, and vapor at 280 F leaves. Liquid at 75 F leaves the condenser. When the refrigerating effect is 20 tons, cooling water passing through the compressor cylinder water jacket picks up heat at a rate of 250 B/min. (a) Calculate the power input. (b) Is the compression process reversible? Prove your answer.

19·18 In an ammonia compression refrigeration cycle, saturated liquid leaves the condenser at 140 psia, and dry saturated vapor leaves the evaporator at 20 psia. These fluids then pass through a heat exchanger in which the vapor is superheated to 20 F while the liquid is subcooled before entering the expansion valve. Compression is adiabatic, and the compressor discharge temperature is 320 F. The refrigerating effect is 50 tons. Calculate the power input.

19·19 A reciprocating ammonia compressor used in a refrigerating system operates normally between pressures of 10 and 180 psia. It is found that, when the suction pressure rises to 20 psia while the discharge pressure remains 180 psia, the overload protection device on the electric motor driving the compressor disconnects the motor from the power line. How do you account for this overloading of the driving motor when the compressor pressure ratio has been reduced?

19·20 A household electric refrigerator is operated in a kitchen which is closed and thermally insulated. If it is operated continuously for 2 hr, will the average temperature of the air in the kitchen increase, decrease, or remain constant if the refrigerator door is kept (a) open, (b) closed?

19·21 A portable emergency refrigerating unit consists of a bottle containing 20 lb of liquid ammonia and a coil of tubing which is fed from the bottle through a small valve which prevents the pressure in the tubing from exceeding 20 psia. The volume of the tubing is negligible compared to the volume of the bottle. The tubing discharges to the atmosphere through a thermostatic valve which is closed only when the temperature of ammonia at the discharge end of the tubing is less than 30 F. Determine the maximum amount of heat that can be absorbed by completely discharging this unit if the ammonia in the bottle is initially at 50 F. (Some assumptions must be made. State them clearly.)

19·22 Refer to Fig. 19·9. Determine the power input to an ideal Freon 12 refrigerating system which operates on the cycle shown with condenser, flash chamber, and evaporator pressures of 100, 35.7, and 12 psia, respectively. Saturated liquid enters each expansion valve, and the refrigerating effect is 20 tons.

19·23 Solve Prob. 19·22 for the same capacity and the same condenser, flash chamber, and evaporator *temperatures* if the refrigerant is ammonia.

19·24 Determine the make-up water flow rate for a system as shown in Fig. 19·10 if 50,000 lb of water per hour at 45 F is to be delivered, the return water is at 70 F, and the make-up water is at 55 F. Assume that the ejector removes only vapor.

19·25 Refer to Prob. 19·24 and Fig. 19·10. If the ejector is replaced by a centrifugal compressor and cooling water is available to maintain a condenser temperature of 65 F, determine the minimum power input to the compressor if it operates adiabatically.

19·26 An aqua–ammonia liquid which is 60 per cent ammonia by mass enters a generator (as in Fig. 19·11) at 300 psia, 80 F. Saturated liquid and saturated vapor, both at 210 F, leave the generator. The flow is steady. Determine the mass of vapor leaving per pound of liquid entering, and the amount of heat added per pound of liquid entering.

19·27 Refer to Fig. 19·11. For pressure limits of 215 and 55 psia, a generator temperature of 200 F, and an absorber temperature of 80 F, determine (*a*) the amount of liquid which must be pumped for each pound of ammonia which enters the condenser, and (*b*) the amount of heat added to the generator for each pound of ammonia which enters the condenser.

19·28 Air is to be liquefied by the Hampson–Linde regenerative process (Fig. 19·15) operating with pressure limits of 200 and 1 atm. It is desired to obtain 1 lb of liquid from every 6 lb of air which flows through the expansion valve. Assume that the regenerative heat exchanger is perfectly insulated from the surroundings and that the minimum temperature differential between the two streams of air passing through this heat exchanger is to be 20 F. Neglect pressure drops in the heat exchangers. In order to maintain steady conditions, to what temperature must the air be cooled by the compressor aftercooler before it enters the regenerative heat exchanger?

CHAPTER **20**

Binary Mixtures

Phase relationships for a pure substance were discussed in Chapter 3, and in Chapter 10 pure substances were treated further by the application of the first and second laws. Chapter 12 treated gas and gas-vapor mixtures, but such mixtures always form a single phase, and, as long as the chemical composition is constant, such mixtures are pure substances, regardless of the number of constituents (i.e., chemical species) present. In the humidification or dehumidification of atmospheric air, the gaseous phase is not a pure substance, because the amount of water vapor in it changes; however, this is still a rather simple case because only two phases are present, and the liquid phase is a pure substance consisting only of the single constituent water. Thus the only multiconstituent phase relationships considered so far in this textbook have been for a rather elementary case.

This chapter considers phase relationships for binary mixtures in which both constituents exist in more than one phase. A binary mixture is defined as one comprised of two constituents. This chapter is therefore an extension of Chapter 3. Extensive applications of the first and second laws and the determination of mixture properties from constituent properties are not considered.

Before taking up the phase relationships for binary mixtures, we discuss briefly the *phase rule* which is a valuable generalization which pertains to many other systems besides binary mixtures.

20·1 The phase rule

The phase rule, which was first published by J. Willard Gibbs in 1876, is a simple, powerful rule for determining the maximum number of independent intensive properties of various types of systems in equilibrium. This number of independent intensive properties is necessary and sufficient to specify the state of each phase in the system, but it is usually insufficient to specify the amount of each phase which is present. The number of independent intensive properties is also called the number of *degrees of freedom* of the system, so the symbol F is used for it.

Although the phase rule can be simply stated, its use requires a thorough understanding of some definitions and of elementary chemistry. Let us review the pertinent definitions.

Two or more properties are independent if each one can be varied without affecting the others. For a multiphase system, a property is an *intensive property of the system* if it is an intensive property of any phase of the system. (Examples are pressure, temperature, and the concentration of any one component in one phase.) As defined in Chapter 3, a phase is any homogeneous part of a system which is physically distinct and is separated from other parts of the system by distinct bounding surfaces. If all the intensive properties of one part of a system are identical with those of another part, the two parts comprise a single phase, even though they may be physically separated. For example, if many drops of water are present in condensing steam, there are but two phases: liquid water and steam.

Most of the difficulty in applying the phase rule stems from difficulty in distinguishing and counting the *components* in a system. By the *constituents* of a system we mean the various chemical substances that comprise it. The *components* of a system are the independently variable constituents from which the system in any of its states can be prepared. By the *number of components* is meant the least number of independently variable constituents from which the system in any of its states can be prepared or in terms of which the composition of any phase can be specified.

Determining the number of components in a given system requires careful analysis. The number of components is not in all cases equal to the number of different substances present. Several systems will be considered in order to demonstrate how the number of components may be ascertained.

A system comprised of ice, liquid water, and water vapor. For this system the number of components in equilibrium is only one; that is, the chemical substance *water*. The constituents hydrogen and oxygen are not regarded as components since they are combined in definite proportions, and cannot be varied independently. A variation in the amount of hydrogen requires a definite variation in the quantity of oxygen.

A system composed of a saturated solution of water and NaCl and excess NaCl. The only phases in this system are the saturated solutions of NaCl and water and solid NaCl. Each phase is completely described in terms of either one or both of the components H_2O and $NaCl$. There are therefore two components.

A system consisting of Glauber's salt $Na_2SO_4 \cdot 10H_2O$ with

solution and vapor. The composition of each phase may be expressed in terms of Na_2SO_4 and H_2O as follows:·

Phase	Relations Specifying Each Phase in Terms of the Components H_2O and Na_2SO_4
$Na_2SO_4 \cdot 10H_2O$ (solid)	$Na_2SO_4 + 10H_2O$
Saturated solution	$Na_2SO_4 + xH_2O$
Vapor	$0Na_2SO_4 + H_2O$

Since two components completely specify the phases, the system may be classified as a two-component system.

A system in equilibrium consisting of calcium carbonate, $CaCO_3$; calcium oxide, CaO; and carbon dioxide, CO_2. Under equilibrium conditions three different substances are present; however, they are not all regarded as components for they are not mutually independent. The three substances are related by the following equilibrium reaction:

$$CaCO_3 \rightleftharpoons CaO + CO_2$$

If any two of the substances are specified, the third is fixed according to this relation. In order to be considered as components, the various constituents must be capable of independent variation. The components to be considered for this system are the smallest number of independently variable constituents which are necessary to specify the substances according to this chemical reaction, which is two. Any two of the three substances may be selected as the components. Choosing CaO and CO_2 as the two components, the composition of each phase may be specified as follows:

Phase	Equation Specifying Each Phase in Terms of the Components CaO and CO_2
$CaCO_3$ (solid)	$CaCO_3 = CaO + CO_2$
CaO (solid)	$CaO = CaO + 0CO_2$
CO_2 (gas)	$CO_2 = 0CaO + CO_2$

From the two terms on the right side of the equations it is apparent that each phase may be expressed in terms of one or the other or both of the components CaO and CO_2. In these equations zero and positive coefficients have been used. If two other components had been selected, zero, negative, and positive coefficients would result.

These examples of determining the number of components are by no means exhaustive. For more complex systems, counting the components may be difficult.

For any system which is (1) homogeneous or comprised of a finite number of homogeneous parts in contact, (2) in equilibrium, and (3) free of electric, magnetic, gravitational, and surface tension effects, the phase rule states that the maximum number of independent intensive properties F is given by

$$F = 2 + C - P \qquad (20 \cdot 1)$$

where C is the number of components and P is the number of phases in the system.

Before applying the phase rule to a few systems, we will outline its derivation. First, consider any one phase of a system which meets the conditions listed in the preceding paragraph. If in a unit mass of this phase the masses of $(C-1)$ components are known, then the relative proportions of the masses of all components are determined. For P phases, this means that $P(C-1)$ properties must be specified in order to fix the relative proportions of the components in each phase. In addition to the composition, it is *assumed* that two other intensive properties, pressure and temperature, are necessary and sufficient to determine the state of each phase. Then the total number of intensive properties needed to determine the states of all phases of the system is $P(C-1)+2$. From the first and second laws it can be shown that, for each component in a system, $(P-1)$ independent equations among intensive properties can be written. Then for the system of C components there are $C(P-1)$ such equations. The difference between the number of intensive properties needed to determine the states of all phases of a system and the number of equations relating these properties is the number of independent intensive properties F of the system:

$$F = P(C - 1) + 2 - C(P - 1) = 2 + C - P \qquad (20 \cdot 1)$$

Notice that the phase rule is based on an assumption which cannot be proved by means of the first or second law and, as the derivation is outlined here, is also based on the first and second laws in a manner that we do not describe in this textbook.

A system for which there are no independent intensive properties is said to be *invariant*; one with one independent property is called *univariant*; one with two is called *divariant*; and so forth. Now we shall apply the phase rule in order to determine the *variance*, or the number of independent intensive properties, of several systems. In each case the system is in equilibrium and meets the other conditions established for systems to which the phase rule applies.

A system comprised of ice, liquid water, and water vapor. In this system there are three phases and one component, H_2O. Application of the phase rule gives

$$F = 2 + C - P = 2 + 1 - 3 = 0$$

This result indicates that there are no independent variables; that is, neither the pressure nor the temperature can be varied as long as the three phases exist together in equilibrium. The system is at the triple point, which is the only state in which these three phases can exist together. This system is said to be invariant.

A system comprised of liquid water and water vapor. There are two phases and one component, so the phase rule gives $F = 1$. The system is univariant, or, in other words, there is one independent intensive property. If either pressure or temperature is specified, then the state of the system is determined, and this is in accordance with the conclusions reached in Chapter 3 from experiments. The phase rule is not concerned with the amount of each phase present; so it might be said more precisely that the *intensive* state of this system is determined by a single intensive property.

A system comprised of water vapor. This system is comprised of one phase and one component, so the phase rule indicates that it is divariant, or $F = 2$. This is in accordance with the observation in Chapter 3 and later, that two properties must be specified to determine the state of superheated steam. Superheated vapor tables are therefore double-argument tables, while tables of saturation properties have a single argument.

A system comprised of ammonia and water in a liquid solution and a vapor. There are two phases, liquid and vapor. There are two components, NH_3 and H_2O (or two components can also be taken as NH_4OH and H_2O in the liquid phase). The phase rule shows that the system is divariant, $F = 2$. This means that specifying the pressure and temperature of this system completely determines the state of the system and hence the composition of each phase. If the composition of one phase and the pressure are specified, then there is only one possible temperature under which the two phases can exist together, and the composition of the other phase is fixed.

A system comprised of liquid mercury, liquid water, and vapor. The water and mercury are immiscible and so form two liquid phases. These plus the vapor make a total of three phases. There are two components, Hg and H_2O. The phase rule shows that $F = 1$, so the system is univariant. This means that, at a given pressure, there is only one temperature at which these three phases can coexist, and the composition of the vapor is fixed under those conditions. Another conclusion is that, in order to have a mercury vapor and water vapor mixture of specified composition coexist with liquid water and liquid mercury, there is no choice of either pressure or temperature of the system.

A system comprised of three gases: phosphorus pentachloride, PCl_5; phosphorus trichloride, PCl_3; and chlorine, Cl_2. There is one phase because any gaseous mixture forms only one phase. There are two components because the equilibrium equation for these three gases

$$PCl_5 \rightleftharpoons PCl_3 + Cl_2$$

shows that the composition of the single phase can be expressed in terms of any two of the constituents. The phase rule gives $F = 3$, so pressure, temperature, and composition must all be specified in order to determine the state of this system.

20·2　Miscibility

If two liquids when mixed in any concentration form a single phase, they are said to be *miscible*. If when mixed they remain in two phases, each identical in composition with one of the liquids before mixing, they are *immiscible*. If the mixing results in a single phase for some concentrations and two phases for the others, the liquids are said to be *partially miscible*. The miscibility of two liquids may change markedly with temperature.

Figure 20·1 is a temperature–composition diagram or phase diagram for two liquids, A and B, which are miscible at temperatures above T_a and partially miscible at lower temperatures. The diagram is for a fixed pressure. Any point such as b, c, or d in the single-phase region represents a solution of the two constituents. For two components in a single phase, the phase rule gives us $F = 2 + C - P = 2 + 2 - 1 = 3$, so pressure, temperature, and composition must all be specified to define a state such as b, c, or d. A point such as k does not represent a single-phase solution but rather a mixture of two phases. Point k represents a mixture of a phase in state e and a phase in state f. The proportion of the two phases present is such that the over-all composition of the system is represented by point k.

Pure B at temperature T_e is represented by point j in Fig. 20·1. If A is gradually added to B, the state point on the diagram moves to the right and represents a single-phase solution until state e is reached. Further addition of A causes the formation of a second phase which is in state f. As more of pure A is added to the system, the total mass in state f increases and that in state e decreases. The mixture of the two phases represented by point g is comprised of about one part in state f and nine parts in state e. The mixture represented by point k is about six parts in state f and four parts in state e. When the state point which has passed from j through e, g, and k reaches f, the last trace of the phase in state e disappears, and further addition of pure A increases the concentration of A in a single phase

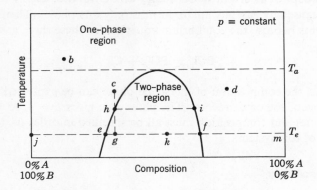

Fig. 20·1   Phase diagram for two liquids which are miscible at temperatures higher than T_a and partially miscible at lower temperatures.

represented by state points between f and m. For mixtures represented by points such as g and k, notice that $F = 2 + C - P = 2 + 2 - 2 = 2$, so there are only two independent intensive properties. This is in accordance with the fact that, for the specified pressure of the diagram and temperature T_e, two phases existing together must be in states e and f, and there is consequently no choice of concentration in either phase.

If a solution in state c of Fig. 20·1 is cooled, only one phase is present until state h is reached, whereupon a separate phase, in state i, begins to form. As the temperature is lowered to T_e, the two phases approach states e and f. The relative amounts of the two phases must be such that the over-all concentration remains constant.

Notice that in a two-phase region on a phase diagram a point always represents a mixture of the two phases represented by state points on the phase boundaries.

Figure 20·2a is a phase diagram for a system comprised of two liquids which are miscible throughout the temperature range of the diagram. Figure 20·2b is for two liquids which are immiscible throughout the diagram temperature range. These two simple diagrams are shown to illustrate that point a in the single-phase region represents a solution, while point b in the two-phase region represents a mixture of two separate phases, pure A and pure B.

Solids, like liquids, show varying degrees of miscibility, and their characteristics can be shown in a similar manner on phase diagrams. Gases are always completely miscible.

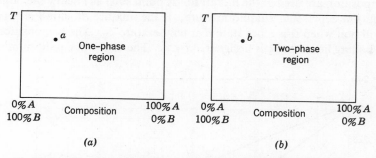

Fig. 20·2 Phase diagrams for (a) miscible liquids and (b) immiscible liquids.

20.3   Liquid–vapor equilibrium: miscible liquids

In studying liquid–vapor equilibrium of binary mixtures, we say that two liquids are miscible as long as they are miscible when in equilibrium with the vapor. If they are immiscible or only partially miscible under other conditions, this has no bearing on the liquid–vapor equilibrium.

In this article we treat only *zeotropic* mixtures. As the composition of a zeotropic mixture is changed from one extreme to the other, the boiling and condensation temperatures change progressively from the saturation temperature of one pure component to that of the other. An *azeotropic* mixture is one which has a minimum or maximum boiling or condensation temperature at some intermediate composition.

For a binary mixture in a single phase, the phase rule shows that there are three independent intensive properties. A complete property diagram for such a mixture would therefore be a three-dimensional diagram. This difficulty is avoided by using plane diagrams on which two of the properties, usually temperature and composition, are plotted for constant values of the third one, usually pressure. On such a diagram there are areas in which points representing single-phase states can be located, inasmuch as pressure, temperature, and composition are independent. For any phase of a binary mixture in equilibrium with another phase, there are only two independent properties; so points representing such states must lie on lines which for the given pressure relate the temperature and composition.

Data on mixtures of benzene and toluene, which are very nearly a completely miscible pair, are shown in Fig. 20·3 for a pressure of 1 atm. Points *A* and *C* are at the boiling points of pure toluene and pure benzene, respectively. The curve *A-B-C* gives the boiling point for any mixture composition. Notice that the composition is expressed in Fig. 20·3 as a mole fraction rather than as a mass fraction. Both methods of expressing composition are used in the literature. A point such as *i* below the boiling-point line represents a liquid mixture. If the mixture of state *i* is heated, it will boil when it reaches state *d* at temperature T_2. The composition of the boiling liquid at T_2 is designated by x_2'. The vapor in equilibrium with

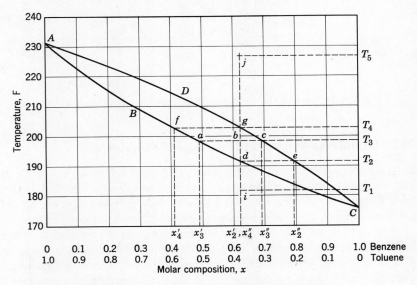

Fig. 20·3 Benzene–toluene Tx diagram at 1 atm.

this liquid has a composition x_2'' and is represented by state *e*. Since two phases exist, the phase rule shows that, at a specified pressure, the temperature and composition cannot be independent; so an increase in temperature causes a change in composition of the two phases along the lines *A-B-C* and *A-D-C*. At temperature T_3 the mixture which was originally in state *i* is comprised of a liquid phase in state *a* with a composition x_3' and a vapor phase in state *c* with a composition x_3''. If the total amount of the two components in the system has remained the same, point *b* at the original composition represents the mixture state at T_3, but remember that this is actually a mixture of a liquid phase and a vapor phase, and no single phase with the composition of state *b* can exist at T_3. For the state represented by point *b* the relative proportions of the liquid and vapor are shown by the lengths of lines *b-c* and *a-b*. For example, if *a-b* and *b-c* are respectively two thirds and one third of the total length *a-c*, then the system is comprised of one-third liquid and two-thirds vapor by moles. As the temperature is increased further, the compositions of the two phases change until temperature T_4 is reached, whereupon the liquid phase disappears and the vapor has the same composition as the original liquid mixture. Further increase in temperature superheats the vapor with no change in composition. ·

If a superheated vapor in state j is cooled, the temperature decreases

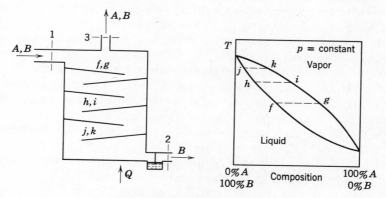

Fig. 20·4   Partial rectification.

until state g at T_4 is reached, whereupon liquid of composition x_4' begins to appear. Continued cooling causes the composition of both the liquid and the vapor to change until a temperature T_2 is reached. At T_2 the last trace of vapor condenses, and further cooling simply reduces the temperature of the liquid.

A temperature–composition or phase diagram is useful in the study of the separation of volatile miscible liquids. If a mixture of benzene and toluene, for example, is heated to the boiling point, and the vapor is removed, the liquid becomes richer in toluene and leaner in benzene. The vapor is richer in benzene than the original mixture. If this vapor is removed and condensed, the resulting liquid is richer in benzene than the original mixture. If this liquid is boiled and the vapor removed and condensed, a still richer liquid in benzene will be obtained. By continuing the evaporation and condensation steps it is possible to obtain complete separation of the benzene and toluene. The separation of a mixture into its components is called *rectification*.

Figure 20·4 shows a method of partial rectification. A binary liquid mixture enters the rectifier or rectifying tower at section 1 and flows downward over the trays which are arranged to produce a large liquid surface area for heat and mass transfer. Heat is added at the bottom of the tower, and only liquid is allowed to leave at section 2. The vapor driven from the liquid flows back up the tower to leave at section 3. Heat transferred from the vapor to the counterflowing liquid causes some of the liquid to evaporate and establishes a temperature gradient throughout the tower. Corresponding to the temperature gradient there are concentration gradients in both the liquid and the vapor streams. Referring to the temperature–composition diagram in Fig. 20·4, if a mixture of A and B in state f enters the tower, the vapor driven from it is in state g. This makes the liquid richer in B and raises its boiling point. As it flows downward, its temperature rises, evaporation continues, and its B concentration increases. The vapor formed lower in the tower is also richer in B. Notice that it is possible to withdraw pure B at section 2 but the vapor leaving at section 3 can be no richer in A than state g. (In an actual rectifier the liquid and vapor at any section are not in equilibrium with each other because heat and mass are being transferred at a finite rate between the phases. This difference between the actual system and the ideal system we are analyzing should be recognized.)

The maximum yield of pure component B can be determined by means of a mass balance and temperature–composition data. Let X'_A stand for the mass fraction of A in the liquid phase and X''_A stand for the mass fraction of A in the vapor phase. Let M represent a total flow rate and M_A and M_B represent the flow rates of components A and B, respectively. Only B leaves at section 2, so a mass balance is

$$M_{B2} = M_2 = M_1 - M_3 = M_1 - \frac{M_{A3}}{X''_{A3}}$$

All A that enters the system leaves at 3, so $M_{A3} = M_{A1} = X'_{A1}M_1$. Also, the liquid entering at 1 and the vapor leaving at 3 are in equilibrium with each other; so $X''_{A1} = X''_{A3}$. These substitutions in the mass balance and rearrangement lead to

$$\frac{M_{B2}}{M_1} = 1 - \frac{X'_{A1}}{X''_{A1}}$$

This is the maximum yield. If less liquid is removed at section 2, the vapor in the tower will be richer in B. Its temperature at each section of the tower will be higher, and this is actually required in order to maintain the required heat transfer from the vapor to the liquid; so the yield given by the equation above is not realized by an actual system.

Complete rectification can be accomplished by means of the system shown in Fig. 20·5. Instead of removing vapor at the section where the liquid enters, the tower is extended above the inlet, and a cooler is provided at the top. Pure B liquid leaves at section 2, and pure A vapor leaves at section 3. The condensate from the cooler at the top of the tower flows back down the tower, so that the transfer of heat from the vapor to the liquid and the transfer of mass from the liquid to the vapor occurs throughout the tower. The liquid which flows down the tower and mixes with the incoming stream is called the *reflux*. The ratio of reflux to incoming flow,

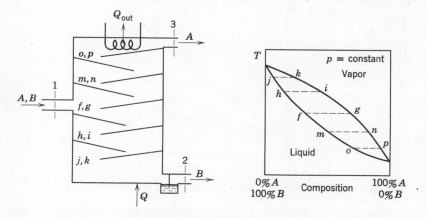

Fig. 20·5   Complete rectification.

M_R/M_1, is a minimum when these two streams are in the same state as they mix and the vapor flowing up the tower past the mixing point at the inlet is in equilibrium with the liquid. It can be shown from mass balances that the minimum reflux ratio is given by

$$\frac{M_R}{M_1} = \left(\frac{1 - X''_{A1}}{X''_{A1} - X'_{A1}}\right) X'_{A1}$$

If mixture enthalpy data (such as that for ammonia and water given in Chart A·5 of the appendix) are available, the required heat transfer of a rectification process can be easily determined by application of the first law.

20·4   Liquid–vapor equilibrium: immiscible and partially miscible liquids

If two liquids are immiscible, each one forms a liquid phase. If they are in equilibrium with a vapor phase, the phase rule shows that $F = 2 + C - P = 2 + 2 - 3 = 1$: There is only one independent intensive property. If the pressure is fixed, then the temperature is fixed, and it is independent of the amount of the phases present. Thus a single saturation pressure–temperature curve holds for all compositions of the liquid mixture. The saturation pressure of the mixture of immiscible liquids A and B is equal to the sum of the saturation pressures of A and B alone at the same temperature as shown in Fig. 20·6. The boiling-point temperature at any pressure is the temperature at which the sum of the constituent saturation pressures equals the total pressure specified.

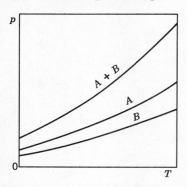

Fig. 20·6 Vapor pressures of immiscible liquids A and B.

A temperature–composition diagram for two immiscible liquids A and B and their vapor is shown in Fig. 20·7. The boiling-point temperature for the constant pressure of the diagram is T_b. As pointed out above, it is independent of the composition of the liquid mixture. Since for a system comprised of two liquid phases A and B coexisting in equilibrium with their vapor there is only one independent intensive property, there is at any specified pressure only one possible composition of the vapor which can exist in equilibrium with a liquid mixture of A and B. This state of the vapor is represented by point a in Fig. 20·7.

As an illustration of the phase relationships of immiscible liquids and their vapor, consider a mixture which is initially in state c as shown in Fig. 20·7. This is actually a mixture of pure B liquid in state q and pure A liquid in state r. The mixture comprises a closed system, so that the total amount of each component remains the same. Also, the pressure is held constant. As the temperature is increased, the mixture goes from state c to state d, always consisting of two liquid phases, one of pure A and the other of pure B. If heat is added to the liquid mixture in state d, evaporation begins, but of course the vapor formed must be in state a as noted previously. Since the vapor formed is richer in A than the system as a whole is, there is an increase in the amount of the liquid phase comprised of pure B, state m. As the last trace of liquid A is evaporated, the system is comprised of two phases: pure B liquid in state m, and a vapor mixture in state *a*. The relative masses of the two phases are indicated by the lengths of the line segments *a-d* and *m-d*. The system is again divariant $(F = 2+C-P = 2+2-2 = 2.)$; so the temperature can be increased at

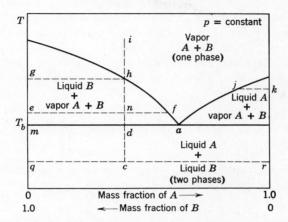

Fig. 20·7 Liquid–vapor equilibrium of two immiscible liquids *A* and *B*.

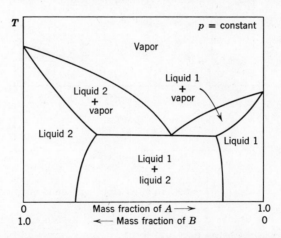

Fig. 20·8 Liquid–vapor equilibrium of partially miscible liquids.

constant pressure. The liquid phase remains pure *B*, and the vapor phase changes composition as its state point moves from *a* toward *f* and *h*. Since the vapor phase becomes richer in *B*, the amount of the liquid phase present decreases. When the temperature reaches the value for which the vapor state is *h*, the pure *B* liquid phase is represented by point *g*. The vapor in state *h* has the same composition as the entire system; so the last trace of liquid evaporates as the vapor reaches state h. Further heating superheats the vapor toward state i.

Figure 20·7 shows three double-phase regions, one triple-phase point a, and one single-phase region. Notice that points c, d, and n represent mixtures of two phases, neither of which has the composition indicated by the single state point. Point i, however, represents the composition and temperature of a single phase.

The phase relationships for two partially miscible liquids and their vapor are shown in Fig. 20·8. Liquid 1 is a solution rich in A, and liquid 2 is a solution rich in B.

20·5 Solid–liquid equilibrium: immiscible solids and miscible liquids

The preceding articles give a general picture of phase relationships in binary mixtures, even though only liquid and vapor phases have been

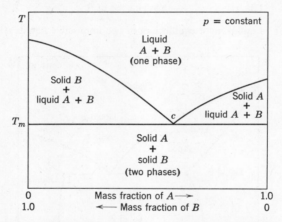

Fig. 20·9 Solid–liquid equilibrium of miscible liquids and immiscible solids.

treated. Similar analyses apply to solid–liquid systems. Figure 20·9 is a temperature–composition diagram for a system comprised of components A and B which are immiscible as solids and miscible as liquids.

The only liquid which can be in equilibrium with both solid phases in Fig. 20·9 is that in state c which is called the *eutectic** point. If liquid of any composition other than that of the eutectic mixture is cooled, one of the components will crystallize and cause the liquid remaining to approach the eutectic composition. When the temperature T_m is reached, the system

---

* *Eutectic* is derived from two Greek words which mean *easy melting*.

is comprised of one single-component solid phase and liquid of the eutectic composition. Further removal of heat causes the liquid to solidify into a mixture of crystals of A and crystals of B. The two components must crystallize in the ratio of the eutectic mixture because the liquid solution must remain fixed in composition as long as it is in equilibrium with two solid phases. The resulting solid mixture of course includes all the single-component solid formed as the temperature was lowered toward T_m as well as the solid formed in the eutectic proportion at T_m.

20·6 Summary

The phase rule which was first formulated by J. Willard Gibbs states that, for any system which is (1) homogeneous or comprised of a finite number of homogeneous parts in contact, (2) in equilibrium, and (3) free of electric, magnetic, gravitational, and surface tension effects, the maximum number of independent intensive properties F is given by

$$F = 2 + C - P \tag{20·1}$$

where C is the number of components and P is the number of phases in the system. By the number of components is meant the least number of independently variable constituents from which the system in any of its states can be prepared or in terms of which the composition of any phase can be specified.

Two liquids are miscible if when they are mixed in any concentration they form a single phase. They are immiscible if when mixed they remain in two phases, each identical with one of the liquids before mixing. If the mixing results in a single phase for some concentrations and two phases for the others, the liquids are said to be partially miscible. Solids, like liquids, show varying degrees of miscibility. Gases are always completely miscible.

In the study of phase relationships of multicomponent systems, temperature–composition diagrams plotted for constant pressure are quite useful. In this chapter such diagrams have been used to analyze phase relationships of a few types of binary mixtures.

REFERENCES

20·1 S. T. Bowden, *The Phase Rule and Phase Reactions*, Macmillan & Co., 1945.

20·2 B. F. Dodge, *Chemical Engineering Thermodynamics*, McGraw-Hill Book Co., 1944, chapter XII.

20·3 A. Findlay, *The Phase Rule and Its Applications*, Longmans, Green & Co. and Dover Publications.

20·4   S. J. Kline and F. O. Koenig, "The State Principle—Some General Aspects of Relationships among Properties of Systems," *Journal of Applied Mechanics, Transactions ASME*, vol. 79, March 1957, pp. 29–34. See also the discussion published in the same volume, pp. 625–630.

20·5   C. S. Robinson and E. R. Gilliland, *Elements of Fractional Distillation*, McGraw-Hill Book Co., 4th ed., 1950. (See pp. 22–25 for sources of data on binary mixtures.)

PROBLEMS

20·1   A system consists of solid sodium chloride, a solution of sodium chloride, water, ethyl alcohol, and vapor. Determine the number of phases.

20·2   How many components are present in a gas mixture at room temperature and atmospheric pressure consisting of oxygen, hydrogen, and water vapor?

20·3   Determine the number of phases for a system consisting of sand and solid salt in the presence of a saturated salt solution and the vapor.

20·4   Determine the number of components and degrees of freedom for a system consisting of CaO, Ca(OH)$_2$, and H$_2$O at 14.7 psia, 100 F.

20·5   Saturated sulfur dioxide exists at 100 F. Is the system invariant, univariant, or divariant?

20·6   A system under equilibrium conditions contains a saturated water solution of sodium chloride, excess sodium chloride, ethyl alcohol, and vapor. Determine the number of degrees of freedom.

20·7   For the system in which solid magnesium carbonate dissociates according to the following reaction, determine the number of degrees of freedom: MgCO$_3$(solid) → MgO(solid) + CO$_2$(gas).

20·8   Derive the expression given in Art. 20·3 for the minimum reflux ratio for complete rectification.

20·9   A mixture of 20 per cent benzene and 80 per cent toluene enters a partial rectifier as shown in Fig. 20·4 at a rate of 6000 lb/hr. Compute the maximum yield of pure toluene.

20·10   A continuous rectifying column is used to separate completely 12,000 lb/hr of a solution of 60 per cent benzene and 40 per cent toluene into its components. Compute the minimum reflux rate.

20·11   An aqua–ammonia solution which is 30 per cent ammonia is to be rectified at 100 psia in a tower like that of Fig. 20·5. Determine the reflux ratio, the heat added, and the heat removed per pound of entering solution. What assumptions do you make?

20·12   Refer to Fig. 20·9. A liquid is initially in a state with a composition which is richer in B than the eutectic mixture. Describe the phase changes which occur as this mixture is cooled to a temperature lower than T_m.

Heat Transfer

In many thermodynamic analyses we are concerned with the magnitude of heat transfer; but considerations of the mechanism of heat transfer and the rate at which heat is transferred are not part of thermodynamics. They are the subject of the separate but closely related discipline of heat transfer. Many engineering curricula include a course in heat transfer, but we include a brief chapter on the subject in this thermodynamics textbook because it is often helpful for a student to have knowledge of the modes of heat transfer at the time of studying thermodynamics. The discussion here is limited to the presentation of the basic equations of heat transfer in elementary form, a few definitions, and some simple applications. We restrict ourselves to the conditions of steady state which means that the temperature at any point is constant with respect to time.

The three methods of heat transfer are conduction, convection, and radiation. We shall see that convection is more accurately classified as mass transfer rather than heat transfer, but established usage is to include convection as a mode of heat transfer.

21·1 Steady-state one-dimensional conduction

Heat transfer is one-dimensional if the temperature variation can be expressed in terms of a single space coordinate. (Compare one-dimensional heat transfer with one-dimensional fluid flow described in Art. 15·1.) Conduction is the transfer of energy through a material as a result of a temperature gradient in the material and involves no motion of the material on a macroscopic scale. The basic equation for one-dimensional heat conduction is

$$\dot{Q} = -kA\frac{dt}{dx} \tag{21·1}$$

where $\dot{Q}$ is the rate of heat transfer, A is the cross-sectional area normal to the direction of heat transfer, x is distance in the direction of heat transfer,

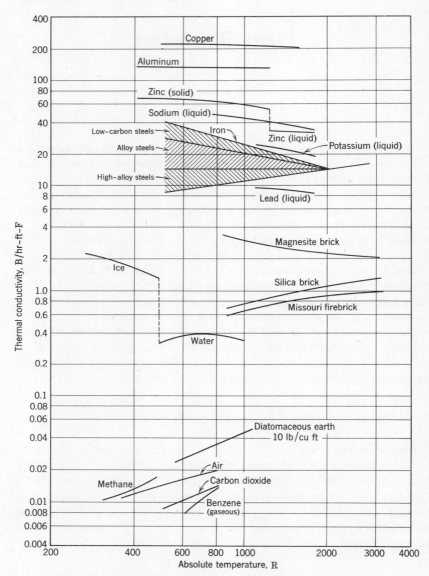

Fig. 21·1 Thermal conductivities of several substances. From M. Jakob and G. A. Hawkins, *Elements of Heat Transfer*, John Wiley & Sons, Inc., third edition, 1957.

t is temperature, and the coefficient k is a property of the material through which heat flows and is called the *thermal conductivity*. The minus sign indicates that heat is transferred in the direction of decreasing temperature.

Inspection of equation 21·1 shows that the dimensions of k are such that typical units are B/hr-ft-F. k is a function of temperature for most materials, but in many cases the variation of k is small enough so that constant mean values can be used. Values of thermal conductivity of several substances are shown in Fig. 21·1.

Let us consider the integration of the basic equation for two cases of a homogeneous material with constant k value: a plane wall and a

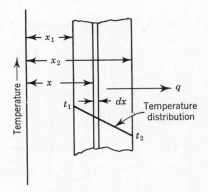

Fig. 21·2   Homogeneous plane wall.

cylindrical wall. Considering first the plane wall as shown in Fig. 21·2, A is independent of x. We are treating the case of constant k, so equation 21·1 can be integrated to give

$$\dot{Q} = -kA \frac{t_2 - t_1}{x_2 - x_1}$$

In the field of heat transfer, Δt is defined as $(t_1 - t_2)$, where t_1 is the higher temperature; so the last equation can be written as

$$\dot{Q} = kA \frac{\Delta t}{\Delta x} \tag{21·2}$$

For the steady flow of heat in a radial direction through a homogeneous cylindrical wall, the heat transfer is one-dimensional because the temperature at any point is a function of the radius only. The cross-sectional area for heat transfer is $2\pi r L$, where r is the radius, and L is the axial length of the cylinder. Equation 21·1 thus becomes

$$\dot{Q} = -2\pi r L \frac{dt}{dr}$$

Integrating for the case of constant k and substituting the limits of temperature t_2 at radius r_2 and t_1 at r_1 gives

$$\dot{Q} = \frac{2\pi L k (t_1 - t_2)}{\ln (r_2/r_1)} \tag{21·3}$$

Now let us consider the case of composite walls. Figure 21·3 shows a

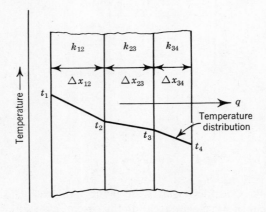

Fig. 21·3 Composite plane wall.

plane wall comprised of three layers. Assume that the k of each layer is constant. Then for steady-state one-dimensional conduction through the wall, equation 21·2 may be applied to each section as follows:

$$\dot{Q} = k_{12} \frac{A(t_1 - t_2)}{\Delta x_{12}}$$

$$\dot{Q} = k_{23} \frac{A(t_2 - t_3)}{\Delta x_{23}}$$

$$\dot{Q} = k_{34} \frac{A(t_3 - t_4)}{\Delta x_{34}}$$

Solving each equation for the temperature difference and adding the expressions gives

$$\dot{Q} = \frac{A(t_1 - t_4)}{\dfrac{\Delta x_{12}}{k_{12}} + \dfrac{\Delta x_{23}}{k_{23}} + \dfrac{\Delta x_{34}}{k_{34}}} \qquad (21\cdot4)$$

In this equation Δx_{12}, Δx_{23}, and Δx_{34} represent the thickness of the first, second, and third layers of the wall. t_1 and t_4 represent the inner and outer surface temperatures, and k_{12}, k_{23}, and k_{34} are the thermal conductivities of the materials, each of which is assumed to be constant.

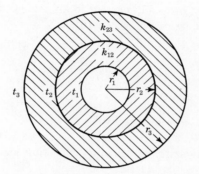

Fig. 21·4   Composite cylindrical wall.

A composite cylindrical wall which might be two layers of insulation on a pipe is shown in Fig. 21·4. The steady-state heat conduction in a radial direction is given by the following equation, which can be derived in a manner similar to that used in the development of equation 21·4:

$$\dot{Q} = \frac{2\pi L(t_1 - t_3)}{\dfrac{\ln (r_2/r_1)}{k_{12}} + \dfrac{\ln (r_3/r_2)}{k_{23}}} \qquad (21\cdot5)$$

The general differential equations representing the current flow in an electric system are similar to those for the heat flow in a thermal system. As a result of the similarity of the basic equations, a close analogy exists between a thermal circuit and an equivalent electric circuit. The use of the analogy is very valuable in the study of complex heat-transfer problems.

The material through which heat flows may be considered as a resistance to the passage of heat. For the plane homogeneous wall shown in Fig.

21·2, the equation for the heat flow may be written

$$\dot{Q} = kA \frac{\Delta t}{\Delta x} = \frac{\Delta t}{\Delta x / kA} = \frac{\Delta t}{R}$$

In this expression R is the thermal resistance. For the composite plane wall shown in Fig. 21·3, the equation for the heat flow in terms of the thermal resistances is

$$\dot{Q} = \frac{t_1 - t_4}{\dfrac{\Delta x_{12}}{Ak_{12}} + \dfrac{\Delta x_{23}}{Ak_{23}} + \dfrac{\Delta x_{34}}{Ak_{34}}} = \frac{t_1 - t_4}{R_{12} + R_{23} + R_{34}}$$

If the temperature difference and heat flow in a thermal circuit are analogous to voltage drop and current in an equivalent electric network, the two following equations may be written:

Thermal circuit:

$$\dot{Q} = \frac{\Delta t}{R}$$

Equivalent electric circuit:

$$i = \frac{E}{R}$$

This analogy is particularly valuable in connection with complex two- and three-dimensional heat-conduction problems.

21·2 Convection

Convection is the transfer of energy by means of a fluid which flows between regions of different temperature. As mentioned in the introduction to this chapter, this is a matter of mass transfer, but it is conventional to classify convection as one of the three modes of heat transfer.

Heat transfer between a solid and a fluid always involves a temperature gradient in the fluid near the solid. The region in which this gradient exists is called the convective film. The temperature gradient is accompanied by a density gradient which as a result of gravity may cause the fluid to flow. If the fluid flow past the solid surface is caused only by this density gradient, the method of heat transfer is referred to as *free (or natural) convection.* If the flow past the surface is caused by other means such as a pump, fan, or gravity flow of the entire mass of fluid, then the heat transfer is said to be by *forced convection.*

The basic equation for convective heat transfer is

$$\dot{Q} = hA \, \Delta t \tag{21·6}$$

where Δt is the difference in temperature between the solid surface and the bulk of the fluid outside the convective film, A is the area of the surface, and h is the *convective heat-transfer coefficient* or film coefficient. h is a complex function of the fluid properties and the characteristics of the flow. The accurate prediction of h values for a particular case may be difficult. Nearly all the references listed at the end of this chapter devote considerable attention to the correlation of h with fluid properties and flow characteristics for various flow and heat-transfer geometries.

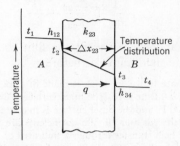

Fig. 21·5 Two fluids separated by a wall.

It is often necessary to compute the heat transfer between two fluids separated by a partition. The heat is transferred through the two fluids by convection and through the separating wall by conduction. Under these conditions it is convenient to express the transfer of heat in terms of an over-all heat-transfer coefficient. The over-all coefficient depends on the two film coefficients and the resistance to heat transfer through the separating wall by conduction. The heat transfer by convection in terms of the over-all coefficient may be expressed as

$$\dot{Q} = AU(t_1 - t_4) \tag{21·7}$$

See Fig. 21·5. The over-all heat-transfer coefficient U has the same units as the film coefficient h.

The over-all heat-transfer coefficient may be expressed in terms of the individual film coefficients by means of relatively simple expressions. Consider the transfer of heat from fluid A to fluid B as in Fig. 21·5. The heat transfer through the fluid and the separating wall is expressed by each of the following:

$$\dot{Q} = Ak_{23}\frac{t_2 - t_3}{\Delta x_{23}}$$

$$\dot{Q} = Ah_{34}(t_3 - t_4)$$

$$\dot{Q} = Ah_{12}(t_1 - t_2)$$

Solving each equation for the temperature difference and then adding the equations gives

$$\dot{Q} = \frac{A(t_1 - t_4)}{\dfrac{1}{h_{12}} + \dfrac{\Delta x_{23}}{k_{23}} + \dfrac{1}{h_{34}}} = AU(t_1 - t_4)$$

Solving for U gives

$$U = \frac{1}{\dfrac{1}{h_{12}} + \dfrac{\Delta x_{23}}{k_{23}} + \dfrac{1}{h_{34}}} \qquad (21 \cdot 8)$$

In this equation h_{12} and h_{34} represent the film coefficients. The other symbols have the same significance as before.

EXAMPLE 21·1. A furnace wall 8 in. thick is made of a material having an average thermal conductivity k of 0.8 B/hr-ft-F. The inner surface is exposed to a hot gas at an average temperature of 600 F, and the outer surface is in contact with air at an average temperature of 90 F. If the gas and air film coefficients are 12 and 1.2 B/hr-sq ft-F, respectively, compute the heat transfer through a wall area of 18 sq ft.

Solution. The over-all heat-transfer coefficient is given by equation 21·8 above. Substitution of numerical values gives

$$U = \frac{1}{\dfrac{1}{12} + \dfrac{8}{12(0.8)} + \dfrac{1}{1.2}} = 0.572 \text{ B/hr-sq ft}$$

The heat transfer is

$$\dot{Q} = AU \, \Delta t = 18(0.572)(600 - 90) = 5250 \text{ B/hr}$$

Consider next the heat transfer from the hot fluid to the cold fluid in a tubular heat exchanger as shown in Fig. 21·6. Heat is transferred from the hot fluid to the metal wall by convection, through the wall by conduction, and to the cold fluid by convection. Surface temperatures of the wall are t_2 and t_3, respectively. Fluid temperatures are designated by t_1 and t_4. No heat flows through the wall of the large outer pipe. The rate of heat transfer from the hot fluid to the inner surface of the small pipe is

$$\dot{Q} = h_{12}(2\pi r_2 L)(t_1 - t_2)$$

where $2\pi r_2 L$ represents the inner surface area of the pipe, and h_{12} the inner fluid film coefficient. Similarly the rate of heat transfer from the outer surface of the inner pipe to the cold fluid is

$$\dot{Q} = h_{34} 2\pi r_3 L(t_3 - t_4)$$

In this relation $2\pi r_3 L$ represents the outer surface area of the inner pipe, and h_{34} the heat-transfer coefficient based on this area. The rate of heat transfer through the inner pipe wall may be expressed by equation 21·3:

$$\dot{Q} = \frac{k_{23} 2\pi L (t_2 - t_3)}{\ln (r_3/r_2)}$$

Solving each of these three relations for the temperature difference and then adding equations gives

$$\dot{Q} = \frac{L(t_1 - t_4)}{\dfrac{1}{h_{12} 2\pi r_2} + \dfrac{\ln (r_3/r_2)}{k_{23} 2\pi} + \dfrac{1}{h_{34} 2\pi r_3}} \qquad (21·9)$$

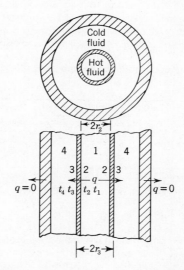

Fig. 21·6 Double-pipe heat exchanger.

Equation 21·7 may also be employed to express the heat flow in the following manner.

$$\dot{Q} = U_2 A_2 (t_1 - t_4) = U_3 A_3 (t_1 - t_4) \qquad (21·10)$$

In this relation U_2 and U_3 are over-all heat-transfer coefficients which are related to the inner and outer pipe areas A_2 and A_3, respectively.

Useful equations may be obtained by equating equations 21·9 and 21·10.

$$U_2 = \frac{1}{\dfrac{1}{h_{12}} + \dfrac{A_2 \ln (r_3/r_2)}{k_{23} 2\pi L} + \dfrac{A_2}{h_{34} A_3}} \qquad (21·11)$$

$$U_3 = \frac{1}{\dfrac{A_3}{h_{12} A_2} + \dfrac{A_3 \ln (r_3/r_2)}{k_{23} 2\pi L} + \dfrac{1}{h_{34}}} \qquad (21·12)$$

Equations 21·11 and 21·12 may be simplified by substituting for the areas the equivalents $2\pi rL$ or πDL. For example, equation 21·11 becomes

$$U_i = \cfrac{1}{\cfrac{1}{h_i} + \cfrac{r_i}{k}\left(\ln\cfrac{r_o}{r_i}\right) + \cfrac{r_i}{r_o h_o}} \tag{21·13}$$

In this expression the subscripts o and i refer to the outside and inside surfaces, respectively.

EXAMPLE 21·2. Compute the over-all heat-transfer coefficients based on the inner and outer areas for a copper condenser tube of $\frac{3}{4}$-in. outside diameter having a wall thickness of 0.1 in. Assume that the inner film coefficient is 280 B/hr-sq ft-F, the outer film coefficient is 2000 B/hr-sq ft-F, and the thermal conductivity of the copper is 200 B/hr-ft-F.

Solution. Substituting in equations 21·11 and 21·13 gives

$$U_i = \cfrac{1}{\cfrac{1}{280} + \cfrac{\pi(0.55)1\ln(0.75/0.55)}{12(200)2\pi(1)} + \cfrac{\pi(0.55)1/12}{2000(\pi)0.75(1)/12}}$$

$$= 252 \text{ B/hr-sq ft-F}$$

$$U_o = \cfrac{1}{\cfrac{\pi(0.75)1/12}{280(\pi)0.55(1)/12} + \cfrac{\pi(0.75)1\ln(0.75/0.55)}{12(200)2\pi(1)} + \cfrac{1}{2000}}$$

$$= 184 \text{ B/hr-sq ft-F}$$

These results show that it is important to use the over-all heat-transfer coefficient based on the proper area in any calculation of tubular heat exchangers.

In the preceding discussion the section of heat exchanger under study was so short that no question was raised regarding the value of Δt to use in the heat-transfer equation. In most heat exchangers the Δt varies from section to section of the heat exchanger, so there is a question as to what value of Δt to use. We now investigate this point for the two special cases of parallel flow and counterflow. In a parallel-flow heat exchanger the two fluids enter at the same end of the exchanger and flow in the same direction. Heat transfer therefore causes the temperature difference between the fluids to decrease in the direction of flow. The fluids enter a counterflow heat exchanger at opposite ends and flow in opposite directions. The initially hot fluid therefore exchanges heat first with cold fluid that has already been through most of the heat exchanger. Whether the temperature difference increases or decreases in a particular direction depends on the flow rates and the specific heats of the two fluids. Figure 21·7 shows the temperature distributions for parallel-flow and counterflow heat exchangers. The problem at hand is to find the value of mean temperature difference Δt_m to use in the relationship

$$\dot{Q} = UA\,\Delta t_m$$

for the simple case where U is constant throughout the heat exchanger.

Consider a parallel-flow heat exchanger, the temperature distribution for which is shown in Fig. 21·7a. For an infinitesimal area dA in the heat exchanger, the infinitesimal amount of heat transferred per unit time equals

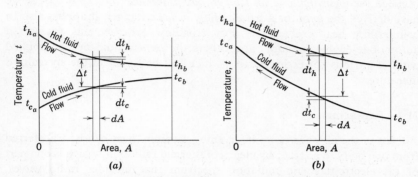

Fig. 21·7 Temperature distributions through (a) parallel-flow and (b) counterflow heat exchangers.

$U(\Delta t)\,dA$ and can also be expressed in terms of the temperature change dt of either fluid which occurs as the fluid passes the area dA. Thus

$$U(\Delta t)\,dA = -M_h c_{ph}\,dt_h = M_c c_{pc}\,dt_c \qquad (a)$$

where the subscripts h and c refer to the hot fluid and the cold fluid, respectively, and the minus sign accounts for the fact that we are concerned with heat which leaves the hot fluid. The change in Δt between the two fluids is

$$d(\Delta t) = d(t_h - t_c) = dt_h - dt_c = -U(\Delta t)\,dA\left(\frac{1}{M_h c_{ph}} + \frac{1}{M_c c_{pc}}\right) \qquad (b)$$

For the entire heat exchanger, if the specific heats are constant,

$$\dot{Q} = -M_h c_{ph}(t_{hb} - t_{ha}) = M_c c_{pc}(t_{cb} - t_{ca}) \qquad (c)$$

where the subscripts a and b denote the end sections of the heat exchanger as shown in Fig. 21·7a. Substituting from equation (c) into equation (b),

$$d(\Delta t) = -U(\Delta t)\,dA\left(\frac{t_{ha} - t_{hb}}{\dot{Q}} + \frac{t_{cb} - t_{ca}}{\dot{Q}}\right)$$

Integration over the entire heat exchanger (i.e., limits of $\Delta t = t_{ha} - t_{ca}$ at $A = 0$ and $\Delta t = t_{hb} - t_{cb}$ at $A = A$) gives

$$\dot{Q} = UA \frac{(t_{hb} - t_{cb}) - (t_{ha} - t_{ca})}{\ln\left[(t_{hb} - t_{cb})/(t_{ha} - t_{ca})\right]} = UA \frac{\Delta t_b - \Delta t_a}{\ln\left(\Delta t_b / \Delta t_a\right)}$$

The quantity

$$\Delta t_m = \frac{\Delta t_b - \Delta t_a}{\ln\left(\Delta t_b / \Delta t_a\right)}$$

is called the *logarithmic mean temperature difference* (*lmtd*). Although we have derived the *lmtd* for a parallel-flow heat exchanger, it applies also to counterflow heat exchangers. For crossflow arrangements (as in an automobile-engine radiator) and others the *lmtd* should not be applied without various correction factors which can be found in the specialized literature.

21·3 Radiation

Even in the absence of an intervening medium, heat can be transferred from one body to another by means of thermal radiation, which is one part of the electromagnetic radiation spectrum that includes radio waves, X rays, and visible light. Thermal radiation covers a broad band of wavelengths which is adjacent to and partly overlaps that of visible light in the spectrum, the thermal radiation having generally longer wavelengths than visible light. The laws of optics regarding reflection and refraction apply to thermal radiation.

Whenever radiant energy falls on a body, part may be absorbed, part reflected, and the remainder transmitted through the body. If we define *absorptivity* α as the fraction of the incident radiant energy which is absorbed, *reflectivity* ρ as the fraction which is reflected, and *transmissivity* τ as the fraction which is transmitted through the body,

$$\alpha + \rho + \tau = 1 \tag{21·14}$$

For the majority of opaque solid materials encountered in engineering, except for extremely thin bodies, $\tau = 0$; for gases, $\rho = 0$. α, ρ, and τ of a given material depend on the wavelength of the incident radiation. Their values for a given wavelength are called the *monochromatic absorptivity*, etc.

A substance which will absorb all the radiant thermal energy incident upon it at all wavelengths (thus reflecting or transmitting none) is called a *black body* or *black surface*. It should not be inferred from this name that the substance is black in color to the eye. A black body can be simulated by means of a box of uniform temperature with a small hole in it. Radiation incident upon the hole from the outside enters the box and is partially absorbed when it first strikes one of the walls. The part which is reflected from this wall strikes other walls from which only a part is reflected. If the box is large in comparison with the hole in it, a very small fraction of the radiant energy incident upon the hole from the outside is reflected back out through the hole which therefore approaches a black body in its behavior.

The hole which acts as a black body not only absorbs radiation from outside the box but also emits radiation from the interior, and the black body is a useful idealization which serves as a standard of comparison for the radiating characteristics of actual bodies as well as for their absorption characteristics.

The Stefan–Boltzmann law* states that the rate of total radiant energy emission from a black body at absolute temperature T is

$$\dot{Q}_b = \sigma A T^4 \qquad (21·15)$$

where A is the radiating area and σ is the *Stefan–Boltzmann constant*, $0.174(10^{-8})$ B/hr-sq ft-R⁴. The subscript b is a reminder that this applies only to black-body radiation. Notice that $\dot{Q}_b$ is the total rate of energy radiation by a black body, not the net rate of heat transfer as commonly used in thermodynamics. $\dot{Q}_b$ is given by equation 21·15 for any black body, regardless of the rate at which energy is being received from the surroundings at the same time. The emissivity of a body is defined as

$$\epsilon \equiv \frac{\dot{Q}/A}{(\dot{Q}/A)_b}$$

where $\dot{Q}/A$ is the rate of thermal radiation per unit area from the body, and $(\dot{Q}/A)_b$ is the rate of thermal radiation per unit area from a black body *at the same temperature*. For a black body, $\epsilon = 1$; for all other bodies, $\epsilon < 1$. Thus for a non-black body,

$$\dot{Q} = \sigma A \epsilon T^4 \qquad (21·16)$$

A few emissivity values for approximately room temperature taken from reference 21·2 are given in the table appearing on page 674 for purposes of illustration.

Kirchhoff's law states that for a body *in thermal equilibrium with its surroundings* the emissivity is equal to the absorptivity. This fact can be deduced by considering a body which is in thermal equilibrium with its surroundings and has a total thermal radiation incident upon it of $\dot{Q}$. If the absorptivity of the body is α, the rate of energy absorption is $\alpha\dot{Q}$.

---

* J. Stefan formulated this law in 1879 from a study of experimental data. Five years later, L. Boltzmann derived the same law from thermodynamic principles.

Since the body is in thermal equilibrium with its surroundings, its rate of energy emission equals its rate of energy absorption:

$$\sigma A \epsilon T^4 = \alpha \dot{Q}$$

ϵ and α must be so related that this equality holds for any body. If it is a black body, $\epsilon = 1$ and $\alpha = 1$. If it is a non-black body, the fraction of $\dot{Q}$ it absorbs must be the same as the fraction of $\sigma A T^4$ it emits. Therefore, $\alpha = \epsilon$ for any body which is in thermal equilibrium with its surroundings. A good absorber of radiant energy is also a good emitter.

Material	Emissivity
Iron oxide, carbon, oil	0.8
Rubber (gray, soft), wood (planed), paper	0.85 to 0.90
Roofing paper, enamel, lacquer, porcelain (glazed), fused quartz (rough), brick (red, rough), marble (gray, polished), glass (smooth)	0.91 to 0.94
Asbestos slate (rough), ice, water	0.95 to 0.99
Polished silver	0.01
Polished aluminum	0.04
Polished steel	0.07
Oxidized steel	≈ 0.8

The emissivity defined above and used in equation 21·16 and in the statement of Kirchhoff's law pertains to the total thermal radiation of all wavelengths from a body. The *monochromatic emissivity* of a body varies with the wavelength. For a black body, the distribution of the radiant energy throughout the wavelength spectrum depends only on the temperature, but for a non-black body it depends also on the variation of the monochromatic emissivity with wavelength. It can be shown that Kirchhoff's law holds also for monochromatic emissivity and monochromatic absorptivity. A body for which the monochromatic emissivity (and consequently the monochromatic absorptivity) is the same for all wavelengths is called a *gray body*.

We have so far discussed the rate of energy emission and the rate of energy absorption of a body, but the problem in engineering is usually one of the net interchange of radiant energy between two bodies. Consider first the interchange between two black bodies. If all the radiation from each body falls upon the other body, then the net interchange is simply the difference between $\sigma A_1 T_1^4$ and $\sigma A_2 T_2^4$, where 1 and 2 denote the two bodies. This would be the case for two infinitely large (i.e., large enough that edge effects are negligible) parallel black planes. Thus

$$\frac{\dot{Q}}{A} = \sigma(T_1^4 - T_2^4)$$

In general, the radiant heat transfer between two black surfaces is given by

$$\dot{Q} = \sigma F_{A1} A_1 (T_1^4 - T_2^4) = \sigma F_{A2} A_2 (T_1^4 - T_2^4) \qquad (21\cdot17)$$

where F_{A1} and F_{A2} are called *configuration factors* or *view factors* based on

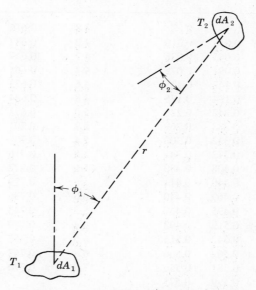

Fig. 21·8 Geometrical arrangement of surfaces.

area A_1 and area A_2, respectively. Configuration factors depend only on the geometry of the black surfaces. If dA_1 and dA_2 in Fig. 21·8 are infinitesimal parts of two black surfaces, the ϕ's are the angles between the normals to the infinitesimal areas and the line joining them, and r is the distance between them, then

$$F_{A1} A_1 = F_{A2} A_2 = \int_0^{A1} \int_0^{A2} \frac{\cos\phi_1 \cdot \cos\phi_2 \cdot dA_1 \cdot dA_2}{\pi r^2}$$

For infinitely large parallel planes, $F_{A1} = F_{A2} = 1.0$. Also, for any case in which all the radiation from body 1 is incident upon body 2 (as when body 1 is completely enclosed by body 2), $F_{A1} = 1.0$. Table 21·1 gives F_A

TABLE 21·1

Configuration Factors for Parallel Squares and Disks,
Directly Opposed*

Ratio of Side (or Diameter) to Distance between Planes	Squares	Disks	Ratio of Side (or Diameter) to Distance between Planes	Squares	Disks
0	0	0	3.8	0.616	0.593
0.2	0.018	0.010	4.0	0.632	0.609
0.4	0.045	0.038	4.2	0.647	0.624
0.6	0.091	0.075	4.4	0.661	0.638
0.8	0.142	0.125	4.6	0.673	0.651
1.0	0.194	0.175	4.8	0.684	0.662
1.2	0.242	0.226	5.0	0.693	0.672
1.4	0.288	0.269	5.2	0.701	0.681
1.6	0.332	0.308	5.4	0.709	0.689
1.8	0.372	0.345	5.5	0.716	0.697
2.0	0.408	0.380	5.6	0.722	0.703
2.2	0.440	0.411	5.8	0.729	0.709
2.4	0.469	0.440	6.0	0.736	0.716
2.6	0.495	0.467	6.2	0.743	0.723
2.8	0.519	0.492	6.4	0.749	0.730
3.0	0.542	0.515	6.6	0.756	0.737
3.2	0.562	0.536	6.8	0.763	0.743
3.4	0.581	0.556	7.0	0.770	0.750
3.6	0.599	0.575			

* Data from "Radiant Heat Transmission," by H. C. Hottel, *Mechanical Engineering*, vol. 52, p. 699, 1930. (Several points adjusted by the authors of reference 21·2.)

for cases of parallel disks and squares of equal size directly opposed. Most of the references listed at the end of this chapter give data on F_A for various configurations.

For the radiant heat transfer between gray bodies, the fact that not all the radiant energy incident upon either body is absorbed must be considered. Therefore equation 21·17 is modified to

$$\dot{Q} = \sigma F_\epsilon F_{A1} A_1 (T_1^4 - T_2^4) \qquad (21 \cdot 18)$$

where F_ϵ is the *emissivity factor*, values of which can also be found in the literature for a number of geometries. For very large parallel planes,

$$F_\epsilon = \frac{1}{1/\epsilon_1 + 1/\epsilon_2 - 1}$$

and this value applies also to the case of one body completely enclosed by another if the inner body is large compared with the enclosure. If the enclosed body 1 is small compared with the enclosure 2, very little of the reflected radiation from the enclosing surface falls on body 1, so the surface 2 acts as though it is black regardless of its emissivity. Then $F_\epsilon = \epsilon_1$. For parallel disks and squares if the distance between them is large compared with their dimensions, $F_\epsilon = \epsilon_1\epsilon_2$.

In this discussion we have ignored the effects of gases between bodies which are exchanging radiant energy. This is a reliable procedure if the gases are transparent ($\tau = 1.0$, $\alpha = 0$, $\rho = 0$) to thermal radiation as nitrogen, oxygen, and hydrogen are. Carbon dioxide, water vapor, and many other gases absorb (and hence emit) appreciable amounts of radiation, however, and this must be accounted for if such gases are present.

REFERENCES

21·1 H. C. Hottel, "Radiant Heat Transmission," *Mechanical Engineering*, vol. 52, 1930, p. 699.

21·2 M. Jakob and G. A. Hawkins, *Elements of Heat Transfer*, John Wiley & Sons, 3d ed., 1957.

21·3 W. H. McAdams, *Heat Transmission*, McGraw-Hill Book Co., 3d ed., 1954.

21·4 A. I. Brown and S. M. Marco, *Introduction to Heat Transfer*, McGraw-Hill Book Co., 3d ed., 1958.

21·5 M. Jakob, *Heat Transfer*, vol. I, John Wiley & Sons, 1949.

21·6 M. Jakob, *Heat Transfer*, vol. II, John Wiley & Sons, 1957.

21·7 E. R. G. Eckert, *Introduction to the Transfer of Heat and Mass*, McGraw-Hill Book Co., 1950.

21·8 P. J. Schneider, *Conduction Heat Transfer*, Addison-Wesley Publishing Co., 1955.

21·9 W. H. Giedt, *Principles of Engineering Heat Transfer*, D. Van Nostrand Co., 1957.

PROBLEMS

21·1 Calculate the heat transfer between the two surfaces of a wall 2 in. thick, made of insulation, if the inner and outer surfaces are at 300 and 100 F, respectively. Assume that the thermal conductivity of the material at an average temperature of 200 F is 0.037 B/hr-ft-F.

21·2 A wall is made up of 9 in. of refractory material A ($k_A = 1.4$ B/hr-ft-F), 4 in. of insulation B ($k_B = 0.05$ B/hr-ft-F), and 4 in. of brick material C ($k_C = 1.1$ B/hr-ft-F). If the outer surface of materials A and C are at temperatures of 1200 and 120 F, respectively, calculate the heat transfer for each 10 sq ft of surface area.

21·3　Calculate the temperature at the contact surfaces for materials A and B and B and C in Prob. 21·2.

21·4　Determine the heat transmitted per hour through 7 sq ft of a wall made up of 9 in. of material A ($k_A = 2.0$ B/hr-ft-F) and 1 in. of material B ($k_B = 0.3$ B/hr-ft-F). Assume that the outer surfaces of materials A and B are at temperatures of 700 and 200 F, respectively.

21·5　Determine the heat loss from 60 ft of horizontal pipe, 2 in. nominal diameter, covered with 1 in. of insulation ($k = 0.04$ B/hr-ft-F), if the inner and outer surface temperatures of the insulation are 500 and 150 F, respectively.

21·6　Calculate the heat loss per linear foot from a pipe 8 in. in nominal diameter covered with 2 in. of insulation ($k = 0.05$ B/hr-ft-F). Assume that the inside and outside surface temperatures of the insulation are 600 and 120 F, respectively.

21·7　Determine the heat loss per square foot of insulation surface for a horizontal steam pipe 4 in. in nominal diameter, covered with 1 in. of insulation A ($k_A = 0.9$ B/hr-ft-F) and 2 in. of insulation B ($k_B = 0.06$ B/hr-ft-F), if the inner and outer surface insulation temperatures are 800 and 140 F, respectively.

21·8　Sketch a curve of temperature versus distance through a plane wall in the direction of heat transfer if the thermal conductivity is given by $k = a + bt$, where a and b are positive constants.

21·9　Sketch a curve of temperature versus radius for one-dimensional heat conduction outward through a cylindrical wall if the thermal conductivity is constant.

21·10　Would the existence of a negative thermal conductivity violate either the first or the second law? Explain.

21·11　Compute the heat loss by convection from 350 ft of bare pipe 2 in. in nominal diameter to the still air of a room. Assume that the pipe surface temperature and air temperature are 300 and 80 F, respectively, and that the film coefficient is equal to 1 B/hr-sq ft-F.

21·12　The wall of a heat exchanger is made of a plate of copper $\frac{3}{4}$ in. thick ($k = 200$ B/hr-ft-F). If the film coefficients on the two sides of the plate are 50 B/hr-sq ft-F and 150 B/hr-sq ft-F, calculate the heat passing through the section per day per square foot. The total temperature drop is 150 F.

21·13　Brass tubes, 1 in. OD $\times$ 0.92 in. ID, are used in a heat exchanger. If the inner and outer film coefficients are 1500 B/hr-sq ft-F and 1000 B/hr-sq ft-F, calculate the over-all heat-transfer coefficient on the basis of the inner surface area. Assume that k for brass is 60 B/hr-ft-F.

21·14　In Prob. 21·13 calculate the over-all heat-transfer coefficient based on the outer tube area.

21·15　A steel tube ($k = 25$ B/hr-ft-F) has an outside diameter of 0.9 in. and an inside diameter of 0.8 in. If the coefficients on the outside and inside are 100 B/hr-sq ft-F and 1500 B/hr-sq ft-F, respectively, calculate the over-all heat-transfer coefficient, using the outer surface area as the basis.

21·16　Cooling water enters a steam condenser at 65 F and leaves at 78 F. If the condensing steam is at a temperature of 115 F, calculate the log mean temperature difference.

21·17　A furnace wall 8 in. thick is made of material having an average thermal conductivity of 0.8 B/hr-ft-F. The inner surface is exposed to hot gases at 600 F; the outer surface is in contact with air at 90 F. Heat loss through the wall by conduction and convection amounts to 292 B/hr-sq ft. If the total wall surface is 300 sq ft, calculate the over-all heat-transfer coefficient U.

21·18 A heat exchanger is to be designed to transmit 500,000 B/hr. If the design maximum and minimum temperature differences are 3 and 30 F, respectively, and the over-all heat-transfer rate is 250 B/hr-sq ft-F, calculate the total heat-transfer surface required for parallel flow.

21·19 In a proposed design of a liquid-to-liquid heat exchanger, the temperature differences are 40 and 10 F, respectively. If 100,000 B/hr are to be transmitted through 50 sq ft, calculate the over-all heat-transfer coefficient required.

21·20 Water at 85 F enters a heat exchanger and leaves at 100 F. Steam at a constant temperature of 140 F condenses on the outside of the tubes carrying the water. If the total heat transfer area is 500 sq ft and the over-all heat-transfer coefficient for the unit is 300 B/hr-sq ft-F, calculate the total heat transferred per hour.

21·21 Water enters a two-fluid heat exchanger at 160 F and leaves at 270 F. Hot gases enter at 580 F and leave at 300 F. If the total heat-transfer area is 5000 sq ft and the over-all heat-transfer coefficient is 100 B/hr-sq ft-F, calculate the total heat transferred per hour if the fluids flow parallel to each other and in the same direction.

21·22 A house is heated by an oil-burning furnace which is controlled by a thermostat which holds the room temperature within ± 2 F of its setting. From the standpoint of fuel saving alone, which procedure is better for winter operation of the heating system: (*a*) leaving the thermostat set at 70 F, or (*b*) leaving the thermostat set at 70 F during the day but setting it at 55 F for 8 hr during the night? Explain your reasoning in not more than one page.

21·23 A gearbox driven by a gasoline engine has an efficiency of 92 per cent when its output shaft delivers 120 hp at 240 rpm. The gearbox is cooled by means of a fan which blows room air over it. Under these steady operating conditions, how much heat is given off by the gearbox? Sketch a curve of gearbox casing temperature versus gearbox efficiency.

21·24 In order to get a uniform temperature distribution over the bottom of a surface cooking vessel, should the bottom be made (*a*) of high- or low-conductivity material, (*b*) thick or thin?

21·25 Why is grease used in a skillet? Is more grease required in an iron skillet or in a Pyrex one?

21·26 Compute the radiant heat interchange per square foot between two infinite parallel black planes, the temperatures of which are 400 and 100 F, respectively.

21·27 Two parallel black disks 2 ft in diameter are located 1 ft apart and directly opposite each other. If the temperatures of the disks are 400 and 200 F, respectively, compute the net radiant heat transfer per square foot of surface area.

21·28 Two black square surfaces of 4 ft side length are located 1 ft apart and directly opposite each other. If the temperatures are 100 and 500 F, respectively, compute the net radiant heat interchange between the two surfaces.

21·29 Compute the net radiant interchange between two parallel square black surfaces of 6 ft side length located directly opposite each other at a distance of 2 ft. The temperatures of the surfaces are 200 and 600 F, respectively.

21·30 Calculate the radiant heat transfer through a hole, approximately 1 in. in diameter, in the wall of an open-hearth furnace, if the average furnace and outside temperatures are 2800 and 110 F, respectively. Assume that black-body conditions exist.

21·31 Determine the radiant heat loss through a crack in an oven door if the inside and outside temperatures are 1500 and 100 F, respectively. Assume black-body conditions; also that the area of the crack is 0.3 sq in.

21·32 The outer surface temperature of a gearbox operating steadily at an efficiency (ratio of power output to power input) of 95 per cent is 140 F when the surroundings are at 40 F. What will the surface temperature be if the gearbox operates at 90 per cent efficiency with the same power input, assuming that the gearbox is always cooled by (*a*) convection alone? (*b*) radiation alone?

21·33 Consider the heat transfer by radiation only between two infinitely large parallel black planes, each at a constant temperature. A third infinitely large black plane is inserted between the original two. Determine the ratio of the rate of heat transfer with the third plane present to the original rate.

21·34 Explain why smudge pots are effective in reducing frost damage in fruit groves. Explain how protection is also provided by large fans which circulate air through the groves.

Dimensions and Units

In this discussion we refer to physical quantities such as length, time, mass, and temperature as *dimensions*. Thus the dimensions of velocity are length/time and the dimensions of pressure are force/(length)². We refer to a small group of dimensions from which all others can be formed as *primary dimensions*. If we denote these primary dimensions by the symbols L for length, M for mass, F for force, τ for time, θ for temperature, and Q for electric charge, we can write the dimensions of other physical quantities in terms of these as shown in the following list:

Linear velocity	L/τ	Density	M/L^3
Linear acceleration	L/τ^2	Specific volume	L^3/M
Angular velocity*	$1/\tau$	Specific gravity*	—
Angular acceleration*	$1/\tau^2$	Energy	FL
Pressure	F/L^2	Specific heat	$FL/M\theta$
Work	FL	Electric potential	FL/Q
Power	FL/τ	Electric current	Q/τ

*Angular measure is dimensionless and can be thought of as a ratio of two lengths: an arc length and a radius. Specific gravity is dimensionless because it is a ratio of two densities.

Any equation involving physical quantities, whether it is an algebraic, differential, or integral equation, must be dimensionally homogeneous; that is, equal quantities must have the same dimensions and only quantities with the same dimensions can be added to each other. Dimensions are not changed by the performance of any indicated mathematical operation such as differentiation or integration. The dimensional homogeneity of an equation such as

$$pv = RT$$

is shown by substituting for each quantity its dimensions,

$$\left[\frac{F}{L^2}\right]\left[\frac{L^3}{M}\right] = \left[\frac{FL}{M\theta}\right]\theta$$

$$\left[\frac{FL}{M}\right] = \left[\frac{FL}{M}\right]$$

681

Also, the dimensions of

$$\left(\frac{\partial T}{\partial v}\right)_s = \left(\frac{\partial p}{\partial s}\right)_v$$

are readily checked for homogeneity by

$$\left[\frac{\theta M}{L^3}\right] = \left[\frac{F}{L^2}\right]\left[\frac{M\theta}{FL}\right]$$

$$\left[\frac{\theta M}{L^3}\right] = \left[\frac{\theta M}{L^3}\right]$$

Notice that dimensional homogeneity has nothing to do with numbers or numerical values. If an equation is valid, it must be dimensionally homogeneous. If it is not dimensionally homogeneous, it cannot be made valid simply by a judicious selection of numerical values or the use of numerical conversion factors. The requirement of dimensional homogeneity thus provides a means of checking equations, and it is also useful in determining the general form of physical equations through a process known as dimensional analysis.

Units are arbitrary magnitudes of dimensions which are used for purposes of measurement. Samples of units of the primary dimensions are given in the following table:

Primary Dimension	Sample Units
Length	inch, cm, ft, mile, light year
Time	hour, minute, second, day
Force	pound, poundal, dyne, newton
Mass	pound, slug, gram, kilogram
Temperature	degree Rankine, degree Kelvin, degree Fahrenheit
Electric charge	coulomb, abcoulomb, statcoulomb

As pointed out above, any equation involving physical quantities must be dimensionally homogeneous. For numerical computations, the additional requirements of unitary homogeneity must be met. For example, although the equation

$$v = \frac{RT}{p} \tag{a}$$

is dimensionally homogeneous, substitution of numerical values as

$$v\left[\frac{\text{ft}^3}{\text{lb}_m}\right] = \frac{0.0686\left[\dfrac{B}{\text{lb}_m\text{-R}}\right]520[R]}{14.7\left[\dfrac{\text{lb}_f}{\text{in}^2}\right]} \tag{b}$$

does not satisfy the requirement of consistent units and leads to confusion.

Consistent units can be provided by means of *conversion factors* or *unitary constants* such as

$$\frac{778 \text{ ft-lb}_f}{\text{B}} = 1$$

$$\frac{144 \text{ in}^2}{\text{ft}^2} = 1$$

which follow from the relations

$$778 \text{ ft-lb}_f = 1 \text{ B}$$

$$144 \text{ in}^2 = 1 \text{ ft}^2$$

(Notice that a conversion factor is always dimensionless.) Thus instead of equation (*b*) we can write

$$v\left[\frac{\text{ft}^3}{\text{lb}_m}\right] = \frac{0.0686\left[\dfrac{\text{B}}{\text{lb}_m\text{-R}}\right] 778\left[\dfrac{\text{ft-lb}_f}{\text{B}}\right] 520[\text{R}]}{14.7\left[\dfrac{\text{lb}_f}{\text{in}^2}\right] 144\left[\dfrac{\text{in}^2}{\text{ft}^2}\right]}$$

$$= 13.1 \frac{\text{ft}^3}{\text{lb}_m}$$

in which the units are consistent or homogeneous. Notice that, in any equation which is dimensionally homogeneous, unitary homogeneity can be obtained by the proper selection of units and the use of conversion factors.

The relationship among force, mass, length, and time is a very important one and often for students a troublesome one. *If we take the relationship for a body of fixed mass to be*

$$F = ma \qquad\qquad (c)$$

then we are saying that the dimensions are related by

$$[F] = \left[\frac{ML}{\tau^2}\right]$$

Thus a relationship among these four dimensions makes it possible to select any three of them as primary dimensions in terms of which the fourth one can be defined. For making numerical substitutions into equation (*c*), consistent units must be used. If the numerical values at hand for *F*, *m*, and *a* are not in consistent units, it may be necessary to use a conversion factor. For example, if we substitute into

$$F = ma$$

numerical values such as

$$F[\text{lb}_f] = 10[\text{lb}_m]10\left[\frac{\text{ft}}{\text{sec}^2}\right]$$

then in order to obtain consistent units, we use a conversion factor

$$g_c = 32.2 \left[\frac{\text{lb}_m\text{-ft}}{\text{lb}_f\text{-sec}^2} \right] = 1$$

This conversion factor is dimensionless (as all conversion factors must be) because we have established above that $F = ML/\tau^2$. Thus it is possible to use g_c as a conversion factor or unitary constant. This is done whenever only three of the quantities F, M, L, and τ are taken as independent primary dimensions. *This is not the practice followed in this book.*

If we treat force, mass, length, and time as independent primary dimensions, then the equation $F = ma$ is invalid because it is not dimensionally homogeneous. We must write instead

$$F = \frac{ma}{g_c} \qquad (d)$$

where g_c is a dimensional constant. Its dimensions can be deduced as $ML/F\tau^2$ from the fact that equation (d) must be dimensionally homogeneous,

$$F = \frac{[M]\left[\dfrac{L}{\tau^2}\right]}{\left[\dfrac{ML}{F\tau^2}\right]}$$

This is the procedure followed in this book. g_c is taken to be a dimensional constant. It is written in equations to provide dimensional homogeneity. It is unlike unitary constants such as J or 144 sq in/sq ft, which are necessary in numerical computations but are not written in equations which should be valid independently of any set of units or numerical values.*

g_c can be written with various units, and of course its numerical value depends only on the units selected. The numerical value of g_c is shown for five systems

* If force, mass, length, and time are used as independent primary dimensions, equations such as

$$\gamma = \rho g; \qquad KE = \tfrac{1}{2}mV^2; \qquad \text{Torque} = I\alpha; \qquad E = mc^2 \qquad (e)$$

are also dimensionally inhomogeneous, and they should be written

$$\gamma = \frac{\rho g}{g_c}; \qquad KE = \frac{mV^2}{2g_c}; \qquad \text{Torque} = \frac{I\alpha}{g_c}; \qquad E = \frac{mc^2}{g_c} \qquad (f)$$

If, on the other hand, only three primary dimensions are used, equations (e) are correct, and equations (f) would include a conversion factor which is superfluous until numerical calculations are made.

of units in the accompanying table. Thus we can write

$$g_c = 32.174 \, \frac{\text{lb}_m\text{-ft}}{\text{lb}_f\text{-sec}^2} = 1 \, \frac{\text{slug-ft}}{\text{lb}_f\text{-sec}^2} = 1 \, \frac{\text{lb}_m\text{-ft}}{\text{pdl-sec}^2} = \cdots$$

F	M	L	τ	g_c
lb$_f$	lb$_m$	foot	second	$32.174 \, \dfrac{\text{lb}_m\text{-ft}}{\text{lb}_f\text{-sec}^2}$
lb$_f$	slug	foot		$1 \, \dfrac{\text{slug-ft}}{\text{lb}_f\text{-sec}^2}$
poundal	lb$_m$	foot		$1 \, \dfrac{\text{lb}_m\text{-ft}}{\text{pdl-sec}^2}$
dyne	gram	centimeter		$1 \, \dfrac{\text{g-cm}}{\text{dyne-sec}^2}$
newton	kilogram	meter		$1 \, \dfrac{\text{kg-meter}}{\text{newton-sec}^2}$

Notice that g_c has nothing to do with gravity or the acceleration of a freely falling body, even though historically some systems of units were founded on the basis of gravitational force measurements on bodies in certain locations.

Difficulty with units and dimensions stems largely from the use of the term pound as a unit of force and as a unit of mass, and the difficulty is compounded by the fact that in some cases mass and a particular force—weight, a gravitational force—can be used interchangeably. Let us look into the relationship which involves weight and mass by applying the basic equation for a body of fixed mass,

$$F = \frac{ma}{g_c} \qquad (d)$$

to a body which is acted upon by a gravitational force and none other. This force we call weight. The acceleration of a body caused by this force alone is called the acceleration of gravity g. Substituting this particular force and the corresponding particular acceleration into equation (d) gives

$$w = \frac{mg}{g_c}$$

Obviously, if g is constant, then weight and mass are in a fixed proportion to each other, and for accounting purposes, such as mass balances, can actually be used interchangeably. This cannot be done if g varies. A serious danger in this practice is that weight, which is a force, comes to be thought of as mass, and confusion then results between the quantities force and mass which are as different from each other as the quantities length and time are.

Another factor in the confusion between weight and mass is that the operation called *weighing* is usually a determination of mass. This is certainly the case when a balance-type scale is used. It is also the case with a spring scale if the scale has been calibrated by means of standard masses (which are commonly and unfortunately called standard weights).

The exercises below provide a means of checking your understanding of units and dimensions.

EXERCISES

1. A body weighs 20 lb in a location where $g = 31.6$ ft/sec². Determine the force required to accelerate this body at a rate of 30 ft/sec².

2. A body has a mass of 500 lb. Determine the force required to accelerate this body at a rate of 5 ft/sec² in a location where $g = 31.6$ ft/sec.²

3. A body has a mass of 15 kg. Determine the force in pounds required to accelerate it at a rate of 10 ft/sec² in a location where $g = 30.0$ ft/sec².

4. A body weighs 30 lb in a location where $g = 32.0$ ft/sec². (a) What is its mass in pounds? In slugs? (b) What are its weight in pounds, mass in pounds, and mass in slugs in a location where $g = 16.0$ ft/sec²?

5. A liquid has a density of 55 lb/cu ft. Determine its specific volume, its specific weight, and its density in slugs/cu ft in a location where (a) $g = 32.2$ ft/sec², (b) $g = 31.6$ ft/sec².

6. What is the value of g_c in a location where a body with a mass of 270 lb weighs 195 lb$_f$?

ANSWERS

1. 19.0 lb$_f$.

2. 77.7 lb$_f$.

3. 10.3 lb$_f$.

4. (a) 30.2 lb$_m$, 0.938 slug; (b) 15 lb$_f$, 30.2 lb$_m$, 0.938 slug.

5. (a) 0.0182 cu ft/lb$_m$, 55 lb$_f$/cu ft, 1.71 slugs/cu ft; (b) 0.0182 cu ft/lb$_m$, 54.0 lb$_f$/cu ft, 1.71 slugs/cu ft.

6. The same as it is in any other location.

Note on Partial Derivatives

Partial derivatives are important in thermodynamics because several properties are defined in terms of partial derivatives (for example, specific heats and Joule–Thomson coefficient), and a knowledge of relationships among partial derivatives is consequently helpful in correlating properties.

B·1 A graphical interpretation of partial derivatives

If three quantities x, y, and z are functionally related, this fact can be stated in any of the following ways:

$$f(x, y, z) = 0 \qquad x = f(y, z) \qquad y = f(x, z) \qquad z = f(x, y)$$

The differential dz is given by

$$dz = \left(\frac{\partial z}{\partial x}\right)_y dx + \left(\frac{\partial z}{\partial y}\right)_x dy$$

and similar expressions can be written for dx and dy.

A physical picture of this differential dz is given by reference to Fig. B·1 in which a-b-c-d is any very small element of a surface which satisfies the equation $z = f(x, y)$. The change in z between points a and c can be evaluated as

$$\Delta z_{a\text{-}c} = \Delta z_{b\text{-}c} + \Delta z_{a\text{-}b}$$

Since b and c both lie in a plane of $y = $ constant,

$$\Delta z_{b\text{-}c} = \Delta x_{b\text{-}c} \times \text{(slope of } zx \text{ curve in plane of } y = \text{constant)}$$

$$= \Delta x_{b\text{-}c} \left(\frac{\Delta z}{\Delta x}\right)_{y=\text{const}}$$

and similarly

$$\Delta z_{a\text{-}b} = \Delta y_{a\text{-}b} \left(\frac{\Delta z}{\Delta y}\right)_{x=\text{const}}$$

Then

$$\Delta z_{a\text{-}c} = \left(\frac{\Delta z}{\Delta x}\right)_y \Delta x_{b\text{-}c} + \left(\frac{\Delta z}{\Delta y}\right)_x \Delta y_{a\text{-}b}$$

If the surface element a-b-c-d is allowed to become smaller and smaller, Δz approaches dz as a limit, and

$$dz = \left(\frac{\partial z}{\partial x}\right)_y dx + \left(\frac{\partial z}{\partial y}\right)_x dy$$

Notice that, at each point on the surface, $(\partial z/\partial x)_y$ has a single fixed value, because it is the slope of a zx curve along a particular path (which in this case

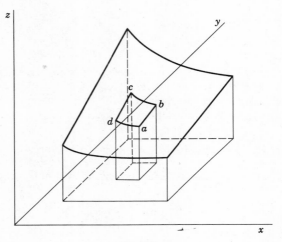

Fig. B·1

is a path along the intersection of the surface and a y = constant plane). dz/dx, however, has many values at each point on the surface, since it can be evaluated along many different paths through any point. In general

$$\frac{dz}{dx} = \left(\frac{\partial z}{\partial x}\right)_y + \left(\frac{\partial z}{\partial y}\right)_x \frac{dy}{dx}$$

where $(\partial z/\partial x)_y$ and $(\partial z/\partial y)_x$ are point functions which have fixed values at each point, and dz/dx and dy/dx have many possible values at each point, depending on the path along which they are evaluated.

EXERCISES

Figure B·2 is a map which bears numbered contour lines of constant elevation H. x is distance measured east of the origin, and y is distance measured north of the origin. At every xy location there is a fixed value of H; so $H = f(x, y)$ or $f(H, x, y) = 0$. The map shows a hill with its summit at 3,5 (i.e., $x = 3$, $y = 5$). A stream flows southwest along a path given approximately by $y = x - 12$.

1. Give the coordinates of a point at which it appears that $(\partial H/\partial y)_x$ is (a) a maximum, (b) a minimum, and (c) zero.

2. Repeat exercise 1 for $(\partial H/\partial x)_y$.

3. Give the coordinates of a point at which it appears that $(\partial y/\partial x)_H$ equals (a) zero, (b) one, and (c) minus one.

4. A path on the ground is given by the relation $y = 2x$. Give the coordinates of points (if any) along this path where dH/dx is (a) a maximum, (b) a minimum, and (c) zero.

5. Repeat exercise 4 for $(\partial H/\partial x)_y$.

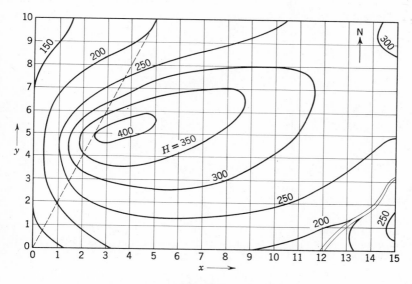

Fig. B·2

ANSWERS

1. (a) Vicinity of 2.7,3.4; (b) vicinity of 2.5,5.8; (c) 11.6,7.0; 1.0,4.2; 5.1,5.4; etc.
2. (a) 1.7,4.8; (b) vicinity of 10.0,6.6; (c) 9.0,8.0; 5.5,2.6; 7.8,7.0; etc.
3. (a) 9.0,8.0; 5.5,2.6; etc.; (b) 10.8,4.8; 8.3,5.5; etc.; (c) 2.2,4.0; 14.4,8.9; etc.
4. (a) Vicinity of 1.9,3.8; (b) vicinity of 3.1,6.2; (c) 2.5⁻,4.9; 5.0,10.0.
5. (a) Perhaps at 2.5,5.0; (b) 5.0,10.0; (c) none.

B·2   Three relations among partial derivatives

If four quantities w, x, y, and z are related in such a manner that any two, but not more than two, are independent (and this is a common case in thermodynamics), then any one can be considered as a function of any other two:

$$w = f(x, y) \qquad x = f(y, z) \qquad y = f(x, z) \qquad z = f(x, y)$$

$$w = f(x, z) \qquad x = f(w, z) \qquad y = f(w, x) \qquad z = f(w, x)$$

$$w = f(y, z) \qquad x = f(w, y) \qquad y = f(w, z) \qquad z = f(w, y)$$

Of course, $f(x, y)$ signifies only *some function of x and y* and does not represent any particular function.

Writing the differentials of two of the quantities as expressed above is the first step toward establishing three relationships which are quite useful in thermodynamics. If we take, for example, the following pair from the list above,

$$x = f(w, y) \quad \text{and} \quad y = f(w, z)$$

the differentials are

$$dx = \left(\frac{\partial x}{\partial w}\right)_y dw + \left(\frac{\partial x}{\partial y}\right)_w dy$$

$$dy = \left(\frac{\partial y}{\partial w}\right)_z dw + \left(\frac{\partial y}{\partial z}\right)_w dz$$

Substituting the value of dy from the second of these two equations into the first one and collecting terms gives

$$dx = \left[\left(\frac{\partial x}{\partial w}\right)_y + \left(\frac{\partial x}{\partial y}\right)_w\left(\frac{\partial y}{\partial w}\right)_z\right]dw + \left[\left(\frac{\partial x}{\partial y}\right)_w\left(\frac{\partial y}{\partial z}\right)_w\right]dz$$

Also, $$dx = \left(\frac{\partial x}{\partial w}\right)_z dw + \left(\frac{\partial x}{\partial z}\right)_w dz$$

w and z can be varied independently, so the coefficients of dw and dz must be the same in these two equations. Equating the coefficients of dw gives the important relationship

$$\left(\frac{\partial x}{\partial w}\right)_z = \left(\frac{\partial x}{\partial w}\right)_y + \left(\frac{\partial x}{\partial y}\right)_w\left(\frac{\partial y}{\partial w}\right)_z \tag{A}$$

Equating the coefficients of dz and rearranging gives

$$\left(\frac{\partial x}{\partial y}\right)_w\left(\frac{\partial y}{\partial z}\right)_w = \left(\frac{\partial x}{\partial z}\right)_w \tag{B}$$

or $$\left(\frac{\partial x}{\partial y}\right)_w\left(\frac{\partial y}{\partial z}\right)_w\left(\frac{\partial z}{\partial x}\right)_w = 1 \tag{B}$$

A third useful relationship can be obtained by first writing an equation such as

$$dz = \left(\frac{\partial z}{\partial y}\right)_x dy + \left(\frac{\partial z}{\partial x}\right)_y dx$$

in the form $$\frac{dz}{dy} = \left(\frac{\partial z}{\partial y}\right)_x + \left(\frac{\partial z}{\partial x}\right)_y\frac{dx}{dy}$$

Since any two of the three quantities x, y, and z can be varied independently, we can assign the condition that z is constant. (This means, referring back to the graphical interpretation in Art. B·1, that we follow a path of constant z.

It does not mean that $(\partial z/\partial y)_x$ or $(\partial z/\partial x)_y$ is zero.)   Then

$$0 = \left(\frac{\partial z}{\partial y}\right)_x + \left(\frac{\partial z}{\partial x}\right)_y \left(\frac{\partial x}{\partial y}\right)_z$$

This useful relationship is often written as

$$\left(\frac{\partial x}{\partial y}\right)_z \left(\frac{\partial y}{\partial z}\right)_x \left(\frac{\partial z}{\partial x}\right)_y = -1 \qquad\qquad (C)$$

and is sometimes called the "rotating partials." Equation (C) shows the absurdity of treating ∂x, ∂y, and ∂z as quantities which can be handled alone and canceled as parts of fractions.

Equations (A), (B), and (C) are frequently used in the correlation of thermo-dynamic property data.

Tables and Charts

TABLE A·1
Dry Saturated Steam: Temperature Table*

Temp. F	Abs Press. Lb Sq In. p	Specific Volume Sat. Liquid vf	Specific Volume Evap. vfg	Specific Volume Sat. Vapor vg	Enthalpy Sat. Liquid hf	Enthalpy Evap. hfg	Enthalpy Sat. Vapor hg	Entropy Sat. Liquid sf	Entropy Evap. sfg	Entropy Sat. Vapor sg	Temp. F
32	0.08854	0.01602	3306	3306	0.00	1075.8	1075.8	0.0000	2.1877	2.1877	32
35	0.09995	0.01602	2947	2947	3.02	1074.1	1077.1	0.0061	2.1709	2.1770	35
40	0.12170	0.01602	2444	2444	8.05	1071.3	1079.3	0.0162	2.1435	2.1597	40
45	0.14752	0.01602	2036.4	2036.4	13.06	1068.4	1081.5	0.0262	2.1167	2.1429	45
50	0.17811	0.01603	1703.2	1703.2	18.07	1065.6	1083.7	0.0361	2.0903	2.1264	50
60	0.2563	0.01604	1206.6	1206.7	28.06	1059.9	1088.0	0.0555	2.0393	2.0948	60
70	0.3631	0.01606	867.8	867.9	38.04	1054.3	1092.3	0.0745	1.9902	2.0647	70
80	0.5069	0.01608	633.1	633.1	48.02	1048.6	1096.6	0.0932	1.9428	2.0360	80
90	0.6982	0.01610	468.0	468.0	57.99	1042.9	1100.9	0.1115	1.8972	2.0087	90
100	0.9492	0.01613	350.3	350.4	67.97	1037.2	1105.2	0.1295	1.8531	1.9826	100
110	1.2748	0.01617	265.3	265.4	77.94	1031.6	1109.5	0.1471	1.8106	1.9577	110
120	1.6924	0.01620	203.25	203.27	87.92	1025.8	1113.7	0.1645	1.7694	1.9339	120
130	2.2225	0.01625	157.32	157.34	97.90	1020.0	1117.9	0.1816	1.7296	1.9112	130
140	2.8886	0.01629	122.99	123.01	107.89	1014.1	1122.0	0.1984	1.6910	1.8894	140
150	3.718	0.01634	97.06	97.07	117.89	1008.2	1126.1	0.2149	1.6537	1.8685	150
160	4.741	0.01639	77.27	77.29	127.89	1002.3	1130.2	0.2311	1.6174	1.8485	160
170	5.992	0.01645	62.04	62.06	137.90	996.3	1134.2	0.2472	1.5822	1.8293	170
180	7.510	0.01651	50.21	50.23	147.92	990.2	1138.1	0.2630	1.5480	1.8109	180
190	9.339	0.01657	40.94	40.96	157.95	984.1	1142.0	0.2785	1.5147	1.7932	190
200	11.526	0.01663	33.62	33.64	167.99	977.9	1145.9	0.2938	1.4824	1.7762	200
210	14.123	0.01670	27.80	27.82	178.05	971.6	1149.7	0.3090	1.4508	1.7598	210
212	14.696	0.01672	26.78	26.80	180.07	970.3	1150.4	0.3120	1.4446	1.7566	212
220	17.186	0.01677	23.13	23.15	188.13	965.2	1153.4	0.3239	1.4201	1.7440	220
230	20.780	0.01684	19.365	19.382	198.23	958.8	1157.0	0.3387	1.3901	1.7288	230
240	24.969	0.01692	16.306	16.323	208.34	952.2	1160.5	0.3531	1.3609	1.7140	240
250	29.825	0.01700	13.804	13.821	218.48	945.5	1164.0	0.3675	1.3323	1.6998	250
260	35.429	0.01709	11.746	11.763	228.64	938.7	1167.3	0.3817	1.3043	1.6860	260
270	41.858	0.01717	10.044	10.061	238.84	931.8	1170.6	0.3958	1.2769	1.6727	270
280	49.203	0.01726	8.628	8.645	249.06	924.7	1173.8	0.4096	1.2501	1.6597	280
290	57.556	0.01735	7.444	7.461	259.31	917.5	1176.8	0.4234	1.2238	1.6472	290

Temp	P	vf	vfg	vg	hf	hfg	hg	sf	sfg	sg	Temp
300	67.013	0.01745	6.449	6.466	269.59	910.1	1179.7	0.4369	1.1980	1.6350	300
310	77.68	0.01755	5.609	5.626	279.92	902.6	1182.5	0.4504	1.1727	1.6231	310
320	89.66	0.01765	4.896	4.914	290.28	894.9	1185.2	0.4637	1.1478	1.6115	320
330	103.06	0.01776	4.289	4.307	300.68	887.0	1187.7	0.4769	1.1233	1.6002	330
340	118.01	0.01787	3.770	3.788	311.13	879.0	1190.1	0.4900	1.0992	1.5891	340
350	134.63	0.01799	3.324	3.342	321.63	870.7	1192.3	0.5029	1.0754	1.5783	350
360	153.04	0.01811	2.939	2.957	332.18	862.2	1194.4	0.5158	1.0519	1.5677	360
370	173.37	0.01823	2.606	2.625	342.79	853.5	1196.3	0.5286	1.0287	1.5573	370
380	195.77	0.01836	2.317	2.335	353.45	844.6	1198.1	0.5413	1.0059	1.5471	380
390	220.37	0.01850	2.0651	2.0836	364.17	835.4	1199.6	0.5539	0.9832	1.5371	390
400	247.31	0.01864	1.8447	1.8633	374.97	826.0	1201.0	0.5664	0.9608	1.5272	400
410	276.75	0.01878	1.6512	1.6700	385.83	816.3	1202.1	0.5788	0.9386	1.5174	410
420	308.83	0.01894	1.4811	1.5000	396.77	806.3	1203.1	0.5912	0.9166	1.5078	420
430	343.72	0.01910	1.3308	1.3499	407.79	796.0	1203.8	0.6035	0.8947	1.4982	430
440	381.59	0.01926	1.1979	1.2171	418.90	785.4	1204.3	0.6158	0.8730	1.4887	440
450	422.6	0.0194	1.0799	1.0993	430.1	774.5	1204.6	0.6280	0.8513	1.4793	450
460	466.9	0.0196	0.9748	0.9944	441.4	763.2	1204.6	0.6402	0.8298	1.4700	460
470	514.7	0.0198	0.8811	0.9009	452.8	751.5	1204.3	0.6523	0.8083	1.4606	470
480	566.1	0.0200	0.7972	0.8172	464.4	739.4	1203.7	0.6645	0.7868	1.4513	480
490	621.4	0.0202	0.7221	0.7423	476.0	726.8	1202.8	0.6766	0.7653	1.4419	490
500	680.8	0.0204	0.6545	0.6749	487.8	713.9	1201.7	0.6887	0.7438	1.4325	500
520	812.4	0.0209	0.5385	0.5594	511.9	686.4	1198.2	0.7130	0.7006	1.4136	520
540	962.5	0.0215	0.4434	0.4649	536.6	656.6	1193.2	0.7374	0.6568	1.3942	540
560	1133.1	0.0221	0.3647	0.3868	562.2	624.2	1186.4	0.7621	0.6121	1.3742	560
580	1325.8	0.0228	0.2989	0.3217	588.9	588.4	1177.3	0.7872	0.5659	1.3532	580
600	1542.9	0.0236	0.2432	0.2668	617.0	548.5	1165.5	0.8131	0.5176	1.3307	600
620	1786.6	0.0247	0.1955	0.2201	646.7	503.6	1150.3	0.8398	0.4664	1.3062	620
640	2059.7	0.0260	0.1538	0.1798	678.6	452.0	1130.5	0.8679	0.4110	1.2789	640
660	2365.4	0.0278	0.1165	0.1442	714.2	390.2	1104.4	0.8987	0.3485	1.2472	660
680	2708.1	0.0305	0.0810	0.1115	757.3	309.9	1067.2	0.9351	0.2719	1.2071	680
700	3093.7	0.0369	0.0392	0.0761	823.3	172.1	995.4	0.9905	0.1484	1.1389	700
705.4	3206.2	0.0503	0	0.0503	902.7	0	902.7	1.0580	0	1.0580	705.4

* Abridged from *Thermodynamic Properties of Steam*, by Joseph H. Keenan and Frederick G. Keyes, John Wiley & Sons, Inc., 1936.

TABLE A·2
Dry Saturated Steam: Pressure Table *

Abs Press., Lb Sq In p	Temp., F t	Specific Volume Sat. Liquid v_f	Specific Volume Sat. Vapor v_g	Enthalpy Sat. Liquid h_f	Enthalpy Evap h_{fg}	Enthalpy Sat. Vapor h_g	Entropy Sat. Liquid s_f	Entropy Evap s_{fg}	Entropy Sat. Vapor s_g	Internal Energy Sat. Liquid u_f	Internal Energy Sat. Vapor u_g	Abs Press., Lb Sq In p
1.0	101.74	0.01614	333.6	69.70	1036.3	1106.0	0.1326	1.8456	1.9782	69.70	1044.3	1.0
2.0	126.08	0.01623	173.73	93.99	1022.2	1116.2	0.1749	1.7451	1.9200	93.98	1051.9	2.0
3.0	141.48	0.01630	118.71	109.37	1013.2	1122.6	0.2008	1.6855	1.8863	109.36	1056.7	3.0
4.0	152.97	0.01636	90.63	120.86	1006.4	1127.3	0.2198	1.6427	1.8625	120.85	1060.2	4.0
5.0	162.24	0.01640	73.52	130.13	1001.0	1131.1	0.2347	1.6094	1.8441	130.12	1063.1	5.0
6.0	170.06	0.01645	61.98	137.96	996.2	1134.2	0.2472	1.5820	1.8292	137.94	1065.4	6.0
7.0	176.85	0.01649	53.64	144.76	992.1	1136.9	0.2581	1.5586	1.8167	144.74	1067.4	7.0
8.0	182.86	0.01653	47.34	150.79	988.5	1139.3	0.2674	1.5383	1.8057	150.77	1069.2	8.0
9.0	188.28	0.01656	42.40	156.22	985.2	1141.4	0.2759	1.5203	1.7962	156.19	1070.8	9.0
10	193.21	0.01659	38.42	161.17	982.1	1143.3	0.2835	1.5041	1.7876	161.14	1072.2	10
14.696	212.00	0.01672	26.80	180.07	970.3	1150.4	0.3120	1.4446	1.7566	180.02	1077.5	14.696
15	213.03	0.01672	26.29	181.11	969.7	1150.8	0.3135	1.4415	1.7549	181.06	1077.8	15
20	227.96	0.01683	20.089	196.16	960.1	1156.3	0.3356	1.3962	1.7319	196.10	1081.9	20
25	240.07	0.01692	16.303	208.42	952.1	1160.6	0.3533	1.3606	1.7139	208.34	1085.1	25
30	250.33	0.01701	13.746	218.82	945.3	1164.1	0.3680	1.3313	1.6993	218.73	1087.8	30
35	259.28	0.01708	11.898	227.91	939.2	1167.1	0.3807	1.3063	1.6870	227.80	1090.1	35
40	267.25	0.01715	10.498	236.03	933.7	1169.7	0.3919	1.2844	1.6763	235.90	1092.0	40
45	274.44	0.01721	9.401	243.36	928.6	1172.0	0.4019	1.2650	1.6669	243.22	1093.7	45
50	281.01	0.01727	8.515	250.09	924.0	1174.1	0.4110	1.2474	1.6585	249.93	1095.3	50
55	287.07	0.01732	7.787	256.30	919.6	1175.9	0.4193	1.2316	1.6509	256.12	1096.7	55
60	292.71	0.01738	7.175	262.09	915.5	1177.6	0.4270	1.2168	1.6438	261.90	1097.9	60
65	297.97	0.01743	6.655	267.50	911.6	1179.1	0.4342	1.2032	1.6374	267.29	1099.1	65
70	302.92	0.01748	6.206	272.61	907.9	1180.6	0.4409	1.1906	1.6315	272.38	1100.2	70
75	307.60	0.01753	5.816	277.43	904.5	1181.9	0.4472	1.1787	1.6259	277.19	1101.2	75
80	312.03	0.01757	5.472	282.02	901.1	1183.1	0.4531	1.1676	1.6207	281.76	1102.1	80
85	316.25	0.01761	5.168	286.39	897.8	1184.2	0.4587	1.1571	1.6158	286.11	1102.9	85
90	320.27	0.01766	4.896	290.56	894.7	1185.3	0.4641	1.1471	1.6112	290.27	1103.7	90
95	324.12	0.01770	4.652	294.56	891.7	1186.2	0.4692	1.1376	1.6068	294.25	1104.5	95
100	327.81	0.01774	4.432	298.40	888.8	1187.2	0.4740	1.1286	1.6026	298.08	1105.2	100
110	334.77	0.01782	4.049	305.66	883.2	1188.9	0.4832	1.1117	1.5948	305.30	1106.5	110

P												P
120	341.25	0.01789	3.728	312.44	877.9	1190.4	0.4916	1.0962	1.5878	312.05	1107.6	120
130	347.32	0.01796	3.455	318.81	872.9	1191.7	0.4995	1.0817	1.5812	318.38	1108.6	130
140	353.02	0.01802	3.220	324.82	868.2	1193.0	0.5069	1.0682	1.5751	324.35	1109.6	140
150	358.42	0.01809	3.015	330.51	863.6	1194.1	0.5138	1.0556	1.5694	330.01	1110.5	150
160	363.53	0.01815	2.834	335.93	859.2	1195.1	0.5204	1.0436	1.5640	335.39	1111.2	160
170	368.41	0.01822	2.675	341.09	854.9	1196.0	0.5266	1.0324	1.5590	340.52	1111.9	170
180	373.06	0.01827	2.532	346.03	850.8	1196.9	0.5325	1.0217	1.5542	345.42	1112.5	180
190	377.51	0.01833	2.404	350.79	846.8	1197.6	0.5381	1.0116	1.5497	350.15	1113.1	190
200	381.79	0.01839	2.288	355.36	843.0	1198.4	0.5435	1.0018	1.5453	354.68	1113.7	200
250	400.95	0.01865	1.8438	376.00	825.1	1201.1	0.5675	0.9588	1.5263	375.14	1115.8	250
300	417.33	0.01890	1.5433	393.84	809.0	1202.8	0.5879	0.9225	1.5104	392.79	1117.1	300
350	431.72	0.01913	1.3260	409.69	794.2	1203.9	0.6056	0.8910	1.4966	408.45	1118.0	350
400	444.59	0.0193	1.1613	424.0	780.5	1204.5	0.6214	0.8630	1.4844	422.6	1118.5	400
450	456.28	0.0195	1.0320	437.2	767.4	1204.6	0.6356	0.8378	1.4734	435.5	1118.7	450
500	467.01	0.0197	0.9278	449.4	755.0	1204.4	0.6487	0.8147	1.4634	447.6	1118.6	500
550	476.94	0.0199	0.8424	460.8	743.1	1203.9	0.6608	0.7934	1.4542	458.8	1118.2	550
600	486.21	0.0201	0.7698	471.6	731.6	1203.2	0.6720	0.7734	1.4454	469.4	1117.7	600
650	494.90	0.0203	0.7083	481.8	720.5	1202.3	0.6826	0.7548	1.4374	479.4	1117.1	650
700	503.10	0.0205	0.6554	491.5	709.7	1201.2	0.6925	0.7371	1.4296	488.8	1116.3	700
750	510.86	0.0207	0.6092	500.8	699.2	1200.0	0.7019	0.7204	1.4223	498.0	1115.4	750
800	518.23	0.0209	0.5687	509.7	688.9	1198.6	0.7108	0.7045	1.4153	506.6	1114.4	800
850	525.26	0.0210	0.5327	518.3	678.8	1197.1	0.7194	0.6891	1.4085	515.0	1113.3	850
900	531.98	0.0212	0.5006	526.6	668.8	1195.4	0.7275	0.6744	1.4020	523.1	1112.1	900
950	538.43	0.0214	0.4717	534.6	659.1	1193.7	0.7355	0.6602	1.3957	530.9	1110.8	950
1000	544.61	0.0216	0.4456	542.4	649.4	1191.8	0.7430	0.6467	1.3897	538.4	1109.4	1000
1100	556.31	0.0220	0.4001	557.4	630.4	1187.8	0.7575	0.6205	1.3780	552.9	1106.4	1100
1200	567.22	0.0223	0.3619	571.7	611.7	1183.4	0.7711	0.5956	1.3667	566.7	1103.0	1200
1300	577.46	0.0227	0.3293	585.4	593.2	1178.6	0.7840	0.5719	1.3559	580.0	1099.4	1300
1400	587.10	0.0231	0.3012	598.7	574.7	1173.4	0.7963	0.5491	1.3454	592.7	1095.4	1400
1500	596.23	0.0235	0.2765	611.6	556.3	1167.9	0.8082	0.5269	1.3351	605.1	1091.2	1500
2000	635.82	0.0257	0.1878	671.7	463.4	1135.1	0.8619	0.4230	1.2849	662.2	1065.6	2000
2500	668.13	0.0287	0.1307	730.6	360.5	1091.1	0.9126	0.3197	1.2322	717.3	1030.6	2500
3000	695.36	0.0346	0.0858	802.5	217.8	1020.3	0.9731	0.1885	1.1615	783.4	972.7	3000
3206.2	705.40	0.0503	0.0503	902.7	0	902.7	1.0580	0	1.0580	872.9	872.9	3206.2

* Abridged from *Thermodynamic Properties of Steam*, by Joseph H. Keenan and Frederick G. Keyes, John Wiley & Sons, Inc., 1936.

TABLE A·3
Properties of Superheated Steam *

Abs Press., Lb Sq In. (Sat. Temp.)		Temperature—Degrees Fahrenheit												
		200	300	400	500	600	700	800	900	1000	1100	1200	1400	1600
1 (101.74)	v	392.6	452.3	512.0	571.6	631.2	690.8	750.4	809.9	869.5	929.1	988.7	1107.8	1227.0
	h	1150.4	1195.8	1241.7	1288.3	1335.7	1383.8	1432.8	1482.7	1533.5	1585.2	1637.7	1745.7	1857.5
	s	2.0512	2.1153	2.1720	2.2233	2.2702	2.3137	2.3542	2.3923	2.4283	2.4625	2.4952	2.5566	2.6137
5 (162.24)	v	78.16	90.25	102.26	114.22	126.16	138.10	150.03	161.95	173.87	185.79	197.71	221.5	245.4
	h	1148.8	1195.0	1241.2	1288.0	1335.4	1383.6	1432.7	1482.6	1533.4	1585.1	1637.7	1745.6	1857.4
	s	1.8718	1.9370	1.9942	2.0456	2.0927	2.1361	2.1767	2.2148	2.2509	2.2851	2.3178	2.3792	2.4363
10 (193.21)	v	38.85	45.00	51.04	57.05	63.03	69.01	74.98	80.95	86.92	92.88	98.84	110.77	122.69
	h	1146.6	1193.9	1240.6	1287.5	1335.1	1383.4	1432.5	1482.4	1533.2	1585.0	1637.6	1745.6	1857.3
	s	1.7927	1.8595	1.9172	1.9689	2.0160	2.0596	2.1002	2.1383	2.1744	2.2086	2.2413	2.3028	2.3598
14.696 (212.00)	v			34.68	38.78	42.86	46.94	51.00	55.07	59.13	63.19	67.25	75.37	83.48
	h			1239.9	1287.1	1334.8	1383.2	1432.3	1482.3	1533.1	1584.8	1637.5	1745.5	1857.3
	s			1.8743	1.9261	1.9734	2.0170	2.0576	2.0958	2.1319	2.1662	2.1989	2.2603	2.3174
20 (227.96)	v		22.36	25.43	28.46	31.47	34.47	37.46	40.45	43.44	46.42	49.41	55.37	61.34
	h		1191.6	1239.2	1286.6	1334.4	1382.9	1432.1	1482.1	1533.0	1584.7	1637.4	1745.4	1857.2
	s		1.7808	1.8396	1.8918	1.9392	1.9829	2.0235	2.0618	2.0978	2.1321	2.1648	2.2263	2.2834
40 (267.25)	v		11.040	12.628	14.168	15.688	17.198	18.702	20.20	21.70	23.20	24.69	27.68	30.66
	h		1186.8	1236.5	1284.8	1333.1	1381.9	1431.3	1481.4	1532.4	1584.3	1637.0	1745.1	1857.0
	s		1.6994	1.7608	1.8140	1.8619	1.9058	1.9467	1.9850	2.0212	2.0555	2.0883	2.1498	2.2069
60 (292.71)	v		7.259	8.357	9.403	10.427	11.441	12.449	13.452	14.454	15.453	16.451	18.446	20.44
	h		1181.6	1233.6	1283.0	1331.8	1380.9	1430.5	1480.8	1531.9	1583.8	1636.6	1744.8	1856.7
	s		1.6492	1.7135	1.7678	1.8162	1.8605	1.9015	1.9400	1.9762	2.0106	2.0434	2.1049	2.1621
80 (312.03)	v			6.220	7.020	7.797	8.562	9.322	10.077	10.830	11.582	12.332	13.830	15.325
	h			1230.7	1281.1	1330.5	1379.9	1429.7	1480.1	1531.3	1583.4	1636.2	1744.5	1856.5
	s			1.6791	1.7346	1.7836	1.8281	1.8694	1.9079	1.9442	1.9787	2.0115	2.0731	2.1303
100 (327.81)	v			4.937	5.589	6.218	6.835	7.446	8.052	8.656	9.259	9.860	11.060	12.258
	h			1227.6	1279.1	1329.1	1378.9	1428.9	1479.5	1530.8	1582.9	1635.7	1744.2	1856.2
	s			1.6518	1.7085	1.7581	1.8029	1.8443	1.8829	1.9193	1.9538	1.9867	2.0484	2.1056
120 (341.25)	v			4.081	4.636	5.165	5.683	6.195	6.702	7.207	7.710	8.212	9.214	10.213
	h			1224.4	1277.2	1327.7	1377.8	1428.1	1478.8	1530.2	1582.4	1635.3	1743.9	1856.0
	s			1.6287	1.6869	1.7370	1.7822	1.8237	1.8625	1.8990	1.9335	1.9664	2.0281	2.0854

Abs. Press. Lb/Sq In. (Sat. Temp)																
140 (353.02)	v	8.752	7.895	7.035	6.604	6.172	5.738	5.301	4.861	4.413	3.954	3.468	.....	.....	.....	.....
	h	1855.7	1743.5	1634.9	1581.9	1529.7	1478.2	1427.3	1376.8	1326.4	1275.2	1221.1	.....	.....	.....	.....
	s	2.0683	2.0110	1.9493	1.9163	1.8817	1.8451	1.8063	1.7645	1.7190	1.6683	1.6087	.....	.....	.....	.....
160 (363.53)	v	7.656	6.906	6.152	5.775	5.396	5.015	4.631	4.244	3.849	3.443	3.008	.....	.....	.....	.....
	h	1855.5	1743.2	1634.5	1581.4	1529.1	1477.5	1426.4	1375.7	1325.0	1273.1	1217.6	.....	.....	.....	.....
	s	2.0635	1.9982	1.9344	1.9014	1.8667	1.8301	1.7911	1.7491	1.7033	1.6519	1.5908	.....	.....	.....	.....
180 (373.06)	v	6.804	6.136	5.466	5.129	4.792	4.452	4.110	3.764	3.411	3.044	2.649	.....	.....	.....	.....
	h	1855.2	1742.9	1634.1	1581.0	1528.6	1476.8	1425.6	1374.7	1323.5	1271.0	1214.0	.....	.....	.....	.....
	s	2.0404	1.9831	1.9212	1.8882	1.8534	1.8167	1.7776	1.7355	1.6894	1.6373	1.5745	.....	.....	.....	.....
200 (381.79)	v	6.123	5.521	4.917	4.613	4.309	4.002	3.693	3.380	3.060	2.726	2.361	.....	.....	.....	.....
	h	1855.0	1742.6	1633.7	1580.5	1528.0	1476.2	1424.8	1373.6	1322.1	1268.9	1210.3	.....	.....	.....	.....
	s	2.0287	1.9713	1.9094	1.8763	1.8415	1.8048	1.7655	1.7232	1.6767	1.6240	1.5594	.....	.....	.....	.....
220 (389.86)	v	5.565	5.017	4.467	4.191	3.913	3.634	3.352	3.066	2.772	2.465	2.125	.....	.....	.....	.....
	h	1854.7	1742.3	1633.3	1580.0	1527.5	1475.5	1424.0	1372.6	1320.7	1266.7	1206.5	.....	.....	.....	.....
	s	2.0181	1.9607	1.8987	1.8656	1.8308	1.7939	1.7545	1.7120	1.6652	1.6117	1.5463	.....	.....	.....	.....
240 (397.37)	v	5.100	4.597	4.093	3.839	3.584	3.327	3.068	2.804	2.533	2.247	1.9276	.....	.....	.....	.....
	h	1854.5	1742.0	1632.9	1579.6	1526.9	1474.8	1423.2	1371.5	1319.2	1264.5	1202.5	.....	.....	.....	.....
	s	2.0084	1.9510	1.8889	1.8558	1.8209	1.7839	1.7444	1.7017	1.6546	1.6003	1.5319	.....	.....	.....	.....
260 (404.42)	v	4.707	4.242	3.776	3.541	3.305	3.067	2.827	2.582	2.330	2.063	.....	.....	.....	.....	.....
	h	1854.2	1741.7	1632.5	1579.1	1526.3	1474.2	1422.3	1370.4	1317.7	1262.3	.....	.....	.....	.....	.....
	s	1.9995	1.9420	1.8799	1.8467	1.8118	1.7748	1.7352	1.6922	1.6447	1.5897	.....	.....	.....	.....	.....
280 (411.05)	v	4.370	3.938	3.504	3.286	3.066	2.845	2.621	2.392	2.156	1.9047	.....	.....	.....	.....	.....
	h	1854.0	1741.4	1632.1	1578.6	1525.8	1473.5	1421.5	1369.4	1316.2	1260.0	.....	.....	.....	.....	.....
	s	1.9912	1.9337	1.8716	1.8383	1.8033	1.7662	1.7265	1.6834	1.6354	1.5796	.....	.....	.....	.....	.....
300 417.33	v	4.078	3.674	3.269	3.065	2.859	2.652	2.442	2.227	2.005	1.7675	.....	.....	.....	.....	.....
	h	1853.7	1741.0	1631.7	1578.1	1525.2	1472.8	1420.6	1368.3	1314.7	1257.6	.....	.....	.....	.....	.....
	s	1.9835	1.9260	1.8638	1.8305	1.7954	1.7582	1.7184	1.6751	1.6268	1.5701	.....	.....	.....	.....	.....
350 (431.72)	v	3.493	3.147	2.798	2.622	2.445	2.266	2.084	1.8980	1.7036	1.4923	.....	.....	.....	.....	.....
	h	1853.1	1740.3	1630.7	1577.0	1523.8	1471.1	1418.5	1365.5	1310.9	1251.5	.....	.....	.....	.....	.....
	s	1.9663	1.9086	1.8463	1.8130	1.7777	1.7403	1.7002	1.6563	1.6070	1.5481	.....	.....	.....	.....	.....
400 (444.59)	v	3.055	2.751	2.445	2.290	2.134	1.9767	1.8161	1.6508	1.4770	1.2851	.....	.....	.....	.....	.....
	h	1852.5	1739.5	1629.6	1575.8	1522.4	1469.4	1416.4	1362.7	1306.9	1245.1	.....	.....	.....	.....	.....
	s	1.9513	1.8936	1.8311	1.7977	1.7623	1.7247	1.6842	1.6398	1.5894	1.5281	.....	.....	.....	.....	.....

TABLE A-3 (Continued)
Properties of Superheated Steam *

Abs Press. Lb Sq In. (Sat. Temp.)		Temperature—Degrees Fahrenheit													
		500	550	600	620	640	660	680	700	800	900	1000	1200	1400	1600
450 (456.28)	v	1.1231	1.2155	1.3005	1.3332	1.3652	1.3967	1.4278	1.4584	1.6074	1.7516	1.8928	2.170	2.443	2.714
	h	1238.4	1272.0	1302.8	1314.6	1326.2	1337.5	1348.8	1359.9	1414.3	1467.7	1521.0	1628.6	1738.7	1851.9
	s	1.5095	1.5437	1.5735	1.5845	1.5951	1.6054	1.6153	1.6250	1.6699	1.7108	1.7486	1.8177	1.8803	1.9381
500 (467.01)	v	0.9927	1.0800	1.1591	1.1893	1.2188	1.2478	1.2763	1.3044	1.4405	1.5715	1.6996	1.9504	2.197	2.442
	h	1231.3	1266.8	1298.6	1310.7	1322.6	1334.2	1345.7	1357.0	1412.1	1466.0	1519.6	1627.6	1737.9	1851.3
	s	1.4919	1.5280	1.5588	1.5701	1.5810	1.5915	1.6016	1.6115	1.6571	1.6982	1.7363	1.8056	1.8683	1.9262
550 (476.94)	v	0.8852	0.9686	1.0431	1.0714	1.0989	1.1259	1.1523	1.1783	1.3038	1.4241	1.5414	1.7706	1.9957	2.219
	h	1223.7	1261.2	1294.3	1306.8	1318.9	1330.8	1342.5	1354.0	1409.9	1464.3	1518.2	1626.6	1737.1	1850.6
	s	1.4751	1.5131	1.5451	1.5568	1.5680	1.5787	1.5890	1.5991	1.6452	1.6868	1.7250	1.7946	1.8575	1.9155
600 (486.21)	v	0.7947	0.8753	0.9463	0.9729	0.9988	1.0241	1.0489	1.0732	1.1899	1.3013	1.4096	1.6208	1.8279	2.033
	h	1215.7	1255.5	1289.9	1302.7	1315.2	1327.4	1339.3	1351.1	1407.7	1462.5	1516.7	1625.5	1736.3	1850.0
	s	1.4586	1.4990	1.5323	1.5443	1.5558	1.5667	1.5773	1.5875	1.6343	1.6762	1.7147	1.7846	1.8476	1.9056
700 (503.10)	v	......	0.7277	0.7934	0.8177	0.8411	0.8639	0.8860	0.9077	1.0108	1.1082	1.2024	1.3853	1.5641	1.7405
	h	......	1243.2	1280.6	1294.3	1307.5	1320.3	1332.8	1345.0	1403.2	1459.0	1513.9	1623.5	1734.8	1848.8
	s	......	1.4722	1.5084	1.5212	1.5333	1.5449	1.5559	1.5665	1.6147	1.6573	1.6963	1.7666	1.8299	1.8881
800 (518.23)	v	......	0.6154	0.6779	0.7008	0.7223	0.7433	0.7635	0.7833	0.8763	0.9633	1.0470	1.2088	1.3662	1.5214
	h	......	1229.8	1270.7	1285.4	1299.4	1312.9	1325.9	1338.6	1398.6	1455.4	1511.0	1621.4	1733.2	1847.5
	s	......	1.4467	1.4863	1.5000	1.5129	1.5250	1.5366	1.5476	1.5972	1.6407	1.6801	1.7510	1.8146	1.8729
900 (531.98)	v	......	0.5264	0.5873	0.6089	0.6294	0.6491	0.6680	0.6863	0.7716	0.8506	0.9262	1.0714	1.2124	1.3509
	h	......	1215.0	1260.1	1275.9	1290.9	1305.1	1318.8	1332.1	1393.9	1451.8	1508.1	1619.3	1731.6	1846.3
	s	......	1.4216	1.4653	1.4800	1.4938	1.5066	1.5187	1.5303	1.5814	1.6257	1.6656	1.7371	1.8009	1.8595
1000 (544.61)	v	......	0.4533	0.5140	0.5350	0.5546	0.5733	0.5912	0.6084	0.6878	0.7604	0.8294	0.9615	1.0893	1.2146
	h	......	1198.3	1248.8	1265.9	1281.9	1297.0	1311.4	1325.3	1389.2	1448.2	1505.1	1617.3	1730.0	1845.0
	s	......	1.3961	1.4450	1.4610	1.4757	1.4893	1.5021	1.5141	1.5670	1.6121	1.6525	1.7245	1.7886	1.8474
1100 (556.31)	v	......	......	0.4532	0.4738	0.4929	0.5110	0.5281	0.5445	0.6191	0.6866	0.7503	0.8716	0.9885	1.1031
	h	......	......	1236.7	1255.3	1272.4	1288.5	1303.7	1318.5	1384.3	1444.5	1502.2	1615.2	1728.4	1843.8
	s	......	......	1.4261	1.4425	1.4583	1.4728	1.4862	1.4989	1.5535	1.5995	1.6405	1.7130	1.7775	1.8363
1200 (567.22)	v	......	......	0.4016	0.4222	0.4410	0.4586	0.4752	0.4909	0.5617	0.6250	0.6843	0.7967	0.9046	1.0101
	h	......	......	1223.5	1243.9	1262.4	1279.6	1295.7	1311.0	1379.3	1440.7	1499.2	1613.1	1726.9	1842.5
	s	......	......	1.4052	1.4243	1.4413	1.4568	1.4710	1.4843	1.5409	1.5879	1.6293	1.7025	1.7672	1.8263

Abs. Press. (Sat. Temp.)													
1400 (587.10)	v	0.8640	0.7727	0.6789	0.5805	0.5281	0.4714	0.4062	0.3912	0.3753	0.3580	0.3390	0.3174
	h	1840.0	1723.7	1608.9	1493.2	1433.1	1369.1	1295.5	1278.5	1260.3	1240.4	1218.4	1193.0
	s	1.8083	1.7489	1.6836	1.6093	1.5666	1.5177	1.4567	1.4419	1.4258	1.4079	1.3877	1.3639
1600 (604.90)	v	0.7545	0.6738	0.5906	0.5027	0.4553	0.4034	0.3417	0.3271	0.3112	0.2936	0.2733	····
	h	1837.5	1720.5	1604.6	1487.0	1425.3	1358.4	1278.7	1259.6	1238.7	1215.2	1187.8	····
	s	1.7926	1.7328	1.6669	1.5914	1.5476	1.4964	1.4303	1.4137	1.3952	1.3741	1.3489	····
1800 (621.03)	v	0.6693	0.5968	0.5218	0.4421	0.3986	0.3502	0.2907	0.2760	0.2597	0.2407	····	····
	h	1835.0	1717.3	1600.4	1480.8	1417.4	1347.2	1260.3	1238.5	1214.0	1185.1	····	····
	s	1.7786	1.7185	1.6520	1.5752	1.5301	1.4765	1.4044	1.3855	1.3638	1.3377	····	····
2000 (635.82)	v	0.6011	0.5352	0.4668	0.3935	0.3532	0.3074	0.2489	0.2337	0.2161	0.1936	····	····
	h	1832.5	1714.1	1596.1	1474.5	1409.2	1335.5	1240.0	1214.8	1184.9	1145.6	····	····
	s	1.7660	1.7055	1.6384	1.5603	1.5139	1.4576	1.3783	1.3564	1.3300	1.2945	····	····
2500 (668.13)	v	0.4784	0.4244	0.3678	0.3061	0.2710	0.2294	0.1686	0.1484	····	····	····	····
	h	1826.2	1706.1	1585.3	1458.4	1387.8	1303.6	1176.8	1132.3	····	····	····	····
	s	1.7389	1.6775	1.6088	1.5273	1.4772	1.4127	1.3073	1.2687	····	····	····	····
3000 (695.36)	v	0.3966	0.3505	0.3018	0.2476	0.2159	0.1760	0.0984	····	····	····	····	····
	h	1819.9	1698.0	1574.3	1441.8	1365.0	1267.2	1060.7	····	····	····	····	····
	s	1.7163	1.6540	1.5837	1.4984	1.4439	1.3690	1.1966	····	····	····	····	····
3206.2 (705.40)	v	0.3703	0.3267	0.2806	0.2288	0.1981	0.1583	····	····	····	····	····	····
	h	1817.2	1694.6	1569.8	1434.7	1355.2	1250.5	····	····	····	····	····	····
	s	1.7080	1.6452	1.5742	1.4874	1.4309	1.3508	····	····	····	····	····	····
3500	v	0.3381	0.2977	0.2546	0.2058	0.1762	0.1364	0.0306	····	····	····	····	····
	h	1813.6	1689.8	1563.3	1424.5	1340.7	1224.9	780.5	····	····	····	····	····
	s	1.6968	1.6336	1.5615	1.4723	1.4127	1.3241	0.9515	····	····	····	····	····
4000	v	0.2943	0.2581	0.2192	0.1743	0.1462	0.1052	0.0287	····	····	····	····	····
	h	1807.2	1681.7	1552.1	1406.8	1314.4	1174.8	763.8	····	····	····	····	····
	s	1.6795	1.6154	1.5417	1.4482	1.3827	1.2757	0.9347	····	····	····	····	····
4500	v	0.2602	0.2273	0.1917	0.1500	0.1226	0.0798	0.0276	····	····	····	····	····
	h	1800.9	1673.5	1540.8	1388.4	1286.5	1113.9	753.5	····	····	····	····	····
	s	1.6640	1.5990	1.5235	1.4253	1.3529	1.2204	0.9235	····	····	····	····	····
5000	v	0.2329	0.2027	0.1696	0.1303	0.1036	0.0593	0.0268	····	····	····	····	····
	h	1794.5	1665.3	1529.5	1369.5	1256.5	1047.1	746.4	····	····	····	····	····
	s	1.6499	1.5839	1.5066	1.4034	1.3231	1.1622	0.9152	····	····	····	····	····
5500	v	0.2106	0.1825	0.1516	0.1143	0.0880	0.0463	0.0262	····	····	····	····	····
	h	1788.1	1657.0	1518.2	1349.3	1224.1	985.0	741.3	····	····	····	····	····
	s	1.6369	1.5699	1.4908	1.3821	1.2930	1.1093	0.9090	····	····	····	····	····

TABLE A-4
Saturated Ammonia: Temperature Table*

$v = $ cu ft/lb; $h = $ B/lb; $s = $ B/lb-R

Temp., °F t	Press., psia p	Specific Volume		Enthalpy			Entropy			Temp., °F t
		Sat. liquid v_f	Sat. vapor v_g	Sat. liquid h_f	Evap. h_{fg}	Sat. vapor h_g	Sat. liquid s_f	Evap. s_{fg}	Sat. vapor s_g	
−60	5.55	0.02278	44.73	−21.2	610.8	589.6	−0.0517	1.5286	1.4769	−60
−50	7.67	0.02299	33.08	−10.6	604.3	593.7	−0.0256	1.4753	1.4497	−50
−40	10.41	0.02322	24.86	0.0	597.6	597.6	0.0000	1.4242	1.4242	−40
−30	13.90	0.02345	18.97	10.7	590.7	601.4	0.0250	1.3751	1.4001	−30
−20	18.30	0.02369	14.68	21.4	583.6	605.0	0.0497	1.3277	1.3774	−20
−10	23.74	0.02393	11.50	32.1	576.4	608.5	0.0738	1.2820	1.3558	−10
0	30.42	0.02419	9.116	42.9	568.9	611.8	0.0975	1.2377	1.3352	0
5	34.27	0.02432	8.150	48.3	565.0	613.3	0.1092	1.2161	1.3253	5
10	38.51	0.02446	7.304	53.8	561.1	614.9	0.1208	1.1949	1.3157	10
20	48.21	0.02474	5.910	64.7	553.1	617.8	0.1437	1.1532	1.2969	20
30	59.74	0.02503	4.825	75.7	544.8	620.5	0.1663	1.1127	1.2790	30
40	73.32	0.02533	3.971	86.8	536.2	623.0	0.1885	1.0733	1.2618	40
50	89.19	0.02564	3.294	97.9	527.3	625.2	0.2105	1.0348	1.2453	50
60	107.6	0.02597	2.751	109.2	518.1	627.3	0.2322	0.9972	1.2294	60
70	128.8	0.02632	2.312	120.5	508.6	629.1	0.2537	0.9603	1.2140	70
80	153.0	0.02668	1.955	132.0	498.7	630.7	0.2749	0.9242	1.1991	80
86	169.2	0.02691	1.772	138.9	492.6	631.5	0.2875	0.9029	1.1904	86
90	180.6	0.02707	1.661	143.5	488.5	632.0	0.2958	0.8888	1.1846	90
100	211.9	0.02747	1.419	155.2	477.8	633.0	0.3166	0.8539	1.1705	100
110	247.0	0.02790	1.217	167.0	466.7	633.7	0.3372	0.8194	1.1566	110
120	286.4	0.02836	1.047	179.0	455.0	634.0	0.3576	0.7851	1.1427	120

* From *Engineering Thermodynamics*, by H. J. Stoever, John Wiley & Sons, Inc., 1951, as abridged from *Tables of Thermodynamic Properties of Ammonia*, National Bureau of Standards Circular 142.

TABLE A-5
Saturated Ammonia: Pressure Table *
v = cu ft/lb; h = B/lb; s = B/lb-R

Press., psia p	Temp., °F t	Specific Volume Sat. liquid v_f	Specific Volume Sat. vapor v_g	Enthalpy Sat. liquid h_f	Enthalpy Evap. h_{fg}	Enthalpy Sat. vapor h_g	Entropy Sat. liquid s_f	Entropy Evap. s_{fg}	Entropy Sat. vapor s_g	Press., psia p
5	−63.11	0.02271	49.31	−24.5	612.8	588.3	−0.0599	1.5456	1.4857	5
10	−41.34	0.02319	25.81	−1.4	598.5	597.1	−0.0034	1.4310	1.4276	10
15	−27.29	0.02351	17.67	13.6	588.8	602.4	0.0318	1.3620	1.3938	15
20	−16.64	0.02377	13.50	25.0	581.2	606.2	0.0578	1.3122	1.3700	20
30	−0.57	0.02417	9.236	42.3	569.3	611.6	0.0962	1.2402	1.3364	30
40	11.66	0.02451	7.047	55.6	559.8	615.4	0.1246	1.1879	1.3125	40
50	21.67	0.02479	5.710	66.5	551.7	618.2	0.1475	1.1464	1.2939	50
60	30.21	0.02504	4.805	75.9	544.6	620.5	0.1668	1.1119	1.2787	60
80	44.40	0.02546	3.655	91.7	532.3	624.0	0.1982	1.0563	1.2545	80
100	56.05	0.02584	2.952	104.7	521.8	626.5	0.2237	1.0119	1.2356	100
120	66.02	0.02618	2.476	116.0	512.4	628.4	0.2452	0.9749	1.2201	120
140	74.79	0.02649	2.132	126.0	503.9	629.9	0.2638	0.9430	1.2068	140
170	86.29	0.02692	1.764	139.3	492.3	631.6	0.2881	0.9019	1.1900	170
200	96.34	0.02732	1.502	150.9	481.8	632.7	0.3090	0.8666	1.1756	200
230	105.30	0.02770	1.307	161.4	472.0	633.4	0.3275	0.8356	1.1631	230
260	113.42	0.02806	1.155	171.1	462.8	633.9	0.3441	0.8077	1.1518	260

* From *Engineering Thermodynamics*, by H. J. Stoever, John Wiley & Sons, Inc., 1951, as abridged from *Tables of Thermodynamic Properties of Ammonia*, National Bureau of Standards Circular 142.

TABLE A·6
Superheated Ammonia Vapor*
v = cu ft/lb; h = B/lb; s = B/lb-R

Pressure, psia (saturation temperature in italics)

Temp., °F	5 −63.11°			10 −41.84°			15 −27.29°			20 −16.64°			Temp., °F
	v	h	s	v	h	s	v	h	s	v	h	s	
Sat.	*49.31*	*588.3*	*1.4857*	*25.81*	*597.1*	*1.4876*	*17.67*	*602.4*	*1.3938*	*13.50*	*606.2*	*1.3700*	*Sat.*
−50	51.05	595.2	1.5025	.....	.....	.....	.....	.....	.....	.....	.....	.....	−50
−40	52.36	600.3	.5149	25.90	597.8	1.4293	.....	.....	.....	.....	.....	.....	−40
−30	53.67	605.4	.5269	26.58	603.2	.4420	.....	.....	.....	.....	.....	.....	−30
−20	54.97	610.4	.5385	27.26	608.5	.4542	18.01	606.4	1.4031	.....	.....	.....	−20
−10	56.26	615.4	.5498	27.92	613.7	.4659	18.47	611.9	.4154	13.74	610.0	1.3784	−10
0	57.55	620.4	1.5608	28.58	618.9	1.4773	18.92	617.2	1.4272	14.09	615.5	1.3907	0
10	58.84	625.4	.5716	29.24	624.0	.4884	19.37	622.5	.4386	14.44	621.0	.4025	10
20	60.12	630.4	.5821	29.90	629.1	.4992	19.82	627.8	.4497	14.78	626.4	.4138	20
30	61.41	635.4	.5925	30.55	634.2	.5097	20.26	633.0	.4604	15.11	631.7	.4248	30
40	62.69	640.4	.6026	31.20	639.3	.5200	20.70	638.2	.4709	15.45	637.0	.4356	40
50	63.96	645.5	1.6125	31.85	644.4	1.5301	21.14	643.4	1.4812	15.78	642.3	1.4460	50
60	65.24	650.5	.6223	32.49	649.5	.5400	21.58	648.5	.4912	16.12	647.5	.4562	60
70	66.51	655.5	.6319	33.14	654.6	.5497	22.01	653.7	.5011	16.45	652.8	.4662	70
80	67.79	660.6	.6413	33.78	659.7	.5593	22.44	658.9	.5108	16.78	658.0	.4760	80
90	69.06	665.6	.6506	34.42	664.8	.5687	22.88	664.0	.5203	17.10	663.2	.4856	90
100	70.33	670.7	1.6598	35.07	670.0	1.5779	23.31	669.2	1.5296	17.43	668.5	1.4950	100
110	71.60	675.8	.6689	35.71	675.1	.5870	23.74	674.4	.5388	17.76	673.7	.5042	110
120	72.87	680.9	.6778	36.35	680.3	.5960	24.17	679.6	.5478	18.08	678.9	.5133	120
130	74.14	686.1	.6865	36.99	685.4	.6049	24.60	684.8	.5567	18.41	684.2	.5223	130
140	75.41	691.2	.6952	37.62	690.6	.6136	25.03	690.0	.5655	18.73	689.4	.5312	140
150	76.68	696.4	1.7038	38.26	695.8	1.6222	25.46	695.3	1.5742	19.05	694.7	1.5399	150
160	77.95	701.6	.7122	38.90	701.1	.6307	25.88	700.5	.5827	19.37	700.0	.5485	160
170	79.21	706.8	.7206	39.54	706.3	.6391	26.31	705.8	.5911	19.70	705.3	.5569	170
180	80.48	712.1	.7289	40.17	711.6	.6474	26.74	711.1	.5995	20.02	710.6	.5653	180
190	.....	.....	.....	40.81	716.9	.6556	27.16	716.4	.6077	20.34	715.9	.5736	190
200	.....	.....	.....	41.45	722.2	1.6637	27.59	721.7	1.6158	20.66	721.2	1.5817	200
220	.....	.....	.....	.....	.....	.....	28.44	732.4	.6318	21.30	732.0	.5978	220
240	.....	.....	.....	.....	.....	.....	.....	.....	.....	21.94	742.8	.6135	240

Pressure, psia (saturation temperature in italics)

Temp., °F	30 −0.57°			40 11.66°			50 21.67°			60 30.21°			Temp., °F
	v	h	s	v	h	s	v	h	s	v	h	s	
Sat.	9.236	611.6	1.3364	7.047	615.4	1.3195	5.710	618.2	1.2939	4.805	620.5	1.2787	Sat.
0	9.250	611.9	1.3371	.....	.....	.....	.....	.....	.....	.....	.....	.....	0
10	9.492	617.8	.3497	.....	.....	.....	.....	.....	.....	.....	.....	.....	10
20	9.731	623.5	.3618	7.203	620.4	1.3231	.....	.....	.....	.....	.....	.....	20
30	9.966	629.1	.3733	7.387	626.3	.3353	5.838	623.4	1.3046	.....	.....	.....	30
40	10.20	634.6	.3845	7.568	632.1	.3470	5.988	629.5	.3169	4.933	626.8	1.2913	40
50	10.43	640.1	1.3953	7.746	637.8	1.3583	6.135	635.4	1.3286	5.060	632.9	1.3035	50
60	10.65	645.5	.4059	7.922	643.4	.3692	6.280	641.2	.3399	5.184	639.0	.3152	60
70	10.88	650.9	.4161	8.096	648.9	.3797	6.423	646.9	.3508	5.307	644.9	.3265	70
80	11.10	656.2	.4261	8.268	654.4	.3900	6.564	652.6	.3613	5.428	650.7	.3373	80
90	11.33	661.6	.4359	8.439	659.9	.4000	6.704	658.2	.3716	5.547	656.4	.3479	90
100	11.55	666.9	1.4456	8.609	665.3	1.4098	6.843	663.7	1.3816	5.665	662.1	1.3581	100
110	11.77	672.2	.4550	8.777	670.7	.4194	6.980	669.2	.3914	5.781	667.7	.3681	110
120	11.99	677.5	.4642	8.945	676.1	.4288	7.117	674.7	.4009	5.897	673.3	.3778	120
130	12.21	682.9	.4733	9.112	681.5	.4381	7.252	680.2	.4103	6.012	678.9	.3873	130
140	12.43	688.2	.4823	9.278	686.9	.4471	7.387	685.7	.4195	6.126	684.4	.3966	140
150	12.65	693.5	1.4911	9.444	692.3	1.4561	7.521	691.1	1.4286	6.239	689.9	1.4058	150
160	12.87	698.8	.4998	9.609	697.7	.4648	7.655	696.6	.4374	6.352	695.5	.4148	160
170	13.08	704.2	.5083	9.774	703.1	.4735	7.788	702.1	.4462	6.464	701.0	.4236	170
180	13.30	709.6	.5168	9.938	708.5	.4820	7.921	707.5	.4548	6.576	706.5	.4323	180
190	13.52	714.9	.5251	10.10	714.0	.4904	8.053	713.0	.4633	6.687	712.0	.4409	190
200	13.73	720.3	1.5334	10.27	719.4	1.4987	8.185	718.5	1.4716	6.798	717.5	1.4493	200
220	14.16	731.1	.5495	10.59	730.3	.5150	8.448	729.4	.4880	7.019	728.6	.4658	220
240	14.59	742.0	.5653	10.92	741.3	.5309	8.710	740.5	.5040	7.238	739.7	.4819	240
260	15.02	753.0	.5808	11.24	752.3	.5465	8.970	751.6	.5197	7.457	750.9	.4976	260
280	.....	.....	.....	11.56	763.4	.5617	9.230	762.7	.5350	7.675	762.1	.5130	280
300	.....	.....	.....	11.88	774.6	1.5766	9.489	774.0	1.5500	7.892	773.3	1.5281	300

* From *Engineering Thermodynamics*, by H. J. Stoever, John Wiley & Sons, Inc., 1951, as abridged from *Tables of Thermodynamic Properties of Ammonia*, National Bureau of Standards Circular 142.

TABLE A·6 (Continued)
Superheated Ammonia Vapor*
v = cu ft/lb; h = B/lb; s = B/lb-R

Pressure, psia (saturation temperature in italics)

Temp., °F	80 *44.40°* v	80 h	80 s	100 *56.05°* v	100 h	100 s	120 *66.02°* v	120 h	120 s	140 *74.79°* v	140 h	140 s	Temp., °F
Sat.	*3.655*	*624.0*	*1.2545*	*2.952*	*626.5*	*1.2356*	*2.476*	*628.4*	*1.2201*	*2.132*	*629.9*	*1.2068*	*Sat.*
50	3.712	627.7	1.2619	.....	.....	.....	.....	.....	.....	.....	.....	.....	50
60	3.812	634.3	.2745	2.985	629.3	1.2409	.....	.....	.....	.....	.....	.....	60
70	3.909	640.6	.2866	3.068	636.0	.2539	2.505	631.3	1.2255	.....	.....	.....	70
80	4.005	646.7	.2981	3.149	642.6	.2661	2.576	638.3	.2386	2.166	633.8	1.2140	80
90	4.098	652.8	.3092	3.227	649.0	.2778	2.645	645.0	.2510	2.228	640.9	.2272	90
100	4.190	658.7	1.3199	3.304	655.2	1.2891	2.712	651.6	1.2628	2.288	647.8	1.2396	100
110	4.281	664.6	.3303	3.380	661.3	.2999	2.778	658.0	.2741	2.347	654.5	.2515	110
120	4.371	670.4	.3404	3.454	667.3	.3104	2.842	664.2	.2850	2.404	661.1	.2628	120
130	4.460	676.1	.3502	3.527	673.3	.3206	2.905	670.4	.2956	2.460	667.4	.2738	130
140	4.548	681.8	.3598	3.600	679.2	.3305	2.967	676.5	.3058	2.515	673.7	.2843	140
150	4.635	687.5	1.3692	3.672	685.0	1.3401	3.029	682.5	1.3157	2.569	679.9	1.2945	150
160	4.722	693.2	.3784	3.743	690.8	.3495	3.089	688.4	.3254	2.622	686.0	.3045	160
170	4.808	698.8	.3874	3.813	696.6	.3588	3.149	694.3	.3348	2.675	692.0	.3141	170
180	4.893	704.4	.3963	3.883	702.3	.3678	3.209	700.2	.3441	2.727	698.0	.3236	180
190	4.978	710.0	.4050	3.952	708.0	.3767	3.268	706.0	.3531	2.779	704.0	.3328	190
200	5.063	715.6	1.4136	4.021	713.7	1.3854	3.326	711.8	1.3620	2.830	709.9	1.3418	200
210	5.147	721.3	.4220	4.090	719.4	.3940	3.385	717.6	.3707	2.880	715.8	.3507	210
220	5.231	726.9	.4304	4.158	725.1	.4024	3.442	723.4	.3793	2.931	721.6	.3594	220
230	5.315	732.5	.4386	4.226	730.8	.4108	3.500	729.2	.3877	2.981	727.5	.3679	230
240	5.398	738.1	.4467	4.294	736.5	.4190	3.557	734.9	.3960	3.030	733.3	.3763	240
250	5.482	743.8	1.4547	4.361	742.2	1.4271	3.614	740.7	1.4042	3.080	739.2	1.3846	250
260	5.565	749.4	.4626	4.428	747.9	.4350	3.671	746.5	.4123	3.129	745.0	.3928	260
280	5.730	760.7	.4781	4.562	759.4	.4507	3.783	758.0	.4281	3.227	756.7	.4088	280
300	5.894	772.1	.4933	4.695	770.8	.4660	3.895	769.6	.4435	3.323	768.3	.4243	300

Pressure, psia (saturation temperature in italics)

Temp., °F	170 86.29° v	h	s	200 96.34° v	h	s	230 105.30° v	h	s	260 113.42° v	h	s	Temp., °F
Sat.	*1.764*	*631.6*	*1.1900*	*1.502*	*632.7*	*1.1756*	*1.307*	*633.4*	*1.1631*	*1.155*	*633.9*	*1.1618*	*Sat.*
90	1.784	634.4	1.1952	....	....	....	....	....	....	....	....	....	90
100	1.837	641.9	1.2087	1.520	635.6	1.1809	....	....	....	....	....	....	100
110	1.889	649.1	.2215	1.567	643.6	.1947	1.328	637.4	1.1700	....	....	....	110
120	1.939	656.1	.2336	1.612	650.9	.2077	1.370	645.4	.1840	1.182	639.5	1.1617	120
130	1.988	662.8	.2452	1.656	658.1	.2200	1.410	653.1	.1971	1.220	647.8	.1757	130
140	2.035	669.4	.2563	1.698	665.0	.2317	1.449	660.4	.2095	1.257	655.6	.1889	140
150	2.081	675.9	1.2669	1.740	671.8	1.2429	1.487	667.6	1.2213	1.292	663.1	1.2014	150
160	2.127	682.3	.2773	1.780	678.4	.2537	1.524	674.5	.2325	1.326	670.4	.2132	160
170	2.172	688.5	.2873	1.820	684.9	.2641	1.559	681.3	.2434	1.359	677.5	.2245	170
180	2.216	694.7	.2971	1.859	691.3	.2742	1.594	687.9	.2538	1.391	684.4	.2354	180
190	2.260	700.8	.3066	1.897	697.7	.2840	1.629	694.4	.2640	1.422	691.1	.2458	190
200	2.303	706.9	1.3159	1.935	703.9	1.2935	1.663	700.9	1.2738	1.453	697.7	1.2560	200
210	2.346	713.0	.3249	1.972	710.1	.3029	1.696	707.2	.2834	1.484	704.3	.2658	210
220	2.389	719.0	.3338	2.009	716.1	.3120	1.729	713.5	.2927	1.514	710.7	.2754	220
230	2.431	724.9	.3426	2.046	722.4	.3209	1.762	719.8	.3018	1.543	717.1	.2847	230
240	2.473	730.9	.3512	2.082	728.4	.3296	1.794	726.0	.3107	1.572	723.4	.2938	240
250	2.514	736.8	1.3596	2.118	734.5	1.3382	1.826	732.1	1.3195	1.601	729.7	1.3027	250
260	2.555	742.8	.3679	2.154	740.5	.3467	1.857	738.3	.3281	1.630	736.0	.3115	260
270	2.596	748.7	.3761	2.189	746.5	.3550	1.889	744.4	.3365	1.658	742.2	.3200	270
280	2.637	754.6	.3841	2.225	752.5	.3631	1.920	750.5	.3448	1.686	748.4	.3285	280
290	2.678	760.5	.3921	2.260	758.5	.3712	1.951	756.5	.3530	1.714	754.5	.3367	290
300	2.718	766.4	1.3999	2.295	764.5	1.3791	1.982	762.6	1.3610	1.741	760.7	1.3449	300
320	2.798	778.3	.4153	2.364	776.5	.3947	2.043	774.7	.3767	1.796	772.9	.3608	320
340	2.878	790.1	.4303	2.432	788.5	.4099	2.103	786.8	.3921	1.850	785.2	.3763	340
360	....	....	....	2.500	800.5	.4247	2.163	798.9	.4070	1.904	797.4	.3914	360
380	....	....	....	2.568	812.5	.4392	2.222	811.1	.4217	1.957	809.6	.4062	380

* From *Engineering Thermodynamics*, by H. J. Stoever, John Wiley & Sons, Inc., 1951, as abridged from *Tables of Thermodynamic Properties of Ammonia*, National Bureau of Standards Circular 142.

TABLE A-7
Thermodynamic Properties of Freon-12 (Dichlorodifluoromethane)*
Saturation States

Temp., F t	Abs. Press., lbf/in.² p	Specific Volume, ft³/lbm			Enthalpy, Btu/lbm			Entropy, Btu/lbm R		
		Sat. Liquid v_f	Evap. v_{fg}	Sat. Vapor v_g	Sat. Liquid h_f	Evap. h_{fg}	Sat. Vapor h_g	Sat. Liquid s_f	Evap. s_{fg}	Sat. Vapor s_g
-130	0.41224	0.009736	70.7203	70.730	-18.609	81.577	62.968	-0.04983	0.24743	0.19760
-120	0.64190	0.009816	46.7312	46.741	-16.565	80.617	64.052	-0.04372	0.23731	0.19359
-110	0.97034	0.009899	31.7671	31.777	-14.518	79.663	65.145	-0.03779	0.22780	0.19002
-100	1.4280	0.009985	21.1541	22.164	-12.466	78.714	66.248	-0.03200	0.21883	0.18683
-90	2.0509	0.010073	15.8109	15.821	-10.409	77.764	67.355	-0.02637	0.21034	0.18398
-80	2.8807	0.010164	11.5228	11.533	-8.3451	76.812	68.467	-0.02086	0.20229	0.18143
-70	3.9651	0.010259	8.5584	8.5687	-6.2730	75.853	69.580	-0.01548	0.19464	0.17916
-60	5.3575	0.010357	6.4670	6.4774	-4.1919	74.885	70.693	-0.01021	0.18716	0.17714
-50	7.1168	0.010459	4.9637	4.9742	-2.1011	73.906	71.805	-0.00506	0.18038	0.17533
-40	9.3076	0.010564	3.8644	3.8750	0	72.913	72.913	0	0.17373	0.17373
-30	11.999	0.010674	3.0478	3.0585	2.1120	71.903	74.015	0.00496	0.16733	0.17229
-20	15.267	0.010788	2.4321	2.4429	4.2357	70.874	75.110	0.00983	0.16119	0.17102
-10	19.189	0.010906	1.9628	1.9727	6.3716	69.824	76.196	0.01462	0.15527	0.16989
0	23.849	0.011030	1.5979	1.6089	8.5207	68.750	77.271	0.01932	0.14956	0.16888

10	29.335	0.011160	1.3129	1.3241	10.684	67.651	78.335	0.02395	0.14403	0.16798
20	35.736	0.011296	1.0875	1.0988	12.863	66.522	79.385	0.02852	0.13867	0.16719
30	43.148	0.011438	0.90736	0.91880	15.058	65.361	80.419	0.03301	0.13347	0.16648
40	51.667	0.011588	0.76198	0.77357	17.273	64.163	81.436	0.03745	0.12841	0.16586
50	61.394	0.011746	0.64362	0.65537	19.507	62.926	82.433	0.04184	0.12346	0.16530
60	72.433	0.011913	0.54648	0.55839	21.766	61.643	83.409	0.04618	0.11861	0.16479
70	84.888	0.012089	0.46609	0.47818	24.050	60.309	84.359	0.05048	0.11386	0.16434
80	98.870	0.012277	0.39907	0.41135	26.365	58.917	85.282	0.05475	0.10917	0.16392
90	114.49	0.012478	0.34281	0.35529	28.713	57.461	86.174	0.05900	0.10453	0.16353
100	131.86	0.012693	0.29525	0.30794	31.100	55.929	87.029	0.06323	0.09992	0.16315
110	151.11	0.012924	0.25577	0.26769	33.531	54.313	87.844	0.06745	0.09534	0.16279
120	172.35	0.013174	0.22019	0.23326	36.013	52.597	88.610	0.07168	0.09073	0.16241
130	195.71	0.013447	0.19019	0.20364	38.553	50.768	89.321	0.07583	0.08609	0.16202
140	221.32	0.013746	0.16424	0.17799	41.162	48.805	89.967	0.08021	0.08138	0.16159
150	249.31	0.014078	0.14156	0.15564	43.850	46.684	90.534	0.08453	0.07657	0.16110
160	279.82	0.014449	0.12159	0.13604	46.633	44.373	91.006	0.08893	0.07260	0.16053
170	313.00	0.014871	0.10386	0.11873	49.529	41.830	91.359	0.09342	0.06643	0.15985
180	349.00	0.015360	0.08794	0.10330	52.562	38.999	91.561	0.09804	0.06096	0.15900
190	387.98	0.015942	0.073476	0.089418	55.769	35.792	91.561	0.10284	0.05511	0.15793
200	430.09	0.016659	0.060069	0.076728	59.203	32.075	91.278	0.10789	0.04862	0.15651
210	475.52	0.017601	0.047242	0.064843	62.959	27.599	90.558	0.11332	0.03921	0.15453
220	524.43	0.018986	0.035154	0.053140	67.246	21.790	89.036	0.11943	0.03206	0.15149
230	577.03	0.021854	0.017581	0.039435	72.893	12.229	85.122	0.12739	0.01773	0.14512
233.6 (critical)	596.9	0.02870	0	0.2870	78.86	0	78.86	0.1359	0	0.1359

TABLE A·7 (Continued)
Thermodynamic Properties of Freon-12*
Superheated Vapor

Temp., F	v	h	s	v	h	s	v	h	s
	5 lbf/in.²			10 lbf/in.²			15 lbf/in.²		
0	8.0611	78.582	0.19663	3.9809	78.246	0.18471	2.6201	77.902	0.17751
20	8.4265	81.309	0.20244	4.1691	81.014	0.19061	2.7494	80.712	0.18349
40	8.7903	84.090	0.20812	4.3556	83.828	0.19635	2.8770	83.561	0.18931
60	9.1528	86.922	0.21367	4.5408	86.689	0.20197	3.0031	86.451	0.19498
80	9.5142	89.806	0.21912	4.7248	89.596	0.20746	3.1281	89.383	0.20051
100	9.8747	92.738	0.22445	4.9079	92.548	0.21283	3.2521	92.357	0.20593
120	10.234	95.717	0.22968	5.0903	95.546	0.21809	3.3754	95.373	0.21122
140	10.594	98.743	0.23481	5.2720	98.586	0.22325	3.4981	98.429	0.21640
160	10.952	101.812	0.23985	5.4533	101.669	0.22830	3.6202	101.525	0.22148
180	11.311	104.925	0.24479	5.6341	104.793	0.23326	3.7419	104.661	0.22646
200	11.668	108.079	0.24964	5.8145	107.957	0.23813	3.8632	107.835	0.23135
220	12.026	111.272	0.25441	5.9946	111.159	0.24291	3.9841	111.046	0.23614
	20 lbf/in.²			25 lbf/in.²			30 lbf/in.²		
20	2.0391	80.403	0.17829	1.6125	80.088	0.17414	1.3278	79.765	0.17065
40	2.1373	83.289	0.18419	1.6932	83.012	0.18012	1.3969	82.730	0.17671
60	2.2340	86.210	0.18992	1.7723	85.965	0.18591	1.4644	85.716	0.18257
80	2.3295	89.168	0.19550	1.8502	88.950	0.19155	1.5306	88.729	0.18826
100	2.4241	92.164	0.20095	1.9271	91.968	0.19704	1.5957	91.770	0.19379
120	2.5179	95.198	0.20628	2.0032	95.021	0.20240	1.6600	94.843	0.19918
140	2.6110	98.270	0.21149	2.0786	98.110	0.20763	1.7237	97.948	0.20445
160	2.7036	101.380	0.21659	2.1535	101.234	0.21276	1.7868	101.086	0.20960
180	2.7957	104.528	0.22159	2.2279	104.393	0.21778	1.8494	104.258	0.21463
200	2.8874	107.712	0.22649	2.3019	107.588	0.22269	1.9116	107.464	0.21957
220	2.9789	110.932	0.23130	2.3756	110.817	0.22752	1.9735	110.702	0.22440
240	3.0700	114.186	0.23602	2.4491	114.080	0.23225	2.0351	113.973	0.22915
	35 lbf/in.²			40 lbf/in.²			50 lbf/in.²		
40	1.1850	82.442	0.17375	1.0258	82.148	0.17112	0.80248	81.540	0.16655
60	1.2442	85.463	0.17968	1.0789	85.206	0.17712	0.84713	84.676	0.17271
80	1.3021	88.504	0.18542	1.1306	88.277	0.18292	0.89025	87.811	0.17862
100	1.3589	91.570	0.19100	1.1812	91.367	0.18854	0.93216	90.953	0.18434
120·	1.4148	94.663	0.19643	1.2309	94.480	0.19401	0.97313	94.110	0.18988
140	1.4701	97.785	0.20172	1.2798	97.620	0.19933	1.0133	97.286	0.19527
160	1.5248	100.938	0.20689	1.3282	100.788	0.20453	1.0529	100.485	0.20051
180	1.5789	104.122	0.21195	1.3761	103.985	0.20961	1.0920	103.708	0.20563
200	1.6327	107.338	0.21690	1.4236	107.212	0.21457	1.1307	106.958	0.21064
220	1.6862	110.586	0.22175	1.4707	110.469	0.21944	1.1690	110.235	0.21553
240	1.7394	113.865	0.22651	1.5176	113.757	0.22420	1.2070	113.539	0.22032
260	1.7923	117.175	0.23117	1.5642	117.074	0.22888	1.2447	116.871	0.22502
	60 lbf/in.²			70 lbf/in.²			80 lbf/in.²		
60	0.69210	84.126	0.16892	0.58088	83.552	0.16556	...		...
80	0.72964	87.330	0.17497	0.61458	86.832	0.17175	0.52795	86.316	0.16885
100	0.76588	90.528	0.18079	0.64685	90.091	0.17768	0.55734	89.640	0.17489
120	0.80110	93.731	0.18641	0.67803	93.343	0.18339	0.58556	92.945	0.18070
140	0.83551	96.945	0.19186	0.70836	96.597	0.18891	0.61286	96.242	0.18629
160	0.86928	100.776	0.19716	0.73800	99.862	0.19427	0.63943	99.542	0.19170
180	0.90252	103.642	0.20233	0.76708	103.141	0.19948	0.66543	102.851	0.19696
200	0.93531	106.700	0.20736	0.79571	106.439	0.20455	0.69095	106.174	0.20207
220	0.96775	109.997	0.21229	0.82397	109.756	0.20951	0.71609	109.513	0.20706
240	0.99988	113.319	0.21710	0.85191	113.096	0.21435	0.74090	112.872	0.21193
260	1.0318	116.666	0.22182	0.87959	116.459	0.21909	0.76544	116.251	0.21669
280	1.0634	120.039	0.22644	0.90705	119.846	0.22373	0.78975	119.652	0.22135

* Reprinted from *Thermodynamics*, by G. J. Van Wylen, John Wiley & Sons, Inc., 1959.

TABLE A·7 (Continued)
Thermodynamic Properties of Freon-12*
Superheated Vapor

Temp., F	v	h	s	v	h	s	v	h	s
		90 lbf/in.²			100 lbf/in.²			125 lbf/in.²	
100	0.48749	89.175	0.17234	0.43138	88.694	0.16996	0.32943	87.407	0.16455
120	0.51346	92.536	0.17824	0.45562	92.116	0.17597	0.35086	91.008	0.17087
140	0.53845	95.879	0.18391	0.47881	95.507	0.18172	0.37098	94.537	0.17686
160	0.56268	99.216	0.18938	0.50118	98.884	0.18726	0.39015	98.023	0.18258
180	0.58629	102.557	0.19469	0.52291	102.257	0.19262	0.40857	101.484	0.18807
200	0.60941	105.905	0.19984	0.54413	105.633	0.19782	0.42642	104.934	0.19338
220	0.63213	109.267	0.20486	0.56492	109.018	0.20287	0.44380	108.380	0.19853
240	0.65451	112.644	0.20976	0.58538	112.415	0.20780	0.46081	111.829	0.20353
260	0.67662	116.040	0.21455	0.60554	115.828	0.21261	0.47750	115.287	0.20840
280	0.69849	119.456	0.21923	0.62546	119.258	0.21731	0.49394	118.756	0.21316
300	0.72016	122.892	0.22381	0.64518	122.707	0.22191	0.51016	122.238	0.21780
320	0.74166	126.349	0.22830	0.66472	126.176	0.22641	0.52619	125.737	0.22235
		150 lbf/in.²			175 lbf/in.²			200 lbf/in.²	
120	0.28007	89.800	0.16629	...	...	...	...	...	...
140	0.29845	93.498	0.17256	0.24595	92.373	0.16859	0.20579	91.137	0.1 480
160	0.31566	97.112	0.17849	0.26198	96.142	0.17478	0.22121	95.100	0.17130
180	0.33200	100.675	0.18415	0.27697	99.823	0.18062	0.23535	98.921	0.17737
200	0.34769	104.206	0.18958	0.29120	103.447	0.18620	0.24860	102.652	0.18311
220	0.36285	107.720	0.19483	0.30485	107.036	0.19156	0.26117	106.325	0.18860
240	0.37761	111.226	0.19992	0.31804	110.605	0.19674	0.27323	109.962	0.19387
260	0.39203	114.732	0.20485	0.33087	114.162	0.20175	0.28489	113.576	0.19896
280	0.40617	118.242	0.20967	0.34339	117.717	0.20662	0.29623	117.178	0.20390
300	0.42008	121.761	0.21436	0.35567	121.273	0.21137	0.30730	120.775	0.20870
320	0.43379	125.290	0.21894	0.36773	124.835	0.21599	0.31815	124.373	0.21337
340	0.44733	128.833	0.22343	0.37963	128.407	0.22052	0.32881	127.974	0.21793
		250 lbf/in.²			300 lbf/in.²			400 lbf/in.²	
160	0.16249	92.717	0.16462	...	...	...	...	...	...
180	0.17605	96.925	0.17130	0.13482	94.556	0.16537	...	...	...
200	0.18824	100.930	0.17747	0.14697	98.975	0.17217	0.091005	93.718	0.16092
220	0.19952	104.809	0.18326	0.15774	103.136	0.17838	0.10316	99.046	0.16888
240	0.21014	108.607	0.18877	0.16761	107.140	0.18419	0.11300	103.735	0.17568
260	0.22027	112.351	0.19404	0.17685	111.043	0.18969	0.12163	108.105	0.18183
280	0.23001	116.060	0.19913	0.18562	114.879	0.19495	0.12949	112.286	0.18756
300	0.23944	119.747	0.20405	0.19402	118.670	0.20000	0.13680	116.343	0.19298
320	0.24862	123.420	0.20882	0.20214	122.430	0.20489	0.14372	120.318	0.19814
340	0.25759	127.088	0.21346	0.21002	126.171	0.20963	0.15032	124.235	0.20310
360	0.26639	130.754	0.21799	0.21770	129.900	0.21423	0.15668	128.112	0.20789
380	0.27504	134.423	0.22241	0.22522	133.624	0.21872	0.16285	131.961	0.21255
		500 lbf/in.²			600 lbf/in.²				
220	0.064207	92.397	0.15683	...	...	...			
240	0.077620	99.218	0.16672	0.047488	91.024	0.15335			
260	0.087054	104.526	0.17421	0.061922	99.741	0.16566			
280	0.094923	109.277	0.18072	0.070859	105.637	0.17374			
300	0.10190	113.729	0.18666	0.078059	110.729	0.18053			
320	0.10829	117.997	0.19221	0.084333	115.420	0.18663			
340	0.11426	122.143	0.19746	0.090017	119.871	0.19227			
360	0.11992	126.205	0.20247	0.095289	124.167	0.19757			
380	0.12533	130.207	0.20730	0.10025	128.355	0.20262			
400	0.13054	134.166	0.21196	0.10498	132.466	0.20746			
420	0.13559	138.096	0.21648	0.10952	136.523	0.21213			
440	0.14051	142.004	0.22087	0.11391	140.539	0.21664			

* Reprinted from *Thermodynamics*, by G. J. Van Wylen, John Wiley & Sons, Inc., 1959.

TABLE A·8
Thermodynamic Properties of Air at Low Pressure*

T, °F abs	t, °F	h, Btu/lb	p_r	u, Btu/lb	v_r	φ, Btu/lb °F	T, °F abs	t, °F	h, Btu/lb	p_r	u, Btu/lb	v_r	φ, Btu/lb °F
100	−360	23.7	.00384	16.9	9640	.1971	1200	740	291.3	24.0	209.0	18.51	.7963
120	−340	28.5	.00726	20.3	6120	.2408	1220	760	296.4	25.5	212.8	17.70	.8005
140	−320	33.3	.01244	23.7	4170	.2777	1240	780	301.5	27.1	216.5	16.93	.8047
160	−300	38.1	.01982	27.1	2990	.3096	1260	800	306.6	28.8	220.3	16.20	.8088
180	−280	42.9	.0299	30.6	2230	.3378	1280	820	311.8	30.6	224.0	15.52	.8128
200	−260	47.7	.0432	34.0	1715	.3630	1300	840	316.9	32.4	227.8	14.87	.8168
220	−240	52.5	.0603	37.4	1352	.3858	1320	860	322.1	34.3	231.6	14.25	.8208
240	−220	57.2	.0816	40.8	1089	.4067	1340	880	327.3	36.3	235.4	13.67	.8246
260	−200	62.0	.1080	44.2	892	.4258	1360	900	332.5	38.4	239.2	13.12	.8285
280	−180	66.8	.1399	47.6	742	.4436	1380	920	337.7	40.6	243.1	12.59	.8323
300	−160	71.6	.1780	51.0	624	.4601	1400	940	342.9	42.9	246.9	12.10	.8360
320	−140	76.4	.2229	54.5	532	.4755	1420	960	348.1	45.3	250.8	11.62	.8398
340	−120	81.2	.2754	57.9	457	.4900	1440	980	353.4	47.8	254.7	11.17	.8434
360	−100	86.0	.336	61.3	397	.5037	1460	1000	358.6	50.3	258.5	10.74	.8470
380	−80	90.8	.406	64.7	347	.5166	1480	1020	363.9	53.0	262.4	10.34	.8506
400	−60	95.5	.486	68.1	305	.5289	1500	1040	369.2	55.9	266.3	9.95	.8542
420	−40	100.3	.576	71.5	270	.5406	1520	1060	374.5	58.8	270.3	9.58	.8568
440	−20	105.1	.678	74.9	241	.5517	1540	1080	379.8	61.8	274.2	9.23	.8611
460	0	109.9	.791	78.4	215.3	.5624	1560	1100	385.1	65.0	278.1	8.89	.8646
480	20	114.7	.918	81.8	193.6	.5726	1580	1120	390.4	68.3	282.1	8.57	.8679
500	40	119.5	1.059	85.2	174.9	.5823	1600	1140	395.7	71.7	286.1	8.26	.8713
520	60	124.3	1.215	88.6	158.6	.5917	1620	1160	401.1	75.3	290.0	7.97	.8746
540	80	129.1	1.386	92.0	144.3	.6008	1640	1180	406.4	79.0	294.0	7.69	.8779
560	100	133.9	1.574	95.5	131.8	.6095	1660	1200	411.8	82.8	298.0	7.42	.8812
580	120	138.7	1.780	98.9	120.7	.6179	1680	1220	417.2	86.8	302.0	7.17	.8844
600	140	143.5	2.00	102.3	110.9	.6261	1700	1240	422.6	91.0	306.1	6.92	.8876
620	160	148.3	2.25	105.8	102.1	.6340	1720	1260	428.0	95.2	310.1	6.69	.8907
640	180	153.1	2.51	109.2	94.3	.6416	1740	1280	433.4	99.7	314.1	6.46	.8939
660	200	157.9	2.80	112.7	87.3	.6490	1760	1300	438.8	104.3	318.2	6.25	.8970
680	220	162.7	3.11	116.1	81.0	.6562	1780	1320	444.3	109.1	322.2	6.04	.9000
700	240	167.6	3.45	119.6	75.2	.6632	1800	1340	449.7	114.0	326.3	5.85	.9031
720	260	172.4	3.81	123.0	70.1	.6700	1820	1360	455.2	119.2	330.4	5.66	.9061
740	280	177.2	4.19	126.5	65.4	.6766	1840	1380	460.6	124.5	334.5	5.48	.9091
760	300	182.1	4.61	130.0	61.1	.6831	1860	1400	466.1	130.0	338.6	5.30	.9120
780	320	186.9	5.05	133.5	57.2	.6894	1880	1420	471.6	135.6	342.7	5.13	.9150
800	340	191.8	5.53	137.0	53.6	.6956	1900	1440	477.1	141.5	346.8	4.97	.9179
820	360	196.7	6.03	140.5	50.4	.7016	1920	1460	482.6	147.6	351.0	4.82	.9208
840	380	201.6	6.57	144.0	47.3	.7075	1940	1480	488.1	153.9	355.1	4.67	.9236
860	400	206.5	7.15	147.5	44.6	.7132	1960	1500	493.6	160.4	359.3	4.53	.9264
880	420	211.4	7.76	151.0	42.0	.7189	1980	1520	499.1	167.1	363.4	4.39	.9293
900	440	216.3	8.41	154.6	39.6	.7244	2000	1540	504.7	174.0	367.6	4.26	.9320
920	460	221.2	9.10	158.1	37.4	.7298	2020	1560	510.3	181.2	371.8	4.13	.9348
940	480	226.1	9.83	161.7	35.4	.7351	2040	1580	515.8	188.5	376.0	4.01	.9376
960	500	231.1	10.61	165.3	33.5	.7403	2060	1600	521.4	196.2	380.2	3.89	.9403
980	520	236.0	11.43	168.8	31.8	.7454	2080	1620	527.0	204.0	384.4	3.78	.9430
1000	540	241.0	12.30	172.4	30.1	.7504	2100	1640	532.6	212	388.6	3.67	.9456
1020	560	246.0	13.22	176.0	28.6	.7554	2120	1660	538.2	220	392.8	3.56	.9483
1040	580	251.0	14.18	179.7	27.2	.7602	2140	1680	543.7	229	397.0	3.46	.9509
1060	600	256.0	15.20	183.3	25.8	.7650	2160	1700	549.4	238	401.3	3.36	.9535
1080	620	261.0	16.28	186.9	24.6	.7696	2180	1720	555.0	247	405.5	3.27	.9561
1100	640	266.0	17.41	190.6	23.4	.7743	2200	1740	560.6	257	409.8	3.18	.9587
1120	660	271.0	18.60	194.2	22.3	.7788	2220	1760	566.2	266	414.0	3.09	.9612
1140	680	276.1	19.86	197.9	21.3	.7833	2240	1780	571.9	276	418.3	3.00	.9638
1160	700	281.1	21.2	201.6	20.29	.7877	2260	1800	577.5	287	422.6	2.92	.9663
1180	720	286.2	22.6	205.3	19.38	.7920	2280	1820	583.2	297	426.9	2.84	.9688

* The properties given here are condensed by permission from *Gas Tables* by J. H. Keenan and J. Kaye, published by John Wiley & Sons, Inc., 1948.

T, °F abs	t, °F	h, Btu/lb	p_r	u, Btu/lb	v_r	ϕ, Btu/lb °F	T, °F abs	t, °F	h, Btu/lb	p_r	u, Btu/lb	v_r	ϕ, Btu/lb °F
2300	1840	588.8	308	431.2	2.76	.9712	3000	2540	790.7	941	585.0	1.180	1.0478
2320	1860	594.5	319	435.5	2.69	.9737	3020	2560	796.5	969	589.5	1.155	1.0497
2340	1880	600.2	331	439.8	2.62	.9761	3040	2580	802.4	996	594.0	1.130	1.0517
2360	1900	605.8	343	444.1	2.55	.9785	3060	2600	808.3	1025	598.5	1.106	1.0536
2380	1920	611.5	355	448.4	2.48	.9809	3080	2620	814.2	1054	603.0	1.083	1.0555
2400	1940	617.2	368	452.7	2.42	.9833	3100	2640	820.0	1083	607.5	1.060	1.0574
2420	1960	622.9	380	457.0	2.36	.9857	3120	2660	825.9	1114	612.0	1.038	1.0593
2440	1980	628.6	394	461.4	2.30	.9880	3140	2680	831.8	1145	616.6	1.016	1.0612
2460	2000	634.3	407	465.7	2.24	.9904	3160	2700	837.7	1176	621.1	.995	1.0630
2480	2020	640.0	421	470.0	2.18	.9927	3180	2720	843.6	1209	625.6	.975	1.0649
2500	2040	645.8	436	474.4	2.12	.9950	3200	2740	849.5	1242	630.1	.955	1.0668
2520	2060	651.5	450	478.8	2.07	.9972	3220	2760	855.4	1276	634.6	.935	1.0686
2540	2080	657.2	466	483.1	2.02	.9995	3240	2780	861.3	1310	639.2	.916	1.0704
2560	2100	663.0	481	487.5	1.971	1.0018	3260	2800	867.2	1345	643.7	.898	1.0722
2580	2120	668.7	497	491.9	1.922	1.0040	3280	2820	873.1	1381	648.3	.880	1.0740
2600	2140	674.5	514	496.3	1.876	1.0062	3300	2840	879.0	1418	652.8	.862	1.0758
2620	2160	680.2	530	500.6	1.830	1.0084	3320	2860	884.9	1455	657.4	.845	1.0776
2640	2180	686.0	548	505.0	1.786	1.0106	3440	2880	890.9	1494	661.9	.828	1.0794
2660	2200	691.8	565	509.4	1.743	1.0128	3360	2900	896.8	1533	666.5	.812	1.0812
2680	2220	697.6	583	513.8	1.702	1.0150	3380	2920	902.7	1573	671.0	.796	1.0830
2700	2240	703.4	602	518.3	1.662	1.0171	3400	2940	908.7	1613	675.6	.781	1.0847
2720	2260	709.1	621	522.7	1.623	1.0193	3420	2960	914.6	1655	680.2	.766	1.0864
2740	2280	714.9	640	527.1	1.585	1.0214	3440	2980	920.6	1697	684.8	.751	1.0882
2760	2300	720.7	660	531.5	1.548	1.0235	3460	3000	926.5	1740	689.3	.736	1.0899
2780	2320	726.5	681	536.0	1.512	1.0256	3480	3020	932.4	1784	693.9	.722	1.0916
2800	2340	732.3	702	540.4	1.478	1.0277	3500	3040	938.4	1829	698.5	.709	1.0933
2820	2360	738.2	724	544.8	1.444	1.0297	3520	3060	944.4	1875	703.1	.695	1.0950
2840	2380	744.0	746	549.3	1.411	1.0318	3540	3080	950.3	1922	707.6	.682	1.0967
2860	2400	749.8	768	553.7	1.379	1.0338	3560	3100	956.3	1970	712.2	.670	1.0984
2880	2420	755.6	791	558.2	1.348	1.0359	3580	3120	962.2	2018	716.8	.657	1.1000
2900	2440	761.4	815	562.7	1.318	1.0379	3600	3140	968.2	2068	721.4	.645	1.1017
2920	2460	767.3	839	567.1	1.289	1.0399	3620	3160	974.2	2118	726.0	.633	1.1034
2940	2480	773.1	864	571.6	1.261	1.0419	3640	3180	980.2	2170	730.6	.621	1.1050
2960	2500	779.0	889	576.1	1.233	1.0439	3660	3200	986.1	2222	735.3	.610	1.1066
2980	2520	784.8	915	580.6	1.206	1.0458	3680	3220	992.1	2276	739.9	.599	1.1083

* The properties given here are condensed by permission from *Gas Tables* by J. H. Keenan and J. Kaye, published by John Wiley & Sons, Inc., 1948.

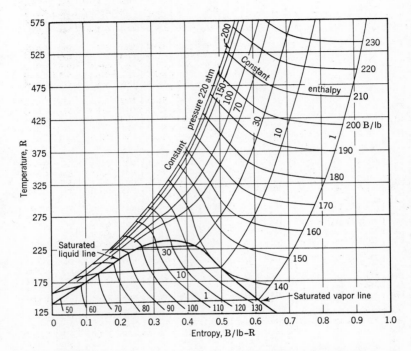

Chart A·I Temperature-entropy diagram for air. Data from "Thermodynamic Properties of Air at Low Temperatures," by V. C. Williams, *Transactions, AIChE*, vol. 39, no. 1, Feb. 1943.

16·12	15.8 B/lb.
16·15	(a) 1033 R; (b) 1098 R; (c) 1162 R.
16·18	0.838.
16·27	5.55 hp.
16·30	26.2 hp.
17·3	5200 hp; 0.351.
17·6	0.182.
17·15	0.428.
17·21	370 cu ft.
17·24	4040 lb.
17·27	2110 lb.
17·30	(a) 0.483; (b) 6.18 B; (c) 1.35 B.
17·33	(a) 411%; (b) 0.621.
17·36	5.25 B.
17·39	10.6 B.
17·42	(a) 13,650 ft-lb; (b) 0.54; (c) 26.0 B; (d) 8.5 B.
18·3	0.365.
18·6	(a) 0.269; (b) 0.0166; (c) 0.425.
18·15	(a) 0.401; (b) 0.400.
18·18	0.387.
18·24	0.456; 645,000 lb/hr.

18·30	0.77 hr.
18·36	(a) 437 kw; (b) 1400 lb/hr.
19·3	4.45.
19·9	2.83 hp.
19·12	6.27; 26.6 tons.
19·15	14.5 hp.
19·18	72.4 hp.
19·21	10,700 B.
19·24	1181 lb/hr.
19·27	(a) 5.67 lb/lb; (b) 1400 B/lb.
20·3	4.
20·6	3.
20·9	2790 lb/hr.
21·3	1122 F; 164 F.
21·6	400 B/hr-ft.
21·12	135,100 B/day-sq ft.
21·15	93 B/hr-sq ft.
21·18	170 sq ft.
21·21	74,000,000 B/hr.
21·27	238 B/hr.
21·30	1077 B/hr.
21·33	$\frac{1}{2}$.

Index

Absorption system, refrigeration, 633
Absorptivity, 672
  monochromatic, 672
Acoustic velocity, 513
Additive pressures, law of, 393, 405
Additive volumes, law of, 393, 406
Adiabatic flame temperature, maximum
  without dissociation, 465
  with dissociation, 495
Adiabatic processes, 40
  irreversible, 291, 293
  isentropic, 279
Adiabatic saturation, 416
Air, composition of, 437
  excess, 438
  properties of, 710
  stoichiometric, 437
Air conditioning, 424
Aircraft cooling, 626
Air-standard analysis, 565
  cold, 566
  with mass of fuel considered, 569
Air-standard cycles, 565
  Brayton, 566
  Diesel, 582
  dual, 585
  Otto, 581
Air tables, 347, 710
Amagat's law, 393
Ammonia absorption cycle, 633
Ammonia properties, 700–705
Answers to problems, 713–715
Aqua ammonia, 634
  chart, *between* 712 and 713
Atmosphere, 363
Atmospheric air, 411
Atmospheric pressure, 15

Availability, 372
  accounting, 382
  of closed system, 372
  of steadily flowing fluid, 373
Available energy, 295, 297
  accounting, 301
Avogadro's number, 176
Azeotropic mixtures, 651

Back-work ratio, 567, 600
Beattie-Bridgeman equation of state, 202
  constants for, 202
Binary-fluid cycles, power, 613
  refrigeration, 631
Black body, 672
Blowers, 540
Boltzmann, L., 673
Boundary layer, 506, 553
Bourdon gage, 15
Brayton, George B., 566
Brayton cycle, 566
  reversed, 624
British thermal unit, 38, 56
By-product power, 611

Caloric theory, 95
Calorimeter, throttling, 353
Carnot, Sadi, 236
Carnot cycle, 236
  efficiency of, 260
  reversal of, 241
  using steam, 596
Carnot engine, 237
Carnot principle, 250
Cavitation, 549
Characteristic functions, 326
Chemical equilibrium, 467

Chemical reaction, application of first law, 448
 application of second law, 468
 rate of, 490
Clapeyron equation, 327, 485
Claude system, 639
Clausius, Rudolph, 212, 236
 inequality, 271
Clearance, 558
 influence on volumetric efficiency, 558
 per cent, 558
Cleghorn, William, 95
Coefficient, constant-temperature, 334
 Joule-Thomson, 329
 of heat transfer, 667
 of performance, 93, 623
 of volume expansion, 343
Combustion, actual mass balance, 442
 chemical equations for, 436
 ideal, 438
Components, 645
Compound engines, 586
Compound power plants, 586
Compressed liquid, 117, 136, 140
Compressed solid, 117
Compressibility, isentropic, 344
 isothermal, 343
Compressibility factors, 188
 for nitrogen, chart of, 189
 for real-gas mixtures, 408
 for reduced coordinates, 195, 196
 for steam, chart of, 190
 generalized, 196
 table of, 191
Compression, 540
 adiabatic, 543
 efficiency, 542
 intercooling, 544
 isothermal, 541
 multistaging, 543
 polytropic, 541
 volumetric efficiency, 558
Compression ratio, 581
Compressors, 540
 axial flow, 554
 dynamic, 553
 multistage, 543
 reciprocating, 557
Condenser, 598, 628
Conduction of heat, 661

Conductivity, thermal, 663
Configuration factors, 675
Conservation of energy principle, 61
Constant-temperature coefficient, 334
Constituents, 645
Continuity equation, 33
Control surface, 7
Control volume, 7
Convection, 666
Convective heat-transfer coefficient, 667
Conversion factors, 683
 J, 56, 57
Cooling tower, 426
Corresponding states, law of, 192
Counterflow heat exchanger, 670
Critical constants, table of, 118
Critical flow in nozzles, 519
 ideal gases, 519
 vapors, 525
Critical point, 111, 117, 133
Critical pressure, 134
Critical temperature, 133
Cycle, 11
Cyclic integral, 11

Dalton's law, 393
Darrieus function, 373
Davy, Humphry, 96, 236
Debye, Peter, 344
Debye constants, 345
Debye specific heat law, 345
Debye's T^3 law, 346
Definitions, 2
 operational, 4
Degree of reaction, 553, 555
Degrees of freedom, 177, 645
Dehumidification, 424
Dense air refrigeration cycle, 626
Density, 13
Derivatives, partial, 687
Dew point, 415
 determination of, 415
Diatomic gases, specific heat of, 178
Diesel cycle, air-standard analysis for, 582
 cutoff ratio, 582
 per cent cutoff, 582
Differentials, exact, 43
 inexact, 44
Dimensional analysis, 682

Dimensions, 681
Displacement energy, *see* Flow work
Dry-bulb temperature, 415
Dry saturated vapor, 120
Dual cycle, 585
Dulong and Petit, law of, 344
Dynamic equation of steady flow, 508

Effectiveness, 573
Efficiency, compressor, 542
  heat-engine, 92
  nozzle, 523
  reversible-engine, 252
  thermal, 92
  turbine, 546
  volumetric, 558
Emissivity, 673
  monochromatic, 674
  values, 674
Emissivity factor, 676
Energy, 60
  available, 295, 297
  conservation of, 61
  geopotential, 64
  internal, 66
  in transition, 60
  kinetic, 65
  potential, 63
  stored, 59
  unavailable, 295, 297
Engineering thermodynamics, 1
Enthalpy, 67
  absolute, 463
  calculation of, 336
  of combustion, 458
  of formation, 458, 461
    table of, 460
  of fusion, 127
  of ideal gases, 160
  of reaction, 451
    tables of, 456, 460
  of vaporization, 127
  stagnation, 505
  total, 505
Enthalpy-entropy diagram, 278, 352
Enthalpy-volume diagram, 354
Entropy, 266
  absolute, 460, 470
  and probability, 308
  as a coordinate, 277

Entropy, calculation of, 273, 336
  increase of, principle of, 288
  uses of, 308
Equations of state, 151
  Beattie-Bridgeman, 202
  ideal-gas, 151
  van der Waals, 197
  virial, 203
Equilibrium, 10
  chemical, 467
  complete, 482
  criteria of, 482
  frozen, 491
  mechanical, 482
  thermal, 18
Equilibrium constant, 488
  data, 490
  relationship with ΔG_R, 498
  relationship with ΔH_R, 497
Equipartition of energy, 177
Ericsson, John, 242
Ericsson cycle, 244
Eutectic, 658
Exact differential, 43
Excess air, 438
Extensive properties, 12
Externally reversible process, 230
  cycle, 232

Fahrenheit, Gabriel D., 19
Fanno line, 530
Fans, 540
Feedwater heaters, 602
  closed, 603
  deaerating, 603
  direct-contact, 602
  open, 602
  terminal temperature difference, 603
Film coefficient, 667
First law of thermodynamics, 55
  applied to closed systems, 68
  applied to open systems, 71, 83
  applied to steady-flow systems, 73
  historical note on, 94
  limitations of, 94, 210
Flame temperature, 465
Flash chamber, 631
Flow energy, *see* Flow work
Flow work, 72
Forced convection, 666

Free convection, 666
Free energy, 307, 499
Free-piston gas generator, 588
Freon 12 properties, 706–709
Functions, path and point, 42
Fusion, 113

Gage pressure, 15
Gas, ideal, 151
    mixtures of, 391
    real, 188
    specific heats of, 161, 203
Gas constant, 151
    of gas mixtures, 397
    universal, 151
    values, table of, 152
Gas liquefaction, 637
Gas-turbine cycles, intercooled, 576
    jet propulsion, 578
    regenerative, 572
    reheat, 577
    simple, 566
Gibbs, J. Willard, 305
Gibbs function, 305, 484
    of an ideal-gas mixture, 486
Gray body, 674

Hampson-Linde system, 638
Head, 549
    "loss due to friction," 548
Heat, 38
    sign convention, 39
Heat engine, 91
Heat pump, 622
Heat transfer, by conduction, 661
    by convection, 666
    by radiation, 672
    over-all coefficient of, 667
Heaters, extraction, 602
Heating and power cycles, 611
Helmholtz, Hermann, 96
Helmholtz function, 305
Humidity, absolute, 414
    relative, 412
    specific, 414
Humidity ratio, 413

Ice point, 19
Ideal and actual systems, 9
Ideal gas, 151

Ideal gas, and kinetic theory, 173
    enthalpy of, 160
    equation of state, 151
    internal energy of, 158
    property tables, 347, 454, 456
    specific heats, 161
    temperature scale, 154
Indicator diagram, 30
Inequality of Clausius, 271
Inexact differential, 44
Intensive properties, 12, 645
Intercooling, in gas compression, 544
    in gas-turbine cycles, 576
Internal-combustion engine, 565
Internal energy, 66
    calculation of, 336
    of ideal gases, 158
    of reaction, 463
        table of, 456
Internally reversible process, 230
Inversion line, 331
Irreversibility, 375
Irreversible process, 218
    and molecular disorder, 245
    characteristics of, 224
Isentropic flow of gases, 516
    converging nozzle, 519
    converging-diverging nozzle, 519
Isentropic process, 279
Isolated system, 8
    energy of, 61
    entropy of, 290
Isothermal compression, 541

Jet propulsion, 578
Joule, J. P., 56
Joule cycle, 566
Joule's law, 156
Joule-Thomson coefficient, 329, 637
    values of, 332
Joule-Thomson expansion, 330

Keenan and Kaye, 347, 471, 523
Keenan and Keyes, 137, 549
Kelvin, Lord (William Thomson), 212,
    236, 256
Kelvin temperature scale, 21, 256, 259
Kinetic energy, 65
Kinetic theory, 13

Kinetic theory, pressure of ideal gas developed from, 174
  specific heat developed from, 177
Kirchhoff's law, 673
k values, 164, 166

Latent heat, 126
  of fusion, 126
  of sublimation, 126
  of vaporization, 126
Leduc's law, 393
Limiting flow, in nozzles, 519
  in pipes, 531
Liquefaction of gases, 637
Liquids, compressed, 117
  saturated, 111
  subcooled, 117
Logarithmic mean temperature difference, 672

Mach number, 515
Macroscopic vs. microscopic viewpoint, 13
Manometer, 16
Mass fraction, 391
Mathematics, language of, 5
Maximum work, 228, 363
Maxwell, J. C., 321
Maxwell equations, 321
Mayer, Julius Robert, 96
Mean temperature difference, 672
Mercury-water cycle, 614
Microscopic vs. macroscopic viewpoint, 13
Miscibility, 649
Mixing of ideal gases, 401
Mixtures, ideal-gas, properties of, 395
  ideal-gas and vapor, 409
  real-gas, 404
Molecular disorder, 246
Molecular structure, gases, 108
  liquids, 108
  solids, 107
Molecular velocities, 109
Molecular weight of gas mixture, apparent, 392
Mole fraction, 392
Mollier diagram, 278, 352, 353
  for steam, *between* 712 and 713
Monatomic gas, specific heat of, 177

Multiple fluid cycles, 613, 631
Munters, Carl G., 636

Natural convection, 666
Newcomen, Thomas, 95
Normal shock, 522, 532
Nozzle, adiabatic flow in, 518, 525
  convergent, 519
  convergent-divergent, 519
  critical pressure ratio in, 519, 525
  critical velocity, 519
  efficiency, 523
  vapor flow in, 525

One-dimensional flow, 503
One-dimensional heat conduction, 661
Orifice, flow through, 529
  vena contracta of, 529
Orsat analysis, 442
Otto, Nikolaus A., 581
Otto cycle, air-standard analysis for, 581

Parallel-flow heat exchanger, 670
Partial derivatives, 687
Partial pressure, 392
  of vapor in mixtures, 409
Partial volume, 392
Path function, 11, 42
pdv, 27
Perfect gas, *see* Ideal gas
Performance, coefficient of, 93, 623
Perpetual-motion machines, 215
Phase, 106
  changes of, 129
Phase diagram, 115
Phase equilibrium, 109, 651, 655, 658
Phase rule, 644
Piston displacement, 558
Planck, Max, 212
Point function, 11, 42
Polytropic exponent, 169
Polytropic process, 169
Potential energy, 63
Pressure, 14
  absolute, 15
  atmospheric, 15
  critical, 134
  gage, 15, 28
  partial, 392
  reduced, 193

Pressure, relative, 349
  stagnation, 506
  static, 506
  total, 506
  vacuum, 15
Pressure-enthalpy diagram, 353
Pressure-height equation, 16
Pressure-temperature diagram for refrigerants, 630
Pressure-volume diagram, 27, 353
Pressure-volume-temperature surfaces,
  122, 152
Probable states, 246, 308
Process, 10
  cyclic, 11
  irreversible, 218
  reversible, 218
Property, 10
  as point function, 42
  extensive, 12
  intensive, 12
  specific, 12
Property diagrams, 118, 352
Pseudoreduced properties, 197
Psychrometric charts, 420, *between* 712
  and 713
Pump, heat, 622
Pumps, 540
Pump work, 600
Pure substance, 109
pv diagram, 27, 353
pV product, 72
pvT surface, 122
  for an ideal gas, 152

Quality, 120

Radiation, 672
Rankine, W. J. M., 21
Rankine cycle, 598
  supercritical pressure, 599
Rankine temperature scale, 21
Rayleigh, Lord, 532
Rayleigh line, 532
Real or actual gases, 188
  and $pv = RT$, 153
  equations of state for, 197, 202, 203
Rectification, 653
  complete, 654
  partial, 653

Rectification, reflux, 655
Rectifier, 635, 653
Reduced coordinates, 193
Reduced properties, 193
Reflectivity, 672
Refrigerants, 630
Refrigeration, 93
  absorption system, 633
  Carnot cycle, reversed, 623
  dense air system, 626
  dry compression, 629
  Servel system, 636
  standard ton of, 624
  steam-jet system, 632
  vacuum system, 632
  vapor-compression, 628
  wet compression, 629
Regeneration, 243, 572
Regenerative cycle, gas turbine, 572
  steam power, 601
Regenerative-reheating cycle, 577, 610
Regenerator effectiveness, 573
Reheat factor or fraction, 526
Reheating cycle, gas-turbine, 577
  steam-power, 609
Relative humidity, 412
Relative pressure, 349
Relative (specific) volume, 350
Reversed cycle, Brayton, 624
  Carnot, 241, 623
Reversibility, 218
  external, 230
  internal, 230
Reversible cycles, 232
  efficiency of, 252
Reversible process, 218
  as maximum work process, 228
  characteristics of, 224, 227
  cycle, 232
Rigorous approach to thermodynamics,
  355
Rotor-fluid energy transfer, 550
Rumford, Count (Benjamin Thompson),
  96, 236

Saturated liquid, 111
Saturated solid, 111
Saturated vapor, 111
Saturation conditions, 111
Savery, Thomas, 95

Second law of thermodynamics, 211
  Clausius statement, 212
  Kelvin-Planck statement, 213
Séguin, Marc, 96
Separation, 553
Shock, normal, 522
Sign convention, for heat, 39
  for work, 23
Sink temperature, 299
Solid, 107
Solid-vapor saturation line, 113
Sonic velocity, 513
Specific gravity, 14
Specific heat, 124
  instantaneous, 126
  mean, 126
  of ideal gases, 161
    equations for, 167
    from kinetic theory, 177
    tables of, 162, 163, 164
  of ideal-gas mixtures, 397
  of real gases, 204
  ratio, 343
  relations, 342
Specific humidity, see Humidity ratio
Specific volume, 13
Specific weight, 14
Stagnation point, 505
Standard state, 470
State, 10
  equations of, 151
  equilibrium, 10
  identical, 10
Steady flow, 32
Steam generator, 599
Steam point, 19
Steam properties, 692–699
Stefan, J., 673
Stefan-Boltzmann law, 673
Stirling, Robert, 242
Stirling cycle, 243
Stoichiometric air, 437
Stored energy, 59, 63
Stream availability, 373
Stress-strain diagram, 354
Subcooled liquid, 117, 136, 140
Sublimation, 113
Superheated vapor, 117
Supersaturation, 525
Surroundings, 7

Symbols, list of, xv
System, 7
  actual and ideal, 9
  classification of, 7
  closed, 7
  fixed-mass, 7
  isolated, 8
  nonflow, 68
  open, 7
  steady-flow, 33

Tables of properties, 135
Tds equations, 285, 469, 483
Temperature, 17
  absolute, 21
  absolute zero of, 258
  adiabatic saturation, 416
  adiabatic wall, 506
  approximate adiabatic wall, 507
  centigrade scale of, 21
  critical, 133
  dew-point, 415
  dry-bulb, 415
  Fahrenheit scale of, 19
  ideal-gas scale of, 154
  Kelvin scale of, 21, 256, 259
  lowest in the surroundings, 299
  maximum combustion, 465
  Rankine scale of, 21
  saturation, 111
  scales of, 18, 21
  sink, 299
  stagnation, 506
  thermodynamic, 20, 252, 335
  total, 506
  wet-bulb, 418
Temperature-entropy diagram, 279, 352
  of a Carnot cycle, 280
  of irreversible processes, 281
Thermal conductivity, 663
Thermal efficiency, 92
Thermal equilibrium, 18
Thermodynamics, 1
  classical, 13
  engineering, 1
  first law of, 55
  second law of, 211
  statistical, 13
  third law of, 469
  zeroth law of, 18

Thermometer, constant-volume gas, 20
    scale, ideal-gas, 154
Third law of thermodynamics, 469
Thompson, Benjamin, 96, 236
Thomson, William (Lord Kelvin), 212, 236, 256
Throttling calorimeter, 353
Throttling process, 133
Ton of refrigeration, 624
Transient flow, 71, 83
Transmissivity, 672
Triple-phase point, 117
Triple point, 111
Turbine, 546, 555
    axial-flow, 556
    efficiency, 546
    impulse, 556
    multistage, 547
    reheat effect, 547
Turbomachines, 550

Unavailable energy, 295, 297
Undefined terms, 4, 6
Units, 682
Universal gas constant, 151
Unsteady flow, 71, 83
Useful work, 371

van der Waals, J. D., 197
van der Waals equation of state, 197
    table of constants, 198
Vapor, 111, 120

Vapor-compression system of refrigeration, 628
Vaporization, 111
Variance, 647
vdp, 36
Velocity, acoustic or sonic, 513
Vena contracta, 529
Virial equations of state, 203
Volumetric analysis, 394
Volumetric efficiency, 558
von Platen, Baltzar, 636

Water, properties of, 114, 692–699
Water gas reaction, 494
Watt, James, 95
Weight, specific, 14
Wet-bulb temperature, 418
Wet region, 119
Wet vapor, 120
Whirl, 552
Work, 22
    maximum, 363
    mechanical, 24
    of closed-system frictionless process, 25
    of steady-flow frictionless process, 34
    sign convention, 23, 27
    useful, 371

Zeotropic mixtures, 651
Zero of temperature, 258
Zeroth law of thermodynamics, 18